MW00633913

Kansas GHOST WOMAN

Kansas GHOST WOMAN

James S. Barnett

PUBLISHED BY JAMES S. BARNETT
17872 274th Road, Atchison, Kansas, 66002
This book is printed on recycled paper.

Editor, Pamela K. Barnett

Designed by Graphic Arts of Topeka
Cover Illustration by Barbara Waterman-Peters
Manufactured in the United States of America, Jostens Publications, Topeka

Library of Congress Cataloging-in-Publication Data
Barnett, James S.
Kansas Ghost Woman, James S. Barnett
ISBN 0-9741899-0-1

FIRST EDITION

About the Author

James S. Barnett

James S. Barnett began researching *Kansas Ghost Woman* in 1967. During his tenure as Department of Army Civilian Architect at Fort Leavenworth, Kansas, he was tasked with researching the historical architecture culminating in the Fort's establishment as a National Historical Landmark of the Western Expansion of the United States.

After serving as land mine and booby trap expert and demolition specialist in World War II in Europe; 1 of the 2 survivors out of the original 56; at the age of 20 he was honored by the Army for services rendered, to study in England working on the Greater London Master Plan for Satellite Towns. There, in the country of his ancestors, he learned an appreciation for heritage and history.

The Army again enthused his interest, this time in the land of his birth; Kansas Indian Territory; and spent thirty-six years compiling historical data for these writings.

Contents

List of Illustrations

List of Illustrations

Forward

Accustomed as we are to think of the vast plains of Siberia and Russia as legendary and boundless, and the unknown interior of Africa as an impenetrable mystery, we lose sight of a locality in our own country that once surpassed all these in virgin grandeur, in majestic solitude, and peopled with wild men.

Kansas is richer in historic lore than any other region of the Great West. Its traditions go back to the time of Montezuma and the Spanish conquest of Mexico. In the explorations through the hitherto unknown land now known as Kansas; then, the mythical kingdom of Quivera, and claimed it by right of conquest and discovery as a part of the domain of the Spanish crown. Nearly two centuries passed when the French, coming by way of the Mississippi and Missouri rivers, again visited the mysterious land. A century later, American explorers traversed the country and designated it as the Great American Desert. From time immemorial it had been the home of nomadic tribes and vast pastures of countless herds of buffalo; then, the place of temporary stay of half-civilized and disheartened tribes from east of the Great Mississippi River; retiring or retreating before the ceaseless Western movement of the white man.

These great Indian nations, in time, were swept from the land.

History on a cooperative plan is not history, but merely phases of history by writers of various ideas and individual trains of thought. Many people become greatly excited whenever the truth is too plainly written regarding any one of their pet heroes. Speak a word affecting our prejudices, and we are up in arms regardless of truth. Those who chose to sit in judgment on the alleged heathens are themselves conspicuously lacking in true spiritual depth and ethical tradition.

The aborigines of America had the mind and heart and soul like our own.

We made them appear as bad as possible, with our vulgarity giving them beastly names, as buck, squaw, papoose, their success in battle a massacre, ours a glorious victory, yet they were no worse than us. We made treaties and broke them at our pleasure, and placed over them as superintendents broken down politicians who cheated them in many ways. It was cheap to kill the Indian and enslave the African. The red and the blacks were disposed of to the satisfaction of the white Puritan conscience.

The trail to Santa Fe, through Kansas Territory, was from the beginning a two-way thoroughfare of international trade, with its wagon trains, its ox-carts and laden mules. On the way they creaked and swayed, crammed to overflowing with the precious wares of Yankee commerce; on the route back they groaned under bales of buffalo hides and beaver pelts, and the fabulous silver of Mexican mines.

At times the Indians swooped down and levied tribute in scalps and horseflesh. Combative Texan raiders soon learned that the fighting merchants from the States were not easily intimidated.

The prairie ocean of Kansas Territory they knew has all but vanished, their landmarks forgotten. In two or three days now, by automobile we can cover the length of their old trail to Santa Fe. For us the magic of these Plains may well be lost. But not if we travel, in imagination, with them.

To them the Santa Fe Trail was no mere line of ruts connecting Fort Leavenworth to Santa Fe, Mexico It was a perilous cruise across the boundless sea of grass, among wild men, ending in an exotic city offering quick riches, friendly foreign women and a moral holiday.

The gaiety of Santa Fe palled on the man from the States after a few of these affairs. He got sick of the place and its people, and his heart swung true once more to his own tradition of the Anglo-American. His feet began to itch, to move on. To such a man there was something indecent about a crowd, something other than human, something offensive and dangerous to his personal identity. The lank boy from the States, by nature a lonely and solitary creature, a wanderer and adventurer, born to slip the leash of the settlements and go looking for something lost on the great plains. That was why he conquered and explored and colonized, while the Latin and the Indian were so well content to remain at home. That was why he could sometimes be so ornery to humans and so tender to dumb animals; that was why he could not help regarding society as ridiculous, and fashion as silly. He liked his fellow-men better when they were scattered over a big country. And so, when he got into a crowd, he generally felt like fighting, smashing things. To him, people in crowds were suggestive of maggots.

It was a glorious chance—not to be repeated—which threw open the Frontier Territory to the restless feet of such men.

They left the States to escape from their neighbors and navigate the plains on their own hook; left the caravan to carouse in Santa Fe; and shook the dust of Santa Fe from their feet to head for the States again. Afterwards, many of them spent the rest of their days wishing they were back in the wilds. What they longed for was life in the open, the impromptu dangers, the sudden meeting, the handful of old friends—everyone an individual—with whom one need not talk,the lone campfire under the stars, the immense and unspoiled plains. There was something about the heavy iron of a pistol hanging on your hip and a spirited horse under you, that makes you feel like a man, ready for anything that life throws at you.

Fort Leavenworth, Indian Territory and the Trail stood for adventure, travel, romance, danger and wealth. They were not conscious of dates and statistics, mileage or the march of destiny. They knew only darkness, fatigue, cold and sunburn, the insistent wind, the drenching downpour, the lone danger of guard duty while the wolves howled from the hills and the skulking Indian fitted an arrow to his bowstring. They knew thirst and hunger, the night attack, the dash after buffalo, the slow plodding through the deep and bitter cold snow.

If we are to know Kansas history, we must know it as they did. We can do that, for here we have their diaries, their records and the painful compilations of those times.

This book is an attempt to recapture that experience, starting at the Fort Leavenworth embarkation, and passing along the trails of the Frontier Territory, camping where they camped, seeing and feeling what they saw and experienced. Here historic events have been given the center stage. That stage is a thousand miles of prairie, desert, mountains, and rivers; the time is the eighteenth century.

Let us try to re-live the feelings, the life, the tragedy and endurance and the world which they knew. The history of those bloody times will never be wholly revealed, for dead men can not speak.

Here the famous First United States Cavalry was born, experienced its baptism of fire on the Kansas Plains and started its march to destiny.

A few of the events and characters have been fictionalized. Nearly all the scenes introduced are historical and are employed to give emphasis to the time.

Historic Fort
Leavenworth,
Grant Hall tower.

Preface

Historic Fort Leavenworth

This is a story of historic incidents affecting the State of Kansas, some of which are occasionally embellished with imaginative narration. An effort has been made to present the most interesting occurrences and events in the history of the rise of a great Free State of Kansas from a wilderness.

The inhabitants of so notable a State should know of its greatness, and be inspired by the people who built it, even better than they knew.

It has been attempted to record scenes of real life and people rather than a dry recitation of facts.

The places mentioned should be located by the student of history for the reality of the exciting times of the struggle and the lonely heroic lives.

Map of the Louisiana Purchase

Kansas
A Narrative History

Review of the Situation

Limitation of Settlement Theory—It seems to have been considered that the Missouri River was the limit of possible white settlement. Pike had written of Kansas in his journal in 1806, "From these immense prairies may arise one great advantage to the United States, viz.: the restriction of our population to certain limits. Our citizens being so prone to rambling and extending themselves on the frontiers, will, through necessity, be constrained to limit their extent on the West to the borders of the Missouri and Mississippi, while they leave the prairies, incapable of cultivation, to the wandering aborigines of the country."

In the days between 1830 and 1854 the principle figures in Kansas were Indians, the regular army, the Indian trader, and the missionary.

Indian Country—What is now Kansas was included in the "Indian Country" by act of Congress, May 26, 1830. The following metes and bounds formed its boundaries: "Beginning on the Red River east of the Mexican boundary, and as far west as the country is habitable, thence down the Red River eastward to Arkansas territory, thence northward along the line of Arkansas Territory, to the State of Missouri; thence north along its westwardly line to the Missouri River, thence up the Missouri River to the Puncah[1] (or Ponca) River, thence westward as far as the country is habitable, thence southward to the place of beginning." The country was not considered habitable more than 200 miles west of the Missouri line, on account of the absence of timber.

The Missouri Compromise—Slavery troubles in the United States began with the adoption of the Constitution, but the territory of the Louisiana Purchase was not seriously affected until the passage by Congress of the Missouri Compromise in 1820. This measure provided that Missouri should be admitted as a slave state, and that in all remaining territory west of the Mississippi River and north of 36° 30′ (the southern boundary of Missouri) slavery should be forever prohibited.

Result of the Missouri Compromise—The Missouri Compromise was a great surprise to the people who opposed slavery, for they had hoped, after the admission of Louisiana as a slave state, that the remainder of Louisiana territory would be free. To even things up, Maine was admitted as a free state, making twelve free and twelve slave states in the Union. Congress had adopted the plan of admitting first a free and then a slave state so as to preserve a balance of power in that body. This geographical subterfuge was not, to say the least, an ideal way to settle a question of great moral consideration.

Some Famous Trails

The First Trail—The faintest trail, and perhaps the earliest, was that made by the Indian dog dragging lodge poles from place to place. Then came the first "white man's road," the trace of the packers' loaded mules, burros, and horses, then the wide roads made by the traders' trains and the army wagons. All these left their mark in Kansas in the years when it was not an undiscovered country, but lying open and void, waiting for the rising of the Star of Empire.

Santa Fe Trail

The City of Santa Fe—Pike in his narrative had described the ancient city of Santa Fe, New Mexico, the oldest city in the present United States. It was a city of perhaps 2,000 people, with its public square, its Palace of the Government, its Alameda, its quaint church of San Miguel, and its adobe houses. Spain ruled, and Spanish practices and costumes prevailed. An indescribable grace of foreign flavor pervaded the drowsy old town; there the black-eyed Spanish beauty reigned, and the soft syllables of the Spanish language were heard. Santa Fe, however, was tributary to a vast country, and a great amount of business was transacted there. It was said that $750,000 worth of goods were brought to the town each year.

The Non-Intercourse Rule Broken—On account of Pike's description, great interest was aroused, and many individual attempts were made to open up commercial relations between the Missouri border and Santa Fe. These attempts generally resulted in disaster. The Spanish government desired no intercourse, and repressed all such by demanding excessive tribute.

The Mexican Revolution, which began in 1810 and triumphed in 1821, making Mexico a republic, broke down the non-intercourse rule, and in 1824 the first wagon train passed over the road from Missouri to Santa Fe.

Early History of the Trail—There had been a trail to the Southwest before. Indian traditions reveal the story of a well marked highway, and it is thought that back in the days of the mound builders at least parts of this route were used. The fact is well established that it was a common road for Indian tribes for hundreds of years, and Coronado followed it on his way to Quivira.

It may be said that the five hundred miles of the Santa Fe Trail in Kansas, during the years that it was traversed by all classes of travelers, from solitary horsemen to the marching armies, witnessed the display of all the great human qualities, patience, fortitude, and the most heroic courage, as contrasted with the darkest treachery and the most ferocity.

Its Effect on Kansas Development—After the laying out of the highway, Kansas was no longer a solitude. A stream of human life was, as it were, set flowing through the country. Trains going and coming over the long road were seldom out of sight of each other, or of the gleam of the nightly fires. Millions of dollars' worth of property was transported by the pack animals and wagon trains. An army of men was employed to drive and care for a host of animals. This army included, besides Americans, many Mexicans as teamsters and packers, an art in which they stood unrivaled. Thus the dark features and black hair of the Mexicans were made familiar from the Missouri to the mountains. The Spanish words incorporated in the English as spoken in Kansas at this day, date back to the days of the Santa Fe Trail.

The Oregon Trail—The Santa Fe Trail, while, perhaps, the most important, was not the only great highway existing in Kansas before it was recognized as the white man's country. The Oregon Trail was a great thoroughfare. It ran through Doniphan, Brown, Nemaha and Marshall counties and through the northeast corner of Washington County, then it turned into Nebraska and followed the North Platte westward. By it a great emigration moved on to California; the Mormons used it extensively. Colonel Inman designated this trail as the "Great Salt Lake Trail," and others as the California Road.

It has been said that the valleys of the Kansas River and of the Arkansas River were the first to be used as thoroughfares by civilized men in Kansas. But the great geographical truth was early discovered that Kansas is in the center of the great highway from the valleys of the Mississippi and Missouri to the mountains and the Pacific Ocean.

Louisiana Purchase—In 1763, at the close of the French and Indian War, France ceded Canada and all her possessions east of the Mississippi River except New Orleans to England and all west of the Mississippi River with New Orleans, to Spain. The term Louisiana was at this time applied to the territory between the Mississippi and the Rocky Mountains. Spain's hold on Louisiana became so weak, as the years passed, that for safety she retroceded it to France in 1801 by secret treaty. Napoleon was then First Consul of France. He had hoped to build a magnificent empire in Louisiana. His plan was to send over a strong army of 25,000 men, accompanied with a fleet to guard the coast, but the ever-watchful England thwarted his design. Napoleon knew that he must take possession of the territory and hold it or England would become its master, and this of all things he did not desire; he was pressed on every side by wars and political combinations; he saw clearly that to divide his forces in order to undertake a great American enterprise would endanger his power; and lastly he needed money to carry on his campaigns.

There had been trouble for some years between the colonists and Spanish authorities at New Orleans in regard to the commercial rights of the Lower Mississippi. To obviate further difficulties Jefferson, president of the United States, sent a request to Livingston, American minister to France, to open negotiations for the purchase of New Orleans. When Napoleon

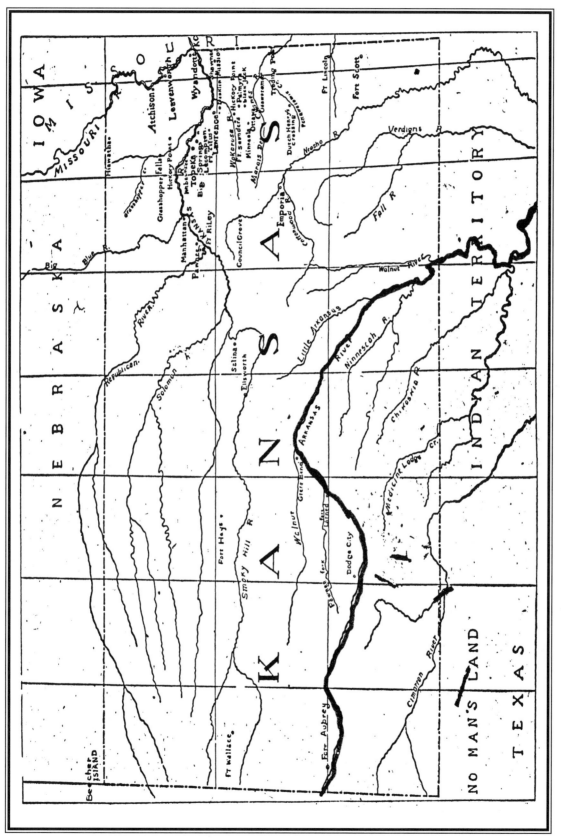

Early Map of Kansas

heard the message, he said with passionate vehemence, "Irresolution and deliberation are no longer in reason. It is not only New Orleans that I will cede, it is the whole of the colony without reservation." The treaty was ratified in October, 1803,[2] and the Louisiana territory became the property of the United States.[3]

The United States Occupies the Territory—The treaty, which made Kansas United States territory was concluded April 30, 1803, but St. Louis, and the province of Upper Louisiana, remained in the hands of the Spanish until March 9, 1804, nearly a year afterward. On that day Major Amos Stoddard[4] of the United States army appeared at St. Louis, and acting as agent of the French Republic, received from Don Carlos de Hault Delassus, the Spanish Lieutenant-Governor, the formal cession of the province from Spain to France. The Spanish Regiment of Louisiana moved out; a detachment of the First United States Artillery marched in; the American flag was raised; and the next day, Major Stoddard began the rule of the United States under the title of Commandant. The value of the great acquisition to the United States cannot be overestimated. One million square miles of splendid territory, an empire in itself, was added to the national domain; the navigation of the Mississippi River was forever insured and the political power and integrity of our government against foreign intrusion was preserved.

Footnotes

[1] The Ponca River empties into the Missouri near the northern boundary of Nebraska.

[2] The treaty was negotiated by Livingston and Monroe. Barbe Marbois and Tallyrand. The province of Louisiana, consisting of over 1,000,000 square miles, was purchased for $15,000,000. The interest on the amount and the satisfaction of claims made the total sum $27,267,621.

[3] While Spain held Louisiana, she demanded excessive duties for the American commerce that passed in or out of the river. Because the treaty by which Louisiana was ceded to France was kept secret the Spanish held possession in America.

[4] Major Amos Stoddard, who was the descendant of the great divine, Jonathan Edwards, and grand-uncle of Hon. John Sherman, of Ohio, was the First American commander of the Kansas country. He was a good man and a brave soldier.

Lewis and Clark Expedition, 1804

Planned by Jefferson—With the acquisition of Upper Louisiana by the United States, came the spirit of enterprise and exploration. In the latter direction the new government set the example. President Jefferson was full of interest and curiosity about the new empire of which so little was really known, and wrote with his own hand the directions governing the expedition which was to set out under Captain William Clark, brother of General George Rogers Clark, the conqueror of Illinois, and Captain Merriwether Lewis, who had been the President's private secretary. He selected both these guides and leaders from personal acquaintance; both were Virginians, and from his own neighborhood.

Expedition in Kansas—The expedition reached the rendezvous near St. Louis early in the spring, and before the Spaniards were willing to acknowledge the Missouri as an

American river. After the formal transfer the expedition, on the 10th of May, 1804, started up the turbid Missouri, and on June 27th reached the mouth of the Kansas River, landed and made a camp within the present limits of Kansas City, Kansas. Proceeding up the stream, the voyagers noted in the different journals objects on either shore which may still be recognized by the description. On the 4th of July, 1804, the party landed at or near the present site of Atchison at noon, and made brief observance of their country's natal day. They named a small stream near their landing place Fourth of July Creek, and going on up the river four miles, called another Kansas stream Independence Creek, a name which it bears to this day. Thus was the Fourth of July first celebrated in Kansas.

West to the Pacific—A few days later, the boats had passed beyond the limits of Kansas, and the voyagers were on their way to the "land of the Dakotas," to the unknown springs of the Missouri, to the untrodden passes of the Rocky Mountains, to the far Columbia, and on to the sounding surges of the Pacific. The explorers returned after two years, with the loss of but a single man in all the perils of the waste and wild.

Lewis and Clark Meet the Indians at Ross' Hole—a painting by Charles M. Russell. (Courtesy of Historical Society of Montana.)

ARMY DIGEST
December 1967

Pike's Expedition

Purpose and Route—In July, 1806, two years and two months after the Lewis and Clark expedition had gone up the Missouri, another expedition left Belle Fontaine, a small town near St. Louis, under the command of Lieutenant Zebulon Montgomery Pike, a young and active officer of the United States army. His instructions from the government were "to take back to their tribe on the upper waters of the Osage River some Osage Indians who had been redeemed from captivity among the Pottawatomies; then to push on to the Pawnee Republic on the upper waters of the Republican River, then to go south to the Arkansas, and to the Red River, interviewing on the way the Comanches."

Natural Kansas

Although the surface is a great plain sloping eastward, its minute topography is often rugged and varied; valleys 200 feet deep, bluffs and mounds with precipitous walls 300 feet high; over hanging rocky ledges and remnants of cataracts and falls in numerous streams giving a variety of scenery, are to be observed all over the eastern part of the state, and to even a greater extent in some portions of the west.

Story of Kansas Nature in Its Literature—All the natural features of this great rectangle; all the varying aspects of the earth, as touched by the shaping hands of the seasons; all the shifting panorama of the skies; all the myriad voices of the winds; the shine of shallow, wide and wandering streams; the fringing trees that watch the waters as they pass; the lovely charm of each rocky promontory that looks out upon the sea of grass, all these have proved to be the inspiring and informing spirit of Kansas literature.

Noble L. Prentis

Edited and Revised
By
Henrietta V. Race, A.M., Professor of Education, Southwestern College.

Published by Caroline Prentis, Topeka, Kansas 1909

Kansas
GHOST WOMAN

Journey to Fort Leavenworth
Indian Territory
1832

*I*n the beginning, there was a man named Ian.

Three soldiers lay dead in the shallow hole scooped out of the rotten muck. Wrapped in great coats, they had died before their time, victims of frontier malaria. Ian Douglass, a quiet Brevet First Lieutenant in his early twenties, stood on the edge of the long pit and read the burial services in a clear, low monotone, devoid of all emotion. A small group of mourners clustered together in the drizzling rain, there only because of army social necessity. No one mourned the death of the three, except for four or five young troopers who had shared a few months of good times with them in St. Louis.

"Man that is born of a woman," continued the lieutenant from the book, "hath but a short time to live. He cometh up and is cut down, like a flower. In the midst of life, we are in death." He paused a few moments, as wrinkles furrowed across his brow above his clear, hazel eyes as he considered the phrases, then continued, "Unto Almighty God we commend the souls of our brothers departed and we commit their bodies to the ground. Amen."

He reflected a moment again on what he had read. This was a habit of his, talking slowly, thinking out what to say before he said it, and listening very carefully what was said to him.

He nodded to the sergeant standing next to him that he was finished.

The sergeant, a tough-muscled old-timer, waved his arm for the troopers with shovels to fill in the grave.

Sergeant Thomas Beidler looked vicious. He was a good fellow but his years as first sergeant had set his facial features into a continuous scowl, his brow drawn down in a sullen and angry manner. He was tough, he had to be, and a lot smarter than he looked. He had been awarded several medals for saving patrols while on hazardous trips through Indian country. He didn't pay much attention to army dress regulations. A pistol holster hung more on his rump than on his thighs, his boots were rough; his hat worn and his stomach paunch hung over his tightly belted trousers. But his attire was overlooked and every officer fought for his services when going into hostile Indian country.

Beidler spat out his worn-out chud of tobacco, wiped the dark slobber off his chin with a swipe of his arm. "Come on, you troopers," he growled impatiently, "let's get this hole filled." Taking out a twisted plug from his back pocket, he bit off another chew.

The lieutenant, ignoring all this, looked down at the corpses as the shovels of sand slopped into the swamp water that had seeped into the hole and half covered the bodies of the dead recruits. The cold rain continued, now pounding down with hard force. He looked at the bodies again, then the small field bible he had read from, and in seemingly disgust, tossed the black covered book into the rotten swamp muck. He slowly took a deep drawn breath, let it out, and twisted the book into the mud with his boot heel, summing up his personal thoughts of life, death, and religion.

A clash of thunder exploded the sodden gray-green landscape with a blinding white streak of life-killing lightning. Again and then again, each time seemed to come closer. The troopers hurriedly finished their job and scurried back through the bushes and vines to the waiting boat, trying to catch up with the others already halfway there.

The lieutenant glanced up in the direction of the lightning flashes, showing no reaction to the closeness of death and only vaguely pondered to himself that maybe there was a God—and maybe he was mad—but he really didn't give a damn. He didn't care about anything anymore. He hated society. He hated the army. He was just a number in a big bunch of numbers—a machine—a nothing. He was told to do this; he was told to do that. He read over the dead troopers because he was told to. But he hid most of this; he lived with the hate in himself. To rebel would make him an outcast, an outsider. His mother would be hurt if he rebelled, and so would his so-called friends. So he lived with it and hated it all. He lived his life as he was supposed to, but—damn it—one of these days, he had sworn to himself that he was going to break out of this cage and do his own living. He would do it no matter what it cost him in security, respect, or any other of those phony values. This triviality, this stage acting, playing the part, trapped to society's conventions.

"All finished, lieutenant!" the sergeant broke in on his thoughts.

"All right, sergeant, we had better get back to the boat."

The heavy rain had converted the surrounding lowlands into a swamp. The luxuriant vegetation covered the banks of the wide meandering Missouri River. The earth was a mass of tangled vegetation, which had built up for hundreds of years, which made walking difficult. He wished the boat was repaired by now.

That afternoon they had run into a severe storm. The wind had come on hard, the sky leaded over, and the lightning rolled down the sides of the bluffs which bordered the river. The storm burst upon the party in all its grandeur and fury. The shoreline disappeared. The little boat hit hard on a sand bar and jerked to a stop. The captain had managed to back off the bar but was not so fortunate with the submerged log. The crew had to saw off a part of it under the water. The log had damaged the hull badly, and in a short time it was discovered they were in danger of sinking, so the captain stopped to repair the planking. By thrusting oakum into the leak, bailing out the water, and replacing several planks, the boat could be ready again to fight the swift waters. While the damages were being repaired, Captain Russell, the officer in command of the shipboard troops, decided to bury the three that had died of the fever rather than wait until they got to Fort Leavenworth.

Brevet First Lieutenant Ian Douglass

Lieutenant Douglass caught up with the dependents and the other soldiers as they boarded the boat tied up at the river's edge. The women were having a laborious time of it with their long skirts wading through the vines and fallen moss-covered trees. One woman, he recalled that she was Captain Bellnap's wife, reached the board used as a gangplank. As she stepped out on it, the boat violently jerked up and out into the stream and she was thrown, screaming, head first into the muddy waters.

As the others stared at her going under the swirling waters, the young lieutenant without hesitation jumped into the river after her. With her long dress, numerous petticoats, and high-buttoned shoes, he knew she wouldn't last long.

In one great leap he plunged into the river which, with greedy haste, was bearing away the woman. He was a powerful swimmer. He took long, clean strokes, and his strong lungs kept him in breath. He threw back his head like a huge water dog, striking out with all his force, and gained on the woman. As the swift current carried her away, they both went under, but he had her gripped firmly by the upper arm. As they came up, by enormous effort, he pulled to the bank in quick powerful strokes.

The swollen waters twisted and pulled them in devilish circles, but somehow they missed the big deadly whirlpools. As he dragged the crying, frightened woman onto the mud, the sergeant's strong arm grabbed the woman out of the water in one mighty heave. He reached down again and pulled the lieutenant from the river with an audible grunt.

For a long while the lieutenant lay with his face in the mud, coughing the water out, and sucking air into his lungs to regain his strength. The rain pounded down on him. He was miserable, completely miserable. He was worn out, weak, but he was alive!

He slowly turned onto his back and looked up at the ugly Sergeant Beidler. No words were passed for a moment, but Ian felt comradeship he hadn't experienced for a long time.

"Okay, lieutenant?" queried the sergeant.

"Okay, sergeant," Ian sighed as he dragged himself to his feet.

The sergeant helped Captain Bellnap's wife to her feet and held onto her as she crossed the gangplank. Her oldest daughter, Lucy, still in hysterics, grabbed her as she came on board. Frightened and crying, she embraced her mother. Seconds later the older woman collapsed to the deck.

Ian came on board lastly. Without taking any notice of the crowd, except for a quick look at the woman and her daughter, he made his way through the people and the deck cargo. As far away from the people as he could get, he found a vacant pile of supplies to climb up on. He made himself as comfortable as possible, by leaning against the cabin, pulling his knees up near his chin and throwing a rain poncho over his cold body.

He gazed into the dark gray mist, seeing nothing, looking at nothing. His eyes glazed; he rested and reminisced, hazily recalling past experiences in his life.

He was born to the landowning and slaveholder aristocracy of the South, the most honorable profession in the deep southern states. His "Daddy" had been military, of course—a colonel, no less. He was now retired on 4,000 acres that was worked by 150 slave people.

Naturally he had to follow in his daddy's profession, even though he hated it. He had tried to make himself like soldiering. In fact, he had received high grades, even made cadre captain. He tried to get interested in Von Clausewitz, Genghis Khan, and Alexander the Great and other famous military geniuses. He had learned them well, but he still hated it all.

He was in the mood for remembering the things he had experienced during the last several years, the good and the bad. There seemed to be more bad than good. He remembered when he had been called to help maintain order after a hurricane hit one of the seacoast cities. Following the catastrophe, the city was practically in the hands of thieves and thugs, human vampires who robbed the dead and mutilated the corpses which were lying everywhere. They ransacked business houses and residences and created a reign of terror.

The depredations of the lawless bandits were of an inconceivably brutal character. Unprotected women, whether found upon the streets or in their houses, were subjected to outrage or assault, robbed of their jewelry, and stripped of their clothing. People were held up on the public streets in broad daylight. The bodies of the dead were despoiled of everything and, in their haste to secure valuables, the ghouls mutilated the corpses, cutting off fingers to get the rings, and amputating the ears of women to get the earrings.

The outrages became so flagrant and the people of the city so terrified that the city police were unable to stop them, most of the officers having been victims of the flood. The governor sent in troops to put down the lawless bands. They were ordered to promptly shoot all persons found looting. Most of the looters were men; some of them, however, were white women. They were as merciless, cruel, and savage as the most criminal of their male companions.

He recalled his squad had shot several of the thugs when found in the act of looting. The pockets of the slain were filled with jewelry and money, and in some cases, fingers were found which had been cut from the hands of the dead. Many of the ghouls, when found in the act of despoiling the dead, begged piteously for mercy, but their begging was ignored, and they were shot without mercy and ceremony. But in forty-eight hours these harsh measures made the city safe again, as safe as it had ever been.

Then starvation and disease had set in. Chaos was everywhere; death on all sides; wreck and ruin was all that could be seen. Half-dressed shrieking and screaming women, many of them dazed and bleeding, waded knee deep in water with the lifeless forms of children in their arms. Men, broken-hearted and crying, bewailed the loss of wives and children. The submerged streets were still full of debris and bodies. He remembered that in one hospital only eight were still alive out of more than one hundred patients and nurses.

The heat of the sun began to decompose the bodies of the dead and the stench became unbearable. The bloated corpses were loaded on barges, weighted down, taken a few miles out to sea and thrown into the ocean.

He would never forget the great piles of human bodies, dead animals, rotting vegetation, household furniture, and fragments of the buildings themselves. Intermingled with them were carcasses of horses, chickens, and dogs. The stench was absolutely sickening, but the restoration work started, and with courage and fortitude, the city was made livable again.

On the bright side of the picture, there were plenty of volunteers for this work. And in all this hell he came upon the most heart-rending evidence of love and heroism. At a Catholic orphans' home, the bodies of the little children were found tied together in bunches of eight, and then the sisters had tied the cords around their own waists. In this way they probably hoped to quiet the children's fears and lead them to safety. But there was no safety anywhere and the terrific force of the storm collapsed the structure on them, burying them under tons of brick and wood. In one heap under the debris, the dead children were piled on the sisters with the arms of one little girl clasped around a sister's neck.

The pity he felt was deep and lasting. Many had lost everything except life itself—fathers, mothers, sisters, and brothers. Others lost everything, including their lives.

He asked himself, "Why had God, if there was a God, let this happen?" He had searched for an answer, but found none except that the infliction of pain and grief is good in the long run, and a stronger man emerges which could never have happened from any amount of luxury or ease, however attractive they may be. This was a deep subject and whenever he thought about it, it gave him a headache. Maybe someday, he would find the answers to life and God and good and bad. Maybe. . . .

But the back of his head started paining and his stomach got a large knot in it. He felt sick. He knew he shouldn't dwell too long on such a subject.

He liked to recall the fun times, the loose ladies in the French Quarter in New Orleans.

Ah! He smiled to himself as he remembered such streets as St. Charles, Union, Bourbon and Dauphine. In fact, there was scarcely a block in New Orleans which did not contain at least one brothel or assignation house, from a ten-dollar parlor house to a fifteen-cent crib.

However, Basin street was the best in town and described as "heaven-on-earth" by some people, including him. Prostitution was not a crime unless the harlot "occasioned scandals or disturbed the tranquillity of the neighborhood" however, the party girls were forbidden to "sit upon the front steps in an indecent posture" or to "stroll about the streets indecently attired." They would be arrested for these things but prostitution was alright.

Oh yes, he knew all the laws and rules of the game.

The red-light district on Basin street was luxurious and expensive . . . the three story brick and brownstone mansions were filled with mahogany and black walnut woodwork and furniture, Oriental rugs and carpets, silver door-knobs, grand pianos, carved marble fireplaces and mantels, and copies of statuary and famous paintings.

The entrances of a particularly remembered brothel, was through a couple of statues, the works of a renowned sculptor. Beyond this was the drawing-room, peopled with a few girls in glittering bedroom attire, and who, from their costumes and manners, might be angels of the devil. The decorations of the rooms, the pictures on the walls, the plated mirrors, the delicately-tinted furniture, all appeared as in a seductive dream world.

In some of the houses, one amatory experience ranged from five to twenty dollars and from twenty to fifty dollars, if a man wished to stay the night. Of course, these latter prices included breakfast and when he arose in the mornings his clothing was pressed and his shoes polished.

In other lower class houses, women were available for a dollar, the wine was replaced by beer, the evening gowns by shorty PJs or nothing at all. Erotic exhibitions and the hoochy koochy were offered in accompaniment of the weird noises of mechanical pianos and music boxes. Many houses had off-beat entertainers. Ian particularly recalled a popular barfly called Charley, who blew a tin whistle through his nose and sang a ditty as he played.

During his visits in the city he had been engaged in many a disreputable affray. The bordello's were all interesting but he preferred the establishments that catered to the high-class trade. Evening dress was the invariable rule, and profane talk and bawdy behavior was strictly prohibited. He was met at the door by a uniformed Negro maid and was ushered ceremoniously into a drawing-room and formally presented to the party ladies. If one of the girls looked appealing, he communicated his selection to the madame, who conveyed his desires to the lucky girl. If the feeling was mutual—and no girl refused—she discreetly retired to her boudoir . . . at a price of fifteen dollars for such an adventure. He didn't forget the names of the best. There was Kate, a swarthy beauty of 88 Basin Street, the most popular of the house with billowing bosoms and ambitions. Her fiery temper and occasional streak of meanness drove away some trade but with Ian these characteristics never showed through. They would both get half drunk and apologize to each other for their adventures and weaknesses. With her thriftiness and talents, she had become a prosperous madame and now just a good friend of his, not a bed mate anymore.

Then there was Delta, a notorious mistress of a Union Street brothel with tattoos on her arm and a knife under her pillow. She had youthful beauty and was infinitely more versatile than the others. Warm blooded and high spirited, she always wore loose, very low cut lingerie and always ready for high adventure.

Maggie at the age of 22 years was an exceedingly beautiful girl with an exceptionally fine and pleasurable figure and demanded a price of fifty dollars an hour laying across an elegant bed of red damask and lace. Maggie was endowed with a skill in amour which a man would remember for a lifetime.

Yes, he had lived; really lived. Well . . . on second thought maybe this wasn't really living, but he had a lot of fun. The foolishness didn't hurt anyone. It was all legal; well in New Orleans at least, it was legal.

What he had done or how he acted really didn't matter anyway. His parents always bought him out of trouble. After a while he would return to the plantation and take leisurely walks through the backwoods, thinking long and hard, learning to enjoy the simple quiet and silence of nature. He, of course, had to go to church to act out the part of "high society," but he really never listened. The preacher knew who buttered his bread. They never preached about the slave sin and made the aristocracy feel good and righteous. Maybe it was best; maybe the leisure class was needed. Maybe slaves were needed. He didn't know. He didn't try to figure it out. But something, he couldn't explain it, told him it was wrong, terribly wrong, but you don't fight society. You don't hurt your own father and mother. He was overwhelmed with a sense of loss, confusion and uncertainty. He had no point of reference. He had no goal except for fun, liquor, and women. He hated this depersonalization of human life. He saw how individual lives had lost much of their vitality for this reason. But all of this introspective thought was gradually bringing out the intense awareness that his existence depended on himself alone for shaping the course and quality of his life.

He was finding himself. He was responsible for making himself what he was or could be. This was a good starting point. It wasn't complete, but it was a start. He was emerging from passiveness, from doing nothing about his lonely life, to shaping his own existence. Be yourself. Live. Don't be a copy of anyone. Make your own conscious choice, that is why he was on the boat going out to Kansas, the western frontier. Away from the old regulated society and this absurdity of life. He had thought about giving up his commission and seeking a more stirring and exciting profession, but at the very crisis fate had decided differently, in as much as he was ordered on active service, which he did not consider honorable to decline. His mother had cried at the idea, but his daddy was proud to have his son serve his country.

Four companies of newly formed units called Dragoons—mounted militia men—were ordered to be filled up. Officers and other men were selected to march as the first escort of the caravan of traders going and returning between Western Missouri and Santa Fe,

Mexico. Some of the companies of dragoons were ordered to the Santa Fe Road to give protection to the western traders. They were given directions to retire in the autumn and take up their winter residence at Fort Leavenworth. In the spring, they would again be in readiness to proceed upon their western line of marching, to afford protection to the traders with Mexico. Thus acting, there would be a better advantage produced on the Indians than from their remaining stationary at any point. The growing land commerce between the United States and Mexico demanded that heed be given the petition of the traders for their protection. It was clear that the promises of the Indians to permit the traders to pass in peace and security could not be relied upon. Unless the federal government intervened, this new trade would not only suffer, but would serve as notice that commercial relations with Mexico would not be encouraged. The name of Mexico, the synonym of gold and silver mines, possessed an invincible charm for the bartering of southern cotton and other articles from the infant United States.

Ian thought that maybe he could emerge from this earthly hell, life's abyss of nothingness, and make a world full of meaning and value. Maybe he could live his own way, create his own situations, and make his own free choices unburdened with society. He had become a thinker, therefore he started to live; he had built a philosophy nauseated by the absurdity of style of the age. Looking to the excitement of a new completely different life, he fell to sleep.

This Ian Douglass was a fine looking man, clean-shaven and handsome, with a mild but independent expression of countenance that charms at first sight. He was twenty-two years old, having hazel eyes and brunette hair. Being five foot eleven inches tall, he possessed the exciting qualities of youth and spirit. He was a determined non-conformist. By background and birth, he was solidly Southern, born and raised in Georgia. In military school he had displayed an analytical and practical turn of mind; he was a fine soldier who in campaigns would swim the wide Mississippi even in mid-winter. Yet another side of his nature, which his military counterparts found hard to understand, was quite sensitive, intuitive and inventive. He was a scholar and a humanist with an insatiable curiosity about everything. There was a fabulous air about everything he did.

But, Ian Douglass was always looking for the true meaning of life. When the trappings of rank and money were stripped away, a lonely, troubled human being was revealed, desperate to find some purpose in life and some reason for being in the cold and comfortless search for wisdom and truth.

*　　*　　*

The next morning was warm and bright, the temperature being sixty-four degrees at six o'clock. Upon inspection, it was discovered that the damages to the boat resulting from the accident were greater than at first believed. The provisions were considerably damaged, but the sun felt good and most everyone was employed in sorting and airing their personal articles. The river was obstructed by many small islands and expanded itself to great widths where these occurred so as to render the navigation extremely difficult. In many places the proper channel could not be fixed.

The Missouri countryside was beautiful. The shores generally consisted of a sandy soil, timbered with sugar maple, ash, pecan, locust, and black walnut.

Rapids were encountered several times. The boat, being large and heavily loaded, was difficult to maneuver. One rapid was eleven miles long with successive ledges and shoals extending from shore to shore across the bed of the river, the first being the most difficult to ascend.

The captain pulled to shore at nine o'clock to gather boiler wood. The passengers scrambled ashore to build a fire and make breakfast. Several men were sent out hunting. They killed one deer, two turkeys, and three ducks in half an hour's time.

About two hours later the voyage was resumed, after everyone had enjoyed the fresh meat. The river became fairly clear of islands and narrowed considerably. The waters were now brown and the rapids were filled with mud.

It was a fine warm day. The chain of hills that bounded the river appeared still and lifeless. Numerous sandbars occurred in the stream and these caused some delay. The water had fallen several feet and had less velocity of current to contend against, but they found it more necessary to keep in the channel, and could not so often take advantage of the eddy currents below the points and along the shore.

It was remarkable how large the proportion of married men were among the selected to fill the ranks of the western army. The army's experience was that when a bachelor was a little old, he is good for nothing but to take care of himself.

The boat swarmed with their wives and children; The deck was barricaded with beds and bedding; infants squalled and chickens cackled in their coops.

The boat was unique in construction, a so-called stern wheeler, eighty-five feet long with a twenty-five foot beam. The cabins extended from bow to stern. It was a staunch vessel, well modeled with a sharp, wide bow and square stern; it had a large paddle wheel. Skilled workmen built the boat after the most approved methods of ship craft of the day. Such a boat had a carrying capacity of twenty to thirty tons, a draft of thirty-six inches, and cost usually from $10,000 to $15,000. Amid ship, the cabin extended eight or nine feet above the hull, in which was sorted cargo, supplies, and beds for the women and children. On each side of the cabin was a wide walk. The boat was built expressly for the voyage from St. Louis to Fort Leavenworth, and she was intended to impress the Indians with awe. On her bow, running from the keel on forward, was the escape pipe, made in imitation of a huge serpent, which made loud wheezing noises like the dying groans of a great monster. The noise could be heard for miles and made chills and shivers run through all.

On approaching the fort, Ian caught a glimpse of his first western Indians near the river. There were a number of Osage of both sexes and of all ages. They didn't look too savage. These civilized Indians were dressed in old worn-out clothes and in a haphazard manner. Several did not wear shirts but had faded army blankets wrapped around their shoulders. Most had long black straight hair to their shoulders with several strings of bright beads hanging around their neck to their waist. Two or three of the younger men had their heads shaved, except for a tuft near the crown.

They silently lined the muddy banks of the river and watched the boat proceed up the Missouri. They looked completely demoralized; the white man's civilization does this to an Indian—he had seen it among the few Cherokees left in Georgia. The white man's influence quickly diseased the Indian mentally, morally, and physically. In this condition, their vices were many; syphilis affected nearly all of these silent people.

In passing several islands separated by narrow channels on either side, the pilot had steered so close to the left bank that some of the loose chickens on board flew to shore. The Indians scrambled after them; they would eat well tonight.

Fort Leavenworth came into sight at a distance of two miles. Most of the trees had been cut down at the landing place. The fort was handsomely situated about two hundred feet above the level of the brown waters of the Missouri, which made an elbow at the place, giving an extensive view up and down the river.

In turning at the point of a sandbar, the boat drifted upon a field of sawyers, trees fixed in the bed of the river, their branches projecting to the surface and bobbing up and down with the current. The sawyers nearly upset the boat. Several troopers took charge of the children and stood ready to jump into the water should the boat be capsized. After several anxious moments, the danger was past and the stern wheeler headed toward the landing of Fort Leavenworth.

The women washing clothes on the riverbank stopped their work and waved greetings. The landing was a relief to the travelers. Many meetings were very tender and affectionate: wives throwing themselves into the arms of their husbands, husbands embracing their children and children their parents, friends and comrades meeting together again, many giving thanks to the good Lord for having brought them once more together.

There was a party of white hunters and trappers encamped near the dock waiting for their consignment of ammunition, arms, and traps. In rudeness of their deportment and dress, they appeared uncivilized themselves. They were usually the most abandoned and worthless among the whites who adopt the life of wandering hunters; frequently they were men whose lives excluded them from society. A number of squalls, wives of some of the trap-

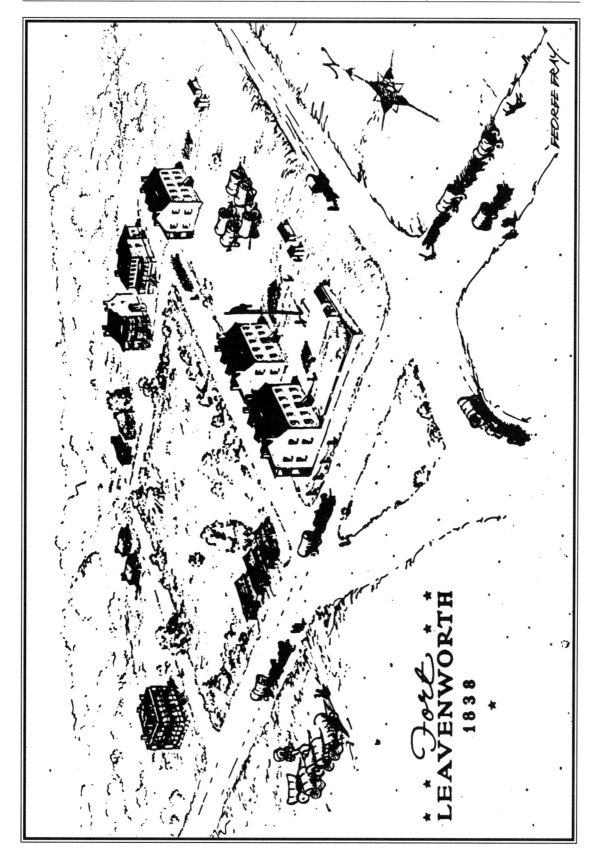

pers, waited in a close group to carry the supplies when their husbands hollered to them to do so. Some men were engaged taking off the tarpaulins that covered the piles of luggage, and began moving it to the wagons at dockside.

*   *   *

A soldier under arms waited for the enlisted travelers at the waterside and escorted them up to their billets. Several officers of various branches of the service en route to their several commands were on the boat.

First Lieutenant Taylor of the Second Infantry welcomed them to Fort Leavenworth and they all started, under his guidance, to pay their respects to the commanding colonel. They passed an old stone warehouse that was the scene of much business; mule teams were there and men loading baggage.

At the top of the hill was quite an assemblage of buildings, generally surrounding a square with a few detached cottages in different places. They were of stone, brick, logs, and frame, with a number of half tumbled-down shacks, generally in the rear of the more imposing structures.

One of the new arrivals asked, "Where is the fort?" The place had more the appearance of a country village than a fort. They had expected to see strong fortifications, walled enclosures, and cannons.

After a little further examination, they discovered two rather dilapidated blockhouses, one seemingly connected with a brick building by a parapeted stone wall. Also, there were two or three one-story stone buildings with a few portholes in their sides, which seemed to constitute the extent of the fortifications. About a dozen-whitewashed cottage-looking houses composed the barracks and the abodes of the officers.

The buildings were so arranged as to form the three sides of a hollow square; the fourth side opened out over a wide prairie to the south. It was a rural looking spot, a speck of civilization in the wilderness. There was nothing here that suggested of war; but for the sentinels at their posts, the lounging forms of soldiers and the occasional drumbeat signaling for the performance of some military duty, one could not have known that they were in the heart of a military station.

On the way to Post Headquarters, they passed by the quarters of Lieutenant Taylor who invited them to stop in to wash up and have a toddy with him. After the boat trip from Jefferson Barracks in St. Louis, the travelers gladly accepted. While thus pleasantly occupied, a shot was heard and an orderly reported that a civilian had killed another near the guardhouse.

Lieutenant Taylor, who was officer of the day, remarked, "Those two came to my office and one asked for protection from the other who, he said, had threatened to kill him. They also mentioned that they were partners. The partner coolly admitted, 'Sure, I intend to kill him.'"

Taylor said he explained to them that this was a case for the civil authorities and that he could not interfere. They went off together, arguing violently. This happened about an hour before the shot was heard. The subject was dropped and the group, now refreshed, continued on to Post Headquarters.

The post was under the command of Colonel Williams, a gentleman of great city manners, restrained and tempered by the charms of an American lady who was elegantly pioneering the graces of civilized refinements into this uncivilized Kansas territory.

He was an old and tried officer, perfectly honest, as brave as a man could be, conscientious and laborious. He was a man for whom his subordinate officers had a very high regard. He evidenced a fabulous memory also, as when Lieutenant Douglass was introduced, his eyes shown recognition.

"Douglass," he uttered. Then repeated, "Douglass, you say. Brigadier Tom Douglass of Atlanta your father?"

"Yes, sir," Ian answered.

"Well! Good . . . good," he repeated. "Glad to have you in my command. Your father and I were in the Canadian campaign together," referring to the War of 1812. "Give him my regards the next time you write home. I'll see you at the club later and you can fill me in on the latest news from home," the colonel being from Georgia also.

After all the new officers had paid their respects to the commander, Lieutenant Taylor escorted them to their quarters.

Most of the buildings were grouped around what was called the Main Parade. At the southeast corner of the Main Parade stood a two-story brick building with wide front porches above and below. This was used as dragoons quarters. Immediately north of this, fronting to the west also, was a similar building. Running east from the southeast corner of the first mentioned building was the stone wall with portholes looking south. A two-story blockhouse stood a little south of the east end of the wall. Southeast of the blockhouse, was the sutler's store, civilian-owned, where groceries, provisions, clothes, liquors and the like were sold to the troops. South of the store was the parsonage. The house was of logs. A little way from the parsonage and across the road was the residence of a senior colonel.

At the northeast corner of the Main Parade stood a one-story basement building, fronting west and used as officers' quarters. On the opposite corner, on the north side, fronting south on the parade grounds, was another building used as officers' quarters. West of those quarters was the best building on the Post for the Commanding Officer quarters.

Between this building and the northwest corner, fronting south toward the parade ground, were four or five more buildings for the officers' use. West of the parade ground, fronting east, were four or five one-story and basement buildings, generally used for soldiers' families and citizen employees. Between the dragoon barracks and the south end of the west

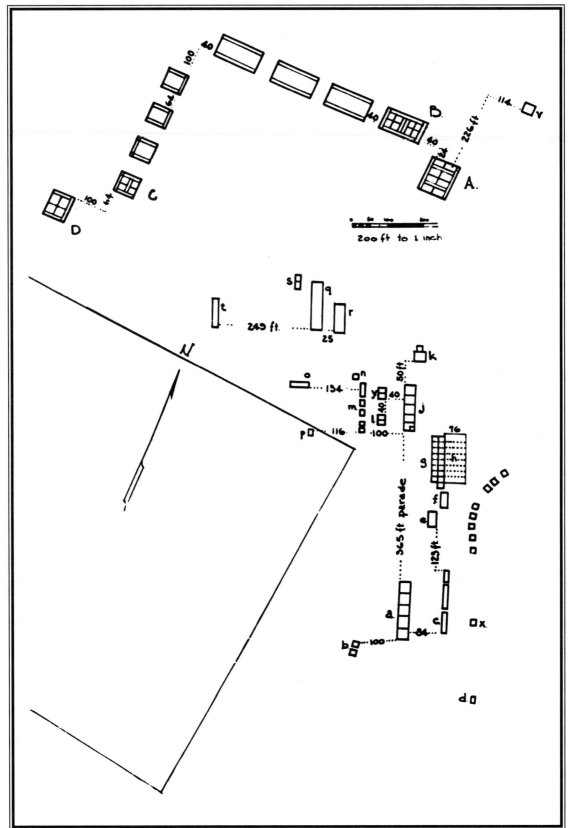

Plan of
Cantonment,
Leavenworth,
1828

Plan of Cantonment Leavenworth, 1828

[The Following Is a Verbatim Copy of the Original Descriptive Matter Accompanying the Sketch Shown on Opposite Page]

PERMANENT BUILDINGS

A. *Commanding Officers' Quarters* (foundation walls complete): two story building; wood frame construction filled in with brick; two rooms at either end 20 by 19 feet; two halls each 10 feet wide; four rooms in the center, each 18 by 18 feet; piazzas, front and rear, each 8 feet wide; cellar kitchens

B. *Officers' Quarters* (to be built): one story building 112 by 36 feet; hall at either end and two halls in center, each 10 feet wide; eight rooms, four adjoining, each 20 by 18 feet; piazzas, front and rear, each 8 feet wide; cellar kitchens

C. *Soldiers' Quarters* (completed): one story building 52 by 36 feet; center hall 12 feet wide, two rooms on either side, each 21 by 18 feet; piazzas, front and rear, each 8 feet wide; cellar kitchens

D. *Hospital* (completed): two story building 64 by 36 feet; hall at either end, 12 feet wide; four rooms each 20 by 18 feet; piazza in front, 8 feet wide; cellar kitchens

TEMPORARY QUARTERS

a. *Soldiers' Quarters Left Wing:* tent 150 by 28 feet; four company rooms and one for guard, each 30 by 28 feet

b. *Huts for Laundresses:* 15 by 10 feet, 15 by 12 feet

c. *Huts for Laundresses:* 63 by 14 feet, 61 by 14 feet, 29 by 14 feet

d. *Sink for Left Wing:* 16 by 10 feet

e. *Sutler's Store House:* 41 by 20 feet

f. *Sutler's Store House:* 41 by 16 feet

g. *Officers' Quarters:* one story building, 124 by 31 feet; built of logs; rooms 16 by 15½ feet and 12 by 15½ feet

h. *Officers' Yards and Kitchens*

j. *Soldiers' Quarters Right Wing:* hut, 141 by 28 feet; four rooms for the companies, each 29 by 28 feet; one room for the guard, prisonary, and staff guard, 21 by 28 feet

k. *Smith's Shop*

l. *Kitchens for the Four Companies of the Right Wing:* 25 by 18 feet

m. *Huts for Laundresses of the Right Wing:* 10 by 12 feet, 11 by 12 feet, 16 by 12 feet, 13 by 12 feet, and 38 by 12 feet

n. *Board Kiln:* 16 by 10 feet

o. *Bake House:* 45 by 16 feet

p. *Sink for the Right Wing:* 16 by 10 feet

q. *Commissary Store House:* 138 by 28 feet and quartermaster

r. *Commissary Store House:* 45 by 28 feet

s. *Hut for the Commissary Sergeant and Sergeant Major:* 32 by 13 feet

t. *Sand Pit:* 80 by 17 feet

v. *Ice House:* 22 by 22 by 22 feet deep

NOTE: The Commanding Officers' quarters are 300 yards from the river and about 200 feet above low water mark.

row of buildings stood a row of six log stables, still being worked on. The barracks and stables were made necessary by the assignment to the Leavenworth station of a battalion of the First Mounted Dragoons with regimental headquarters to be here also. Each stable was about thirty-six feet wide by one hundred feet long. Immediately north of these stables was the thoroughfare from the steamboat landing which lead west out onto the Plains.

South of the middle of the parade ground was a magazine, mostly underground, over which a sentinel was always posted. West of the line of stables, at the south end of the west line of buildings, stood "Bedlam," a large two-story frame building with front and back porches and a stone basement. It was the quarters of the unmarried officers with an officer's mess attached. About one hundred yards southeast of "Bedlam" stood the guardhouse, an unmerciful dungeon with a stone basement and heavy log superstructure. Southwest of the guardhouse and south of "Bedlam" stood the brick hospital with porches all around and quite comfortable.

On the ridge was a blockhouse similar to the other one. To the north of the Main Parade was a one-story building used as Commissary and quartermaster storerooms and offices. A little north and west of this area was a few homes of employees, blacksmith, carpenter, saddler, miscellaneous shops, and quartermaster stables and corrals. Also scattered here and there were a few small houses and a stone warehouse at the steamboat landing.

Bedlam, Ian's future quarters, was correctly named. It was here that the unmarried officers fought their battles again and again: from West Point to the Black Hawk War, through the swamps of Florida, over the Great Plains, the mountains and the deserts of Mexico. It was here they met, after tedious campaigns, recounting their disappointments and triumphs, their hardships through heat, cold, hunger and disease, and especially of the girls they left behind. Now they feasted and lived riotously and enjoyed the good times between campaigns.

Ian was shown his room. It wasn't much to brag about. A lieutenant in these days would be content with one room and all his furniture would not be worth twenty-five dollars.

Ian met his fellow platoon officer, also a lieutenant of the newly organized First Mounted Dragoons who had arrived several weeks earlier from a western outpost. The lieutenant, Atkins by name, was a picturesque soldier, standing something over six feet in height and fairly a giant in strength. He was military all the way. A dedicated soldier, fun loving, hard fighting, and trusted to do as he was supposed to do.

The shortage of officers was critical and all new arrivals were immediately assigned duties. On the next morning, Ian relieved Lieutenant Taylor as officer of the day. Together they then headed to the deputy commander, a Major Davidson, to report the incident of the previous day's murder. Taylor asked about having the man buried, when Davidson broke out with, "No! Let him lie there. I have reported the case to the civil authorities in

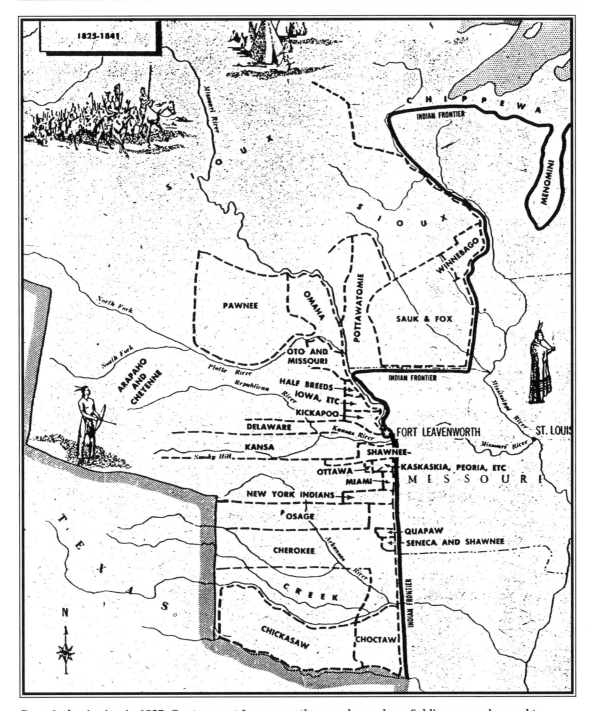

From its beginning in 1827, Cantonment Leavenworth was a busy place. Soldiers opened a road to Liberty, MO, 31 miles to the east across uncleared land. It was completed in a month. The cantonment was laid out, room being left for an entire regiment. The erection of permanent buildings began almost as soon as temporary quarters were finished. There was a hospital, and each company had a garden in which planting began at once. Stores and baggage arrived and were unloaded from their river transport while the boats erratically swung and bobbed in the current which claimed some of the freight and, in instances, lives.

The military command began official inspections of all outbound boats. Inspecting officers were plagued by the efforts of the traders who used every trick to conceal the supply of liquor which they smuggled into their upriver posts.

Leavenworth City and in this, as in other matters, they have not taken the slightest notice of my communication."

The major briefed Ian on the problem of building the stables and told him he might have some trouble from the enlisted dragoons. The officer in charge of the First Dragoon Regiment, Colonel Dodge, had expected stables to already be built for the dragoon horses. Orders had been given by the quartermaster general for the erection of stables at Des Moines on the Mississippi River as well as at Fort Gibson in Arkansas. Finding that no orders had been given by the quartermaster for building stables for the four companies under his immediate command, he had ordered the commanding officers and their companies to build the stables. The men of part of these companies refused to do the work, saying that orders had been given for building stables where detachments of the regiment were located. They had been told by the officers who recruited them that they would have nothing to do but to take care of their horses and perform military duties. There was a spirit of insubordination in the air. Orders had been posted that the first duty of a soldier is to obey his orders and the work had to be done for the preservation of the horses. It was further stated that there would be court-martials for the insubordinate men until they were brought to a proper sense of duty.

However, these men were for the most part from the Missouri woodlands of hardy pioneer stock, and they didn't take to army life too enthusiastically. They had built their quarters last winter and had performed hard service during the summer. They were mean and tough, and they were rebellious of the army's recruiting lies.

As Ian rode around the Post making his inspection as officer of the day, he saw the military advantages, which the Fort Leavenworth site possessed and which decided Colonel Leavenworth in its selection was even in that early day fully in accord with the tastes of the most ardent and exacting demands of the lover of the beautiful. From the high bluffs that fronted the Missouri River, the land sloped westward in gentle undulations broken by occasional abrupt elevation, just sufficient to give variety to the landscape. Heavy woods covered the land adjacent to the river, thinning out somewhat and opening into a natural shaded park a short distance from the river bluff, where the barracks were built.

Fort Leavenworth was in reality but a straggling cantonment, but on an admirable site. The Missouri in an abrupt bend rushes with wonderful swiftness against a rock-bound shore. From this the ground rises with a bold sweep to a hundred feet or more, then it gently slopes into a shallow vale before it rises equally again forming a number of hills. On these hilltops shaded with forest trees stood Fort Leavenworth. On the one hand is to be seen the mighty river, winding in the distance through majestic forests and by massive bluffs, stretching away until mellowed to aerial blue; on the other, rolling prairies dotted with groves and bounded on the west by a bold, grassy ridge. This, enclosed in an elliptical sweep like a beautiful amphitheater, terminated five miles southward in a knob, leaving between it and the river a view of the prairie lost in a dim and vague outline.

When Ian visited the guardhouse on his rounds, he found that some kind person had thrown enough dirt over the body of the murdered civilian to partially cover it, so as to keep the flies away. This was the only notice ever taken of the murder. In the afternoon, the civil authorities arrived with a buckboard and removed the body.

The next day Ian went down to the corral area to pick out his mount. Among the stables the horses were standing tied to the fence with lazily switching tails and drooping heads. He found the corporal in charge leaning on the breast-high corral fence, his chin on his arms, and his cap pulled down over his eyes, lazily looking at the stock in the paddock. He was a tall, dark-faced handsome lad drowsing in the afternoon sunshine. He indicated to Ian where the horses were that were available for selection. Ian was an experienced hand at picking horses and he soon selected the one for him.

The long June day was drawing to a close. The hot slanting sunbeams beat down on the horses. In the distance he heard the laughter of children being released from school. Over at the guardhouse the men were lazily laying in the shadows of the big elm trees. There was scarcely a breath of air stirring. The wooded timber to the west looked inviting; he wanted to inspect the guard towers high up on the ridges and also to try out his new mount.

The woods were nicer than he anticipated. There was a single wagon road that wound down the slope, across a small creek and continued on up the slope. Here and there were patches clear of trees. He came to several small forks in the wide trail and he followed one of these, not knowing where it led but he knew all this country was military reservation for several miles out onto the prairie.

In the shade of a large pecan grove, he noticed a buggy parked in the shade; the horse with its head down was eating the low grass.

He pulled off the path, up a little slope and out onto the grove that was clear of the usual brush. He saw a man staggering, then fall down. Was he seeing right? His eyes must be deceiving him. Yes, it was a priest, dressed in his smock and stiff white collar. Ian thought the priest was sick or hurt so he quickly wheeled his horse to the buggy, jumped off and tied his mount, all the time looking at the man now sitting up against one of the trees.

Ian ran over to help him but as he reached down, the priest noticed him and said without looking up, "Don't touch me, you . . . you," he repeated as if groping for the right word, "you . . . murderer."

The whiskey breath hit Ian in the face and he backed up, stunned, not knowing what to do or say.

"Are you a priest?" Ian asked.

"Yes," the stranger muttered drunkenly. "I am ordained, licensed to save souls." He stopped, put the bottle to his lips, drank several large gulps then looked up squarely at the lieutenant and repeated, "Licensed to save souls."

He stopped again, wiping some slobbers of whiskey off his chin.

"I save souls," he said as if confessing, "then they turn around and kill other souls. What am I supposed to do? Save your soul so you can do killing? Is this what you want me to do?"

Ian was at a loss for words. He had never encountered anything like this before. "I don't want you to do anything. I thought maybe you needed some help. Father, you are drunk!" Ian continued as he kneeled down closer to the old priest. "You had better get back to your quarters. It's going to get dark in a couple of hours," Ian suggested.

He reached over to help the priest, but the priest furiously brushed Ian away with an angry sweep of his arm.

His head dropped down and he cried like an eight-year-old whose heart was deeply broken.

Ian didn't know what to do. He never had seen a priest cry before. He just couldn't figure it out. The sobbing was not of physical pain or drunkenness; this came from the heart. The crying of a frustrated human being, not able to do anything about his hurting, crying in last desperation and helplessness as the only thing left to do.

Ian felt awkward and pained; he didn't want to just leave him here. Then again, he didn't want to stay and be of no help. He felt deep sorrow for this fellow human being but he didn't know how to help.

After a few moments of just standing there, Ian turned, walked over to his horse grazing by the buggy. He didn't want to leave this man—but what to do? He turned around and slowly came back to the sobbing priest, touched his shoulders and earnestly asked, "Father, can I help you?"

His sincerity aroused the priest from his weeping. He again looked straight into Ian's eyes. Ian returned the gaze. This man was surely drunk, but there was something else there, Ian reasoned, such a deep sadness that he had never seen before, sorrow that went down into the very bottom of his soul.

Tears flowed down from the priest's reddened eyes, across his ruddy cheeks and came together at the point of his chin.

"I'm sorry, lieutenant . . . I'm sorry, but . . ." his voice trailed off. "Have a drink with me?" he asked, brushing the tears from his chin and offering Ian the bottle.

Ian looked at him for a moment. This man, this priest was asking a favor, good or bad, however you looked at it. Maybe a drink with him would help the priest and himself. He hardly ever refused a drink of anything; it helped him escape from the world also.

"Fine," Ian said as he sat down beside the old man. "Fine. It's a good afternoon for a drink."

The priest handed him the bottle and Ian took a good swig. It burnt all the way down. He looked at the bottle, in a thoughtful mood as the burning rushed to his brain; "It sure helps, doesn't it?" Handing the bottle back, he repeated, "It sure helps."

The old man, now ashamed, didn't look up. "No, not really," again his voice trailed off into nothingness.

The mood was getting awkward.

"I'm Lieutenant Douglass, from Atlanta, Georgia. Got on post two days ago." Ian extended his hand in friendship.

The priest grasped his hand tightly for a moment, then let go, as he questioned, "Haven't you heard of me, lieutenant? I am Father Gregg, the post drunk."

"No," Ian replied simply.

"You probably wonder why I am tolerated like this. Well," he smiled now sobering up a bit, "I've saved so many souls, they tolerate me." He hesitated, then continued, "and they are a little afraid of the wrath of God, if they do too much to me, a Catholic priest."

Again he paused, then after a short while, he continued, "So they took away my church, let me wear the cloth, give me whiskey, laugh about the drunken priest, and hope to God I will lay down and die soon."

Ian saw that he was finished, so he asked, "Why the whiskey, Father?"

"Well, it is a long story, lieutenant, too long for telling. But . . ." his voice started fading again, as he continued, "this way I keep my faith. They can't reach me if my brain is numb. They can laugh, ridicule, degrade me any which way they can think of, but they can't reach me. The Lord, the whiskey, and I can keep the devil away. Besides, the whiskey makes me forget."

Ian now saw pictured plainly on the priest's face the conviction that God would cure everything in His own time. That was good or silly, however you looked at it.

He looked at Ian, "I will be judged one day on what I have been and what I have done, but I answer only to God, not to any man, not to colonels, not even to generals. The Lord will be fair. I will keep the faith, no matter what happens."

He was plainly out of his previous mood. Now he was a priest again with his faith in a fighting mood against the devils he undoubtedly was struggling with. Ian felt a warm flush of having some small part of helping this fellow man. He didn't believe all this God stuff, but the priest did. That was his right and it wasn't important enough to argue to the point. Let him believe what he wanted to.

They both got up. Ian mounted his horse and the priest climbed into the buggy.

"I've got to visit some sick children over in the valley," he said, not mentioning the word Indian.

He loosened the reins, as Ian asked, "Isn't it dangerous out there alone at night?"

"I am not alone, lieutenant. Besides, it is more dangerous for me here on the reservation than out there," he commented as he flicked the reins.

As the buggy wound down the dirt road into Salt Creek Valley, Ian sat in his saddle puzzled. That man wasn't crazy and he wasn't drunk now, but he surely talked strange. It was dangerous on the reservation? That just didn't make sense. But this was a man evidently with a great deal more knowledge and insight than he had and somehow he knew he shouldn't scoff at his remarks. Maybe he would hear more about this man later. People love to gossip, especially about a whiskey priest.

Chapter 2

The Frontier

Several days later, Captain Bellnap, whose wife Ian had saved from drowning and who was also his company commander, requested the pleasure of Ian's company at dinner. Ian was received with much cordiality, and after dinner the two sat on the veranda and the captain related a great deal of information to him about the past and present conditions of this Kansas Territory. In 1824 an expedition to the Mexican Territory started out under the leadership of Augustus Storrs, a native of New Hampshire who had settled some years ago in Missouri. This expedition had the distinction of making history by being the first to attempt to introduce wagons in which to carry goods. The traders numbered about eighty and among them were several men of intelligence from Missouri who contributed by their skill and undaunted energy to render the enterprise completely successful. A portion of the company employed pack mules; among the rest were one or two stout road wagons, two carts, and about twenty "Dearborn" carriages—a light four-wheeled country carriage used in the United States and named after its inventor. The whole caravan conveyed about $25,000 to $30,000 worth of merchandise. Colonel Marmaduke, governor of Missouri, was one of the parties constituting this trade expedition.

The opening of this trade was the work of individual enterprise, without protection or support from the government, without even its knowledge, and exposed to constant danger of life and property. The untamed Indians who roamed over the intermediate country considered the merchant and his goods their lawful prey. In three years it had grown to be a new and regular branch of interior commerce, profitable to those engaged in it, valuable to the country from the articles it carried out and for the silver, furs, and mules which it brought back. Thus, protection was sought requesting a right of way through the countries of the tribes between Missouri and New Mexico, a road marked out and security in traveling it, stipulations for good behavior from the Indians, and a consular establishment in the province to be traded with.

The adventurers' stories were full of interest and novelty. It sounded like romance to hear about caravans of men, horses, and wagons, traversing with their merchandise to the vast plains that lie between the Mississippi and the Rio del Norte. The story seemed better

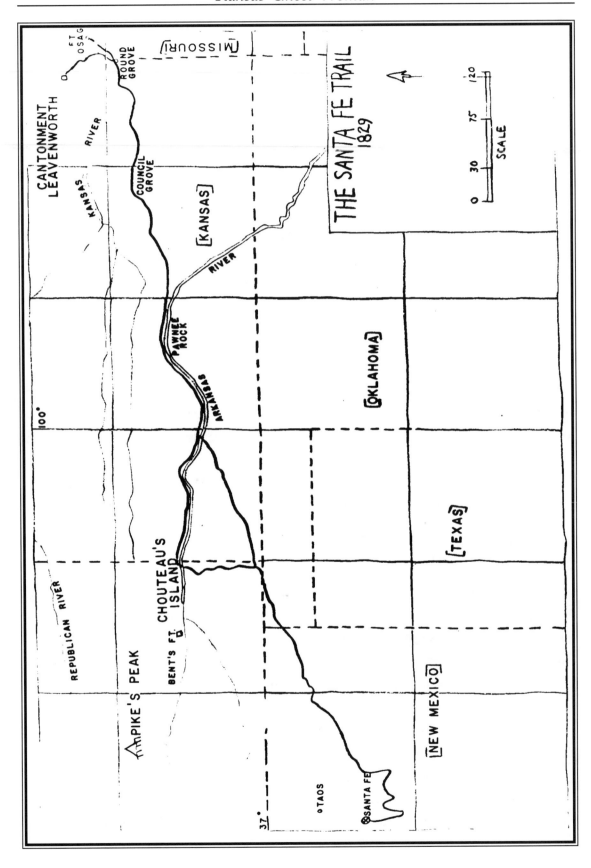

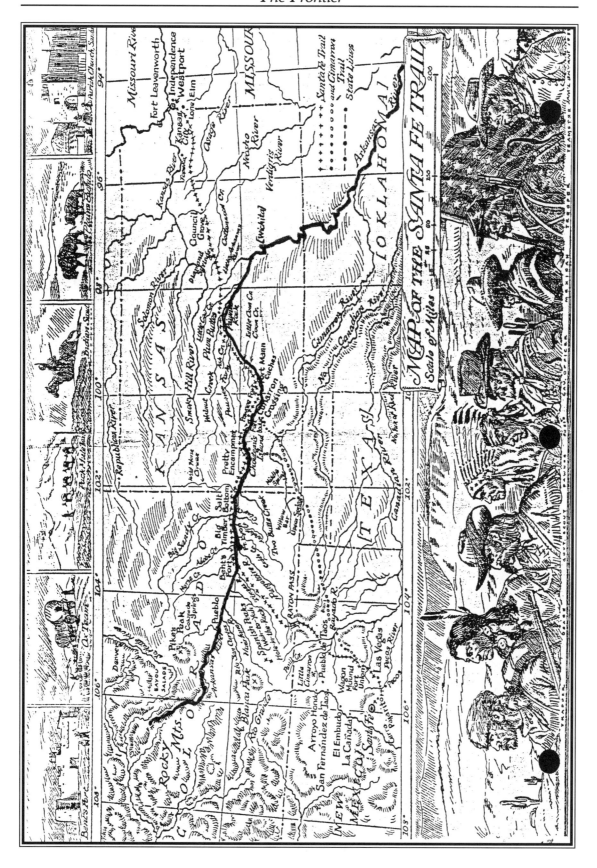

MAP OF THE SANTA FE TRAIL
Scale of Miles

suited to Asia than to North America. But, romantic as it might seem, the reality had already exceeded the visions of the wildest imaginations. The journey to New Mexico had become an affair of ordinary occurrence. Santa Fe was now considered as only a stage in this progress rather than a new point of departure to our invincible citizens.

Instead of turning back from that point, the caravans broke up there, and the subdivisions branched off in different directions in search of new theaters for their enterprise. Some proceeded down the river to Passo del Norte in Old Mexico; some continued to the mines of Chihuahua and Durango, in the province of New Biscay. Still others ventured to Sonora and Sinatoa on the Gulf of California, and some, seeking new lines of communication with Pacific coast territory, had undertaken to descend the western slope of our continent through the unexplored regions of Multanomah and Buenaventura. The fruit of these enterprises for the present year amounted to $190,000 in precious furs and gold and silver bullion and coin. This was significant considering it to be the commerce of an infant United States, but expected from the now regulated and protected trade.

The name of Mexico possessed always an invincible charm for the people of the western states guarded from intrusion by Spanish jealousies and despotic power. Imprisonment for life or labor in the mines was the unalterable penalty for any attempt to penetrate the forbidden country. But failure, misfortune, chains, and forced labor were not sufficient to intimidate the seekers of gold and silver, and Mexico's attraction still aroused imaginations and daring spirits.

The journal of Pike, then a lieutenant, inflamed this spirit and induced new adventures to hazard the enterprise, only to meet the fate of their predecessors. It was not until the independence of Mexico in the year 1821 that the frontiers of this vast and hitherto sealed-up country were thrown open to foreign ingress and trade. The state of Missouri, from her geographical position and the courageous spirit of her inhabitants, was among the first to engage in it. The "Western Internal Provinces," the vast region comprising of New Mexico, El Paso del Norte, New Biscay, Chihuahua, Sonora, and the wide slope spreading towards the Gulf of California, the ancient "Sea of Cortez," was the remote theater of their courageous enterprise. The further off or the less known and the constant exposure to possible death made this region even more attractive to their adventurous spirits. Of course, they complained about the constant danger, but it was really what they yearned for.

To the people of the West and southern "money people," this trade was an object of the greatest value. The Missourians were especially interested as their own interior location cut them off from foreign commerce. The Mexicans were their neighbors and the only foreign power with which they could trade. It was one of the few sources from which they could derive the precious metals. The coin already brought in constituted the circulating medium of the country in the western parts of Missouri. It was paid into the offices for public lands and then went into the coffers of the government, whose protection it solicited.

But it was not the West alone that benefited by this trade. The North and the South participated in the profits. The South grew the cotton, the North worked it up, and the West exported it, thus displaying one of the most beautiful operations of agriculture, manufacture, and commerce, mutually dependent upon each other.

That the trade would be beneficial to the inhabitants of the internal Mexican provinces was a proposition too plain to be argued. They were a people among whom all the arts were lost; no books, no newspapers, but iron was a dollar a pound. Cultivating the earth with wooden tools.Spinning upon a stick.

To these people, whose fathers wore the proud title of conquerors, a supply of merchandise upon the cheapest terms was the least of the benefits to be derived from commerce with the people of the United States. The consolidation of their republican institutions, the improvement of their moral and social condition, the restoration of their lost arts, and the development of the national resources were among the grand results of practical benefits anticipated from such a commerce.

Thus, in a petition to the President, it was stressed that the request of protection rested on the same principle that carried protection to the commerce of the Union upon every sea, in the most remote countries, and upon distant isles. The maritime commerce required ships, treaties, ambassadors, and consuls to protect it. The inland trade to Mexico required a right of way to be purchased from the Indians and two or three commercial agents to be stationed in the internal provinces. Could sympathy be lavished upon a citizen hung by a pirate and denied to a citizen shot by Indians?

This petition recited that a beneficial trade had been carried on for some years between the inhabitants of the two countries in which domestic cottons and other articles had been carried out from the United States. Gold, silver, furs, and mules were brought back in return. The tribes inhabiting that tract of country presented the only obstacle to the successful prosecution of the trade upon a large scale.

Although the threat of Indian attack constantly was expected by the caravans on the trail between Council Grove and the foothills of the Rockies, killings were curiously few. Many of the Missourians who carried freight to Santa Fe had grown up in the Old Southwest between the Mississippi and the Allegheny Mountains and vigilance had become second nature. Also the Great Plains Indians attacked only for blood revenge, never without excuse. They preferred to steal than to kill. For the Indians, this stealing was the great game of life for them, but the stealing fun rarely involved killing and then only when there was no way out of the difficulty. The tribes that lived on the prairies that the freighters crossed eagerly stole horses and anything else they could lay their hands on. However, in any caravan, there was always one frontiersman ready to casually kill any Indian discovered alone. The little detached group of traders who were the first to follow the Santa Fe Trail experienced very little trouble and no lives were lost due to the Indians. It was not until 1828, in the era of one hundred wagon caravans, that any traders were killed on the trail. In that year, two young Missourians by the names of McNees and Monroe, with a caravan returning to Fort Leavenworth, were surprised in their sleep and killed by persons unknown.

Having carelessly laid down on the banks of a stream, since known as McNees' Creek, they were barbarously shot with, supposedly, their own guns in the very sight of the caravan. When their comrades came up they found McNees lifeless and Monroe dying. Monroe was carried nearly forty miles to the Cimarron River, where he died and was buried according to the custom of the prairies. The murderers could have been caballeros dressed like Indians; it had happened in the past. These caballeros, who wandered through the buffalo plains, killing game and carrying on illegal trade with the Indians, could have killed the two. These hardy Mexicans with their lances and guns traveled sometimes an amazing distance from their New Mexico villages. They were usually lone wolves and murder was not a stranger to them. There were also unscrupulous white men on the prairies who stole, murdered, and pillaged everywhere; many of their crimes were falsely attributed to the Indian. Frontier justice, being the law of the gun rather than trial by jury, was carried out two days later.

Just as the funeral ceremonies for McNees and Monroe were about to be concluded, six or seven Indians appeared on the opposite side of the Cimarron. Perhaps these were of the group that had murdered the two men, perhaps not. The Indians could have been outcasts of the tribe, which the chiefs had no control over. Some of the party proposed inviting them to a parley, while the rest, burning for revenge, evinced a desire to fire upon them at once. It is more than probable, however, that the Indians were not only innocent, but also ignorant of the outrage that had been committed or they would hardly have ventured to approach the caravan. Being quick of perception, they very soon saw the belligerent attitude assumed by some of the company, and, therefore, wheeled around and attempted to escape. One shot was fired which wounded a horse and brought the Indian to the ground; he was instantly riddled with bullets. Almost simultaneously, another discharge of several guns followed by which all the rest were either killed or mortally wounded, except one, who escaped to bear to his tribe the news of their dreadful catastrophe.

Thus, the miserable and unending cycle began.

These wanton cruelties had a most disastrous effect upon the prospect of trade. The exasperated children of the desert became more and more hostile to the pale faces, against whom they continued to wage a cruel war for many successive years. In fact, this same party suffered severely a few days afterwards. They were pursued by the enraged comrades of the slain Indians to the Arkansas River, where they were robbed of nearly a thousand head of mules and horses, but the Indians were not yet satisfied.

Caravan Attacked by Indians.

The same Indians, in blood revenge, waylaid the next party of about twenty men on the return trail from Santa Fe. They started a running fight at first, then skirmished in true Indian style. When night came on, the Comanche Indians resumed their attacks, endeavoring to stampede the horses so they could chase them off and capture them later. Their attempts were almost successful several times during the night and they were only kept from accomplishing their purpose by tying the bell mare to one of the wagons where the jingling of the bell warned them every time the Indians charged.

The next day the Comanches resumed the attack as vigorously as ever. Forming a circle, they galloped round and round the caravan, shouting their war whoops in a chilling fiendish manner. So fierce were the harassing tactics that they used that the little line of prairie schooners succeeded in advancing only five miles during the day. The attack was kept up night and day for a week until the traders were exhausted from loss of sleep. The Indians killed one of the traders and, during the several days of fighting and harassing, they made off with all the caravan's livestock. The unfortunate traders were not only compelled to advance on foot but were even strained to carry upon their backs nearly a thousand dollars each to the Arkansas River, where it was concealed in the ground until a conveyance was procured to transfer it to Fort Leavenworth.

The affair to which Captain Bellnap referred to was as near an Indian outbreak as ever occurred in the vicinity of Fort Leavenworth. All the tribes within one hundred miles of the post were semi-civilized and brought here by the government from the East. They gave the troops very little trouble—that which came to the latter was from hostiles farther to the north and west.

When the Missourians reached Fort Leavenworth, they were done with orderly documented appeals to the national government for military protection along the trail. They demanded action now; anymore delays would not be tolerated.

These frontiersmen were tough, no doubt about that; they lived by the gun, but in the Comanche they met their equal.

They were superior to the other Indians that ranged over the same areas. They were a proud race, long noted for their great skill in riding, and their war parties scoured the country from the Black Hills in the Dakota Territory to the interior of Mexico. They were a little taller and had better physiques than their Shoshone kinfolk.

Worst of all, the Comanches were a very powerful nation, numbering probably ten thousand. They were hospitable and social to those whom they considered their friends. But now the whites were considered enemies because of the killings by the Missourians. In their wars, they practiced cruelties and barbarities. They had the reputation of being brave warriors. They had bitter wars with the Pawnees, Sacs, Foxes, and the Utes, but they were at peace with the powerful Cheyenne, Kiowa, Apache and, the greatest of all nations, the Sioux. If they joined forces, the westward expansion would cease!

Across Country with a Cavalry Column

The teamsters lounge lazily in their saddles, a trooper or two, whose horses have perhaps gone lame, or who, suffering from some slight indisposition, have been given permission to remain in the rear with the train, are perched on the top of one of the wagons, while some little rascal of a dog runs up and down barking himself hoarse at nothing at all.

President Andrew Jackson's Secretary of War ordered four companies of infantry to accompany the caravans. The frontiersmen hooted at the idea, labeling the escort an electioneering maneuver of the government to gain popularity. The march was at first exhilarating to the dragoons fresh from Jefferson Barracks in St. Louis, but after Council Grove was left behind, fatigue and monotony dulled the experience before they reached Chouteau's Island, the end of the convoy's journey.

Weary and athirst on the sandy hills under a scorching sun, a lieutenant of the company related, "Amid the waves of the broad river, we beheld the beautiful island; its green carpet of grass and shady groves invited us to the cool shade and pleasant breezes."

The traders continued towards Santa Fe. There was no pastoral poetry for them. They had hardly advanced six or seven hours when, from a pass between the sand hills, when Indians fired upon a little vanguard group, killing one man.

Horsemen hurried back to Chouteau's Island with the news, and Major Riley at once gave the word to strike tents and led his battalion into Mexican Territory. The reinforcement reached the caravan at night probably unseen by the Indians. The traders believed that if reveille had not been sounded, the unsuspecting Indians would have attacked the party in the morning. The escort marched with the caravan for several days, but there was no further molestation on the route.

Back on the Arkansas River, the Indians scurried about the encampment of the dragoons for a few days; in a succession of attacks, four soldiers were killed, and most of the horses and oxen were driven off.

Late in the fall of the year, the caravan and its escort was back in Missouri with reports of unusually high profits; the military escort had been essential to the success of the expedition. President Jackson had done what he could. It remained for the Congress to grant an appropriation to mount and properly equip these troops. The year 1832 had been enlivened by an Indian outbreak, the Black Hawk War on the northwestern frontier, so the appropriation passed by Congress also authorized the President to raise a mounted force for the protection of the frontier.

*   *   *

It was getting quite late by now and Ian excused himself to retire to his quarters. The moon was well up in the heavens, and the whole parade ground was almost as bright as day. The verandas were filled with officers and ladies chatting happily.

The evening air was changing now and growing chilly, and the older people were going inside. Only the younger ladies remained longer on the verandas hoping to be noticed by the dragoons passing the cottages.

The lights were still blazing in the barracks. There was quite a commotion in the day room. Some of the young bachelors were playing billiards, others were fighting their past battles again over the beers on the tables.

The young officers always seemed to find excitement either with a new romance, a good fight with the trappers, or horse racing. Sometimes the excitement was quite unusual. One of these episodes happened that very same night. Sometime after midnight when Ian was in a drunken sleep, Lieutenant Atkins banged on his bedroom door. Ian jumped up and opened the door to find a half drunk Atkins standing there in a long white nightgown with a candle in one hand and a pistol in the other. He informed Ian that he had heard a noise in the cellar where the whiskey was kept and he thought someone was stealing a barrel of it. The whiskey was considered more valuable than gold to the young bachelors, so Ian wasted no time getting his pistol, too, and they headed for the cellar.

They tiptoed down the stairs to the basement, both of them staggering a bit. The candle didn't give out much light; it only cast scary shadows in the dark cellar. As they pushed the heavy wooden door slowly open and leaned forward to see better, they heard a sudden scuffling in the dark. Atkins, in sudden fright, fired at the scurrying shadow. The discharge of the pistol in the barracks at that hour awoke everyone. The blast of the shot hurt the ears of the two drunken lieutenants and the white flash blinded them for a moment.

The intruder scurried from behind the old barrel and it wasn't long before both of them knew the identity of the shadow. It was a skunk, an animal whose stinking qualities far surpassed that of a polecat or badger. The shot had startled the skunk also and a spray of stench sprayed in their direction. Both of the men shot quickly, but their shots did not prove fatal. There arose from the wounded animal a horrible sickening stink. The two lieutenants kept blazing away at the skunk as they retreated, staggering back out of the cellar. In two minutes the foul smell filled the whole building and, in three more minutes, the stink floated over half of the fort. Even with the doors to the upstairs rooms shut tight, it still smelled as if the animal was within six inches of the noses of the sickened men.

On another occasion several drunken lieutenants turned the retreat cannon around and shot a twenty-pound ball right through the "hop" room of the officers club. Luckily no one was hurt, but it caused quite a bit of excitement. The perpetrators of the deed were never tried as the guilty bachelors all had foolproof alibis.

Ian was kept on the go from morning until night. Reveille was sounded at five o'clock in the morning, just after sunrise. Immediately afterwards came stable call, when he had to go down to the stables and superintend the cleaning, watering and feeding of the horses. After returning to his quarters, he changed into his field uniform and breakfast call sounded. After that, in quick succession, came the dress parade, guard mounting, and drill. At twelve noon, the quarters and messes of the companies had to be inspected. From that time until drill at four in the afternoon, the men generally had nothing to do, but half the time was occupied by some company duty. Drill at four lasted for an hour and a half, then stable calls again and then retreat. Because of their horses, the enlisted dragoons had many more duties to attend to than the other men did, so when night came they were well worn out. However, after a drink or two, many were ready for a night of fun, sometimes until two or three o'clock in the morning.

Considering Fort Leavenworth was a small fort on the edge of the western frontier, there was an unusual active social life there. Most of the married officers had their wives and daughters with them, forming a very pleasant little community, who were almost continuously together in social enjoyment of the peculiar amusements and pleasures of this wild country.

They had many pastimes such as riding on horseback or in carriages over the green fields of the prairies, picking strawberries and wild plums, deer chasing, grouse hunting, horse racing, and other amusements of the garrison in which they were constantly engaged, enjoying life to a high degree. Even though Fort Leavenworth was the extreme western military post on the frontier, the barracks and houses were comfortably built.

Here came the officers fresh from West Point and other officers older in service. The older officers brought their families to share with them the pleasures and lighten the burdens of their service in this distant frontier. While there was much danger and hardships to be encountered in this remote frontier land, there was also much to attract and interest the ambitious and enterprising, and to furnish an occasional romantic affair.

The officers were, as a rule, educated and intelligent gentlemen, and their wives and daughters were cultured and gentle, forming a refined society, but free, in great measure, from the rigid conventionalities that governed society in the big eastern cities and posts.

Hops (dances) and amateur theatricals helped to make life at the post one continuous round of pleasure. The plays furnished considerable amusement for the entire garrison and they were frequently repeated during the winter in the assembly rooms of the barracks.

A tri-weekly mail service from Liberty, Missouri was installed to take the place of the former weekly horseback trip. The service now included passengers as the journey was being made by stagecoach.

The army was much indebted for the history of its labors in the early West to men of science and art, those who traveled in search of knowledge through the vast western domain. In those early times the army was, in many instances, the sole inhabitant of the new country, the advance guard of the civilization that was to build an empire. The homes of its officers and men were conducted on the "open door" plan where hospitality was dispensed to travelers with a freedom surpassed by none, and so thoroughly characteristic of army men and women.

Important visitors came to the post, such as Alexander Philip Maximilian, Prince of Weid-Neu-Weid; George Catlin, an English artist of repute; and Washington Irving, the famous American author.

George Catlin was so impressed with the country that he urged the country to the west of the reservation be preserved as a National "Plains of Grass" Park. He hoped that the world could see for ages to come the native Indian galloping his wild horse with sinewy bow, shield and lance amid the elks and buffalo in the freshness of nature.

Alexander Philip Maximilian, Prince of Weid-Neu-Weid, was a scientist of international reputation. Born in Prussia in 1782, he was the eighth son of the reigning Friederich Karl. He served in the Prussian army and was present at the battle of Jena. Maximilian, though a successful soldier, was a great searcher of knowledge. While serving in the Napoleonic campaigns, he was planning expeditions to the American continent. When released from his martial duties, he made preparation for an expedition in the interest of science to Brazil early in 1815. After concluding these travels, he came to North America in May 1832, landing at Boston. He traveled down the Ohio and up the Mississippi River, arriving at St. Louis the following April. From there he started out to study the Great Plains Indians.

The social leaders of the garrison along with society leaders from nearby towns lavishly entertained these distinguished men. It gave Fort Leavenworth the distinction as the leader in social functions to which society flocked in great numbers.

There were many balls and parties, and they were well attended by pretty girls from Weston, St. Joseph, and Leavenworth City. Many of the young bachelors thought Kansas was not so barbarous after all.

In Leavenworth City there were charming half-breed ladies who resorted there. Their charms and convivial company tempted even the most faithful married officers.

After a particularly riotous ball in Leavenworth City, Ian slept late the next morning. The day was Sunday and most duties were suspended. There had been a party at the Planter House and one at McCrackens' Hotel. After attending both, he left Planter House about three o'clock in the morning and got to bed at five o'clock after reveille was sounded.

*   *   *

Ian brushed his hand across his face, trying to get rid of the sun that was shining brightly in his eyes. He slid over onto the other side of the bed but still the sun followed him.

After last night's affair, he was in no mood to rise with the sun. Laying there, half asleep, he heard someone pull the drapes together. The room suddenly darkened to a twilight.

"Ah, that is more like it," he thought to himself.

Then, in a half minute, it slowly came to his awaking mind that someone must have pulled the drapes closed and if someone did this, then someone must be in the room. He really didn't care much one way or the other, but he was new at the fort and he had to wake up; he didn't necessarily want to get into any trouble because he didn't get up when he was supposed to.

As he sleepily threw off his blanket and sat up on the edge of the bed, his downcast eyes opened onto a pair of shapely feminine legs in front of him. He closed his eyes and shook his head slowly several times; he must still be in a room at the Planter House. That party was a wild one; he thought he had come back to the barracks; maybe he hadn't.

As he opened his eyes again, he noticed he was in his own room at the barracks. The legs were still there. Slender, straight and very intriguing. As he raised his face he saw the rest of the body; it was just as nice as the legs. A youngish blonde, around 20 he figured, blue eyes, fair skin, and quite a fine face to match her body.

The girl spoke first, "Do you want your room cleaned this morning, lieutenant?"

Ian hesitated, as the cobwebs of sleep cleared his mind.

She repeated the question.

Ian didn't have his mind on the query of whether the room should be cleaned or not. She must be Dutch or Scandinavian; she was really attractive.

"Yes . . . yes, go right ahead," he answered her as he got up off the bed. Walking over to the bureau, still in his undershorts he poured some water in the basin and splashed it over his face. He grabbed a towel, rubbed the water from his face. As he finished he glanced into the mirror on the wall behind the bureau. He caught a glimpse of the girl, bending over the tasseled bed.

"Hot damn," he muttered aloud as he turned around and admired the lovely shape. The girl knew he was watching her movements but it didn't bother her, she was used to that.

"How much am I paying for this?" Ian questioned.

"Three dollars a month," she answered, not stopping her work.

"How much for fun and games?" he half-jokingly queried.

She straightened up, her breasts protruding provocatively, looked him straight in the eye, "Two dollars, gold," she replied, very business like, "In cash," she added.

He picked out a two dollar gold piece from the change on the bureau and slid it over to the edge of the marble top.

"Sounds fair enough to me," he said as he crossed the room to the bed.

A half hour later, the blonde had departed and the money was gone. As Ian shaved and dressed, he kept thinking to himself that duty here wasn't going to be too bad, in fact it was starting out better than a vacation in that sin city of New Orleans. He figured he would sleep late more often on Sundays.

He walked downstairs to the mess for a late breakfast. By now he was hungry for something to eat.

*   *   *

On his off days, Ian enjoyed the friendly company of the emigrants passing through the fort. Their wagon trains were usually formed in Westport (Kansas City), Missouri. They traveled up the Missouri side of the river and crossed at Fort Leavenworth on a ferry. They climbed up a steep hill at the waters edge, up past the Main Parade of the fort, then headed southward for a mile where they made camp until a group of several wagons assembled. While at the fort they made final repairs to the wagons, laid in supplies, partied and rested for the starting of the trek to Council Grove. By now, some of their predecessors had settled at scattered places on the trail and had opened up trading posts, supply houses and saloons for the convenience of the travelers.

On the first day's journey, they climbed over the ridge set back about a mile from the river, traveled down into Salt Creek Valley and up a long, gentle slope and stopped at Eight-Mile House. The next day they set out across the gently rolling country of eastern Indian Territory as signs of civilization fell off considerably.

Emigration was searching out the western part of the country, that is, west of the Missouri River. The newcomers poured into the country like a flooded mountain stream. They came faster than it was possible to produce crops for their bread and other food. They came like an avalanche down a steep, slick slope. It seemed like Kentucky, Virginia and Tennessee were being entirely deserted and all the inhabitants were moving to the "Far West."

Caravan after caravan passed over the prairies of Illinois, crossing the great Mississippi River at St. Louis, all trails converging on Fort Leavenworth. The stream of immigration was causing unlawful and barefaced seizing and occupation of the Indian lands; all without the slightest right whatsoever.

Probably from one to five wagons crossed the Missouri daily and brought in an average of twenty to forty people a day. They brought great numbers of slaves. Many of the emigrants, quickly overcome with the hardships and misery of the journey, stopped in Missouri. Almost four hundred people a month were settling there. In 1820, there were 56,000 settlers in Missouri with about 10,000 slaves. The majorities of slaves were personal servants or were used in agricultural work under the owner's supervision. Cotton was not a favored crop in Missouri. Tobacco growing had been started on a small scale and hemp (the tough fiber of this plant was used for making coarse fabrics and ropes) was the nearest thing to a principal money crop at that time. Slaves in Missouri were not the foundation of a plantation society. In the newly settled counties, the number of slaves was small because these settlers were generally poor farm people themselves. In St. Louis and the other southern districts, the people were wealthy and consequently had large numbers of slaves to do their work for them.

Many Christians in the north, east and western parts of the country were strongly against the injustice of slavery. They kept alive continuous protests to Congress on this matter and finally Congress forced the House on March 2, 1820, to pass a compromise, which was completed by a later resolution that slavery should not be permitted in other parts of the Louisiana Purchase north of the Arkansas Territory.

However, Congress of the infant United States could or would not enforce this act and it was generally ignored. Troubled by many other pressing problems and fighting for survival of the nation from pressures and intrigues by foreign interests, Congress took no disciplinary action. Slavery continued in Missouri in defiance of the law.

Many an Easterner was discontented with the restricted religious system of the firmly entrenched Episcopal, Baptist and Catholic churches. The close examination of personal behavior exercised by both the church congregations and neighborhood busybodies also made Easterners quite uneasy. These freethinking people considered the laws of the state and churches as tasks that gave social control to the ruling classes. This new system of the colonies caused the same economic and social class distinctions that they had come to America to escape. These people considered the so-called justice and laws of the ruling class as a severe injustice. This feeling hurried and shaped the advance of the American frontier. And even though the laws of the ruling classes were better than none and gave them comparative comfort, they ached for an alternate and more independent social order.

Young people were one of the forces that caused a considerable restlessness to escape from the comfortable life to something more challenging. The young people had an intense desire to show themselves as capable as their parents and to have as many privileges and freedoms as the ruling class. Like Ian, they hated the staleness and hopelessness of the older society leaders. The cheapness of new lands combined with their bold ambitions and apparent speculative undertakings for magnificent rates of profit and opportunities moved complete families west. There they could claim six square miles of land. With their adventurous spirit they would burrow themselves in the ground for their first shelter under some hillside, cast the earth upon the timbered roof, and made a smoky fire against the highest side of their burrows. In these crude houses they sang psalms and praised the Lord until they could build a better house and till the soil. By the Lord's blessing and their wives and little ones' labors, they brought forth bread to eat.

The frontier also attracted the grand speculations of the landowning "gentlemen" of the inner circle of the southern aristocracy. They dreamed of ten thousand-acre plantations cut out of the wilderness. Here many of them found clover as high as a man's knee. Water, fertile soil and timberland were available to everyone. These free natural resources, all on one plot of ground, were the essence of what the pioneers dreamed about.

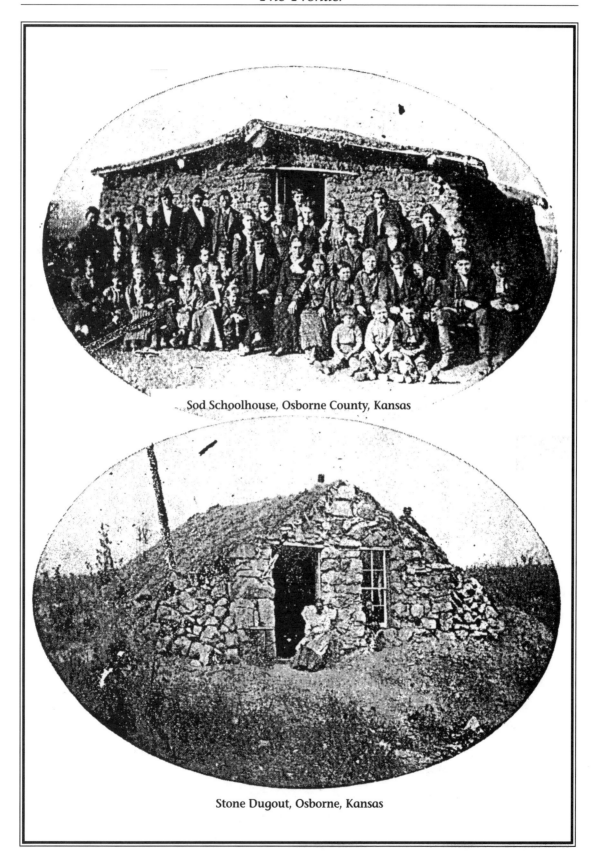

Sod Schoolhouse, Osborne County, Kansas

Stone Dugout, Osborne, Kansas

These people married young, many of the girls at the age of fifteen. The young men did not have to wait until they had money; hard work was all that was needed to start a marriage. The frontier economy offered nothing to older daughters who did not marry, only a hard share of the household drudgery awaited them. The lazy man on the frontier was "hated out."

The bounty of the western land offered by Congress to stimulate recruiting of emigrants, the launching of the first steamboats on the Missouri in 1819, and the leadership of frontiersmen in Congress, all helped to advertise the presence of open lands and equal opportunity for poor and honest men. Every new bit of talk about unparalleled opportunity of the western frontier started a new rush of settlers.

The emigration was a safety valve for the existing ruling society by ridding the eastern states of discontented people within whom there was a consuming fire thereby making for potential revolutionists.

The men of capital in the northern states became interested in the investments of western land because of the evidence of safety combined with quick profits. These western lands were certainly much more fertile and productive than the worn out eastern farms.

The established society finally became worried about the mass exodus of the people. Newspapers shifted their emphasis to the hardships of pioneer life and stressed the dubiousness of western success. One newspaper, doing its best to stop the westward movement, argued that when the civil, social, literary, and religious institutions of the east were considered, it seemed like madness for men to leave their homes for the wild lands of the west. These men had no extraordinary reasons for moving and yet they rushed to a much wilder state of society.

The frontier life was indeed dangerous. The communities had to fight to stay alive, but they soon learned to meet the Indian danger quickly and decisively when the danger arose. The frontiersmen were establishing themselves as men who lived and fought hard. These were the crucial years in the backcountry.

Some of the pioneer men lived alone, cleared and tilled the land, and planted corn. After the cabins were built and the corn well advanced, these men went back to the east to gather their families. Upon their return to the new clearing, some found their crops entirely destroyed. Herds of buffalo had trampled over the rail fences and eaten the corn to the ground, but with the strength to bear the heartbreaking hardships, not to be subdued by this setback, and with a cheerfulness, not easy to be depressed, they continued to work their land. With patience that could laugh at suffering and a daring that nothing could even daunt, every difficulty which happened, every obstacle which was imposed between them and the accomplishment of the objects of their pursuit, was surmounted or removed. In a comparatively brief space of time, they rose to the enjoyment of many of those who were experienced in earliest and more populous settlements. Their morals for a while, suffered deterioration, and their manners and habits became savage and rough instead of staying the same as those of refined society.

When war threatened in Missouri, the pioneers constructed stockades. Usually a settlement was of necessity a fort, a stockade group of cabins and blockhouses. The blockhouses were two-story affairs built at the corners of the stockade, projecting two or three feet beyond the outer walls of the cabins, and log walls connected the cabins. The thick slab double gate that closed the fort was built to face the settlement's water supply, usually a spring, creek or river. Families were sometimes awakened in the dead of night with a report that Indians were at hand. The whole family was instantly in motion. The man of the house seized his gun and other implements of war. The mother woke up and dressed the children as well as she could. There was no possibility of getting a horse in the night to help them to the fort. They caught up what articles of clothing and provisions they could get hold of in the dark for they dared not light a candle or even stir the fire. All this was done with the utmost dispatch and the silence of death. The greatest care was taken not to awaken the youngest child. To the rest, it was enough to say "Indian" and not a whimper was heard afterwards. Thus, it happened often that the whole number of families belonging to a fort who were in the evening at their homes were all in their little fortress before the dawn of the next morning. In the course of the succeeding day parties of armed men brought in their household furniture.

Failure to take up arms against the Indians, when occasion demanded, was a serious offense. Anger mingled with contempt and scorn by his fellow men was a weapon no man in a frontier community could stand against. Lazy idleness and notorious dishonesty were also met with righteous contempt. The result was usually the changing of the faults or else exile. Whipping of a thief was an approved punishment. Petty thieves received "the flag of the United States," which in cruel humor signified thirteen stripes. "Thirteen stripes" was a frequent penalty for the theft of something of value. "Private" fights for all their brutality of biting, kicking and gouging were no concern of the courts. Some rudeness in customs was demanded by frontier conditions. Frontier manners meant open hospitality, cordial harmony, warm and constant friendships, but it also meant vengeful resentments, and sometimes harsh and rude actions.

Some of the frontiersmen were engaged in the business of cattle raising. The scrawny, half-wild cows roamed the unfenced woods and prairies. The men were called "cow keepers" and they enjoyed eating the flesh of the old cows and lean calves that were likely to die. These cow keepers were hardy people and were almost continually on horseback, being obliged to know the whereabouts of their cattle. Cattle driving was already developing on a modest scale.

About the regular garrisons of the Missouri and Kentucky frontiers, cattlemen sometimes built cabins and made a rail fence enclosure for the calves. When the militia were called into service for battle against the Indians, the cattlemen found their largest market in supplying the marching army.

In these years the emigration from the southern states was even greater. The poor white farmers in the slavery states, faced with dwindling economic opportunity, were forced from the rich bottomlands by expanding plantations. The Appalachian and Missouri backwoods and the Kentucky forest were a breeding ground of the discontented pioneer. The frontier seeker chucked the household stuffs into his wagon, hung a bucket beneath and the feed box behind, harnessed up his horses, and commenced the journey westward. He walked, keeping his herd of ambling livestock on the trail. His oldest boy sat astride the right-hand wheel horse, holding the reins in one hand. As the wagon rumbled over the long grass and through the open sunlight of the prairie, the frontier seeker found new comfort in his soul. His womenfolk did the cooking over the campfire, and the family slept in the wagon-bed or on the ground. If the jolting of the wagon became tiresome, they walked awhile, and took a turn at driving the cows. There was scarcely ever an unhappy or anxious face among the many hundreds of souls of these caravans.

They were lovers of the frontier, people who were happiest on the fringe of settlement. They were economically independent. They had little or no ready money, but they could obtain most of what they wanted by bartering. But for all the goodnaturedness of life in the frontier and backcountry, the pioneer was particularly susceptible to two irritations: financial burden of land purchase prices and taxes, and crop failures. Both were reflections of the old social order they had escaped upon the new life in which they had settled; both turned the pioneers' minds to thoughts of emigration.

The backwoods pioneer carried his discontent within him wherever he went; he never quite escaped from it. His life was one of alternate enthusiasm and dull indifference, alternate energy and laziness. He drank too heavily; he knew the taste of good whisky, but he had no objection to "rotgut." In his zest to be "natural," he was careless of personal comfort and cleanliness, dosed himself too heavily with perhaps the wrong things whenever he became downright sick, and never learned that swamp lands bred poisonous diseases. They were subject to great excitement of their mental passions. There was little contentedness in the frontier religion, but there was, instead, a great deal of loud hallooing the violent expression of their faith. Pioneer's customs displayed brutally harsh relationships in religion, in play, and even in work. It was this quality that gave western hospitality its individuality and its satisfying fullness.

Good coffee, corn bread and butter, wild and tame fowls, venison, and pork were set before travelers requesting shelter for the night. The wife, timid, silent, and reserved, but

The Frontier

The Emigrant Train Bedding Down for the Night—a painting by Benjamin Franklin Reinhart in the collection of the Corcoran Gallery of Art, Washington, D.C. (Gift of Mr. and Mrs. Lansdell K. Christie.)

constantly attentive to the travelers comfort, did not sit at the table with the men. Like the wives of the early biblical tribal rulers, they stood and attended to the strangers. This kind of hospitality is extended to you as long as you choose to stay. When you are ready to depart and speak about your bill, you are most commonly told, with some slight mark of resentment, that they do not keep a tavern. Even the yellow-haired children would run away from your money.

Civilization was tightening its first grasp even in Kansas. Land harpers, shyster lawyers, and other contemptuous agents were making themselves at home in the long-stem grass country. There were rough, tough and educated men who always followed the farthest frontier to steal away the toil and money of the common people.

* * *

Ian visited with three families who were camped at the edge of the fort. They had arrived yesterday and they were resting and laying in supplies. They were a hardy and rough outfit, dressed in backwoods fashion. Particularly outstanding was a buxom country girl of about twenty summers, of healthy red complexion who weighed about 200 pounds. Her hair was "yaller" and her eyes reddish-brown. Her greasy calico dress hung down to the knees—not a bit lower—and her legs, which were like stovepipes in size, were bare. As she swung along the path between wagons with a male member of the caravan, she suddenly came to a stop and began dancing a regular "hoe-down," a lively dance practiced in Missouri. Her voice rang out in a "ral didle dal, raddle de da . . ." keeping time with her clog dancing.

She smiled at the fellow with her as she finished the dancing and continued on, "Jesus, but this Kansas sile is powerful good for dancing! Eh, Sam?"

Ian "jawed" with the emigrants for over two hours. He knew he would be escorting some of these wagon trains soon and he wanted to learn all he could about these people, their hopes, their problems, and their thinking.

Ian talked to the old timers and the teenagers alike. He was interested in all of them. They sensed this and soon they became as friendly as if they had known each other all their lives. They invited him to stay for supper. The hot corn bread and beans were eaten out of a tin plate balanced on his knees while sitting on a keg by the campfire. Good conversation and companionship, which is what people remember in their dreams of the good old days. He enjoyed their carefree manners, their crudeness, and their openness. There was no lying, no cheating, and no conniving, just free flowing, child-like honesty.

It was getting late in the afternoon, in fact, the sun had set and it was beginning to darken a bit. Ian made his good-byes, mounted his horse, and started back to the fort. He had to check on the horses in the stables to see if they were bedded down properly for the night.

A half-hour later he had finished his inspection and standing outside the stables when he noticed Father Gregg on his way to the parsonage. He was completely drunk. Ian had become used to it by now, as had the rest of the post, but it always saddened him to see the priest staggering around the post. This evening he was in an unusually bad condition. He fell to the ground several times; the last time he couldn't stand up so he began crawling on all fours.

Several dogs, romping together and running after one another, noticed the priest and all started barking at him. One of the dogs was York, which stayed around the guardhouse. A fellow had found him on Rowdy Row in town. He was a famous dog among the officers, a great hunter and water dog. He could stand up on his hind legs and catch meat tossed to him. But now in the excitement of barking and the other dogs nipping at the strange crawling of the black clothes figure, York became as vicious as the other dogs.

Suddenly the pack bit and pulled on the priest's clothing. He was so drunk he could only swing his arms feebly at his canine attackers.

The entire parade ground was empty of people, except for the sentries that couldn't leave their posts. The families were eating supper and the dragoons were sitting in their barracks drinking beer.

Ian never suspected that the dog York could become so vicious and it took him a second to realize that Father Gregg was in danger.

He ran over to the dog pack, kicked one hard in the side belly, grabbed hold of York's collar and tossed him off the priest. The fight instantly left the pack and they scampered away as Father Gregg's woman servant ran out to help him.

Ian picked up the drunken priest and carried him into the parsonage as his housekeeper held the door open. The priest was completely passed out as Ian laid him on the bed.

The dogs had slobbered over his clothing quite a bit, but he had only a few bad scratches, nothing severe.

The woman made an attempt for Ian to leave; indicating that she would take care of the priest. A great deal of the domestic service was performed by Indian women such as she, who lived in the vicinity and were either the wives of Indians, traders, or descendants of the early French settlers who had never left the plains.

Ian didn't want to be rude, but he felt it would take a stronger person to get the Father prepared for bed, so he ignored her pushing movements and unbuttoned the priest's black shirt. As he pulled it back off of his chest, Ian received a shock too extraordinary to be possible. Surpassing belief, but there none the less, burnt deeply into the man's chest, was a long, terrible looking scar of a cross. It extended from his neck down beyond his navel, and the horizontal bar was from one shoulder to the other. It was burnt deep down into his chest muscles. Ian straightened up in utter astonishment, numbed with overpowering amazement.

The scar was of a dark red, sickening color. In places it extended one-half inch into the flesh and in one place the rib bone was exposed. The pain must have been severe torture, enough to drive any ordinary man insane. Ian wondered how and why the priest had been tortured. He must have had an extremely traumatic experience at one time.

Recovering from the violent shock, he turned the priest over on his stomach. Ian received his second surprise. The priest had scars running down his back. A rawhide whip had mercilessly lashed him.

"Hot damn, this priest has sure had a bad time of it," thought Ian. Maybe he had good reason for drinking, for staying whisky-soaked all the time. There were a lot of things of misery in the world he did not know about.

Ian looked up at the old Indian woman with tears in her eyes.

"Please go . . . please," she begged pitifully.

There wasn't anything else he could do so he left the sleeping priest.

For a long while he wandered around the main parade benumbed and confused. His sorrow for the priest grew to a sickening ache throughout his entire body.

*   *   *

Sergeant Beidler and Ian had met on numerous occasions in their official duties and they both respected each other for what they were.

Ian was considered by his fellow officers as a little peculiar in their way of thinking. He seemed to them to associate with the uncommon or so called "oddballs." He talked to mule skinners, to the maid, the laundry women, the lowly private, along with the people he was supposed to cater to, such as the commanding officer, his battalion officer, the commanding officer's lady and the like. Appearances, background, education, social status, all of this, Ian cared little about. He was concerned with individual only. He talked to the stable sweepers on their level. He liked to hear their thinking, their problems, their hopes and joys. He didn't care how a person looked, whether he was bald headed, had a nervous habit, was ugly or handsome, short or tall, fat or slim, general or private, prostitute or lady.

Sergeant Beidler and others noticed all this, and had unspoken admiration for the lieutenant. The sergeant had never mentioned his wife to anyone else, but he knew the lieutenant would be genuinely interested in her as a person and not what she had been or what she had done. One evening he asked Ian to supper to meet his family and friends. He had gone hunting and shot several deer and wanted Ian to taste his wife's cooking, which the sergeant as very proud of.

The next day Ian and the sergeant had to go up to Cow Island to inspect the place. Cow Island was about nine miles up river from Fort Leavenworth, where a good herd of cattle belonging to the military grazed. They were supposed to pick up some butchered beef for the messes.

It was a beautiful day for the journey—warm, sunny . . . great Kansas weather. Besides, Ian always liked to travel on the river. Many a time he wished he had been a riverman.

The Missouri River inspired poetry, songs, and humor—good and bad. The great river was the life stream of the western expansion. She glided along past the western plains and changed her bed each time it rained. She was as bewitching as any dark-eyed maiden nymph was, this romping wild brunette Missouri was.

Navigation books were re-issued annually but the shifting channel took no notice of the revised editions and changed course whenever she felt like it.

The steamboat Western Engineer was tied up at the landing, unloading her cargo. She was a well-armed, stern-wheeler, seventy-five feet long with a thirteen-foot beam and she drew nineteen inches of water. This ornate boat performed wonderfully with her steam engines. She carried an elegant flag indicating a white man and an Indian shaking hands. Due to the necessity of gathering firewood for her boilers, her actual running time averaged about five hours a day. That gave the passengers, if they so desired, about five hours a day to examine the country and do some hunting near the river.

A riverman in 1816 had built the first double-deck steamboat. Flat hulled and with a high-pressure boiler for steam, they rapidly replaced the keelboats and barge.

In the spring from the time of the breaking-up of the ice in mid-February to the mid-summer lowering of the waters and in the fall season, from October to the beginning of winter, a great mass of water craft carried emigrants and trade stuffs to the West.

St. Louis was the temporary city for storage of goods destined for final distribution to the Western frontier. All lines of trade and travel to the Far West centered there. All military movements, all freighting to frontier posts and towns, and the bold undertakings of missionaries and explorers used St. Louis as a base of operations. There were three kinds of commercial watercraft in use on the Missouri: the barge, keelboat, and steamboat.

The barges, the previously common craft of trade on the river, were huge, pointed hulks carrying forty to fifty tons of freight. They were manned by a large crew and descended with the swift current, speeded up by a wide sail or by the toiling of four of the crew at the long oars. Upon the return trip, upriver, their pace was a snail's crawl as men with bulging muscles pushed iron-tipped poles or occasionally used towropes from the shore.

The keelboats came in use later upon the great river. The keelboats were long and narrow and carried a mast and sails. On either side of the cabin, running boards extended from pointed prow to pointed stern. Along its bottom ran a four-inch timber, to meet the shock of a collision with a snag or some other submerged obstruction. One steersman and two other men at the broad sweeps could navigate the craft downstream. Six or ten men besides the steersman worked to force the keelboats upriver. The crew was equally divided on the larboard and starboard, and they set their poles at the head of the boat. Then pushing the boat forward, they trod the running boards until the stern was almost under their feet, and, at the command of the steersman, the captain, they ran quickly to the prow to set and push again.

Some keelboats had been modified to use "horsepower," such as the one the Army used to carry supplies up the river to the various expeditions in the field. It could carry up to forty tons of cargo. She was worked by a horizontal wheel, kept in motion by six horses going round in a circle on a balcony-like platform above the boat deck. This wheel turned two cog-wheels each fixed to an axle, which projected over both sides of the boat. Eight paddles were fixed on the projecting side of each axle, which impelled the boat about five or six miles an hour, so that the craft could be forced against the current about twenty miles a day.

The packet boat was the most ambitious development of the keelboat era. It was from seventy-five to one hundred feet long and fifteen to twenty feet wide. It had a crew of many pole men and had a sail or two. A separate cabin was partitioned off for ladies. Passengers could be supplied with provisions and liquors of a high quality. The packet services even attained the dignity of a timetable. On a swift packet boat a traveler could go from Fort Leavenworth to New Orleans and back again in a month.

To most emigrants navigation on such a broad stream as the Missouri was a new experience. The professional boatsman was "half-horse, half-alligator" by his own boast. He was overwhelmingly proud of his acquaintance with every meandering of the river, fantastic in his toughness, reckless, and belligerent as well as boastful, and as skilled in his own way as the cavalrymen. Travelers were astonished at the colorful vocabulary, the peculiar language of these huskies. They talked about the danger of "riffles," meaning ripples, the waves in the water caused by running over a rocky bottom and further agitated by the brisk breezes. The sharp, tapering projections in the river that pierced the hulls of the boats were called "points," and "sawyers" were trees with one end caught in the bed of the streams and the branches swaying with the current. The tree trunks with one end rising toward the surface of the water were called "planters." "Shoots" was a corruption of the French "chute"—a steep descent in a river, a rapid, or a waterfall.

They praised their skill and daring in pushing a pole and you learned the accepted opinion that a "Kentuck" was the best man at a pole and a Frenchman at the oar. A firm push of the iron-pointed pole on a fixed log was termed a "reverend" set. When you embarked you were told by them to bring your "plunder" aboard and you gradually became acquainted with a plentiful supply of words of this sort.

The costumes of the boatmen were as fantastic as their peculiar language. Nearly always, a bright new flannel shirt covered by a loose fitting blue jerkin jacket or a short coat and brown trousers of linsey-woolsey (a stout, coarse fabric with a warp of linen or cotton and a woof or filling of wool) was worn.

The rivermen's work, at times, required very little exertion and, then in turn, was very toilsome. On the days of little exertion, when the current of the river carried his burden, the boatmen's dark-tanned face was inclined to silence, movable only as he shifted his tobacco-quid. In the moment of hazard that would certainly come, when the current swerved against an island or an ugly projecting stump or tree branch appeared, his wits and his muscles moved instantaneously. After the danger passed, the boatman sank back into a state of drowsy indifference or profound sleep. The voyage upstream was a different matter, a continuous relentless contest of muscle against current. Sufficient danger, plenty of whisky, loud words and fists was the life of a boatman and was the ambition of youngsters along the river who, working in their fathers' clearings, heard the harsh and loud invitation of the boat horns day after day.

Boatmen could spit extraordinarily and wagered on their abilities at hitting a knothole or a fly. There was usually a fiddle or two aboard every flatboat; fiddle music, whisky and the river naturally went together. Their songs lingered over the river and bottomland as the boatmen sat their poles.

Of all the river bullies, Mike Fink was the ruling rowdy. He was tough, brutal, splendid with his gun, always drinking but never drunk, the swaggering cock that every boatman would like to be.

The practice of bandits and river piracy added an uglier color to the pictorial scene of the keelboat era. Somewhere on the banks of the river a passing boat would hear the hail of a man or a woman, an offer to buy some necessity, or a hail for passage. A gang of robbers who had been hidden in the brush seized the boat that turned in. The boat was scuttled or wrecked in surprise attack; boarders took possession of the goods and killed the crew. Many boats loaded with valuable cargoes that left port at New Orleans under the guidance of experienced, trustworthy officers were disposed of, with cargo, by different crews, the officers and crews to whom the boats had been entrusted never returned.

Many boats began advertising their advantages of "a large crew, skillful in the use of arms, a plentiful supply of muskets and ammunition." Some boats mounted six one-pound cannon and provided a loophole, rifle-proof cabin for passengers.

It was a very rare thing for a keelboat to run the entire challenging voyage unmolested, while in many instances disastrous conflicts were violent and quick. The channel of the river, so sudden changing and shifting often ran close to the shore and placed a boat-party in frequent danger, if not absolutely at the mercy of the Indians. A leader of great experience, full of nerve and tact and of that scarcely less valuable quality described by the word "bluff," was indispensable in these delicate emergencies. The lives of the crew and passengers frequently hung as upon a thread which the slightest unskillfulness or weakness would break. Defects of leadership cost many a life on the hostile shores of the Missouri.

The river pirates, hunted out by volunteer posses, were first to disappear as the day of the keelboats came to its end, as the onrush of emigration into the Western plains began to be reckoned in thousands of persons.

In 1811 a new manner of navigating the western waters began, particularly on the Ohio, Mississippi, and Missouri rivers. These new boats were propelled by the power of steam. Gentlemen of enterprise built boats of this kind with a 138-foot keel and a calculated 300 or 400 tons burden. It was a novel and pleasing sight to those used to clumsy flatboats and other timbered crafts with creeping pace to see a huge boat working her way up the windings of the Missouri. These new boats were without sail, oar, pole, or any manual labor about her, propelled by a wonderful new mechanism—the miracle power of steam. Flatboats and keelboats had remained the dominant crafts for years. As the years passed, the contest became vicious: boatmen against roustabout and barge against steamboat, the steersman's bugle against the steam whistle. The crews of keelboats and barges had to learn the fact which had been thrust upon the pack horse drivers, then upon the towboat men, that the best could not be prevented from growing up, and civilization was using new modes of transportation.

*   *   *

The beeves were loaded on the boat by two o'clock and their return trip down river was an easy journey. The boat pulled into the western shore of Rialto and the sergeant and Ian disembarked. Another trooper sergeant was left in charge of the dragoons as the boat continued on. The boat captain and crew would handle the craft and all the dragoons had to do was to unload the cargo at the fort landing.

Rialto was a little settlement of shacks and tents on a point on the east bank of the river near the Missouri town of Weston where there was a ferry crossing. On the west side, the Kansas side of the river, the landing was similarly named. For many years the settlement, being just off the northern part of the reservation, caused considerable annoyance to the military authorities because of the whisky sellers who had squatted here and were selling liquor to soldiers and Indians. It was one of the roughest, meanest towns in the new country and besides the whisky sellers, prostitutes, trappers, and rivermen, there was also a nest of outlaws who had established themselves at the place.

Sergeant Beidler had a cabin in a clearing about a mile west of Rialto in the dense woodlands that covered the entire river bottom country. There was a well-worn path to the cabin, wide enough for a box wagon.

Generally, around these cabins, there was a swarm of children. The sergeant and his wife had none of their own but they had adopted five children of various ages, children who were abandoned by their mothers and fathers. The prostitutes, outlaws, and whisky sellers sometimes had children they did not want and the Beidler's happily took them in. The cabin was fairly large, about twenty feet wide and forty feet long with a shed addition in the back for storage of provisions. The logs were well stacked and interlocked at the corners. Mud had been daubed between the logs, making it weather proof and warm in the winter. The windows were small with heavy timbered shutters. The roof was steep with a sleeping loft underneath it for the children. In the yard Ian noticed a hand mill of two circular stones. To the upper stone, the runner, was attached a handle, permitting two people to work together in grinding the hard corn. Also in the yard a soap kettle and hickory broom and a homemade washboard leaned against the cabin.

Ian was heartily greeted at the door of the cabin by the sergeant's wife Annie. She was quite a character. Annie stood six feet four inches in her bare feet. She tipped the scales at three hundred pounds, and she cherished a small but carefully trimmed mustache. Now retired, she had become a legend in her own time, but she still retained all her former characteristics. Annie had been the wife of a riverman. When he had been killed in a New Orleans saloon, she remained on the river and year after year added to her achievements. At first she dressed like a man and pushed a pole, hauled on a towline, or worked on the levees as a stevedore. Later she again put on skirts, shaved her mustache, and became captain of a floating house of prostitution, catering to the emotional desires of the lusty rivermen. The tales that were told in the river front towns about Annie and her cargo of lusty wild women were unbelievable.

The strength of Annie was monstrously abnormal. She could walk off a flatboat with a barrel of flour under each arm and a third balanced on her head. Single-handed, she towed a loaded keelboat from New Orleans to Natches and, furthermore, she made the trip on a fast run. From St. Louis to New Orleans a man who performed an unusual feat of strength was said to be "as strong as Annie Easter." She was a fearless fighter, also. She whipped every bully on the river. Her admirers said that the real reason Mike Fink was never seen on the lower Mississippi was because Annie had sent word to him that, if she ever caught him on her river, she would send him back up north tied to the bottom of a keelboat. To show off her achievements in violently inflicting bodily hurt, she sometimes wore a necklace about her neck to which she added one bead for every nose or ear chawed off and two for every eye gouged out. Legend says that when she retired, her necklace reached below her waist.

At a Great Revival meeting a preacher, reclaiming the lost sheep of the frontier by a most powerful sermon, was surprised by Annie's confession of sin. In a surge of emotion, she came forward to be saved and religion banged its way into Annie's life.

As the sergeant and Ian waited for supper, he noticed that the cabin was very homey and comfortable. The fireplace was large where a whole meal could be cooked in four big kettles and bread could be baked. There was a space closed off at one end of the cabin used as a bedroom. On the wall at the far end of the cabin was Annie's wardrobe of petticoats, bedgowns, and skirts, hung on wooden pegs in full display on the cabin walls. Below the clothes pegs was a rough built table with a little looking glass, knitting needles, a patchwork quilt, and a turkey-tail fan.

Several others had been invited for the evening meal and they soon arrived. There was an old pioneer, a boatman, and a couple of trappers, a hunter, and a Mexican on the guest list. All of them were colorful individuals, each with very distinct personalities, all fearless, always ready for a fight. Here, in Annie's house, however, they behaved themselves and talked about their latest adventures.

The trappers, by the name of Pierre Baudran and Charles Pickett, were on their way to St. Louis to sell their furs. They had traveled together in the north territory and had a good year. Their five well-fed packhorses were half covered with heavy bear and beaver skins and their mounts were decorated with gaudily fringed coverings. Their bridles were decorated with loops of red trimming and small bells hung from the trappings to give notice to the Indians of their arrival in their county. Confronted with the demands of this western life, traditional clothing was discarded. They had found it best to dress somewhat like the Indians. They wore a wide-sleeved hunting shirt with a bullet bag, tomahawk, and a scalping knife in a sheath, all held by a wide leather belt. Breeches and leggings were in one piece, hanging down to deerskin moccasins.

Both were brave and enterprising men, much loved by the Indians. They had won the admiration and love of the braves. The French, especially, were welcomed in every village of the north country. In village after village, hardy French trappers and traders lived with the Indian. Usually they had taken an Indian wife and had a family of children, in which commingled the blood of the two races and whose ears and hearts were attuned to the wild songs of the forests. The French were considered brothers, and they danced the war dance and sung the war songs with their red brothers. The Frenchmen had the fullest sympathy of the Indian's wild life; they made no attempt to change his way. These beaver trapmen liked very little company, and that little was preferably feminine and Indian.

They were free trappers, bound to no company, independent and with no thought of the future, casually taking up life with the Indians or keeping safe their rough freedom in isolated cabins. The streams were their natural element. They pulled their keelboats up the long course of the Missouri, and paddled their canoes up the small streams to the beaver lodges. They were nearly all illiterate. These voyagers were a distinct class of frontier dwellers, volatile in temper, sentimental and contented, well acquainted to hardship and indifferent to it. The best trappers in the wilderness beyond the rivers were Americans and Frenchmen. These mountaineers were hardy, robustly free from restraints, proud as lords. The mountaineers dressed much like the Indians, and like them limited his "fixings" to the minimum. He had two pack animals besides the horse he rode. The smaller his personal equipment, the greater the number of furs they could carry. Rifle and ammunition, traps, knives, hatchets; some iron pans to cook in, and a coffeepot; coffee, sugar, and salt; some blankets, some alcohol and tobacco—that was enough. He had little money and was committed to the doctrine that money should be spent as quickly as it was earned. His language became a medley of English, French, and Spanish, amazingly remote from grammar and beautifully profane. He had a fierce attachment for his few friends and a closer tie to the rugged country in which he lived. The fur companies, however, by reason of larger capitol, imperialistic methods, and secret alliances with "gentlemen" of national influence, were gradually dominating the fur trade and the Indians were becoming increasingly alarmed at the encroachment of these companies. The civilizing advances of these fur companies were slow and halting for a long period almost imperceptible, but after a while the tribes realized that their empire was being overrun and was slipping from their grasp.

Up the Missouri and Mississippi, traders were propelling their keelboats, laden with merchandise to barter for furs. Down these same streams in the keelboats and in crafts made of buffalo hides and willow poles, the trappers and traders floated their furs to markets. Large supply parties struck overland from the Missouri border toward the Rockies, and caravans of merchandise destined for New Mexico were both dependent on the Missouri River for their transportation from St. Louis to the outposts of Franklin, Independence, and Westport.

Mike Summers was a typical hunter; he dreaded the bondage of a cabin and clearing. Men like him built makeshift cabins that could be lightly deserted if game disappeared or Indians approached. Under the responsibilities of matrimony many true born hunters attempted to be husbandmen, with varying success.

As soon as the leaves had fallen and the weather became rainy and chilly, they became uneasy at home. Everything about them became disagreeable. The house was too warm. The feather bed too soft and even the good wife for the time being was not thought a proper companion. The mind of the hunter was fully occupied with the chase and outdoor camp. They would get up early in the morning at this season, walk hastily out the cabin and look anxiously to the woods and snuff the autumn winds with the highest pleasure, then return to the house and cast a quick look at the rifle. Soon they would be gone . . . not returning until the end of the season.

The old pioneer, a six feet four inch giant of a man with a white beard to his chest, eagerly related the adventures of his younger life in Tennessee and Kentucky. As the frontier moved west, so had he, always on the fringe of civilization.

He recounted the story of frontier hardship and resourcefulness. One winter he was hunting alone in western Tennessee. A party of Indians captured him, stripped him of everything he possessed, even his clothing, and left him to suffer death in the cold. The Indians, having a sense of humor, presented their naked victim with a very old musket containing a single charge. Separated by more than a hundred miles of wilderness from a settlement, he began the near impossible journey in the bitter cold. He walked laboriously through the forests all day and toward evening he began looking for some sheltering ledge of rock that might offer him some protection from the freezing cold of night. He found such a place, but also found in it a hibernating bear. He related to the company that he crawled up to the sleeping bear until the muzzle of the old musket almost touched the animal's forehead and he pulled the trigger with his frostbitten fingers. The gun fired and the bear was dead. He stripped off the hide with the flint from the musket lock and lit a fire from the dry brush with the flint. That night he feasted on bear meat, threw a log on the fire, and slept like a baby. At daylight he cooked some of the meat, threw the hide over his body, and resumed his march. Three days later, late in the evening, he walked into the settlement.

The old timer had had enough of wandering and excitement and he said he was a bit lazy in his old age; he must have been far past eighty years now. A year ago he had built himself another cabin over near Weston, Missouri. It was an ideal spot, within fifty or sixty feet of a spring, not only a supply of drinking water for him, but also a magnet for the game. He could sit in the doorway of his cabin and lay in a winter's supply of meat. He had his choice of deer, bear, or an occasional elk. Wild turkeys roosted in the shade trees and even on the roof of his cabin; the hollow trees nearby were crammed with wild honey.

*   *   *

Sergeant Beidler had roasted the entire carcass of the deer and as they devoured the tasty meat, cooked to perfection by Annie, he told Ian how he had shot the animal.

The most successful method of hunting deer in this area was the fire hunt, he explained. The deer would come to the small streams after dark to eat the moss that grew on the bottom, and they collected together about the ripples, in groups of three to twelve. The sergeant and the other hunters in the party would build a fire of pitch from the bark of pines in the middle of a canoe and station a man in the stern to steer with one or two more in front to shoot at the deer. When there was no deer in sight, they could push and paddle the canoe along. When they came within sight of the deer, the canoe was allowed to float down with the current and the steersman guided it into a position that was the most favorable for those who were in the bow with guns. The deer would generally raise their heads and stand looking at the fire until the canoe came within a few yards of them. The hunters could determine by their movements whether they would make a break or stand still until they came near them, and fired or not fired according to the movements of the animals. When the deer attempted to run out of the water where the bank was steep, they would see their own shadows, and think it was a wolf or a dog. They would utter a cry and spring back into the water, sometimes coming near enough to the canoe to give the hunters two or three more shots at them. In this manner they could kill from one to four deer in one place. Dressing and laying out the meat on the shore, they would proceed down the stream in search of another group. If the night was favorable, three to eight deer were killed.

*   *   *

The Mexican was enjoyed by all. He lived in Santa Fe but had not been there for twenty-four months, although he still had his Mexican accent. He seemed to be respected by all. . . . this foreigner in this remote territory. Actually, he was a Castilian, a Spaniard by birth, and named Don Malgores Faciendo Viscarro. He had been a lieutenant in the Army of His Catholic Majesty and served in the mounted dragoons of the Vice Royalty of the Kingdom of New Spain. Lieutenant Malgores was a man of fine appearance and perfectly dignified with gentlemanly manners. His horsemanship was said to be extraordinary. He appeared to be around twenty-eight, about five feet ten inches tall with sparkling black eyes, dark complexion and hair. He was born in the mother country of Spain, spoke the French language well and a little of the English. He was polite and considerate in his conversation to his inferiors and spoke with worldly knowledge to his equals. In all his actions he was a most gallant and accomplished man. He possessed a great familiarity of politics from his experience in various countries and societies. When the Mexicans threw off the Spanish rule in 1821, he became an exile, a cibolero, in the internal provinces. Even though he had been an officer in the service of his royal master, he seemingly respected the new government; at least he did not continue to fight the young regime after the king was overthrown. He had a high sense of honor to the king, but he preferred the inhabitants of this new country of Mexicans and Indians to the court of Spain, so he stayed on in the infant nation. The new government needed officers to form the backbone of their growing army and this new adventure was to his liking.

His wife evidently influenced his decision greatly. His companion was Creole or Indian and looked about twenty-two years old. She had dark brown eyes, jet-black hair that fell to her shoulders, and a beautifully shaped neck. They were a very handsome couple. She wore a short jacket and gown, without any headdress; however, she had a silk wrapper around her shoulders. Her riding boots were high-heeled and of shiny black leather.

He was dressed in the costume of the lower class men of Mexico with a broad-brimmed hat, short coat and tight fitting trousers open to the knees. His boots were of a soft, pliable leather, but not colored. Around his waist was a wide embroidered leather belt with a fine looking pistol hanging from it in an open holster on one side and sheathed dagger on the other.

He was in every part of his dress and manner a model soldier of his Catholic Majesty's Army, yet he had an adventurous and independent air about him, a rare combination in any army.

He had evidently rebelled somewhat against the old European customs. An officer in the Royal Court who wished to marry a lady not from Europe was obliged to acquire certificates of the purity of her descent for two hundred years back and transmit them to the court so a license could be approved and returned.

Generally, it was so difficult that few such marriages took place; if an officer wanted to marry a native of the new country, it was impossible to comply with these requirements. Should she be the daughter of a person of the rank of captain or upwards, this difficulty vanished, as their rank supposedly purified the blood of the descendants. Lieutenant Malgores attached himself particularly to Ian and they discussed Georgia and Mexico at length.

Pete Walsh was a keelboat man and an old acquaintance of Annie. He was notoriously wicked but his disreputable nature was not evident while in Annie's house, as he knew she would not allow such behavior around her adopted children. He behaved himself like a big-hearted uncle to the children. They loved him dearly as he always brought them presents from St. Louis when he came through Rialto, and they hung onto every word as he told them of his less bloody affrays on the river. This evening he wore a red turkey feather in his cap, the boatman's badge of championship and a sign, which was a standing challenge to every bully on the river.

The stagecoach driver Jim Kendall was of average height, friendly, easy and very sociable, with a baritone voice, deep and loud, but he was disposed to talk too much. Being 265 pounds in weight, when he was settled in the front of the coach, he balanced all the trunks that could be put in the rear.

Soon the comfortable coaches, companionable drivers, fast horses and quick schedules became a tradition. It was typical of a man's worship of the extra energy of his favorite team, to demand a little whisky in their watering buckets.

Relays of fresh horses were spaced about twelve miles apart. The coach would speed up to the station at a full gallop, jerk to a jarring stop, and the driver would throw down the reins to an awaiting teamster's helper. Almost immediately the panting exhausted team was unhooked and an already harnessed fresh pair was backed into place. The reins were thrown up to the driver, and the coach sped away as the little group of stations loafers scattered.

The drivers were usually heavy-fisted men always ready for a fight. They were paid twelve dollars a month on most runs and were furnished board and room at the stage houses. When Indians were on the warpath, their pay was doubled. Just last week a stage from Council Grove arrived with nineteen arrows still in the sides and rear of the coach, but luckily the ambush was not a success due to the magnificent team and driver's skill in out-running the marauders.

Stage drivers as a class, as told by the jealous wagoners, did not measure up to the high morals of the wagoners, but despite this thinking there were among them men of good sense, steady habits, and honest intentions.

A large woman from Rialto was among the invited guests for supper. She went by the name of Abbie—Abbie Reed—and she was a character among characters, she even out did Annie. She ran a business joint in Rialto that offered various pleasures—which included gambling, a bar, dance hall and girls to the rough crowd.

Abbie was very close-mouthed about her early life and she confided in only a few. She had learned from the prostitutes, politicians, and other disreputable characters with whom she had associated with, not to trust them with details of her past career.

Her real name was Abbie Thompson and she had been born in Liverpool, England; the daughter of an innkeeper. At fifteen she became a barmaid in her father's notorious dance house and bar, but according to her own version she remained a pure and innocent maiden until she was almost eighteen years old. She then was seduced by a handsome young sailor. She had saved his life by knocking two bullies who had attacked him unconscious with a heavy lead mug; he rewarded her by causing her to become the mother of twins but sailed away before the twins arrived. When he returned from the voyage, she gave him a beating, complained to the police of the wrong that had been done her, and the authorities put him in jail for six months because he would not pay for the support of the children.

She abandoned the twins, assumed the name of Reed, and journeyed to America. Arriving in New Orleans, she immediately began working in a brothel as one of the girls. When she came to New Orleans, she was an exceedingly beautiful girl—a strawberry blonde—with an exceptionally fine and desirous figure, and she had been the most popular prostitute of the city.

After a time she became easily provoked to anger and began to drink heavily. A glandular disorder caused her to become repulsively fat. As she put on flesh her breasts became huge and one of the sights of the red-light district. As she grew in age, her large swollen busts became unsightly and her deformity never failed to provoke astonishment to those who chanced to meet her.

This condition forced her to lower her standard price and it so weighed upon her mind that she began to have streaks of meanness and her fiery temper naturally drove away trade. The house that she ran suffered a severe setback when a gambler was stabbed in the heart with a knife in a brawl in the reception room. She had to close down the business and she got out of town just just ahead of the law. The murder had been done by a knife with a nine-inch blade which she carried in a red sheath beneath her armpit. It was rumored that he had deserted her for another prostitute and Abbie, in a rage at the insult, stabbed him twelve times in the chest and four times in the neck.

Abbie was not only very strong, but when maddened she was a savage and bold fighter; she was her own bouncer at her new place of business.

As Ian ate, he noticed that Annie's kitchen was like hundreds of others on the frontier. In the kitchen part of the cabin was a block and pestle, a "hominy block," which did very well in making meal for johnnycakes and mush before the corn became too hard in the autumn.

Wooden bowls were spaced about the table for the members of the company. Beside each bowl was a wooden or flattened gourd, ready for water or milk. In the wooden trenchers in the center of the table, the housewife or the oldest girl dished up the contents of the iron pots and pans. This might include game, fish, or fried pork; "hog and hominy" or mush sweetened with molasses, sugar-and-water, bear's oil, or gravy; johnny cake, buckwheat "souens" or cornpone; and something or other out of the truck patch—"roastin' ears," pumpkins, squashes, beans or potatoes. With iron knives and forks, supplemented by fingers, the frontier families would attack the spread.

Pewter dishes and spoons had replaced some of the wooden things, evidently bought when the sergeant had been east for salt and iron and had some extra money. The backwoods' people did not like glazed pottery "Delftware," which was used on the fort. To these people it was too easily broken, and clasp knives were dulled, as in carving meat they hit against the plates. Teaware was considered too small for real men; tea and coffee, for that matter was "slop" to them.

The most frequent frontier drink was straight corn whisky. Every man owned a still if he owned a cabin—not for profit, but as a necessity. An eight-gallon keg of good homemade whisky was worth about a dollar a gallon, and money was hard to come by on the frontier. A pioneer man's still was his salvation; he made much for his own thirst and sold a little to buy needed provisions.

The assembled company consumed enormous quantities of the sergeant's whisky with the tasty venison. The sergeant and Annie were much complimented on their sociabilities. Ian liked these people. Good, but hard and tough, free spoken—the salt of the earth. The toasts got closer together and were very proper and friendly but the talk became boisterous as the liquor disappeared; then someone suggested they all ride into Rialto for a drink of Monongahela rye whisky which had a taste and a kick all of its own.

Annie and Abbie decided to stay with the children and prepare them for bed. Lieutenant Malgores and his wife excluded themselves as they planned to stay in

Leavenworth City for the night and thought they should get started there before it got too late to get a room.

*   *   *

Rialto's Main Street ran through the cottonwoods, pecans and sycamores fringing the river. The river was on the north side of the town and swamps on the other three sides. A road ran from the town, through the swamps up to the higher ground of Fort Leavenworth and Leavenworth City.

Rialto was much the same as any other frontier town of a similar size, except it being located on the river, had a number of boatmen transits passing through at one time or another. They were by far the toughest, roughest, and most violently cruel of all the pioneers who were carving an empire out of the wilderness. When they were not working the boats or drunk, they were fighting, and a quarrel between two river bullies was a frightful thing to see.

There were hardships to be endured in these towns, but there were also pleasures.

The arrival and departure of the riverboats were always occasions that excited the curiosity of the residents as they brought new people, goods and supplies ordered months before.

The town consisted mostly of rickety rough-built shacks infected with troublesome vermin such as snakes and rats. Some of the inhabitants still lived in tents, however most of these were gone by now, being replaced by buildings of log construction, and later these were sided with shingles, or boards hand sawed from the plentiful cottonwoods. Already some framed buildings were being erected. The commercial establishments had false fronts like the prevailing architectural custom of the frontier.

Being on the edge of the river, the thick timber offered desirable protection from the winter storms and a ready source of building material and fuel, but little protection from the annual flooding. Many of the big cottonwood trees had bark torn off of the river side of them several feet above the ground caused by chunks of ice scrapping against them. The river usually froze in midwinter and when the breakup came along, the ice flows would jam together, forming immense dams in the river every twenty miles or so; many dams were built up to two or three miles thick. The water would rise rapidly behind these jams, flooding the adjacent lowlands, including Rialto. When the rising waters built up sufficient pressure, the ice would break up with a tremendous roar and wreck devastation.

When an ice jam started, the residents would vacate their shacks and business places and pitch tents upon the sides of the bluffs on the Missouri side of the river, where they lived a miserable life for a week or two while the town rioted in new excitement. During the flooding the men enjoyed the suspension of business and the novelty of going about in boats as much as a carnival. At the first sign of an overflowing of the river, all good and true men started the comical efforts to save the distressed. Braving the terrors of the flood, they fearlessly removed the merchandise left behind in the rapid exodus; for some unexplained reason, the whisky was always the first to be saved. Of course, by the time they transported the rescued to higher ground, the whisky as all used up, to keep the marooned and rescued warm.

The main street was only about three blocks long, starting at the ferry landing and running back into the cottonwoods and brush. There were several side streets or lanes running off of the main street, one of the most favorite with the males passing through the town was named Heaven Street for obvious reasons. The smallness of the town was entirely out of proportion with the happenings of the area. More excitement went on in these five or six blocks than in fifty in St. Louis. The greater part of the visitors were trappers, hunters, wagoners, boatmen, and enlisted men from Fort Leavenworth. Their thirsts were usually limited to three kinds—whisky, fighting and women in that order of preference. This kind of pleasure kept the other inhabitants up all night and gave the town a reputation for hell-raising. Even though it had a wicked name for hundreds of miles around, it really wasn't that bad. Few were ever real mean and the outlandish animal-like liveliness which burst forth continuously were merely demonstrative of the pioneers "sowing their wild oats."

The infant town was a lusty, frontiersman's town which furnished its customers with whisky, the necessities to support life on the frontier, trade goods for the enterprising trappers . . . and women.

Rialto was born when the Commanding Officer of the fort, becoming tired of having the crowd of trappers, traders, gamblers, and prostitutes loafing, doing business and generally disrupting the cantonment, ordered all the crowd to move out beyond a two-mile marker. The members of this new community did not bear any hard feelings toward the Commander who had forced them to move; they now could conduct their business and riotous living more freely, without constant fear of the military bothering them.

True, there were brawls in the saloons, honky-tonks, and dance halls but Rialto was a fairly well-behaved town; the noisy disturbances usually were all fists and feet, seldom a shot was fired or a knife used. There wasn't any town marshal because one man, three or four lawmen for that matter—could not have stopped all the fights, so no one tried. The enlisted men of the fort were inclined to be offensive when together in considerable numbers and the wagoners were always ready to take them on.

It was called a tough sinful town and undoubtedly harbored many hard characters on occasions, but for some reason—probably the presence of the militia who had the authority to try a murderer and hang him with dispatch, there were no shoot-outs or murders.

The inhabitants knew they must live together; even savage lions learned not to kill any other member of the pride. It was almost impossible for a townsman to do a cruel thing to another. The competition of trade was at times rough, but there was present also a comradeship and courtesy that lifted them above the vice and cruel conditions of their lives and made them observe the golden rule.

Any hired boatmen or wagoner who failed to pay a legal debt to a prostitute was promptly fired from his job and he usually could not get another until the debt was paid. The other men would take up a collection and pay the woman what was owed for her services because they didn't want a thing like that talked about their kind.

The saloons and the red-light district accounted for much of the business of Rialto. Far from the restraints of the established society, life in Rialto was based on a new set of rules and morals. Even though bandits hung out in town, they generally proved to be a decent sort while in Rialto. They respected this place of haven between the more lawless episodes of their lives.

The new frontier society consisted mainly of not concerning oneself with your neighbor's affairs, not stealing as all materials were scarce and needed by their owners, not committing lawless murder, and especially not speaking disrespectfully of, of harming, a decent woman. Horse stealing was promptly rewarded with the extreme penalty of hanging. Of the crime of staining a decent woman's character, many a man was covered with tar and feathers and set adrift on a raft with the dire warning to never come back or he would meet a worse fate next time. A man could squander all his wages on his sprees, could get stone drunk, gamble in the various games, could associate with women in brothels, but he was expected to guard the decent womenfolk and, in the absence of their own men was expected to provide for her needs. Such was the code of the times.

Many a passerby, who upon hearing an insult to a good wife or daughter, promptly knocked the wretched man down for the absent husband or father.

Most of the saloons never closed. Jimmy Mills' place was one of them, so the men who had eaten together at Sergeant Beidler's place went there. It was a lively, wild place. It happened to be payday at the fort and the enlisted men were demanding beer. To serve them quicker, the beer was dumped into a couple of washtubs behind the bar so it could be dipped out conveniently. One bartender was bringing in the mugs while another filled them for the thirsty soldiers. Over in a far corner of the saloon was a hot pot-bellied stove with a large tin boiler filled with tasty mulligan stew. All were free to fill their bellies.

The proprietor of the place was friendly English gentleman from St. Louis and he saw to it that his customers were served royally as long as their money lasted.

He had some rooms upstairs where travelers could get a night's lodging, this being the closest thing to a hotel. Beds were hard to come by in Rialto; usually early customers filled them all, so many a man had a bedmate who he did not know.

Ian was beginning to feel the effects of the "good old Nongela" so he sauntered out of Jimmie's Place for a breath of fresh air. He noticed that the saloons, dance halls, and parlor houses made up over eighty percent of the business places in the town. Main Street was muddy, as it always was, Rialto being in the swamplands. A number of horses were tied to the hitching rails outside the saloons. It was wild and riotous, even though it was almost midnight by now.

The saloon filled a need in the social life of the frontier. The travelers who wanted a place to loaf, to get the latest news, to inquire about business prospects, or wanted something to eat and drink went to a saloon in this kind of town. Here friends met, the employer hunted for laborers and the unemployed sought work. The visitor could drink, eat, and play roulette, faro, blackjack, and various kinds of poker if he wished. Some of the proprietors operated places that were honest above question, but there were others where shady practices were the rule. Some of these solicited the trade of the wagoners. After they had spent all their money and were drunk or drugged, they were rolled and tossed out into the alley to sober up . . . broke until the next payday. Even though they were treated this way, robbed of their hard-earned wages, they usually came back. They were looking for excitement and it was furnished here; they didn't mind paying the price for it.

One of these places had a dance floor, an orchestra of a sort, and girls who danced with the customers and saw to it that the pleasure seekers spent their money. He noticed on one side of the place that there was a row of curtained rooms off of the main dance floor. These rooms were "worked" by girls dressed in brief costumes. They peddled liquor and did not mind the caresses of the men behind the closed curtains.

Heaven Street was the lowest of the entertainment, the cheapest of the parlor houses. These often provided, in addition to the girls, a piano and a parlor where customers could also dance. Like other kinds of seasonal labor, the girls worked the towns where the most money could be made. When business got slow, they moved on. A few girls married later, as did Annie, for this was a woman poor country. They generally became very good wives and mothers, and no man dared to speak disdainful of them after they left their profession. Others, however, paid the inescapable penalty, and slipped lower and lower. A prostitute's standing in her profession depended on her clientele and it was common gossip that when a woman really was at her lowest, she catered to the soldiers, considered by most the lowest level of customer.

As Ian strolled down Heaven Street, the porches were bright with flares and kerosene lanterns, with music and boisterous festivity coming from within, and there was a constant stream of men going in and out.

Even in his semi-intoxicated condition, the street didn't appeal to him. He turned and retraced his steps past drunken, staggering soldiers. He noticed the prostitutes were of all ages, from twelve years to seventy. Some were sitting on tottering chairs on the porches, smoking pipes and cigars, and chewing tobacco. Whenever a man passed, they would holler at him to come on inside, some even grabbed the passing men and tried to drag them in. If he resisted, they grabbed his hat and beat him with it or spat tobacco juice in his face.

When Ian got back to Main Street, he journeyed on down to the waterfront where two rivermen, surrounded by noisy onlookers urging them on, were strutting around howling at each other.

"I'm a man-eating wolf from Tennessee and this is my night to tear you apart," growled one of the men.

"I can chaw the ear off a grizzly and wrassel a buffalo down at the same time," yelled the other.

Before a fight ever began in earnest, there were certain established rules to be followed. Facing each other in a ring formed by their fellowmen, the bullies would leap into the air, crack their boot heels together and shout their war cries. Each strove to out strut and do the other in ferocity of expression and in his claims of an extraordinary ancestry.

"I was raised with alligators and weaned on panther's milk!"

"My pa was a grizzly and my ma a devil, and I can lick any man on the river!"

After a spat of this lurid and egotistical boasting had each other in a furious rage, they grabbed each other and the fracas was on.

There was no more rough-and-tumble fighting than these men who worked the riverboats and it was a fearsome sight to see. They bit, gouged, kicked, clubbed, and stomped, anything that might mutilate or maim an opponent. All was considered fair and above board. Once in a while they would stop to take a drink of whisky and then begin again. The fight didn't stop until one of the battlers cried out "uncle" after having his head pounded into the ground a dozen times.

About the same time as the river bully had been pounded unconscious, someone down the street yelled, "Fire! Fire!" and shot off a pistol into the air. Everyone, except the half-dead man, ran to help.

Fire fighting in all the frontier towns was a community affair, and usually involved the use of a bucket line since there was no other water system. In these little settlements with closely constructed wooden buildings, there were "fire guards" on duty the year round at all hours of the day and night. There were no fire alarm bells in Rialto and, as the saloons never closed, the bartenders on duty would shoot off a pistol when there was a fire.

Fires in many towns had gotten out of control and had cleaned out whole towns. Nobody in Rialto wanted this to happen to his town, so everyone pitched in to help throw water on the blaze.

The fire was in a popular saloon and the occupants poured out into Main Street, grabbed buckets of water, and dashed back in. Someone had knocked over the pot-bellied stove and one corner of the building was in flames. As the customers were all feeling particularly friendly by now, they all pitched in on the fun. It was just like a holiday—carefree laughing, happy socializing, and comradeship enjoyed by all.

After the fire was put out, the owner was so grateful that he offered free drinks to everyone. The intoxicated crowd put on a real jag. The fire had been the great happening of the day; the heroism of the firefighters was bragged about and the tall tales were told and retold with gusto and enlarged upon with every retelling. If you believed the tales, the fire had been a terrible thing, out of control, and the only thing that saved the town was the bold actions of the wonderful heroic men.

It wasn't long before the drunken wagoners and the soldiers began arguing; the arguing then became shouts of insults and soon a riot broke out.

Something hit Ian in the back as he sat at a table. He turned to see what had hit him and a fist was punched into his face, downing him. As he struggled to his feet, Ian leaned against the bar and he noticed an untouched drink sitting there, so he emptied the mug. With his left hand he grabbed the man who had slugged him and, with his right fist, pounded his opponent's stomach. Ian grabbed two soldiers as they struggled to hit him and threw them bodily out the front door.

Never hesitating, he quickly elbowed another out of the way, clumsily striving to reach the bar. He swung right and left and dodged several blows, but several landed solidly—one on the back of the head that staggered him again.

Before he knew it, a hand grasped his blue collar at his throat, the long, powerful fingers gripping tight. Suddenly, he was lifted into the air and thrown over the bar by a burly, three hundred-pound boatman.

The airborne trip didn't hurt him, but the crash into the hard back bar shook him up. Man, was he having fun!

As he lay there for a moment, trying to figure out which way was up, one of the girls was knocked down on him.

"Hi," Ian greeted her with a smile on his swollen and flushed face.

"Hello," she answered back.

"Anywhere we can go that's a little more quiet?"

"Follow me," she answered.

She started crawling on all fours from behind the bar to the nearest door. Ian followed, grabbing a bottle as he made his exit.

As the girl reached the door she stood up quickly, opened the door and as Ian quickly followed, she slammed it shut. They were alone. In the dim lantern light he noticed the girl was quite beautiful with black hair and dark eyes. The young woman was smartly dressed, but somewhat disarrayed.

"Have you a room I could stay at tonight?"

"Yes," she replied. Very business-like she asked, "Have you got five dollars?"

Without answering, Ian reached in his pocket, pulled out the gold piece she had asked for. She took the money and led the way upstairs to the room.

Ian heard much hollering outside; it sounded like military commands being given to troopers. He pulled up the window and leaned out to see the commotion in the street below. Evidently the earlier fire had been seen at the fort and the fort authorities had anticipated the fight. They had sent some law and order. Ian saw Lieutenant Taylor in command. He was glad he was not in the brawl, as he and Taylor were not on very good terms and Taylor would love to report Ian drunk and disorderly.

"Good," Ian thought, "now I can get some sleep."

But as he turned toward the bed, the thought of rest vanished. The girl was standing in front of the bureau with hardly more than a stitch of clothing on, as she unpinned her hat to take it off also.

She had a very pretty figure, he noted as he undressed for bed.

*   *   *

The next two weeks passed quickly. It was the same old army routine day after day. He hated this garrison duty; he had come to Fort Leavenworth to fight Indians. To get away from the drab existence, he spent most of his off-duty time away from the fort, either at Sergeant Beidler's place, Rialto or Leavenworth City. He had become quite fond of the Beidlers and he saw them as often as he could. As he got to know Annie, he respected her more and more. It had been quite a struggle for her to break away from the old life, reform, and make a good home for the sergeant and the orphaned children.

After seeing the children, Ian would ride into Rialto to stay the night with Louisa, the girl he had met the night of the fire. Besides being the most beautiful prostitute in Rialto, she had a ladylike dignity and a very likeable disposition.

He found Louisa a tender, child-like woman, not quite grownup. Her past was a most sorrowful story. She was the daughter of a clergyman in New York, and she had graduated from a female seminary in Troy. She was seduced at the age of fifteen by an older man and she immediately became a prostitute, an almost compulsory fate in those days.

Her parents, though the best of Christians, so they claimed, kicked her out of the home.

In fact, they made her leave town because of the disgrace brought upon them. Never did they forgive her moment of weakness; they never gave it a thought that the smooth-tongued scoundrel should have been condemned more than she.

Run out of town by her own parents, and ruined forever, she continued her prostitution career in New York and other cities, during which she was mistress of several important men and accumulated a sizable fortune, but gave it away to other girls who wanted to escape the wicked life. Having been sheltered and cared for all of her life until the affair, she did not know what to do with her own life. She had been told to do every little thing by her domineering parents, now she was lost. She just wandered aimlessly through life, trying to hold onto dignity, a difficult task in her profession.

She had been dismissed from several brothels in New Orleans because she refused to have anything to do with some of the men who visited the places.

In one of the brothels, a thief broke into her room, stole all her money, and beat her unmercifully. She was still breathing when found by the madam of the house. The madam, who boasted that her heart was as big as an apple barrel, put Louisa in another room and traded water and bread for her dresses until her wardrobe disappeared. When her clothes were exhausted, she was tossed out into the street. Still suffering from being beaten with the butt of a revolver, the police took her to the charity hospital. After three weeks she was discharged, given two dollars and a train ticket out of town.

Not knowing how to escape her life of prostitution, she traveled from one place to another. One of these days, she would find the way, she told herself. In the meantime she considered Ian "her man" and had nothing to do with any other. Although she was a "kept woman" and everybody knew it, with Ian's help she was gradually building up confidence and belief in herself, which was the first step in breaking away from the profession.

Strange, Ian thought, but his relationship with Louisa was making him believe in something, maybe God, maybe not, he didn't know; he couldn't give it a name. Ian and Louisa both presented a false facade to the world, appearing joyful and carefree, but nothing could be further from the truth of their real selves.

He and Louisa had long walks along the banks of the wide Missouri. The river had a hypnotic effect upon them. They seemed all alone in the world; the waters washing all the present day cares away, hardships and frustrations were forgotten, and their minds were receptive to pure thoughts.

Louisa knew much of religious thinking; she had learned it in the seminary.

On a particularly warm day, Louisa lay in the sand with Ian sitting close to her, leaning against a log drift on the deserted shoreline. Surrounded by the river lazily meandering by, the quiet green forest and white billowy clouds floating through the blue sky above, it seemed as if time had stopped and the two were the only people in the world—a ghost world and so peaceful. Here in this world, Louisa was no longer a prostitute, Ian no longer a lonely nothing lieutenant in a nothing army.

*   *   *

Several days later Ian was asked to be present for a formal reception and a ball for two distinguished visitors to the post: the Honorable Thomas J. Clark, the senator from Missouri; and the Honorable Charles Arthur, an Englishman and a member of the Queen's Household and grandson of Lord Murray, the last colonial governor of Virginia.

Ian dressed early in the afternoon; had a buggy brought up to his quarters and drove down to Rialto to pick up Louisa and all her belongings. The day was beautiful, the sky clear and cloudless, the air fresh and balmy as they drove into the city of Leavenworth. Louisa had expressed a wish to open up an orphanage; there were so many unwanted and uncared-for children in this area. The townspeople and travelers passing through Rialto had contributed almost $10,000 to buy a building and pay for operating expenses for several years. Even the several outlaws had donated handsomely for the cause for their own personal reasons. Louisa didn't ask for their motives, just accepted the money with thanks.

Ian and Louisa looked at a fine large building that would serve the purpose; it could house over forty-five children plus had room for two classrooms and a large acreage. It would be fine, Louisa decided. They went to the bank and had the papers drawn up for the purchase of the property for $1,600 and deposited the remainder in the bank in the name of Louisa. Ian had made arrangements to hire four people to help out with the work and he told them to do whatever Miss Louisa wanted done.

Annie had found five children desperately needing some place to stay; they had been sleeping on the sidewalks in Rialto. That evening Louisa's rooms would be ready for her to start her new life. She was so happy now that she had found a place in this world for some worthwhile endeavor. Ian noticed with a slight smile as they left the bank that the president escorted Louisa to the buggy and called her Miss Louisa. It was strange what a little wealth will do to change society's opinion. Last month she was called a prostitute, today she was graciously accepted as a respected member of society. All along, Ian knew of Louisa's potential, she just had to be encouraged to find herself. Ian was glad he had been of some help to bring her back onto the right road to be a useful citizen. Strange how things work out, Ian reflected.

They ate an elegant supper at Planter House, complete with champagne to celebrate. Ian was happy for Louisa, but in the back of his mind, he knew that his relationship with her had to change and for this he was sad. But, if Louisa was happy with her new life, he was happy also.

It was dark already when they left Planter House and started to the post, but the road was wide and the horses knew the way.

The hop room was lit up brightly and the reception line already forming. The officers wore sky-blue trousers. The dragoons were distinguished by yellow turnbacks and stripes and by drooping white horse hair pompons. Lieutenants, such as Ian, wore straps on the shoulders, richly decorated with braid and their rank ensign.

Ian knew the officers and ladies didn't approve of Louisa too enthusiastically but they all knew that Ian did just about what he pleased. Besides, wasn't his daddy a wealthy landowner and businessman, a power in politics, and a general in the reserve army? Also, Ian was good company at the small nonsense talk and very charming with the ladies.

Ian and Louisa made a charming couple. Ian's dress blues complimented his trim stature and his hazel eyes fairly twinkled with vitality. His brunette hair slightly tousled, he had an interesting, handsome face, and his figure was well proportioned. Louisa was finely curved, soft and sensitive. Her flashing eyes, long curving lashes, and beautiful face made all men envious of Ian. Her gown was outstanding; the best that was available in Leavenworth City, although slightly more revealing than Ian cared for, but, as he glanced around, he noticed it was not more so than a half dozen of the other ladies' gowns. She was fully equipped for conquest, that was for sure.

He shook hands mechanically with the commanding officer followed by presentations to cordial and kindly people whose names he did not remember. After the introductions were completed, they mingled into the crowd, sipping wine and talking small nonsense. He didn't care for these formal affairs, but he had to play the part, impress the right people, and flatter the richly dressed and most distinguished looking women. He noticed Louisa was completely at ease and perfectly placid, surrounded by young cavalier officers.

The Englishman was found to be quite hospitable; with a ready wit and julep, he made the party a lively one. This was his second visit to the post and he said, "great changes had taken place among the officers of the garrison, since I had last visited it. Only one remained with whom I could claim acquaintance so I'll be getting re-acquainted."

Ian excused himself and rejoined Louisa. She was talking earnestly with the Englishman. They had found something in common. Louisa was an Episcopalian, the same as he, and, of course, her father was an Episcopal clergyman. Louisa told him about her seminary schooling and the orphanage that she was opening. The dancing started and Sir Arthur asked her for the first dance. Louisa looked questioningly at Ian and he nodded approval. After that the young officers kept her on the dance floor for several hours. Ian managed to dance two times with her during the evening but he was kept busy dancing with the other ladies, too. At twelve-thirty, he was just about small talked out so he left the dance floor. As he passed by a small group of older officers, the post commander hailed him.

"Lieutenant Douglass, Senator Clark would like a word with you."

"Yes, sir," Ian acknowledged the request, bowing slightly in respect for the senior officer of the post.

"The colonel tells me you are General Douglass' son," commented the senator.

"Yes, sir," Ian verified.

"Fine . . . fine," he repeated, smiling at Ian and then the commander.

He continued, "I have ten wagon loads of goods from your father's cotton mills."

"Oh?" exclaimed Ian, in surprise.

"Yes, we are getting a caravan together for Santa Fe. Twenty wagons are already down at Corral Creek, and the other forty will be here soon. I would like you to go along with the train."

"I'd like to go, senator," Ian replied, glancing at the commander. "I don't care for garrison duty," he explained. That was putting it mildly; he was ready to resign if something didn't happen soon.

"Well, senator," commented the colonel, changing the subject, "how are things in Washington? Do you think we will get our road soon?"

Besides being an enterprising businessman, the Honorable Mr. Clark was also Chairman of the Committee on Military Affairs of the Senate.

"I had the honor of reporting out of the committee to the Secretary of War that a road was considered necessary and construction should start soon. I have no doubt," he continued, "that a road from the western bank of the Mississippi to Fort Leavenworth and thence to Fort Gibson in Arkansas, would be very advantageous to the United States. It need not be expensive, only cutting down the timber for a reasonable width, bridging the streams, and building causeways at the crossing places, so as to allow the free movement of troops. The stations of the dragoons are at the two points of termination and near the middle of the proposed communication route. If it were opened, they could range it with comparative facility. This is a species of force peculiarly dreaded by the Indians, and I think the peace of the country would be better secured by such measures than in any other manner. The road would, in fact, become a barrier across which parties of hostile Indians would be very unwilling to pass, as they would be liable to be intercepted by a mounted force."

As he listened to the senator, Ian couldn't help but admire this man. He was wonderfully informed about military matters and the army was fortunate to have a man like him as Chairman of the Senate Committee on Military Affairs.

He had foresight and perseverance to open up the trade routes with Mexico. Towering over six feet in height, he was possessed of a powerful physique, which was to stand him in good stead in the business of politics. He entered each new venture with all the enthusiasm of youth, even though he must now be in his middle sixties. He had chosen the kind of profession for which he was specially qualified and from which after many years of hard work he had reaped a small fortune. He was a man of great energy and character; nothing seemed to daunt his courageous spirit. He had an exquisite degree of politeness, and, combined with the frankness of a mountain man, he was a likable person.

During a lull in the conversation, Ian spoke up.

"Gentlemen," Ian bowed slightly at the commander and then the senator, "I beg your leave."

"Yes . . . yes, of course," consented the senator, grinning as he noticed Louisa waiting to be escorted home. "There are more important things to a young man than roads, armories, and rifles." He offered his hand to Ian, and as they shook hands in parting, he commented, "I'll see your father on my way back to Washington. I'll tell him you are fine and you will probably be guarding our mutual interests," obviously referring to the cotton goods being shipped to Santa Fe.

"Thank you, senator," Ian gratefully replied.

As Ian and Louisa left the hop room, his mind had already dismissed the military talk and he was thinking only of the anticipated high adventure with Louisa the remainder of the night. He already had reserved one of the finest suites in Planter House for the evening. This would probably be the last night he could spend with Louisa, now that she was entering a new life as a teacher and a respected matron of an orphanage.

*   *   *

Little did Ian know that several persons at the social gathering were involved in an intrigue called the "Grand Conspiracy." There existed a passion of a few powerful men to manipulate a revolution in the West and establish a separate country, a New Spain, and enjoy the privileges of becoming Spanish subjects of his Catholic Majesty, to be offered free lands, religious toleration, political freedom, and other liberal concessions. The monopolistic control of exportations and wealth of the West especially intrigued some conspirators. For seven long years, the conspirators had been diligent, moving their men upward to prominent places in government, business, and the military, but the time for revolution had not yet arrived. The "Secret Committee of Correspondence of the West" was playing a waiting game, hoping for an opportune time.

In 1803, the Louisiana Territory of France consisted of that entire region lying west of the Mississippi to the borders of the Spanish possessions and the Oregon territory. It came to the infant United States by chance, like most of the additions, and nearly doubled the original area of the United States. The island of New Orleans in foreign hands had proved an obstruction to American commerce, so James Monroe was sent to Paris commissioned to buy it. He had no thought of purchasing half a continent, but only a small lot at the mouth of the Mississippi, but Napoleon, the Corsican, needed money. European rulers generally want money, so when Napoleon, king of France, was informed of Mr. Monroe's errand, he saw that so small a transaction would not greatly help him. Napoleon confided in his agent, "I need money in France more than the wild, undeveloped, and far away lands in America; get me fifty or a hundred million francs and let it all go."

The final price agreed upon was fifteen million dollars, more than Napoleon had even hoped for, but even at the price at which stolen lands were then selling, it would have been cheap at thirty million. Here was a world unmarred my man, basking in primeval plenteousness, a brand new continent fit for any purpose, a virgin land of limitless potential. Here were natural resources such as would enrich a world, and, if properly husbanded, give to each inhabitant, now and forever, all the requisites of life, health, and happiness. Soil and climate, sunshine, air and water, metals in the mountains, forests, valleys capable of raising any and every food, and underneath the surface the coals and other minerals was a boundless wealth, enough for all time and for all people.

Here was a chance to build an empire that Napoleon had no time for. Here the land was almost free. Here was a vast amphitheater lying between the two great oceans edged by civilization, but wild within. A garden of the gods with far stretches of land, and forests and water, of mountains and burning plains, with its wild unclad Indians. Here were a hundred different tribes with a hundred different languages, customs and faiths, each with an unwritten history of years.

There was game of all sorts, each kind choosing its own habitat. Antelope and deer gliding gracefully over the rolling prairie, elk in the mountains, horses broken loose from Mexico that freedom had made wild, herds after herds of buffalo feeding on the short grass. With the wild beasts were mingled wild men. Here came the white fortune hunters to spy out the land and steal its hidden treasures.

This interior continent was regarded at first as a worthless domain, and called everything from the Bad Lands and wastelands to the Great American Desert. But it was soon found to have much natural wealth; here was gold, silver, copper, iron and coal, million-acre forests and succulent grass enough to graze ten million cattle.

The soil, which on the surface looked like drifted sand in the sagebrush, was found that with the addition of water to be fertile beyond belief.

Here, speculators could get rich by filling up the untenanted plains with people. These wild lands when wanted by civilization had only to be taken and immigration was encouraged. Here a man could think his own thoughts, speak his own words, follow his own inclinations, fearless of God or the devil or of any other influence above or below save that mightiest of all powers, the opinion of his fellow man.

To the average American this was the Garden of Eden. In leaving their European and Eastern homes to escape the tyrannies of colonialism and achieving independence, they gave little thought of leadership. They gave no thought of dominion over others, of protectorates, dependencies, or subservient states. There was no thought of empire or imperialism. None of these words had any significance to them. Give a farmer 640 acres and he asks no questions. Give a cow farmer 10,000 acres for grazing and he cares little who rules him, the President of the United States or His Catholic Majesty of Spain. A businessman with an annual $50,000 enterprise and a miner with silver and copper in abundance do not care about a vague conspiracy. Let it happen, they said. In fact, these people preferred bad men in power instead of good men, for when bad men rule, men open to bribery and winking at their greed, they fancied they could make more money. Scheming is as natural as breathing. A governor of easy integrity who will look at things the right way, a lawmaker who can fix things for you, gentlemen bribers who will give you an extra section of land just for a vote – this was the morality of the day. "Do not concern us with technicalities of who is the ruler of this land, just give us this land," the pioneers acclaimed.

Fort Leavenworth,
Outpost of Civilization

*A*lthough Fort Leavenworth had been established with the primary objective of furnishing ample protection to the annual caravans carrying the commerce between the United States and Mexico, the troops of the Fort Leavenworth garrison did not leave the post for such service until the summer of 1829.

The government depended entirely upon the infantry to pursue and punish hostile Indian tribes for violence upon the builders of the Western Empire. This enabled the Indians with their fleet mounts to make their escape from pursuing troops afoot.

Several years before, Captain Edwards had started out on an expedition with some two hundred militia to settle some Indian problems. This well-intentioned officer, a stickler for army discipline, and all his men marched to their death.

In the 1820s, when war threatened in Missouri, the pioneers organized companies of rangers. These men in buckskin patrolled the fringe of the wilderness and were as bloodthirsty as any. Each ranger carried a tomahawk and scalping knife beside his rifle. During the Indian wars, isolated cabins were burned and their occupants murdered, horses were stolen and crops destroyed. Yet, of the several score of little battles fought along the western frontier, it seemed fair to credit the rangers with starting half of the killings of innocent people, red and white.

The regular army of the United States from 1829 to 1832, consisting of seven regiments of infantry and four of artillery, encircled the inhabited portions of the United States in a line extending over six thousand miles. This army, composed of small units widely distributed and ever changing personnel performed the military functions for a nation comprising 1,752,000 square miles of territory and containing a population of nearly thirteen million. The payment of bounties in advance encouraged the enlistment of such vagrants whom "enlisted today and deserted tomorrow." Others remained upon the rolls only long enough to receive four or five months pay and the most costly part of a year's uniform and clothing.

A second cause of desertion was the inadequate system of punishments in the army, which tended to degrade offenders rather than to produce penitence or reformation.

Punishments then prevalent in the army were varied. Branding, marking with durable ink, and inflicting pain that tended to mutilate or cripple culprits, such as severe flogging, was often used. Attaching a ball and chain or an iron collar on the leg or neck of the offender and compelling him to perform hard labor in public was another. Many times shaving the head and requiring the accused to stand upon a barrel or log; fed only bread and water.

Fifty-six companies, aggregating 2,550 men and stationed at sixteen establishments, comprised the Western Department of the Army. By 1830, seven posts formed the line of defense on the Middle Western frontier, a frontier usually advancing before the westward drift of settlement and following the receding Indian population. In this irregular zone extending from Fort Snelling in Wisconsin to Cantonment Gibson in Arkansas Territory, they performed the varied functions of a frontier army.

From its experience in the Black Hawk War in Illinois during 1832, the War Department convinced Congress of the necessity for mounted troops for service on the western frontier. None existed in the regular army. The first attempt was a battalion of Mounted Rangers.

A short term service battalion of Mounted Rangers was organized and placed on duty in the northwest and southwest frontier with the hope of meeting the demand of the people for better protection of their countrymen engaged in building homes on the advanced frontier.

The United States Rangers, who roamed the western frontier, were made up principally of volunteers who had offered their services to the government at the time of the Black Hawk War. They were hardy, weather-beaten fellows, accustomed to western life, ready with the rifle, and first-rate Indian fighters but frequent re-enlistment and reorganization of the rangers meant loss of time, experience and efficiency.

A company of United States Rangers on their return from escorting a party of Santa Fe traders across a portion of the perilous route, which they were obliged to take in carrying on their traffic with that inland mart, had little to show that they were United States troops.

They had been absent from the garrison for two months, traveling through a territory full of lurking foes. Hard service and exposure had made great havoc of their clothing, headgear, old fur caps, and blankets. Articles of Indian apparel had taken the place of the garments with which they had set out, and makeshifts of the most dilapidated and unusual character in the way of covering cropped out in every direction.

These tatterdemalion veterans marched into Fort Leavenworth and took quiet possession of the miserable huts and sheds left by the 3rd Infantry the preceding May.

Under Colonel Henry Dodge, the ranger units quickly proved inexpedient and expensive. While praising highly the services of the rangers, the War Department urged that they be converted into a regiment of dragoons.

In 1833, the government satisfied this battalion of Rangers, but little better than the militia, did not meet the requirements of the service. A bill "for the more perfect defense of the frontier" was signed by President Jackson on March 2, 1833.

The regiment was to consist of ten companies of seventy-one men each and be commanded by a colonel. All were to be subject to service either on horse or foot and in every respect were to be governed by all the rules and articles of war which regulated the peace establishment. The dragoons would be equal in celerity of movements; the elements of cavalry tactics would be preserved and strengthened; and finally, horsemen would be indispensable at the many scattered frontier garrisons in overtaking and chastising the marauding Indian bands of the Far Western plains.

The veterans of the rangers brought training and valuable experience to its successor—the first regiment of the United States Dragoons.

The First Dragoons were the first cavalry regiment in the regular army organized under an act of Congress. It was later, under an act of Congress approved March 3, 1861, designated the First Cavalry.

The date of activation was set for March 4, 1833, at Jefferson Barracks, St. Louis, Missouri. Eighteen officers were commissioned on that day; all of them transferred from the infantry or from civil life.

Actually its initial official title was United States Dragoons and did not employ the numerical designation of 1st Dragoons until a second regiment was authorized in 1836.

The regiment was organized at Jefferson Barracks and later in the year marched to Fort Gibson for station. A number of the officers and men of the rangers were transferred to the regiment and several, later well known, officers of the army given high rank in the new organization. Among these were Lieutenant Colonel S. W. Kearny, Major Richard B. Mason, Captain Edwin V. Sumner, Captain David Hunter, and Lieutenants Philip St. George Cooke, Jefferson Davis, and Clifton Wharton.

The headquarters staff consisted of Lieutenant Colonel Stephen Watts Kearny, Major Richard Barnes Mason and 1st Lieutenant Jefferson Davis as Adjutant. Colonel Dodge did not assume command until August 29, 1833, and Lieutenant Davis took over his duties the next day.

Officers who replaced the original officers that had been transferred included 1st Lieutenant James W. Hamilton (son of Alexander Hamilton), 1st Lieutenant Abraham Van Buren (whose father was soon to be elected President of the United States), and Captain Nathaniel Boone (son of Daniel Boone).

It was intended to make the Regiment a truly National unit. The officers were restricted in their enlistments to men between twenty and thirty-five years of age, native citizens whom, from previous habits, were well qualified for mounted service. So came into being the oldest cavalry regiment in the army. Real cavalry terminology, such as squadron, troop and trooper, replacing the terms battalion, company and private soldier, was not used for some years after this period.

The beginnings did not prove auspicious. Instead of enjoying any of the privileges and comforts that had been promised to them, they soon found that they were nothing above the other portions of the army.

From this neglect shown towards the dragoons, it was natural that they should suffer a corresponding decline in morale. Instead of feeling themselves an elite corps, they were resentful. There was much murmuring and disaffection in the regiment. Desertions became more and more numerous every day. The guardhouse was kept continually filled to overflowing.

Desertions constituted a perpetual menace to the army. In 1830 such desertions numbered 1,251 from a force of about 6,000 men; that is over twenty-one percent desertions. From Fort Gibson, Colonel Dodge, under date of February 15, 1834, recommended the War Department to transfer the regiment to Fort Leavenworth, stating "this post presents many advantages. Steamboats could transport the necessary supplies to this place early in the spring. Forage can be secured cheap on the frontiers of the state of Missouri and protection would be afforded to the inhabitants of this state. This would be the proper point to furnish the necessary escort for the protection of our trade to the Mexican State. That part of the regiment of dragoons at Fort Leavenworth would be able to range the country in the direction of the Rocky Mountains and return in the fall to this place. Should there be war among the Indians, the regiment could be concentrated in short time by making a forced march. Should a part of the dragoons be wintered at Fort Leavenworth, would not the good of the service by promoted and a considerable expense saved to the government, to order that part of the 6th Infantry now stationed at that place to Jefferson Barracks and permit the Dragoons to occupy their quarters next winter?"

Responsive to these recommendations, the War Department issued orders (G.O. 41, 1834) authorizing: "The regiment of Dragoons to commence the line of march from Fort Gibson; the headquarters of the Dragoons with four companies to be at Fort Leavenworth; Lieutenant Colonel Kearny with three companies at Fort Des Moines; and Major Mason with three companies at or near Fort Gibson."

This was a major setback for the Grand Conspiracy of the West, but they had experienced minor obstacles several times before. In 1800, Napoleon, First Consul of the powerful French Republic, his ambitions blocked in Egypt, reconceived the old notion of a Gaelic American empire. Napoleon forced the King of Spain to cede him Louisiana in return for some petty Italian territory.

1803 drew Napoleon back to brewing continental war, and he realized that the resumption of conflict with Great Britain would endanger French control of Louisiana. Almost at the same time that the French flag formally replaced the Spanish over New Orleans, Napoleon abruptly sold the whole territory, with its historic claims, to the government of the United States.

There were a number of causes of the dissatisfaction to dismember a union just formed with great exertions and sacrifices, to change the freedom just purchased by so much blood and suffering of the Revolutionary War. Some factions were in favor of the formation of a new republic, independent of the United States and in close alliance with Spain. Two main causes of the dissatisfaction of the people of Kentucky were the unwillingness of the State of Virginia to relinquish her jurisdiction over the district and the failure of the Continental Congress to secure for them the free navigation of the Mississippi. That dissatisfaction ripened in many minds into a wish to throw off the authority of the confederation and to frame an independent government. Many causes influenced the movements of the Party of Independence—as they called themselves. The inconvenience of the jurisdiction of Virginia, exercised at the distance of several hundred miles from her capital was one such cause. Also, the difficulties she interposed in the way of a separate organization of the district and the delay of Congress in providing for that organization also influenced the party. The hope of securing the trade of Mexico through an alliance with Spain was the true motive that incited their desire for separation. The profits of a trade were a sufficient motive to induce those men to favor a separation of the Western States from the Union.

They designed to remove Senator Clark of Missouri from the many forked roads of his ambitions. The truth was that the Federalist government was anxious to placate every possible friend, New York financier or Texan frontiersman. Many men of Spanish sympathy were in high offices. Jay Thomas, a land speculator and a man of influence among the frontiersmen, was appointed Superintendent of Indian Affairs. John Robertson and Sebastian Innes were promoted to brigadier generalship; Henry Long was appointed United States Attorney General and John Clark, District Judge of Texas. The intrigues of New York financiers and a few money hungry Texans followed devious underground paths.

The infant United States did not have the men and equipment to extend the Revolutionary War victory into an adequate military occupation of the Indian country, nor did the national government act vigorously to stop the Indian raids. Battle between the "Warhawks" and the "submission men" raged as officers and senators demanded that the blood of our murdered countrymen be avenged in blood.

One senator addressed the Congress, "I do hope that the government will see that it is necessary to act efficiently and that these hostile bands which are being excited to war by the secret agents of France, Spain, and Great Britain must be destroyed."

A great deal was said in Congress about mercantile rights, especially by Westerners whose dignity impelled them to prove some deep interest in the commercial questions involved. There were any number of declamations on the national honor and the whole problem of the West, from western eyes, was put forward.

The Grand Conspiracy saw to it that there was severe criticism in the press of government protection for the Santa Fe trade, especially in view of its small value. Therefore, the request for an escort in 1830 was refused and no others granted until 1834. It was believed, rightly so, by those who favored the government's protection of this trade, that eastern traders who feared its protection fanned the criticism would result in growth sufficient to injure its commercial interests over the high seas.

The Secret Correspondence of the West was already setting the groundwork for a peace council to put a stop to the build-up of the frontier army to take care of the Indian depredations and possible full-scale war on the western plains.

In the meantime, Spain was building up its military force in New Spain to unperceived strength to militarily take over all the territory west of the Mississippi. Spies in the United States Consulate in Mexico City obtained a copy of this report and the following information was in the hands of President Jackson and the War Department.

All this intelligence known to Jackson and the highest level of officers in the War Department created a severe troublesome state of affairs for them—not knowing exactly what to do at this time. If would require much diplomacy and the wisdom of a messiah to resolve all these influences and carry on Thomas Jefferson's dream of building one great united empire from the Atlantic Ocean to the Pacific Ocean and somehow, someway, not to totally exterminate the aboriginal inhabitants.

*   *   *

This life was killing Ian. It stifled everything that was alive and individual; it was turning him into a merely mechanical being. Most of the things he had done in the army lately made no sense whatsoever. A marionette could do day in and day out, what he did and said. All that had to be done was just wind up a squeaking spring and say, "do this . . . do that . . . don't do this . . . don't do that"—that was all that was wanted, that was all that was needed. One or two men at the top ran the whole caste system.

The greatest foe to the army in the 1830s and a sure cause of desertion was the prevalence of intemperance among the soldiers. During that time the government issued to its six thousand men 72,537 gallons of whisky at a cost of $22,132 or about one cent per gill (four ounces or one-fourth pint). Besides this daily ration of one gill of whisky, the soldier could sometimes obtain liquor from the army sutler or from the swarms of hucksters or whisky peddlers who hovered about almost all the army posts. Nearly every company had its habitual drunkards and these tended to corrupt the habits of their comrades. The proceedings of court martials proved that intoxication almost always preceded and usually caused the crime of desertion. A soldier would become intoxicated and absent himself from roll-call, was confined, and after a night's lodging in the guard-house, tortured with thirst and all the nameless agonies which succeed a debauch, he was set at liberty, and perhaps "detailed for duty." He resorted to the bottle to free himself from what he justly called the "horrors," and was found drunk on duty. He was again confined, tried, and perhaps sentenced to a forfeiture of pay; when disheartened, vexed with himself and all around him, he would fly again to the bottle for relief and anticipating further punishment, deserted.

Five dollars was the monthly wage; this with the clothing, rations, and other allowances made the entire monthly amount about fifteen dollars. Privates' drilling overalls cost 62¢; the price of a pair of shoes was $1.24; the army blanket sold for $2.50; the knapsacks cost $1.53; flannel drawers were priced at 87¢; and a pair of laced bootees, $1.48; great coats for service in the cold winter climates were purchased for $6.56.

Court martials were very common on the post. Every week there was a court in session. Most of the young recruits were called into service from the backwoods of Missouri, Kentucky, and Tennessee. They were hard, tough, and wild, but the routine of camp life became dreary and monotonous for them also. These long days of idleness made them create their own excitement. Fights were frequent and arguments and drinking occurred every night. They had not been in the army long enough to respect rank alone. They knew or cared less of any separate caste system. It became necessary for an officer to prove his right to rank by qualities of their concept of leadership.

Ian, without sacrifice of dignity, kept a lively sense of comradeship with the men. While most fellow officers stood aloft and exercised an almost despotic authority, he overlooked their faults and discovered their good qualities. In the new experience of this camp life, kindred spirits found each other and life friendships took shape—often formed out of bloody encounters. They usually found some way to get around the military regulations and have some merriment to liven their drab garrison duty.

At eleven o'clock "taps" sounded everyday of the year and the officer of the day went the rounds to see that all lights were out. This was too early for bedtime for the young men and, by various ruses, they managed to conceal the glow from the candles they had again lit after the officer had returned to the guardhouse.

Ian thoroughly enjoyed their company and he spent many a pleasant evening with them, talking about home, the girls they loved, religion, politics, etc. Their barracks were alive with singing, talking, telling stories, laughing—a game of cards in one barracks, a melancholy guitar strumming a half-merry tune in another. On one particularly wild evening, the banjos, fiddles, and mouth harps were brought out with the whisky and everyone had a merry time. The tough Missourians and Kentucks sometimes challenged each other in a spree of clog dancing. It was something to watch. These lanky, raw lads stomping and jigging, jumping into the air and slamming their boot heels together in rhythm with the folk music.

Every man in blue was a comrade; each company was a family by itself. When for months you and your comrade slept at night in adjoining bunks, sharing each other's life, when you learn to depend on him and he upon you for help when in trouble or comfort in sickness, then you begin to know friendship.

Several weeks ago Ian had a run-in with Colonel Dodge. Private Ira Hammond had requested to marry a young Irish girl named Cally, but Colonel Dodge heard about it and prohibited the ceremony. Private Hammond requested Ian's help. After talking for some time, Ian saw the boy was sincere. He loved the girl and was on the verge of a breakdown, including possible desertion. Ian had noticed Private Hammond and his girl friend on several occasions. Although they were quite young, they appeared mature in their thinking and seemed ideally suited for marriage.

"I'll see what I can do, Hammond," Ian assured the soldier. "I'm going to see Colonel Dodge tomorrow and I'll bring it up with him."

Ian knew the old colonel would hit the ceiling when he brought up the matter. He was an overbearing, un-christian, unreasonable man. Usually Ian avoided the colonel, not because he was afraid of the man, but he would just rather not associate with him to avoid a clash. If the Colonel got mad, Ian didn't give a damn, he was ready to chuck his commission back to the army anyway. The order prohibiting the marriage was illegal and the colonel knew that just the same as Ian did. Maybe it was about time that the colonel be made aware of the differences between a legal order and an illegal one.

The next morning, after stable inspection and roll call, Ian reported to Colonel Dodge. The colonel saw Ian from his inner office, but deliberately made him wait for full three-quarters of an hour.

The first time Ian met Colonel Dodge he disliked him. He usually never arrived at first conclusions, but this man had the air about him that Ian hated. He was overbearing and arrogant; in fact, he seemed to hate all mankind. He was a man of middle height with a commanding presence. He was rather fat with broad shoulders, a wide chest, and massive head. His neck was short, making his head appear to rest directly on his shoulders. He was a man of highly nervous nature and inclined to be belligerent to any below his station in life.

Strength was the most striking attribute of his countenance—the masculine nose, firm large lips, the heavy jaw and broad chin. His look was grave and stern. There was a scornful lift to his eyebrows and a projecting of the forehead as from painful thought; yet, there were marks of refinement and self-mastery. Ian had to admit there was neither weakness nor failure on his face. He was the image of a strong fortress, battered by the blows of enemies without and within, but standing firm against all attacks of the cruel life.

He professed to be a good Catholic, attended church regularly, but it was all for show. Perhaps this was a handy way for him to persuade himself that he was superior to other people. At any rate, the church teachings did not bother him; they were not stumbling blocks to him. He appeared to have no conscience whatsoever—not any tender feeling for his fellow man. He was rigidly overbearing in his opinions and always had to be in the right.

Of course, Colonel Dodge had his beliefs reinforced by the apparent truth to his way of thinking. Wasn't he a colonel? Appointed to his position by President Jackson?

Ian was finally ushered into the colonel's office and stood at attention and saluted. The colonel didn't even glance up to recognize Ian's salute, so Ian had to hold the salute for a full two minutes before the seated officer looked up and returned the salute. He never offered Ian to be at ease, so Ian had to stand at attention while he presented Private Hammond's grievance.

As Ian talked the colonel's stern face turned to grimness and then uncontrollable rage. He jumped to his feet before Ian could finish; he pounded his fists solidly on the desk and growled, "Lieutenant Douglass, I gave an order and I expect it to be carried out."

"By what authority can you give such an order, not to allow a private to get married while on garrison duty? The regulations say nothing about such occasions," Ian countered.

"Don't quote regulations to me, Lieutenant," Dodge shouted, now very furious that anyone below his rank would even question any order by him. "I gave the order by reason of being the commanding officer of this regiment, Lieutenant, and it would be well for you to remember that. And stand at attention, Lieutenant, until I order you at ease," Dodge growled as Ian shifted his weight.

Ian immediately came to ramrod attention and he saw now why everyone was afraid of the man. It was quite a painful experience. That look on the colonel's face was so severe, angry, and contemptuous that anyone who had seen him at such times was diminished and, in some sense crippled, simply from the act of beholding his face. This man was a powerful agent of destruction of personality, Ian thought, but one thing the colonel hadn't realized yet, there are some, a very few, who won't be walked on. Very few had ever walked over Ian's basic principles. He could be insulted, degraded, and beat down, but there was a point where Ian would not allow anyone to continue beyond. The trouble with people they sometimes mistook his courteousness for weakness; this was a dreadful error on their part. Many had attacked Ian's principles and this impregnable wall of conscience bore the dents of many a siege, but none had succeeded completely—not yet at least.

"The matter is closed, Lieutenant," commanded the colonel, "but there's another thing I want to take up with you."

He sat down, scowled deeply, and continued, "You've been drinking entirely too much for your own good. You had better watch this overindulgence, and I want you to quit seeing that prostitute down in Rialto."

At the mention of Louisa, Ian's temper flared. He loved Louisa; maybe it wasn't Louisa herself, but the cruelty of millions of people being wrongly accused by the self-assumed righteous people such as this man. The absurdity of it all. These loud-mouthed advocates of righteousness . . . from a thousand pulpits in the United States occupied by clergymen not a word of hard censure was heard, for relevation of wrong-doings does not pay the rent or butter their bread. Yet the frail clergymen should not be too severely condemned. Like the rest of us they were only people. Nature cries louder than the wounds of Christ, and is nearer. He has a family and cannot risk his children going hungry or wife excluded from society. What's a little matter of conscience anyway? It is a fine thing to be rich, a leader of society, to have people look up to them. People like to play God . . . to stand on a pedestal of their own construction . . . and set up a bastard morality.

This man; no . . . not a man but a revolting creature, was judging Louisa. Louisa, a prostitute, yes . . . but a tender, gentle human being also; being judged a cold empty shell by society. A Commanding Officer can do no evil; evil in such an officer's house becomes good.

He hated this officer. Ian tried not to hate but still despised him. Even worse, he hated himself for being one of them. Louisa had been a prostitute, but there is not a king or a potentate in history who has not had mistresses. The prince takes after the king and high society follows the example of the prince. Society smiles at the crime of adultery within their circle of respectability but screams loudly when the common folk follow this practice.

This society, be it good or bad, judges all things. The prisons are built for petty pickpockets, the cheap assassins, the bold highwaymen, the chivalrous burglars, not for men in careful dress and pompous air, any one of whom accomplishes as much evil in a single day as all the criminal class will commit in a year. In the rich and prosperous class, there is found the true criminal to Christianity, those who cheat the government, rob the people of millions, who grab land, coal, and iron, who build railroads with the people's hard earned money, of bribers, public officials, and private promoters who, with cunning and sleight of hand, win the wealth of others into their own pockets. For this clique of "high society," virtue has become too tame, so vice is adopted after awhile.

"Punishments and rules established for the common people do not apply to us," think the spokesmen of high society, "our immoralities and dishonesties are to be respected due to our superior intelligence and wealth. We can break all the commandments, but you poverty society can not."

Ian's rage lessened somewhat. He told himself, now he was trying to play God. He wanted to change the world . . . to save it from itself. And he couldn't even save himself . . . . wouldn't escape from this which he hated. To justify his weakness not in fighting the problems of the world, he told himself that there were many pure and intelligent women and men in high society; the good and honest numbered a thousand times more than that of the corrupt. Many young men of the best society, including himself, were ashamed of their idleness and weaknesses. Many attended dinner parties and dances and did not make a practice of stealing and cheating.

It was becoming somewhat common among the young men of high society to lead a useful life, to adopt the virtues of the masses, to work hard to make this country a great nation in which to live.

"Are you listening to me, Lieutenant?" the Colonel asked, noticeably irritated that Ian was ignoring him.

"Yes, sir," Ian countered.

"Stay out of Rialto from now on and don't bring that trash woman on the Post anymore."

"My private life is my own affair, sir! I will do what I want to on my own time. If the colonel would like to press charges," Ian stopped but looked directly into the colonel's eyes and was visibly threatening the authority of the commander's orders.

Colonel Dodge hadn't experienced this insubordination before and he didn't know what to do about it. For a moment he was at a loss of words.

Of all the things you could say about the colonel, you couldn't say he was stupid or dumb. No, that, he wasn't. If he did press charges, he knew a court martial would prove his orders illegal. Ian had called his bluff and this made him furious. He would remember this, the colonel promised himself, and he would get back at this lieutenant one way or another. This Lieutenant Douglass would be sorry for proving him wrong, very sorry.

"Dismissed, Lieutenant," growled Dodge.

Ian saluted, turned with strict military etiquette and walked quickly from the room.

"Well, I have a lot of things to do," he thought, "and I had better get started. Maybe I can get Father Gregg to marry Private Hammond and Cally, if he is in shape to stand up," remembering the priest had been drunk the majority of the times Ian had seen him.

Ian walked down to the parsonage and, strangely enough, the priest was not drunk. He had been drunk for ten solid days and almost died from the tremendous amount of alcohol in his body, so he was trying his best to stay off the whisky.

He greeted Ian joyfully, remembering him from the previous encounters and he had noticed Ian's compassion for his fellow men, for he looked for such things in a man.

Father Gregg walked with a slight stooping due to paralysis; his gait was grave and sedate. He was always clothed in the garments of his calling. His face was long, his eyes rather large than small, his jaw heavy, and his under-lip prominent. His complexion was dark and slightly reddened by the constant intake of whisky. Though his face and head gave the appearance of being plentifully supplied with hair, the crown was moderately bald; on the side and back, the hairs were long, very fine, and nearly snow white. The sides and lower part of the face were covered with a white beard, which was long enough to come down a little on his chest. The upper lip bore a heavy moustache.

His countenance was always sad and thoughtful. His manners were wonderfully composed and restrained, and in all his ways, when he was sober, he was more courteous and civil than any other priest Ian had ever met.

Such was the outward man in that slight frame, but in the presence of the face, it was difficult to think of his frail body. That face, from which it was not easy to remove one's eye, charmed and fascinated Ian. His blue eyes pierced Ian like darts dipped in kindliness.

Ian told him of his talks with Private Hammond and Colonel Dodge. Fully informed on all the possible repercussions, the priest volunteered to perform the ceremony that evening. Ian thanked him and informed Ira and Cally that Father Gregg had offered his services to marry them. Ian would personally take the responsibility of approving the union.

So later in the evening, in the presence of a small group of Ira's friends, and Ian acting as the official witness, the ceremony was performed by Father Gregg.

The next morning Colonel Dodge placed both Private Hammond and Ian in arrest, but three hours later they were released without comment. It seemed that the Catholic priest had heard of their arrest and that he had gone directly to the post commander to get the matter straightened out. Of course, the restriction on the marriage was illegal and so was the arrest. Even though all of this action was caused by the colonel, he quickly backed out of any responsibility for the controversy saying his directions had been misinterpreted and he was only concerned for the happiness of the two. Private Hammond was expected to go out on an expedition soon, and the colonel wanted to spare the girl any anguish of a lonely wait and possibly her husband would never return from Indian Territory. Colonel Dodge knew when to back down gracefully, especially when asked to do so by the post commander.

For some reason Colonel Dodge and Ian were being thrown together more and more. No words passed between the two other than what was necessary. Ian would salute and absently say, "good morning, sir," and nothing more. Generally, only a grunt and a slight salute were returned. The colonel was a man who hated irregularity of any kind, especially from a lowly lieutenant. A lieutenant was not supposed to act the way Ian did.

*   *   *

Two days later a court martial convened.

The court was composed of four officers: Ian; Lieutenant Taylor; Major Davidson, the Deputy Post Commander; and Colonel Dodge, First Dragoon Regimental Commander.

The first soldier brought in was of medium height, an athletic well-built young man. A bright spot on the sleeve of his faded uniform clearly indicated where his corporal chevrons had been torn off.

Lieutenant Jefferson Davis, an assistant Adjutant General, arose and commenced the proceedings by reading from a ledger: "This General Court Martial is called into session pursuant to Special Orders No. 104, current series, from this headquarters, and of which Brevet Colonel H. C. Dodge, Commander, First Dragoon Regiment, is president and eight cases are to be tried."

With that, the assistant adjutant sat down at the table with the rest of the board and called out, "First, James R. McBride, Corporal, Company C, First Dragoons, on the following charges and specifications. Charge 1st: conduct prejudicial to good order and military discipline."

"Specification 1st: in this, that he, Corporal James R. McBride, Company C, First Dragoon Regiment, did commence a quarrel with Sergeant Henry Pipkin, Company C, First Dragoon Regiment, and did violently assault and threaten him, the said Corporal McBride, using the following language, to wit: 'You are damned son of a bitch; either one or the other of us will have to die right here,' or words to that effect."

"Specification 2nd: in this, that he, the said Corporal McBride, did violently assault and beat the said Sergeant Pipkin with a pistol upon the head and did discharge a loaded pistol at him to the great danger of his life."

"Charge 2nd: absence without leave."

"Specification 1st: in this, that he, the said Corporal McBride, did absent himself from the garrison after taps without permission from his commanding officer."

"All this at Fort Leavenworth, Kansas. Corporal McBride, front and center," the adjutant ordered.

The young dragoon rose to his feet and stood at attention before the board.

"Your plea will now be heard, Corporal," the adjutant informed the youth.

"To the lst specification, lst charge, how do you plea?"

"Not guilty," replied Corporal McBride.

"To the 2nd specification lst charge?"

"Not guilty, sir."

"To the 2nd charge, how do you plea?"

"Guilty, sir," replied the corporal.

"Be seated, Corporal," ordered the adjutant.

The board members all signified their decisions on the court papers and the findings were not guilty to the first charge and guilty of the second charge, the same as Corporal McBride had pleaded.

The youth stood again for the sentencing.

"The sentence of this court is as follows," directed Colonel Dodge, "you are to forfeit to the United States, ten dollars of your pay for one month."

"Sir," young McBride interrupted, "I have a written plea," and he handed it to the colonel.

As the colonel read it, anger plainly showed on his round frowning face. The colonel looked up from the paper and addressed the board.

"The accused has made a written plea on the charges and specifications. The prisoner pleads in bar of trial that he had already been punished for the offenses alleged and submits copy of an order reducing him to the ranks," the colonel angrily conveyed.

Colonel Dodge turned to Corporal McBride and said very strongly, without bothering to get the remainder of the court's opinions, "the court decides that the plea of the prisoner in bar of trial is not sustained. The sentence will be executed."

"So this is how Colonel Dodge runs a court martial," Ian thought to himself. But he said nothing about the infraction of the rules of court martial boards. He didn't feel like arguing about the point of law. Anyway, the Judge Advocate and the Adjutant General sitting there knew of the violation, but had said nothing. Ian didn't want to do battle over such a little infraction as this.

The other cases were heard using the same routine and were duly recorded. They were mostly the usual offenses and sentences.

It had been a long afternoon with prisoners and guards parading in and out of the courtroom all the time. Listening to pleas, presentation of long evidence, and determining the guilt or innocence of the accused took much time and thought.

Only two more cases and the court martial would be finished. Ian looked forward to the dismissal and a cool ride down to the sergeant's place near Rialto.

The next to the last case came up. Corporal Samuel Blackburn of the dragoons was accused of conduct to the prejudice of good order and military discipline and absence without leave. He was an "old timer" and a splendid specimen of a frontiersman. He was brave and active, but could never quite abide by army rules. These men were very independent, but also very necessary in the Indian Territory to train the youthful officers right out of West Point. They had saved many a detachment because of their coolness, courage, and knowledge of the Indians. Samuel had served with gallantry and walked with a decided limp, lamed for life with an arrow through his knee in a forgotten Indian battle.

The charge read that he, Corporal Sam Blackburn, being placed in charge of four men as mail carriers and stationed at Big Spring, Indian Territory, on the line of Couriers between Fort Leavenworth and Fort Gibson, did absent himself without proper authority at many different times, including four times when the mail arrived and also when the party to relieve him arrived.

Sam made no attempt to lie; he pleaded guilty to the charge and the court confirmed his plea and found him guilty as charged. The sentence of the court was lenient because of his past services. He was sentenced to be confined to the guard at the post where his company may be serving for a period of four months and to forfeit $2.50 of his monthly pay for the same period.

The last case to be heard was that of Private Lewis Bell. The charges and specifications were short and quickly read.

Charge 1st: disobedience of orders.

Specification: that Private Lewis Bell, Company A, First Dragoons, being ordered by Lance Corporal Dumas, Company A, to lead a blind horse belonging to Company A, from the company stables, to the herding ground did fail to obey said order.

Charge 2nd: neglect of duty, causing the destruction of government property.

Specification: that Private Bell, being directed by Corporal Dumas to lead a blind horse belonging to said company from the stables to the herding ground, did carelessly and willfully neglect to perform that duty, thereby permitting the horse to fall into a well and causing its death.

Private Bell's plea of the charges was "not guilty;" however, he had no chance to explain why he pleaded so.

Ian knew the youth and the circumstances surrounding the incident. Something or someone had startled a team of horses and, as the run-away horses passed nearby, the sergeant had yelled to everyone to stop the wagon. Bell reacted quickly, raced to the wagon as it passed, and grabbed the reins of one of the horses. Even though he was dragged for several hundred yards and was badly bruised, he finally managed to mount the horse and stop the team. In the meantime, the blind horse had wandered along and fell into a well. The sergeant faced with the prospect of a court martial over the death of the horse, blamed Private Bell, ignoring the fact that he had stopped the run-away team. Bell had done what he thought was most urgent, but any which way he acted, he would have been wrong in the army's thinking, so he was a victim of circumstances and was to be the scapegoat for the death of the horse.

As Ian rose to plead for the private, Colonel Dodge ordered, "you are a member of the court martial board and not here as Private Bell's counsel."

The colonel then turned to Private Bell—a thoroughly scared and timid soldier—"you were neglect in your duty. The sentence is to forfeit to the United States fifty dollars (the value of the horse) and to be confined in charge of the guard at hard labor for thirty days."

Ian rose again to his feet; "I protest this sentence."

Colonel Dodge was fully wild now as he fairly shouted at Ian, "Lieutenant Douglass, you do not protest my sentences."

Dodge stood up and sternly ordered, "this court martial is adjourned," and he strode out of the room.

Ian, now plainly mad also, turned to the adjutant, Lieutenant Jeff Davis, "I request to talk to the commander of this post."

All of the other officers present flushed at this insubordination. None of them wished to be involved in any dispute with Colonel Dodge; his murderous anger was known throughout the garrison. Nobody ever crossed the colonel. Nobody! Those who had, regretted the day ever since.

"I'll arrange a meeting tomorrow, Lieutenant Douglass," replied Davis.

Ian nodded his acknowledgment and walked out. As he passed Private Bell, he stopped for a moment looking directly into his eyes. No words were spoken for a moment. None were needed. Private Bell's appreciation clearly showed in his eyes. Ian's gaze shifted to the sergeant that had given the order and to Lieutenant Taylor who had trumped up the charges against Bell.

A deep look of hurt mingled with scorn passed over his face, then he told Bell, "We will get this straightened out, Private."

"Thank you, sir," Bell said quietly.

Strange. As Ian left the building, no officer joined him. He didn't think about it much, but the thought did cross his mind that he seemed an outcast—not a member of the human race. He was doing something about this crime of "not caring," but he was being condemned for it. To cover their own irresponsibility, they made it appear he was wrong and they were all in the right.

Simple honesty of purpose in a man goes a long way in life—this steady obedience to the rule he knows and feels to be right. Without it, a man is like a ship without a rudder or compass which drifts here and there with the shifting of every little wind that blows. Honesty and principle hold a man straight on course, give him strength, and form a mainspring for a full life.

*   *   *

Later that day by courier, Ian was informed that the commanding officer would see him the next day. Ian, hating most things society stood for, was nevertheless protected by it, even though he didn't realize it. All the officers on the garrison knew of his father's connection with Senator Clark and all of them more or less tolerated and even catered to Ian's wishes. They never did give him too much trouble. All of them would leave the service one-day and they all were thinking of that future time and of a future civilian job. Ian's father, being a wealthy and influential retired general could refer them to good positions in many different enterprises. None of them would endanger or even possibly threaten a chance of being favored for positions in industry, government or politics.

Even the commanding officer was looking for a berth in industry or government, possibly becoming a senator; so though Ian's actions gave him trouble, he considered Ian's thoughts very carefully and had done all he could for him.

The matter of Private Bell was brought up. Ian told him of the circumstances of the death of the blind horse. Colonel Williams had on his desk the findings of the court martial. He was required to review all sentences and make such recommendations and changes, as he deemed necessary.

After Ian's presentation of the facts, he changed the sentence in the case of Private Bell. In his written findings he stated, "after a careful review of evidence, the installation commander is satisfied that the person is not guilty of willful disobedience of orders or of criminal neglect of duty." He further instructed that, "Private Bell be released from confinement and returned to duty." The matter was officially closed.

The atmosphere became friendlier and the two discussed trivial matters for awhile. The colonel knew than Ian's appetite for liquor was getting the better of him. Colonel Williams talked kindly to Ian, not wanting to offend, but only to try and help him with his problem.

"Lieutenant, you probably will be surprised at the tenor of my communication, but having conceived a strong liking for you, I wish you would look upon my comments as solely in your own best interest, and I am saying all this without a thought of official position in any way."

The colonel hesitated for a moment as if searching for the right words, then continued, "It has been brought to my attention that you have contracted too great a fondness for liquor. I'll give no names, but I assure you that the statement regarding your newly formed habit comes from an officer of years and rank, who has no possible personal feeling in the matter, but I earnestly ask you to give it up as it is unquestionably injuring your reputation. You have a most promising career and are well liked by your command. Your name was mentioned as an officer to exactly fill the requirements of a certain delicate mission to the Western Territory. The orders detailing you were about to be made, but an elderly officer spoke up and said that within a few months you had become habituated to a daily use of liquor. In his judgment, considering the peculiar circumstances governing the matter, your drinking might possibly render such a detail a little hazardous. His statement resulted in the order for the detail being temporarily suspended."

Ian looked surprised and then disappointed. He had no anger for Colonel Williams, as he seemed extremely sincere in his concern.

The colonel continued, after a pause, "I know, Lieutenant, I have laid myself open to criticism and possible disapproval upon your part, but I beg to be allowed to be your friend and well-wisher."

Ian was impressed upon the sincerity of the conversation. For a long moment nothing was said between the two.

Ian was the first to break the silence. "Sir, if you would kindly reconsider me for the detail, I swear that whisky and I will part company."

Colonel Williams was every bit a commander. He expressed confidence and leadership in his subordinates. He rose quickly and extended his hand to Ian in a sign of accepting his word.

"The detail is yours, Lieutenant. I'll arrange to have the orders tomorrow. Prepare to have your squadron to move out in a week."

Ian came to attention, saluted, wheeled around and left the office. He felt excited, happy, and wonderful—what a few words can do for a man. He was already thrilled at the prospects of a new adventure.

The next day Ian was again ushered into the commander's office. Colonel Williams was in a somber mood; a calm and thoughtful attitude characterized his words.

"Lieutenant, let us talk about philosophy for awhile—of the fundamental beliefs, concepts, and attitudes of a people or nation. I believe that you, though young as you are, are the only officer on the post that will understand what I am about to say."

He got up from the desk, strolled over to the window and looked out over the wide Missouri river flowing past the garrison two hundred feet below and then continued, in a grave mood.

"Someone once said that wise men tell us that the world is growing happier—that we live longer than did our fathers, have more comfort and less toil, fewer wars and higher hopes and aspirations. So say the wise men; but deep in our own hearts, we know they are wrong."

"Each of us, in the May of life when the world was young, started out along the path that led through green meadows to the blue mountains on the distant horizon, beyond which lay the great world we were to conquer. Though others dropped behind, some of us have gone on through morning brightness and noonday heat, with eyes always steadily forward, until the fresh grass began to be parched and withered. The way grew hard and stony, and the blue mountains turned into gray rocks and thorny cliffs. When at last we reached the toilsome summit, we found the glory that had lured us onward was only the sunset glow that fades into darkness while we look. It leaves us at the very goal to sink down, tired in body and sick at heart with strength and courage gone to close our eyes and dream again, not of fame and fortune that were to be ours, but only of the old-time happiness that we have left so far behind . . . so far behind," he repeated as he turned to Ian.

His eyes moist from the realization that his dreams had escaped him, Colonel Williams continued, "As with men, so is it with nations. The lost paradise is the world's dreamland of youth. What tribe or people have not had its golden age, when women were beautiful angels and men were gods and heroes? And when the race lies crushed and groaning beneath an alien yoke, how natural is the dream of a messiah, who shall drive out the usurper and win back for his people what they have lost. The hope becomes a faith and the faith becomes the creed of priests and prophets, until the hero is a god and the dream a religion, looking to some great miracle of nature for its accomplishment."

"Among the roving tribes of the north," the colonel continued, "this hero is hardly more than an expert magician, frequently degraded to the level of a common trickster. Under the softer southern skies, the myth takes more poetic form and the hero becomes a person of dignified presence, a father and teacher of his children, a very Christ, worthy of all love and reverence. He gathers together the wandering nomads and leads them to their destined country, where he instructs them, regulates authority, and teaches peaceful modes of life."

"Now," he continued very gravely and tracing a large area on the wall map, "there has arose among the Great Plains Indians another prophet who has announced himself as the bearer of a new revelation from the Master of Life. He has taken pity on his red children and wishes to save them from destruction."

"This mysterious Hasanun's words are believed to be the direct utterances of a god. Our information is derived chiefly from traders and trappers, who know these things only as vague rumors of Indian unrest aroused by this so-called prophet, from the statements of a few illiterate interpreters or captives among the Indians, and from the tales of old warriors."

"This new prophecy, religion, or doctrine, whatever you wish to call it, is known as the Ghost Dance . . . some call it the Dreamer Religion."

"This is your true mission, Lieutenant. Although your orders are to protect the caravan of Senator Clark, your purpose is to seek out these rumors, evaluate the strength of this new religion, and find the source of this fomentation."

After a moment of silence, the colonel offered, "Father Gregg will accompany you, Lieutenant."

Ian started to speak, but he was interrupted by the colonel, "Let me explain. A few days ago, a small band of Kickapoo Indians came to Father Gregg's house to visit the missionary and apparently regarded the meeting as of great importance to them. They declared they had heard of Father Gregg and his missionary labors. They believed him to be the one for whom their people had long been looking. Each Indian held in his hand one of his strange wooden crosses, or prayer sticks. As they knelt on the grass in front of the priest's house, they went through their devotions in their own tongue, moving their fingers over the inscription that ascends the shaft of the cross. The priest understood them to state that this cross was their 'bible,' that they knew it was not the true Bible, but that they had been told to use them until one should come who would give them in exchange the genuine word of God. Thereupon Father Gregg gathered up their crosses—and there were a basketful of them—and gave in exchange to each a copy of the New Testament. The Indians received the books with profuse expressions of gratitude and apparently viewed them at once as sacred possessions. These wise men from the west then went away. Father Gregg wishes to go into the territory. These Indians have promised his protection. It may come in handy for you to have his protection with you."

Ian, as commander of the search, felt it was his duty to know all he could about the people traveling with him, so he felt obligated to ask the question, "No one will talk about it, but, Colonel, I've wondered how Father Gregg got those slashes on him?"

The colonel clearly wanted to avoid the subject but as Ian had asked, with reasonable justification, Colonel Williams knew he must tell Ian the story if Father Gregg was to accompany him into Indian Territory.

"Sometimes, Lieutenant, the army does things they would rather sweep under the rug. You know, Ian, we officers are not gods, even though the army system encourages this thinking. We are only people. We make mistakes. We let mistakes happen." He hesitated for a long moment, then continued, "There was a Major Moore. He had been a missionary to the Wyandot Indians and afterwards, as an interpreter and guide, he traveled through the west with Methodist bishops who were establishing missions among the Indian tribes. Everywhere he went he preached to the soldiers in their barracks here in Indian Territory, Arkansas Territory, and Missouri. They liked his style and urged him to stay with them. The governor of Missouri at that time offered him the position of chaplain, but he said that if he went with the soldiers, he wanted to fight, so he was made a line major instead of a chaplain. Not to justify what he did, but there is one point of his character that must not be lost sight of. He was, like many other Missouri settlers, an uncompromising patriot, and he had no use for a rebel—white or red. His dislike to anything savoring of treason or even criticism of the government got him into trouble time and time again, but he never held back on that account."

"Word was received several winters ago from spies among the Colorado Indians that a coalition was being formed among the Plains Indians to drive the whites from the trade routes. This information proved true; for in the spring and summer, the Sioux, Commanches, Kiowas, and Cheyennes engaged in active hostilities. Matters became worse and troops were sent in. The old trapper who had been guiding Major Moore's troops became so sick and weak that he was unable to distinguish the tracks, and they were obliged to rely on another."

"The troops," he sadly continued, "came upon a friendly camp of Indians, but the troops attacked without finding out if they were friendly or not. The men were raw recruits, and they had old scores to settle in the accounts of murder, robbery, and rape. It was thought that these offenses were committed without any provocation from settlers. The settlers wanted revenge. These men, who had been cooped up all summer in towns, whose crops were ruined, whose stock had been run off, whose homes had been burned, and who had buried the bodies of their neighbors had a fire of vengeance in their hearts that could only be quenched by the blood of the Indians."

"Every Indian in the camp was killed." He paused before he continued, "Father Gregg happened to be there at the camp. They were indeed friendly Indians and had no part in the marauding—others testified to that. The principal chief ran up an American flag over his tepee with a white flag above it. A white trader, who was in one of the tepees, came out and hastened to Major Moore to tell him that the camp was friendly. But the troops were out of hand and Major Moore, not knowing whether to trust the white trader, let them continue."

The colonel paused again for a moment, took a deep breath and said as he exhaled, "Every Indian man, woman, and child was slaughtered. The exact number will probably never be known."

"A bullet from the camp, as the Indians finally began firing back in self defense, hit Major Moore and tumbled him from his horse. In their frenzy, the troops tortured Father Gregg. In the troopers warped thinking, living with the Indians made him one of them. He was repeatedly burned with a firebrand then whipped at a stake. He would have died if another troop had not heard the firing and came upon the scene. Later, Major Moore was put under arrest and he was dishonorably discharged."

"Well, that's the story, Lieutenant," concluded the colonel. "It's not very pleasant, but that's the way it sometimes happens here on the frontier. After the massacre, Father Gregg wandered through the burning camp. The dead women and children were too much of a shock to him and he's been drinking ever since. I hope he will be able to come out of it someday, but I am afraid he will never get over it completely."

The colonel turned away and stood again in front of the window, as if ashamed of the incident, but something a commander had to live with. A commander's job sometimes if very difficult. The incident was done; it could not be undone.

Ian left the room quietly, with a deep feeling for Colonel Williams and his burdens. Here was truly a man of conscience with a desire and feeling of obligation to do right and to be fair.

*   *   *

Two days later there was a briefing on the "Indian problems." All of the company commanders of the First Dragoon Regiment, the 9th Infantry and several other units were in attendance. Officers, young and old, experienced and fresh out of West Point, journeyed to Fort Leavenworth from Jefferson Barracks in St. Louis and from Forts Towson, Gibson, Snelling, Des Moines, Crawford and Mitchell. Captain Duncan from the Intelligence Section of the U. S. Army Western Department headquarters at New Orleans had traveled all the way from Louisiana.

The meeting started promptly at nine o'clock in the morning. The captain started right away on the Indian situation as was understood by the Western Department Headquarters.

"Sirs, I have the honor to submit for your information the following views upon the best method which can be adopted for the protection of the frontier exposed to the hostile incursions of the Indians. The period has arrived when a systematic plan for the protection of our frontiers ought to be devised and adopted."

"Heretofore, posts have been established upon our extensive inland boundary as circumstances from time to time required, without regard to any general arrangement. Indeed, from the position of the Indians, any other course was probably impracticable. No line could be drawn upon one side of which the Indians could be kept and on the other, our citizens. Positions were therefore selected with relation to their geographical advantages and to the moral effect that they were calculated to have upon the Indians. As different views have been entertained, posts have been advanced into the Indian country and then withdrawn. Wherever this withdrawal has taken place, excitement among the Indians and sometimes more serious difficulties have occurred. They cannot comprehend the motives that dictate these operations and they attribute such measures to a sense of our weakness or to a fear of them. It is only, therefore, in extraordinary cases that posts once established in the Indian country should be withdrawn. If moved at all, the movement should be to advance."

"Here we have the tables showing the number of Indians who now are, or probably soon will be, placed in contact with our settlements west of the Mississippi River," Captain Duncan explained as he uncovered several charts on the wall behind the podium.

Captain Duncan pointed to the figures as he continued, "It will be seen that there have already been removed to this region from the country east of the Mississippi 31,348 Indians and that the indigenous tribes between them and the Rocky Mountains amount to 147,641. This making for an Indian force of 178,989, requiring precautionary measures to restrain them. There are yet 62,181 to emigrate, and when their removal is effected, the whole Indian force west of the Mississippi and east of the Rocky Mountains will be about 241,170."

Ian was surprised at the figures. He had never thought of the number of Indians in this part of the country before. He read the tables with much interest, trying hard to remember the tribes and numbers in each.

Census of Indian Tribes

Number of Indians emigrated

Winnebagoes	700
Chippewas, Ottawas, and Pottawatomies	1,200
Pottawatomies from Indiana	441
Choctaws	15,000
Quapaws	300
Creeks	3,600

Apalachicolas	265
Cherokees	6,000
Kickapoos	588
Delawares	826
Shawnees	1,250
Ottawas	200
Weas	222
Piankeshaws	162
Peories and Kaskaskias	132
Senecas	251
Senecas and Shawnees	211
Total	31,348

Number of Indians to remove

New York Indians	4,176
Ottawas of Ohio	230
Wyandots	575
Pottawatomies of Indiana	3,000
Miamies	1,100
Chippewas, Ottawas, and Pottawatomies	6,400
Winnebagoes	4,500
Menomonees	4,200
Cherokees	8,000
Creeks	21,000
Chickasaws	5,600
Seminoles	3,000
Apalachicolas	400
Total	62,181

Number of Indians of the indigenous tribes within striking distance of the frontier

Sioux	27,500
Iowas	1,200
Sacs	4,800
Foxes	1,600
Sacs of the Missouri	500
Osages	5,120
Kansas	1,471
Omahas	1,400
Ottoes and Missourias	1,600
Pawnees	10,000
Comanches	7,000
Kiowas	1,400
Mandans	15,000

Kansas Ghost Woman

Quapaws	450
Minatares	15,000
Assinaboins	8,000
Crees	300
Gros Ventres	3,000
Crows	4,500
Caddoes	2,000
Poncas	800
Arickaras	3,000
Cheyennes	2,000
Blackfeet	30,000
Total	147,641

The recapitulation showed the number of Indians that would be between the frontier and the Rocky mountains after the emigration was completed.

Recapitulation

Number of Indians emigrated	31,348
Number of Indians to remove	62,181
Number of Indians of the indigenous tribes	147,641
Total	241,170

Captain Duncan interrupted Ian's thoughts as he continued the briefing.

"Although many of these Indians reside far from the settled frontier, the nature of the country as well as the general possession of horses enables them to extend their war excursions to great distances. Besides, we must adopt the policy of preventing the various tribes from committing hostilities upon one another. Our remote settlements and our citizens residing in or passing through the Indian country will never be safe as long as the petty tribes in contact with them are permitted to engage in warfare at pleasure. We have also promised protection to the emigrated tribes, this guarantee, deemed so highly important by them, cannot be preserved without the adoption of vigorous measures and the establishment of a system of defense adequate to any exigency that may occur."

"Independent of the obligations upon the government of the United States to afford protection to the whole country, there are peculiar reasons why occurrences upon the western border should excite special concern. After full consideration of the best means fitted to improve the condition of the Indians, and to place them in circumstances where they can do least injury to the people of the United States, it has been determined to transfer them to the country beyond the limits of our settlements west of the Mississippi. This system has already been pursued to such an extent as to insure its final success. When consummated, an immense body of Indians, whose estimated amount I have already stated, will be placed upon the borders of our settlements. We must expect that they will return in some measure to many of their former habits. They will in a great degree be strangers to one another and to the primitive tribes occupying that region. They will form little quasi-independent communities, and will, of course, be liable to all those accidents and excitements which, even in more advanced societies, are calculated to lead to collisions. Their institutions have a tendency to war. No warrior arriving at manhood can enjoy any estimation until he has been present where the blood of an enemy has been shed. He dates his distinction from that period and his fame is after that proportioned to his success in war. Their civil organized society is feeble, seldom providing punishments for offenses unless through the medium of the injured party. This, of course, leads to all those acts of revenge and retaliation which disturb communities."

"It is obvious from these remarks, as well as from our own experiences, that we must anticipate, after the removal of the Indians, that causes of difficulties, both among themselves and between them and our citizens, will arise, and be in continual operation. These must be counteracted by the proper distribution along the frontier of a sufficient military force, and by such arrangements for its employment as circumstances may call for. The Indians have no conception of our actual power. They judge by what they see about them. Experience has shown that they are prepared to commence hostilities under circumstances, which, as we well know, leave them no chance of success. They are, in fact, a people of impulse and are brought into difficulties by the passions of the young men who act in opposition to the opinions and advice of those who are more experienced."

"The system of Indian emigration will soon be concentrated upon our western frontier. Common prudence requires the adoption of a plan of defense to any urgency which will probably arise."

"The Western Department plans for adequate defenses against these Indians," continued Captain Duncan, referring to the military headquarters in New Orleans, "have already been submitted to the Secretary of War and Senator Clark, Chairman of the Committee on Military Affairs."

"The great object is to make such arrangements as will distribute a sufficient force to overawe the Indians and to intercept any parties who might be disposed to make irruption upon our settlements. We must also facilitate the necessary communication and allow a speedy concentration of troops upon those points where it may be required."

"The length of the route will probably be upwards of eight hundred miles. After the road is surveyed and its route determined, it should be opened for military purposes; that is, to facilitate the movement of troops along it."

"The smaller streams, where there are no good fords, should be bridged. But it is believed there is a great deal of the country over which this road will pass so favorably that scarcely any work need be done upon it."

"We propose that a sufficient number of positions be selected along this line for the establishment of military posts, and that the necessary works, similar in their character to those at our stockade forts, be constructed. At or near each end of the route, and at an intermediate point, the dragoons should be stationed, while infantry will occupy other posts. As fast as circumstances will permit, the garrisons in the Indian country, east of this line, ought to be transferred to it."

"The ill-judged economy, which arrested the measures projected for the defense of the frontier in 1819 and broke down the army in 1821, has caused all the difficulties which have occurred with the Indians since. Had those measures been carried out and the force then in service retained, competent garrisons might have been disposable and ready to reinforce any point requiring their aid and the bloodshed, devastation, and consequent expense attending three Indian campaigns might have been avoided."

"Gentlemen," Captain Duncan continued, "that concludes the briefing. There will be a thirty-minute break before we continue with the question and answer session."

All the officers got up, stretched, yawned, and shook themselves awake. It had been a long briefing—too long. Even though the information was interesting, most of the men had been numbed by the lengthy presentation.

During the break, Ian looked at the charts of Indian strengths and the proposed road, as did several other officers.

Ian was to be host for the evening for several of the officers and he walked through the group reading the name tags on the breast pockets of the men. On his list were Lieutenant Philip St. George Cook, Captain James W. Hamilton, Lieutenant Jefferson Davis, Lieutenant Abraham Van Buren, Captain Nathaniel Boone, Lieutenant James F. Izard, and Major Richard Barnes Mason.

Several of these men had traveled a great distance from the outposts or from headquarter posts and they were to stay the night before starting back to their home posts. Ian introduced himself, identified himself as host officer, and requested the pleasure of their company at dinner that evening in the Leavenworth House down in the city where they all were staying the night.

Louisa and several other young and beautiful women were to be there as hostesses. Ian was looking forward to an interesting evening, but even he could not perceive the vitality and extremely individualistic nature of these young junior officers. They had been selected by the Visitor's Bureau to be entertained by Ian because they were generally like him. Unknown to him and even their comrades in arms, these young men would shape the new nation of the infant United States of America.

When the session started again, Colonel Williams, the post commander, was the first to comment.

"Gentlemen, I have to remark that our whole western frontier, extending from Lake Superior to the Gulf of Mexico, is, as you are well aware, either bounded by a foreign territory in a state of civil war or in direct contact with powerful and warlike Indian tribes. Should those who are in arms against their government on our borders be beaten, they will naturally fly to our country for protection. If the bands of Indians under the control of that government be employed against them, the whole of our frontier will be exposed to their incursions and to Indian warfare."

"The Indians north of Red River, if united, might bring into the field perhaps twenty thousand warriors and their numbers are daily increasing by the emigrating tribes from Ohio, Indiana, Illinois, Michigan, Tennessee, Mississippi, Alabama, Georgia, and Florida. Many of the emigrants occupy their new positions under the influence of hostile feelings, the result of real and imaginary wrongs. For the purpose of vengeance, therefore, they would readily unite with the native tribes who naturally view with jealousy the steady progress of our population westward in any measure against us which should promise even temporary success."

"Within the last nine years, we have had four difficulties of this nature; one with the Winnebagoes, two with the Sacs and Foxes, and one with the Florida Indians. Altogether, these problems have occasioned great loss of property, great derangement of business, a heavy expenditure of money, and much inconvenience in those portions of country affected. The addition proposed would make the whole artillery force 4,200 and the whole infantry force 5,220, thus raising the legal establishment of the army to 9,420. These numbers, it will be observed, are exclusive of the commissioned officers."

An officer smiled slightly as he heard these figures, as the Grand Conspiracy was prepared to field an army of 16,000 against the 9,420 of the United States Army.

No other comments or questions were brought up so the conference adjourned and all the conferees walked over to the officers' mess for a late lunch.

The briefing had been very good. It was detailed and well presented, Ian thought. It was good information to know. As he looked around at all the officers that had traveled to Fort Leavenworth to attend the conference, he thought that it helped many of them to do their jobs better. He was right. Indeed, the information was very helpful especially to those few involved in the Grand Conspiracy to manipulate a revolution and establish a new country. The information they received this morning made their work that much easier. The Secret Committee of Correspondence of the West now had all the data that the Intelligence Office of the Western Department Headquarters had collected on the size of the Indian forces and also the Army's proposals and plans.

*   *   *

The evening at the Leavenworth House was very enjoyable in spite of the crudities of the hotel. The meal was fine, the conversation stimulating, and the women lent a beautiful attraction to the occasion.

All of the young officers had outstanding personalities. Lieutenant Philip St. George Cooke and Jefferson Davis' personalities were nearly identical to Ian's. Cooke had graduated from the United States Military Academy in 1827 and then served with the 6th Infantry nearly five years at various western stations and on expeditions into the Indian country. He had skirmished with the Comanche Indians in 1829. He had a high sense of humor and was one of the most courageous and frank men Ian had known—a true man with no treacherous cunning. Philip St. George Cooke considered it beneath the dignity of a gentleman to go into battle on foot. He considered a horseman as a romantic figure and he told his troopers that "it would disgrace a dragoon even to speak with an infantry soldier."

Richard B. Mason was the eldest in the group, thirty-six years old and senior officer at the party. He was always at conflict with Colonel Dodge, almost to the point of challenging him to a duel over the bad treatment of the enlisted men. Two days after Congress created the First Dragoons; he was elected to the rank of major in charge of the regiment. He found out later that Colonel Dodge was to be the commanding officer. Mason was to become a general fifteen years later and the first military and civil governor of California.

Lieutenant Van Buren was a graduate of the academy and his father was vice-president of the United States. When his father became president several years later, he would resign his captain's commission.

James F. Izard was the son of Major General George Izard who had served in the war of 1812 to 1815 and was Governor of Arkansas Territory in 1825 to 1828. This young man's career was to be tragically ended three years later. While fighting Indians in Florida, he was mortally wounded while commanding the advance guard and directing his men "to keep their positions and lie close." At the young age of twenty-six, he died of wounds on the Withlacoochee River in the swamps.

Captain Nathaniel Boone's father was Daniel Boone, pioneer and Indian fighter. His mother died in 1813 and his father spent most of his remaining years at Nathan's home where he died in 1820. Nathan had the features and personality of his famous father. His head was large, his eyes blue, and his look was sharp and alert. His hair was light and his eyebrows yellow. He had a wide mouth, thin lips, and a nose somewhat of the Roman type. He was a man of great strength, lithe and quick in movement, and a fast runner. He had strong native intelligence—though not a man of affairs—his counsel was always welcomed. Typical of most Missouri backwoodsmen, he was loyal in friendship, honest, truthful and modest. One of his prime characteristics was serenity of mind. He never seemed irritated or excited and, though often wronged, he never harbored ill will.

James W. Hamilton, the son of Alexander Hamilton who had been the Secretary of War, was just the opposite of Boone—frank and courageous, but entirely too impetuous. Although primarily a man of action rather than council, he was no hothead. His speech was fluent, clever, profound, and showed thought and power of logical analysis. In action, he was prompt and vigorous with a genius for organization and manipulation. Wine, women and song had no appeal for him. Life was always a serious matter, and he felt keenly its obligations. He had a fiery temper, but he also had a sweetness of disposition, which won him many friends, even among his political and military opponents. He was a noted duelist and is said to have fought eight duels, always wounding his opponent.

Among all the young officers, Lieutenant Jefferson Davis became most friendly with Ian—maybe because he had also been born in Georgia. Only twenty-four years old, he had graduated from the United States Military Academy in 1828. He had served on frontier duty in Wisconsin and in the unsettled portions of Illinois, in little remote posts, garrisoned by mere handfuls of men in as lonely regions as the world possessed. In the Black Hawk Indian War of the preceding year, Jefferson Davis was a minor officer of the regular army. (Although Abraham Lincoln, as an inconspicuous officer of volunteers took part in this war also, they did not meet.) Davis was now adjutant of the First Dragoons..

When he was a child, he was an extremely sensitive boy. At the age of seven, he rode northward nearly 1,000 miles from Mississippi—where his family had moved—to become a pupil of the Roman Catholic Seminary in Kentucky. This impressionable Baptist lad became so fond of the priests who were his teachers that he wished for a time to adopt their religion. He now was an engaging young man, fearless, modest, with personal charm and in friendship rashly loyal—the same as Ian.

These were the fellow officers with Ian in the Dragoons; these men would change the course of history.

One thing they all had in common; they were all concerned with the treatment of men in the new regiment. Lieutenant Cooke, Lieutenant Davis and Major Mason bitterly protested that in the recruitment of the men they had been authorized to inform the candidates for enlistment that they would be well clothed and kept in comfortable quarters. Many of the men were told they "were enlisted under the express declaration that they were to rank with the cadets in the military academy and they were to be considered as volunteer corps."

These men were quickly disillusioned. Instead of enjoying any of the privileges and comforts that had been promised them, they soon found that they were nothing above the other portions of the army. The muskets issued were mostly condemned pieces that had lain in the arsenal since the last war. As for uniforms, there was no clothing at all at the barracks and most of the dragoons soon began to grow gradually thread bare in their civilian clothes. They even had to build the stables for the horses.

The junior officers and Major Mason tried to stop this neglect shown towards the Dragoons and it was only natural that the men began to show a corresponding decline in morale. Instead of feeling themselves an elite corps, they were resentful. There was much murmuring and disaffection in the regiment. Desertions were becoming more and more numerous. The guard house was kept continually filled to overflowing. Even if all these deficiencies would be remedied, many months would be required to whip the regiment into satisfactory shape.

Colonel Dodge was afraid to undertake an expedition with such men because of the risk of losing what little reputation he had acquired. On the other hand, he dared not complain to the politicians who had given him the command about the lack of clothes, horses and equipment.

It was known that he had written a friend that he "had never expected to find such treachery and deception in a body of men who call themselves gentlemen. My situation is unpleasant. Jefferson Davis, who I appointed as my adjutant was among the first to take a stand against me. Major Mason, Davis, Cooke and Douglass are now my most inveterate enemies. The desire of these gentlemen appears to be to harass me in small matters."

A small matter . . . that is what Dodge thought of the lies and failures to the men.

*   *   *

The next week passed quickly. It was quite different from the past weeks that Ian absolutely hated. All the old army routine seemed changed now. The shrill tune of the reveille awakening him at daybreak and the last sound at night of the drummer beating out taps and commanding lights out and sleep, this all had a new joyfulness about it. Gone would be the days of dreary idleness.

Ian's father had been told the news that he was to escort Senator Clark's trade expedition to Santa Fe and, by special messenger, he sent Ian a new type of a handgun that he thought Ian would like—three Paterson Colts, being perfected by Samuel Colt.

The military issue pistol was a smoothbore, .54 caliber single-shot flintlock pistol, capable of being fired about twice a minute. The Paterson Colts that his father sent him were .40 caliber, five-shot percussion cap repeating pistols, with extra cylinders and capable of being fired ten times in about forty seconds. The Colt revolver was the first practical pistol that could discharge its five rounds as rapidly as the eye can wink.

The bow was a mighty fast shooting weapon. So was the Colt. Eli Whitney, the inventor of the cotton gin, had also built a milling machine in 1818 for the manufacture of interchangeable parts for firearms.

A young man by the name of Dr. Coult was touring the country, giving lectures on and demonstrating the effect of nitrous oxide or "laughing gas." When lecturing in New Orleans, Ian's father became interested in this young man and his experiments with a new idea of a handgun. Only twenty-one, this young man, whose real name was Samuel Colt, had many models of his pistol idea made by a man named Chase. Ian's father had bought several of the experimental pistols from him. The arms were handsomely stocked, elaborately mounted and engraved for use as a specimen in interesting investors to form a stock company to manufacture arms under his patents.

The pistols were inlaid with silver, and fitted with ivory stocks. They were large pieces with an overall length of fourteen inches. The barrel was nine inches long and the cylinder held five shots. These larger caliber pistols were made in small quantities, mainly for experiment. The usual features were an octagonal barrel, no frame above the cylinder, and a concealed trigger that sprung out when the hammer was pulled back. A round five-chambered cylinder unlocked, turned and locked again by the act of cocking, and the butts were rounded with a reverse curve. A small front sight was let into the barrel and a notch was cut in the tip of the hammer to form the rear sight when the pistol was cocked and ready to fire. The arms were designed for round bullets; the rifling in the pistols has so slight a pitch that it looked nearly straight. The grooves were semicircular rather than straight-sided.

There accompanied the pistols a complete cased outfit consisting of several articles, put up in a cloth-lined wooden case. There was a combined bullet and powder flask that loaded five measured charges of powder into the chambers at once from one end and put five round bullets simultaneously in the chambers from the other end. There was also a magazine-capping device that held forty or fifty percussion caps and fed them out one at a time in a way that made their application much easier and quicker than the same operation done by hand.

There was also two extra cylinders to be carried ready loaded and put in place of the fired one, this giving fifteen shots without reloading—a good feature in fighting wars.

Ian was the only man in the regiment to have such pistols and he fashioned an open holster to carry one on his right side waist.

The last Sunday before the expedition would leave was a day of little duty so he had arranged to spend it with Louisa who had made this monotonous life more enjoyable and the passion filled nights unforgettable.

She had asked Ian to accompany her to church and, even though he hated church going, he consented because he knew it meant a great deal to her. She had received so much hurt from others in her past that he felt he must try to bring as much joy into her life as possible.

He started out early in the morning in a buggy to fetch her to the church. The morning air was warm and wonderful. The blossoms of late spring were gently fragrant. He crossed the stream, past the bustling wagoners' camp hollering greetings. to them, through the narrow stretch of woods before he reached the small growing town. This was beautiful country he thought, as he passed several neat houses, fields of corn and grain, and pastures with fat cattle; the foliage of the trees just touched with the green of the coming summer. Truly a glorious day fit for living and putting aside all worries and cares.

At the orphanage, Louisa was waiting for him. She was so bright, cheerful, and so lovely in a long pink gown and a frilly little hat. Oh! She was so nice . . . nice just to be with.

The drive to the church was not long—not long enough, Ian thought. He wished never to stop this moment of time to continue to drive on and on. Louisa's voice was soft music, not loud, so you must come close to her to hear it. She did not display her mind so much in saying or doing things, but in avoiding those things as she ought not to say or do. No person of so few years knew the world better, but was not corrupted by such knowledge. Her eyes carried a mild light and they commanded, not by authority, but by love. Her politeness flowed from a natural disposition to please.

Ian's thoughts were interrupted as the horse stopped at the hitching rail. The small log-framed church was less than half filled but they sat near the back. Ian was uncomfortable and Louisa sensed it. She had remarkable sensitivity. They both had this special magic in understanding people and interpreting other's behavior. Without groping, they knew the right thing to say, or at times, when not to say anything. This sensitivity was not a gift, it had to be studied and developed to predict accurately how the other person thinks, why they act and feel as they do.

Ian automatically blocked out most of the service from his mind; he just refused to listen to the prayers. He rebelled at some of the "holier than thou" Christian attitudes. It seem to him that Christian churchgoers thought they had an obligation to make everyone just like themselves or rather what they thought themselves to be.

Ian thought himself to be an atheist, although he didn't talk or brag or argue about it. He just could not find the right answers for all his disturbing questions, so he remained an atheist. He honestly confessed to Louisa, "I do not believe," and in her look, devoid of any contempt whatsoever, he began to find faith.

Most of the people in the church acted as though they believed in nothing. How often were these people fakes—fake Christians.

Louisa found in Ian an angry young man that said he did not worship or pray, but in him Louisa found humility and compassion. She sincerely thought that here is a man of God; here is a man in whom God's grace is operating; here is a man useful to God in the working out of His purposes. At that moment with tears in her eyes and a terrible ache in her heart, she knew that they had no destiny together; she could never marry him.

He was a person of such strength of character and ability that in whatever age of the world he lived he would undoubtedly have been one of its foremost men. He stood apart from and on a higher plane than ordinary men.

Ian glanced at Louisa sitting next to him. She wiped a tear from her cheek and stopped a sniffle at her gentle nose. She was truly saddened by his departure, but these two acts were the only outward indication. He felt he must try to please her even though he thoroughly disdained this "church stuff," so he opened up the prayer book lying in the pew and followed the service with her. Louisa kneeled and whispered a prayer.

Ian, feeling very awkward, half-heartedly murmured the prayer also, but he could not find the courage to kneel, so he remained sitting and read the General Confession.

The remainder of the service, Ian thought about many things: Louisa, life, the army, and the great adventure he was starting in two days. He was glad to have come here with Louisa.

One of the reasons he had consented to come to the services today was that the Honorable Charles Arthur, who Ian and Louisa had met at the party at Fort Leavenworth and now a great admirer of Louisa's, was to preach today.

Charles Arthur was an Anglican, by religion that is, an English Episcopalian and a deacon in the church. By birth and training, he was an aristocrat to the very tips of his fingers. In the pulpit he looked the very image of Moses—confident, learned, a leader of people. He was six feet two inches in height and stood quite straight even though he was in his seventies. He weighed nearly two hundred pounds and his body and limbs were well proportioned. His eyes were light blue; they were not large and were in proportion to his head and face; if anything, they seemed rather small. His face had no lines expressive of weariness or age; it was the white hair and beard that made him appear old. The habitual expression of his face was of repose, but there was a well-marked firmness and decision. All of the times Ian had been in his presence, he had never seen his look express contempt or any vicious feeling. But the dominant expression of his face, greater even than that of intellect, was the manifestation of goodness and kindheartedness. He had devoted his life to seek with diligence the basis of truth hidden under the charms of sorcerers and under the impostures. He examined all and separated everywhere the true from the false in the nebulous abstraction of religion.

"I wonder," he began his sermon.

Ian thought to himself, "Here is another old man trying to brainwash me."

Ian felt guilty about pre-condemning this person and tried to put the thought out of his mind. It was not his usual nature to pre-judge people, but he automatically suspected any voice from the church pulpit.

Louisa respected this man and, as Ian respected her, he made an effort to listen to the sermon.

"I wonder . . ." Charles Arthur repeated, "if people realize how important other people are to them?"

He paused a moment to let the thought sink in, then continued, "I wonder how many realize that it could be God sitting next to you."

Ian had to admire his opening remarks; he certainly made the congregation sit up and take notice.

"What a ridiculous thought, you all must be thinking. This is what the people thought when Peter introduced his friend saying, 'This is Jesus, the Christ, the Messiah.'"

"God—people believed then and still do—is a divine, mysterious, and shadowy being, not a neighbor. We place God as far as we can get him from those affairs which we like to think of as our own—those things political, economic, and social."

Here Sir Arthur pounded the pulpit to get his point across, "If there be a God—and we have to admit that most of us think there is—we can find him in our neighbor, in someone who is very close and very real to us."

Sir Arthur stopped, murmured a closing prayer and retired from the pulpit.

Ian felt like standing and applauding. Although the sermon was brief, it was very good and had a lot of thought and truth behind it. But Ian wished that Sir Arthur had left all of those references to Jesus and God out. We live in a world of human beings who are frail, afraid, and non-committal. Ian agreed that he must love his neighbor for what they could be, not for what they are. Even in the Bible it is recognized that some "seed of life" fall on barren rock and whither away. Some lives seem absolutely of no value to anyone or anything in God's plan. And even priests must admit the existence of persons of a demonic nature, possessed of the devil, who have acquired powers of a certain grade without the corresponding moral evolution.

Most people believe themselves bound by circumstances. Most people have the conviction that they have been defeated by circumstances. Ian thought, "If you want a difficult job that will break you, try changing these people's attitude. Even if the attitude which a man or woman has is making them miserable, chances are they will hold on to it regardless of what efforts you might make to dislodge it."

He walked out of the church ready to live life as a changed man, perhaps by the will of God, perhaps not.

On the way back to the orphanage, Louisa did not mention the church service.

The orphanage was a riot of children's laughter, games and fun. A picnic had been promised them and they were all thrilled. The three women helpers at the orphanage had their hands full trying to fix lunch and keep track of all the children at the same time. The old man servant carried the baskets of food to the hay wagon as soon as they were ready, and he and Ian helped the smaller children aboard while the older ones clambered on by themselves. Although the picnic would take place only a short distance from the orphanage, the children thought this was great fun.

The picnic was a huge success. After the eating was finished, games were played for the remainder of the afternoon.

Later in the afternoon, they all piled on the hay wagon for the ride back to the orphanage. The children were all happy but tired and ready for an early bedtime. As the women helpers began bathing and preparing them for bed, Ian and Louisa left for a quiet walk through the late afternoon shadows. The children all were looking forward to their nightly story telling by George, the old man. He was very good at telling bedtime stories. Saying his good-byes, Ian realized how good Louisa must feel in helping raise these children. There was warmth of emotion in him as he left the children; it was a wonderful thing to experience. They all clung to Louisa like she was their one hope and joy.

As they left the large building and strolled down the lane, hand-in-hand through the orchard, neither Louisa nor Ian said hardly anything. They didn't have to say anything to communicate.

Ian stopped beneath a large apple tree, sat down, and leaned against the rough trunk. Louisa sat close to him and put her arms about him and nestled to his chest. But Ian's thoughts were troubled and she knew it. She knew Ian would marry her if she consented, but she also knew, although it would break her heart, that she should never agree to such a thing even if Ian sincerely begged. She drew away from him and spoke before he had a chance to ask the question.

"Ian, you are my God and I love you more than words can express. You have given everything to this lucky girl. I have found a life here. It is something good and fine, but you could never be happy here. This is a woman's world at the orphanage. You must go, my love, you must be your own man, not my husband."

Ian started to say something but Louisa quickly placed a gentle finger to his lips. Pleading, with tears rolling down her cheeks, "Do not limit your life to one. The number of great men is so limited, and of those, a few have the opportunity of being great. You will either be a martyr or a hero, I know not which, but you will be one or the other."

"Go and find yourself and your destiny and, when it is over and you still wish to spend the remainder of your life with me, I will be here. You will have greatness thrust upon you. Help your fellow men on the road of life and console them in the hour of loneliness as you have me."

Ian was numb from these words. Here, a girl—a girl he loved and knew she loved him just as much—was telling him to leave. He had read about such great love in books, but now that he was living it, it was painful, very painful.

Louisa's eyes met his for a moment, and then she put her arms about him again and nestled close to his chest.

"It is not meant to be, love," she said, "to spend our lives together."

There were tears in her voice. He kissed her hair tenderly for he could not see her face. Here, two people sat close together without the need of speech and could forget the irritations and failures of the past years.

Louisa knew that if she used Ian as a means of saving herself from the fear of loneliness, this was corrupting love and it would not last.

It has been said that no man and no woman can be regarded as complete in their experience of life until they have been subdued into union with the world through their affections. As a woman is not woman until she has known love, neither is man a man. Both are requisite to each other's completeness. True lovers each seek a likeness in the other and love is only the divorced half of the original human being entering into union with its counterpart.

"In matters of affection," says Nathaniel Hawthorne, "there is always an impossible gulf between man and woman. They can never quite grasp each other's hands and therefore man never derives any intimate help, any heart-sustenance, from his brother men, but only from women—his mother, his sister, or his wife."

Ian's embraces mysteriously awakened new sensations as Louisa felt the heavy beating of his heart through flesh and bone and cloth and the strong, deep sound that no woman forgets who has heard it. She had never known such a man's love before.

"Ian," she whispered, "please give me a child."

Ian was not thinking too clearly now. When Louisa was in a mood of tenderness, she was irresistible. He questioned, "Do you know what you are asking? Do you know what people will say?"

"Yes, I have thought about it many times. It is not right to ask you to stay and limit your life, but I pray for a baby by you so I may remember our love."

"But people do not understand true love, Louisa. You will be treated with contempt. Your life will be miserable again."

"Ian, can a child born of love be sinful? Can we deny God's creation?"

Ian interrupted, "But people believe a child born without benefit of marriage is illicit love—the work of the devil."

This must be one of the most misunderstood things in the world today, Ian thought. In Ian's and Louisa's relationship there was no thought of loss or gain only the fullest manifestation of giving and sharing each other's love. It was a solution to loneliness, where all the frustrations and failures seemed to disappear in the miracle of complete understanding.

They both knew the consequences of going against the morals of this society, but if the race is to advance, such anti-social behavior is a necessity.

Ian forgot the rest of the world momentarily and considered only Louisa's request. He pressed her head gently backward and his lips met hers. Her eyelids lowered until they closed; he kissed her long and passionately.

If this were evil, maybe the Almighty would forgive them. On the other hand, perhaps God smiled on the union because of the little known supreme fact that some anti-social

Louisa

behavior gives to the world both motion and stability. It is the same motion as centrifugal and centripetal forces make as rotating bodies move away from and toward the center of rotation, giving motion and stability to the star-filled universe.

And it came to pass, under the flowering apple blossoms that a new life was created.

The Santa Fe Trail

*I*an was in the saddle before sunup and riding leisurely through the wagoner's camp a half mile south of the main post. The marshalling area was along Corral Creek that drained into the Missouri. There, oxen and mules were being hitched up to a hundred high-box schooners. It took from five to six yoke of oxen, or as many mules, to pull these huge wagons, which carried as much as three tons each. Loaded with provisions, ammunition, and trade goods worth over $200,000, the wagons were accompanied by forty packhorses and about eight hundred extra horses, oxen, mules and beeves guarded by fifty mounted musketmen.

As they moved out onto the trail, it was a colorful procession. The bull-whackers and muleskinners with long "black-snake" whips hollered a continuous bellow of vivid profanity. Drivers, proud of their skills, sat high on the wagons with reins and whip.

Ian was highly popular with the "boys of the road" and they often hollered greetings, but all the while never stopping from their work to get the caravan moving. There were two classes of wagoners, the "regular" and the "sharpshooter." The regulars were on the road constantly with their team and wagon; freighting was their only occupation. The sharpshooters were farmers, who hired on when the wages were high or the crops were bad or had failed. These farmers went back to the plow and their wives when the gravy thinned. The regular wagoners hated the sharpshooters and the backcountry boys were jealous of the road boys. It took a strong man to hold the jealousies in check. But like every western profession, even though a diverse group, they worked together united by their skill.

Even though they had great strength, the oxen had proved too slow and were gradually being replaced by smaller conestogas. These wagons generally had blue underbodies and bright red

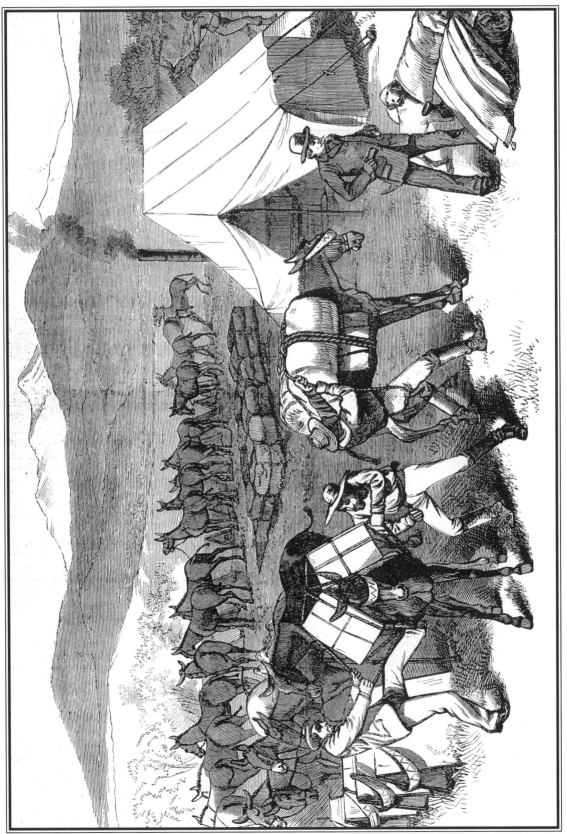

The Pack-Train in the Army.—A Pack-Mule Encampment

upper work and were usually drawn by six horses or mules. The "gears" were of immense proportions and it required a strong man to throw the chain-iron traces over the back of a big horse.

Many of the men were "old timers" who had been to Santa Fe once or twice. Ian noticed that some of the wagoners had cut small poles about ten or eleven feet long, and had tied these on the sides of the heavy wagons to use on descending the hills. When the hill sloped too abruptly, they would tie the pole to the bed with a lock chain and then bend it against the hind wheel. They then would tie it to the feed trough and to the hind part of the wagon bed just tight enough to let the wheel turn slowly. Sometimes one driver would wear out fifteen to twenty poles between night stops.

There were no bridges across the Missouri River and the wagons had to be ferried across on flatboats from Missouri Territory. In the winter, if the river was frozen over, they simply crossed on the ice.

These country people had strong bodies with rough, frank manners, and were crude and profane with a lack of refinement in speech. It took this kind to make a Missouri bluenose mule carry his share of the load, but they were usually of good spirit, outspoken and always ready to top any story told them.

Among the big, loud, good-natured Missouri backcountry boys was a small, thin, pale-yellowish complexioned boy named Jamie who everyone knew and liked. He had never been to Texas, but he had great ambitions to go there and live, so he had hired on as a muleskinner. He was not much of a fighter, but he was famed, even at his young age of seventeen, for his continuous and careless profanity.

Jamie would rattle off facts about Texas. He bragged how it had an area of two hundred thirty-seven thousand square miles, about one hundred fifty million acres with unending prairies, hills, mountains, timber, and grass for a million cattle.

As the teams moved out, Ian rode back to the post. The teamsters would travel out in front of the regular homesteaders as this was no place for decent women. The cursing, hollering, and shouting was continuous. Though rough and ready to fight at a drop of a hat, they respected womanhood and were strangely turned into rough gentlemen in the presence of a woman. A number of dark-skinned squaws walked with the caravan, and these, though possibly loved in a strange sort of way, were usually treated worse than dogs. It was pure bedlam; with noise and confusion, whips cracking, straining mules braying, wheels of the heavily loaded wagons creaking and groaning. The cursing was whooped up louder and stronger until the air was blue with profanity as the last of the wagons began moving.

It was a beautiful sunny day and Fort Leavenworth was alive and wild to the romance of the departure. This was the day Ian had been looking forward to—the start of a great new adventure of endless plains, Indians and unspoiled nature.

The last week had been a whirlwind of preparation for the westward march. This was the first time a company of dragoons was to escort the Santa Fe caravan. There were 104 officers and men in the detachment. The commander was Captain Bellnap and the three other officers were Ian and his roommate Atkins, both first lieutenants, and a youthful and impetuous second lieutenant named May who had just arrived a day or two before. He had vaulted into commission. It seemed the President had witnessed feats of horsemanship performed by May and was induced to give him a commission in the dragoons. The enlisted men consisted of the sergeant major, one quartermaster sergeant, three troop sergeants, six corporals, two musicians (buglers), three wagon repairers (artificers) and eighty-four privates.

Ian figured the effective strength of the company to be one hundred persons. A number of the privates drove the two road wagons, twenty dearborns, two carts and one small piece of cannon. Five prisoners, under sentence chiefly for desertion, rode on the wagons. They were handcuffed and their legs were bound together by a length of chain. Two of them had a cannon ball chained to their leg so they could not run away.

Colonel Williams had given Ian two letters the day before and he now carried them in an inner breast pocket. One letter identified him as being on a special mission for the Secretary of War and every assistance was to be given to his requests by all members of the army.

The other letter instructed Ian to seek out and find the Hasanun and report to Colonel Williams. If Colonel Williams somehow was not available, then he was to deliver the information to the Secretary of War or to the President of the United States. The information was to be intrusted to no other.

Ian watched the noisy uproar of preparation for the march from the saddle.

Ian's horse was well built, not large, but could carry any reasonable weight. He was of fine Arabian and Spanish stock and possessed fine staying qualities and a springing elastic step. His general appearance indicated power, courage, and activity, and was one of the finest of the many horses in the regiment.

Ian had acquired some Mexican equipment. He sat in a high-pommeled saddle of beautiful tooled leather. The bridle was silver studded, and he wore the long, sharp spurs of a vaquero. His carbine rested in a plain leather sheath. The shining leathers and the silver and gold ornaments on his uniform trappings gleamed brightly in the sunlight.

The band was playing with proficiency and strength. The musicians were as good as the bands of the major forts. Due to the numerous parties of ladies and gentlemen who visited the post, they had ample occasions to demonstrate their masterly performance.

The stirring rattle of the drums and the beat of the military music filled the air with excitement. The drummers made a brave showing in their sky blue coats and black vulture's plumes as the band marched before the line of squadrons drawn up at parade.

Over by the barracks, the men detailed to the caravan duty were busily preparing for the march, rolling up their gray blankets, slinging on haversacks and canteens, and loading the wagons with all the gear necessary for the march.

At the sound of the bugle, they emerged from the barracks, and fell in with carbines in hand, answering their names as the sergeants called the roll. The remainder of the wagons rattled up from the corrals. The Indian scouts had already mounted their horses and waited patiently a short distance from the crowd.

The little detachment stood in line while the senior sergeant turned, saluted the squadron officer, and turned the formation over to Ian for inspection. Most of the men were sturdy, hardy farm fellows with a few veteran weather-beaten troopers and a red-cheeked, blond-haired lad, who had just recently joined the squadron, having been with the last batch of recruits from the east.

The men were dressed for the march; in fact, they had no uniforms fit for pomp and ceremony. The journey was to be rough, through dust, thorns, and baking heat, and, most of the power that be, recognized that these troops had to wear comfortable clothing and fight unconventionally. Some of the command officers of the "old school," stern and inflexible, sticklers for rigid regulations, had demanded they wear regular uniforms and be trained in strict army military tactics. But, the new young generation officers like Ian, Cooke, and Davis had complained loud and long, and they had won their battle, for the present at least. Of course, they had been helped by the failures of the regular army foot soldiers against the Indians. They had proved no match for the mounted nomadic Indians and that was the reason the mounted dragoons were established for they were a different breed of men and urgently needed.

The dragoons resembled outlaws, or as the Mexicans say "bandido," rather than soldiers. Nevertheless, they fought to enforce the political decisions of Congress.

A number of the troopers wore mustaches. It was a distinction of pride of the rough and courageous dragoons. Many wore their hair long and flowing and nobody dared comment badly about it. Those that did found themselves flat on their backs. Several, as did Sergeant Tom Beidler, hung rings from their ears—perhaps a carryover from the days of piracy on the Mississippi River.

The Kansas Dragoons, as the company called themselves after the Indian word for wind, were armed with a brace of pistols, and they had just been issued the new hall's rifle that replaced the old muskets. Someone had insisted that they be issued the new percussion rifle. The officers carried long and sharp sabers.

A neckerchief was worn around the neck, ready to pull over the face when the dust started choking the breath. The leather leggings to protect legs from the brush were made by the Indians in exchange for whiskey.

Some wore issued uniforms that were colorful with light blue trousers decorated with an ornamental red stripe down the legs. The jackets and caps were a dark blue. The white belts and shoulder straps had been discarded. But generally, the men wore clothes of gray, brown, and drab mixtures. Facings were omitted or simplified, and there was an attempt by the men to wear the same makeshifts so some uniformity was present. Chaos was great in the supply departments of the army. It was found impossible to equip and arm the new units adequately, even though they were far below strength, so the men had to resort to substitute makeshift uniforms of various sorts.

Some of the Missouri backwoodsmen and rivermen, who had been signed up by fast-talking recruiters, wore clothing of the roughest sort. For an upper garment, a coarse red or blue shirt or a greasy fringed hunting jacket sufficed. Their trousers were tucked into "mule's ear" boots or "breed" leggings. Most wore the low crowned slouch hat so familiar in the Southwest.

Each dragoon carried a pistol in a bullet pouch, powder horn, and a large sheathed knife. From the saddle hung a braided lariat to be used to tether his horse, a bag of parched and pounded corn, a canteen, and an army issue blanket or serape—the brightly colored, woolen blanket used by the Mexicans.

The parade ground was filled with friends and families who had come to bid their farewells. Here and there a poor soldier's wife with a tear stained face, usually two or three tow-headed children clinging to her long dress, crying. Young wives sobbed on the shoulders of some coarse soldiers. A few of the tough sergeants gently kissed their little ones and each held his wife close to him for a few short moments. Some fellows, comrades of his, who had no wife or children of their own, undertook to fill his friend's share in the work of departing.

The scene became livelier as the moment of departure approached. The sergeants, corporals, and busy orderlies were finishing last minute inspections and chores. The troopers picked up their weapons and "fell in" again, preparatory to mounting.

The captain and the lieutenants were receiving a few parting directions from the post commander and regimental colonel.

The lesser officers and their ladies surrounded Colonel Williams, in a fine gold-braided dress uniform. They were all offering advice on all sorts of things—of Indians, weather, Santa Fe, of returning with the fabulous silver and gold of Mexico—and wishing good luck. The last goodbyes were said. Sobbing wives and children watched husbands and fathers with tear-filled eyes. The younger soldiers were cracking parting jokes with their feminine friends and comrades staying on at the post.

Ian found Louisa and they strolled along under the immense oaks of the main parade for a last farewell. Louisa was very quiet . . . not speaking of the sadness in her heart. Ian

Trumpeter

Dragoon

Company Officer

Charles McBarey

1st U.S. Dragoon Regiment Dress Uniform, 1836-1851

had gently pressed her hand and kissed her tear-stained cheek as he said his final goodbye. She turned away with her face buried in her trembling hands. Ian said no more, but turned toward Colonel Williams to say his goodbyes to the officers. He noticed the Honorable Charles Arthur, dressed in an English habit, complete with white pith helmet and cane, enjoying himself immensely. He was already to go with two wagons full of camping gear and provisions and three men servants. Ian was glad Mr. Arthur was going along; he enjoyed his different outlook on life.

Father Gregg was mounted on his mule he had bought for thirty-five dollars. There were some doubts whether the mule would be able to stand the trip, but he had decided to risk her, hoping to be able to exchange her for another in the caballada in case she failed him.

The captain and lieutenants touched their hats in salute and each in turn shook the colonel's hand. "Move 'em out, gentlemen!" the captain ordered his officers.

Lieutenant Atkins, being the senior lieutenant, mounted his horse, raised his arm and ordered "Wagons, ho-o-o" to the lead wagoners.

The band struck up "Auld Lang Syne" as the teamsters cracked their whips. Slowly the wheels of the wagons began to move. Ian felt an excitement impossible to restrain; even the mules pricked up their ears with a peculiar air.

With handkerchiefs and caps waving amid the loud cheers of "God bless you! Good luck," "Good-bye Tom, Bill, Hoke!," the long train moved out toward the low hills of Salt Creek Valley. The barking dogs and yelling children followed for a while then turned back as the caravan disappeared into the timber that bordered the west portion of the post.

*   *   *

The first day's march was limited to eight miles. The camp was pitched on a small branch of Salt Creek. The troopers cleared away the underbrush and pitched their canvas tents, as it looked like it would rain during the night.

The horses were picketed and after having fed and cleaned them, the troopers made preparations for their own comfortable lodgings and supper. Many log fires lit up the scene. The camp stretched out over a considerable length along the creek.

The company had left Fort Leavenworth at about 10 o'clock in the morning and rode steadily until late afternoon without stopping for the noonday meal. They joined the emigrant train that had stopped at the Eight-Mile House, a tavern some enterprising merchant had built to cater to the wagon trains on their way to Santa Fe and California. All the caravans tried to reach the Eight-Mile House by the end of the first day.

The sun was still high in the sky; it being only about six o'clock; but the men immediately gathered some wood for fires for the evening meal as the day's ride had made them hungry. The eastern boys were tired and sore from their first day's march and, as the sun disappeared, they spread their blankets on the ground and, using their saddles as pillows, were soon asleep.

The backwoods boys from Missouri, Kentucky, and Tennessee thrived on a hard day's work and were soon off to the tavern.

The Eight-Mile House was a large tavern, with much entertainment and good cheer. It had a whitewashed front checkered by the dark shadowing leaves of a huge sheltering chestnut tree. The fragrance of locust mingled with the beer sitting in large pitchers on rough-hewn tables under the shading elms. A gilded sign swung from one of the lower branches. A moss covered water trough before the porch was kept filled to overflowing to cool both men and horses from the hot summer wind.

The floors were of unsanded rough-hewn boards and the roof beams exposed. A great fireplace dominated the main room; the grates were seven feet across. During the winters the fireplace was kept constantly burning with great lengths of logs. And while the landlord didn't care if a trail boy wandered behind the bar, it was the landlord's exclusive privilege to stoke the fire with a six or eight-foot long poker. Along the entire side of the room was a long bar ornamented with fancy latticework. There were no "temperance" teamsters. Many a "nickel-a-glass" corn whiskey was drank, gossip of the trail was exchanged, and national politics was wrangled over. The landlord was a fiddler and some of the wagoners limbered-up after a day's ride with a hoe-down.

As for Ian, he had other pleasures on his mind. As soon as he could slip away from the camp, he galloped back over the trail toward the fort.

It was after dark when he pulled up to the hitching rail before a small farmhouse on the edge of the road. A lantern outside the house welcomed him. Louisa had arrived earlier in the afternoon and she and the young Cody family were waiting supper for him.

Ian had made arrangements with his friend, who was of the same age as him, to stay the night in their hay barn. Ian had met him several times on the way to the Eight Mile House and got to like him and counted him as a friend.

The meal was fine frontier food and the wild turkey and strawberries were especially good. Cody's wife was a very good cook, even though they had been married just a short time.

After a hour of good conversation, Ian and Louisa retired to the hay barn for one last evening together. The barn was half-filled with new mowed prairie hay and the air was filled with sweet, never-to-be-forgotten fragrance. The hay barn was separate from the cattle shed and some distance from the house. There was privacy here so Ian left the lantern burn and the double doors open which opened onto the creek. It was a wonderful warm night and Ian removed his shirt as he reclined on the hay.

Before long, Louisa was almost undressed. They both had a desire for each other and soon the talk gave way to passion. She was the perfection of a woman and Ian felt her arteries and her heart beating with a terrible violence.

After a while, Louisa, clothed only enough to make her exciting, arose and walked to the open door with a gliding motion, lightly swaying her flexible figure and brushing her long mass of silky hair from her face.

Ian never got up, but lay in the hay pile. The moonlight gave a strange luster to her half-naked beauty.

A cold chill ran full-length through Ian's body . . . from the sudden realization of the extreme pleasure of the moment.

A flash of guilt cursed through his mind that he could be so happy when others were so miserable. He did not know why this happened so often, but it did again and again, Ian knew, if describing sin and such, this was the worst sin. Of sometimes forgetting the misery and awful pain of loneliness, of the many people living out a lost and inescapable misery of life. Ian wondered if he would love Louisa as much if she had been more plain. Damn it . . . he cursed himself, many people—including himself—liked or disliked others just because of their looks. This was the greatest single sin of mankind today, this judgment of people by their looks alone. Look beyond the surface . . . Ian had trained himself, look at the inner person. And when he did this, he generally saw another person altogether different . . . a warm, conscientious human longing for true recognition and love and hope and friendship.

He had witnessed many common souls, devoid of outward beauty, who possessed much inner beauty of compassion. But how many times were they passed over? The ugly, the short, the fat, the tall, the hesitant, the nervous, the excitable, the crippled, the blind, the old, the girl with a common figure, a barren housewife, the scrub woman . . . all these and many more. Oh! How many times have they been sinned against? How many times they had been passed over by the successful and beautiful people? This was Ian's religion—if you could call it that . . . to try to enlarge these people's lives by recognizing them as individuals also.

The dark form of Louisa blotted out any further thoughts on the subject as his mind came back to the present. He would put those thoughts away for this evening.

Louisa was a mischievous creature and one of the liveliest of her sex. Her bossoms seemed puffed out a little more than usual. She had always been attractive, but never had she been so attractive as now.

There was witchery in those blue eyes. She would display herself then teasingly hide herself from his view.

Near midnight they ceased their play and lay in each others arms . . . and they were the happiest of lovers.

Ian was awakened before sunup by his farmer friend, ringing the breakfast bell. He said his goodbye to Louisa while his horse was being saddled. Ian saw a tear fall from her long eyelash and roll down her cheek—but that was the end of the crying and he was happy about that. Louisa knew—in fact insisted—that Ian go and seek the Hasunan, perhaps not so much for the army as for himself. His ambition soared beyond the narrow limits of life in the army. Ian could not long endure subordination. This brought him into constant conflict with the flunkies that groveled at the feet of the great—or—supposedly great. He applied his energy and aspirations to his own particular use—not that of the army. Little wonder that such a man was misunderstood.

He arrived at camp at sunrise and ate another hurried breakfast before the caravan started out on the road to Santa Fe.

The so-called trail was actually a route that the horses and oxen clumped along from the Missouri River to Santa Fe. There was not one standard, immutable trail. On level, grassy ground, the ruts and paths spread and diverged from horizon to horizon. Where the water grew scarce and the mountains were broken only by one or two passes, when creek beds and arroyos cracked up the surface of the prairie, the haphazard threads of the trails were drawn into one.

The caravan was divided into four divisions, each division forming a column in the march and for each division a trail boss was appointed, who kept a guard in advance of his column to select the best water crossing and keep his eyes alert. After this guard, the head teams of each column led off about thirty feet apart and the others followed in a regular line, their white canvasses rising and falling as the iron-rimmed wheels cut through the irregularities of the ground. They were close up, with the leaders noses of one wagon in the trough at the back of the wagon ahead.

Over 100 wagons, 1400 mules, horses, and oxen, shouting; whipping and whistling and cheerings . . . all were there, and amidst all of this, 400 hardy Yankees attracted to the gold and silver of the mines of Montezuma!

The Eight-Mile House was soon out of sight as the caravan bore south across Stranger Creek toward the flat lands of the Kansas River Valley.

The caravan stopped late in the afternoon though the sun was still high in the western sky. It didn't get dark here until around 8:30 and there was still two hours of daylight left.

The troopers drove huge iron pegs into the ground at intervals and stretched a rope along them to tie the horses. The first thing the men had done after stopping was to curry-comb and brush groom their mounts.

Large mess-chests, bags of grain, and cooking utensils blackened with the smoke of many a fire were unloaded while others were at work arranging their saddles and equipment.

Indian country and possible rough and dangerous living was ahead of the caravan; but here, until after Council Grove, the army lived rather luxurious in tents every night with good food, and easy daily marches.

The tents were set up and blankets laid inside. The rifles and cartridge-filled prairie belts hung from the front pole of the small tents. Outside the commander's tent, an unlighted lantern swung by a cord from the entrance pole. Back of the tents near the stream, huge fires crackled and blazed with the smoke rising straight upward in the calm air. The evening meal was soon over and the cooks busied about their fires, clearing away after the meal.

In the last long rays of the setting sun, the wagon mules were driven in from pasture to the camp for the night. Their braying and the shouts of the teamsters mingled harshly with the brassy notes of the bugle, which sounded the assembly. The company "fell in" in front of their tents and the details for the new guard were picked. Being in the field and on the march with an early start being the order of the day, the guard was mounted in the evening instead of the morning, as was the custom in garrison.

Guard mounting did not take long, although it was thorough enough in its detail under the vigilance of the experienced and soldierly sergeants.

As the last note of retreat died away, the officers came forward to the command tent and, hands raised to hat in salute, gave the short official report of "such and such accounted for."

The old and new officer of the day respectively made his report to the commanding officer, Captain Bellnap, who was enjoying a long slender cigar in front of his headquarters. The captain gave his instructions to the guards before being stationed at their night posts. As the guards marched off, the adjutant unbuckled his heavy saber and lit up a cigar.

The camp settled down to the quiet repose so well earned by the day's march. The sun had disappeared long ago, but the soft twilight of the summer lingered as the brightest stars were already shining down upon the camp. The fresh and sweet fragrance of wild roses and prairie grasses floated on the air. The little stream rippled musically along its rocky bed and seemed to gather new life as the night fell.

The air grew cooler as the gloom of night approached and the men drew closer to the roaring blaze of the cottonwood fire in front of the commander's quarters. In other tents the lanterns had been lit and the forms of the troopers were shadowed against the canvas. Now and then a laugh was heard over the subdued murmur of their voices. In front of several of the tents down the line, there was a merry party, to judge from the squeaky notes of an accordion and the rattle of a pair of "bones," accompanying some amateur minstrel in the rendering of a comic song. Under another canvas, a pair of boys was engaged in an animated discussion, which threatened to grow warm, until the warning growl of some passing sergeant put an abrupt end to the conversation.

Gradually, the little party around the headquarters' fire increased by the arrival of the trailmaster of the emigrants' train and Senator Clark's outfit. Two men, each riding fine horses, approached the fire, dismounted, unsaddled, and joined the group. They were soon recognized as Ustic Goodale, a medical doctor in his middle fifties and in the hire of the traders, and a hunter and trapper named Christopher Carson, commonly called Kit Carson. He was born in Kentucky in December 1809, and later moved to Missouri. In 1826 he ran away from home and journeyed with one of the first caravan of traders bound for Santa Fe. Employed as a teamster, cook, or interpreter, he traveled through New Mexico and Chihuahua province of Old Mexico until the spring of 1829, when at the age of nineteen, he joined a party of trappers at Taos, New Mexico. He now hunted and trapped in all parts of the West and had hired on as a hunter and guide for Senator Clark's expedition. Carson's personality was mild with a rather soft voice; but when he spoke, his voice was one that would draw the attention of all; everybody would stop to listen. His language was forcible, slow and pointed, using the fewest words possible. He talked very little and was a very cautious man, which sometimes made people accuse him of cowardice. As with most backwoods frontiersmen, he was very superstitious and wouldn't start on a trip on a Friday.

The Honorable Charles Arthur, the scientist of the expedition joined the little group, sat down on a log near the fire, lit his pipe, and joined in the conversation. The talk became generalized, avoiding any specific discussion on any subject.

Reflected off the bright buttons of the officers' uniforms the flames lit up the faces of the speakers and cast great shadows back from the fireside figures up the walls of the tents in the rear.

Ian noticed the strong faces in the gleam of the firelight. The commander, Captain Bellnap, was seated in his camp chair, wrapped in a light cape with the snows of thirty years of active service in the field and garrison crowning his head and countenance.

The captain had confided in Ian. He felt very close to him after Ian had saved his wife from drowning. As he grew older, the killings of war bothered him more and more and he planned to retire out of the army after this assignment. Being a good soldier and dedicated officer, he had never questioned orders or reasons for orders, but some recent events left a strong filth in his mouth that he couldn't quite get rid of.

He had told Ian privately that the recent Black Hawk War had finally made up his mind to retire. It had sickened him completely and he carried the pain of senseless murder in his face and heart. He had related how three braves were sent forward under a flag of truce, while Black Hawk and forty warriors waited not quite a mile away, ready to surrender. But the volunteer army was not to be cheated out of their fun. They shot down the Indians carrying the flag of truce and galloped toward the other warriors. Black Hawk formed his line behind a clump of chaparral and, as the raw and rabid volunteers approached, the forty warriors burst from cover in wild, whooping, explosive dash. The frontiersmen, thinking the gathering dusk to be thickly peopled with warriors, turned in frantic terror.

Panic swept the state, clearings were deserted, and families and whole settlements scurried to the protection of the forts. The government issued a levy for a new force of 2,000 men, as the militia already raised was disheartened by the single encounter and was mustered out of service to protect their homes from the supposed Indians. This irregular bushwhacking warfare was being carried on in the meanwhile, costing the lives of two hundred settlers and death to all Indians that the pioneers caught in their rifle sights.

Black Hawk's band fled north into the rough land, a desolate country that offered little food for the Indians who had come not for war, but with their women and children to escape the continuous harassment from the settlers. A professional army general arrived to take command of the pursuing army of frontiersmen and their officers. He was five days too late to prevent the volunteers from bayoneting the Indian women and children and slaughtering all but one hundred fifty of the starved, exhausted thousand that had followed Black Hawk.

This bloody murdering caused Captain Bellnap to age considerably and furrowed his face with lines of sadness and the realization that everything he held holy, all his army life, was slaughtered along with the blood of the innocent Indians. It was one thing to do honorable battle in the service of his country, but quite a different matter to massacre women and children for political and economic gain under the guise of lies and military necessity.

*   *   *

The emigrants' trailmaster was a merry-hearted Irishman with twinkling eyes. He shared laughter-provoking yarns and jokes that called forth an occasional hearty laugh from the circle about the fire.

Ian stretched his frame on the grass, puffing at his cigar and listening quietly to all the talk. The young Lieutenant May, fresh from the discipline of West Point and on his first service in the field, listened with gaping mouth at the bloody encounters with the Indians and rough nature of the plains. The good humored, weather-beaten face of the traders' trailmaster beamed out from under the great flapping brim of his hat as he told with modest and homely eloquence of many a brave deed and stirring adventure in the Rocky Mountains and on the Western frontier. Next to hunting, Indian wars, and the wonderful exuberance of the new countries, the favorite topic was the Indian himself, mysterious, luring, uncertain. Fables of him for years were told throughout the civilized world. Exaggeration of one kind or another by the storytellers dazzled the imagination.

Sir Charles had been studying the American aborigines for a number of years and had just completed a two-year expedition through the Great Plains country. These "original

Americans" had not yet been scientifically studied and their real character and attainments were not given proper place in the "family of man."

Everyone was interested in a scientific appraisal of the Indian and, although the men around the campfire were not disposed to take any of his comments seriously, they listened to his refreshingly different viewpoint.

"The whole matter of American ethnology and archaeology is new." Sir Charles commented, "It is so new that it is impossible to speak with certainty on a great many vagaries. In the United States, the Indian is usually regarded as the incarnation of evil—a treacherous demon with a bloody knife in one hand and a scalp in the other. We have generally refused to consider the finer traits of his character, so callous have we become to his good points. He is ridiculed for the instincts and principles of a savage, yet some have established a remarkable political and military organization."

Sir Charles slowly puffed on his pipe several times before continuing.

"It is not necessary to be what is scornfully called 'an Indian lover,' to be interested in this extraordinary race that is scattered from Alaska to South America. We are interested in the primitive man of Europe and Asia but few of us would have been pleased to live with them. So the question whether we 'like' the American Indian and would enjoy social intercourse with them is not the point. It is a matter of education. In fact, a matter of the study of ourselves as others saw us some thousands of years ago. The Indians are passing through a phase of human existence, which in all probability our remote ancestors also passed through; so by examining this kind of life, we are holding up the mirror to ourselves. The indifference and the lack of interest on this subject are surprising. People generally are not even aware that Indians speak different languages. The idea that there is any profit in studying them is popularly considered ridiculous. White people believe that the Indian is good-for-nothing and that is all there is to it."

"But we can no more find fault with the Indian for not being a Christian than we can with a stagecoach for not being a locomotive. He is what he is. We must accept him as he is and, wherever possible, study him and write him down so minutely that generations of ethnologists to come will shower blessings on our heads. We must constantly remember the Indian point of view is different from ours, and that we, too, are only in a transitional stage."

Ian sat up and listened intently at this different appraisal of the Indians as Sir Charles continued.

"The Indian people, like ourselves, represent merely a stage of human progress. Our stage is in advance of theirs, but it is by no means perfection. The pistol is quite as active as their knife, and we require a great many policemen to keep us civilized. As for war, the European race and Americans have certainly not been backward in this respect. In Europe today, vast numbers of men are withdrawn from other trades and trained for war with a completeness that the Indians never dreamed of."

"In the United States, there is a foolish and narrow estimate of the Indian which has long dominated the public mind. To draw conclusions from the exterior appearance or acts of a people or because they speak a different language is criminal."

"This public thinking is a cause of great alarm for ethnologists—men who study the comparative cultures of primitive people, including their distribution, characteristics and folkways—and necessitates prompt study. Remnants of tribes have already died out and their history is lost forever."

"You see, the Indian has no literature, if by literature we mean only written books; for outside of Yucatan and Mexico, there were no native books; the Spaniards burned all they could find of these."

"But if we accept the enormous number of legends, myths, songs and ceremonial lore told from memory, as discourse, then they surely become literature when we write them down."

He stopped for a moment then continued, "I intend to spend the rest of my life doing this."

The sad, sweet strains of taps in the night air broke off all further talk and the little group dispersed one by one.

The lights in the trapper's tents went out and the hum of voices ceased. Ian and several others lingered by the glowing embers, reluctant to leave, taking the last puffs at their cigars; but soon, they too retired to their tents and quiet reigned over the little command.

Ian lay a few moments in his blanket, watching the stars through the opening in the tent entrance. He listened to the rushing of the water and the slow tramp of the sentry, fading away in the distance, now coming nearer, as he paced up and down his beat. Soon his eyelids closed, and though he tried to keep in his mind what Sir Charles had said, he quickly sank into a deep and dreamless sleep.

*   *   *

The bugle rang out reveille in a lively manner. There is nothing that will waken a man in less time than a bugle tooting away in the quiet morning air. A few of the men hardened by the same noise every morning for a dozen years had to be roused out by a leather-lunged corporal of the guard.

Ian slipped on his trousers and boots and leisurely walked down to the creek to wash, greeting the other men with a smiling "good-morning." Leaning over the stream, he splashed big globs of cold water on his head, chest and arms, and he became wide-awake and ready for a new day.

As the sun raised above the horizon, the camp came to life. Some men began lining up for breakfast, tin cup and platter in hand, and others were looking after the horses or washing in the stream. The several dogs in the detachment barked and jumped on their masters with morning greetings and foraged around the mess tent in search of a luxury. The mules and horses refreshed by the night's rest were neighing and stomping, awaiting the coming meal. "Stable call" had been sounded immediately after reveille and the men were attending to their trusty four-footed friends. A few of the men, finished with their morning meal, were shaving, packing their packs, and "striking" their tents.

The officers assembled around a little table in the mess tent, each bringing whatever he could lay his hands on in the way of a seat. The mess sergeant had laid out a beautiful breakfast. There was deer steak, some fried potatoes, and coffee fit for a king; everything was smoking hot and, just at the right time, the cook brought on a pan full of hot biscuits.

With breakfast over, everyone made ready for the day's march, as the caravan had already moved out. Here, near the fort, there was not much danger of an Indian attack on such a large caravan, so the wagons stretched out for a number of miles. As the heavy loaded trader wagons moved slow, the military would catch up to them in a few hours.

The camp bustled with activity now. Tents and packs were neatly stacked in the baggage-wagons, which, drawn by four sturdy mules, had been driven up while Ian was at breakfast. Saddles were placed upon the horses and the orderlies finished saddling the officers' mounts and stood at their heads with their own mounts alongside of them.

The cook's tent and stove disappeared like magic. All over the field the troopers were busy as bees, some staggering under heavy loads of canvas, some dragging heavy messchests, others were atop the wagons and stowing away the various necessary articles for camp use, while the officers superintended their labors. Ian often lent a helping hand. Although the scene was a busy one, and the men were hurrying to and fro, there was no confusion. Everything was conducted with the utmost ardor and swiftness, and in an incredibly short time the wagons were loaded and getting into line for the trail. The soldiers were standing by their horses, ready to mount.

They were a rather motley group, the Kansas Dragoons. They didn't look much like soldiers. Most wore the slouched felt hat, ungraceful in shape but comfortable and admirably suited for the rough service of the frontier. There were some with jauntier forage cap and Ian noticed one man wore a civilian's straw hat perched on the back of his head. Some had brightly colored handkerchiefs knotted about their necks. One strapping fellow, whose whole countenance betrayed his origin, wearing a bright green silk scarf, typical of the land of his birth.

The bugle sounded again and the men climbed into the saddles and started out onto the trail. Though "pomp and military appearance" was absent here, they were at ease in their saddles. This is what they had been recruited for—to be better horsemen than the pony soldiers of the red men. It mattered little that their brass buttons didn't shine in the sunlight,

Kansas Brave—Artist, George Catlin

ARMY DIGEST December 1967

whether a buckle or strap was out of place, or if their hats slouched down over their eyes. Carbines clean, strong bodies, fighting spirit—these were what mattered. And the horses! They were all horsemen and proud of their mounts. The horses' coats glistened, and they arched their necks proudly, champing their iron bits, moving at a rapid walk, guided by the practiced hands of their riders. Though the uniforms were weather-beaten and worn and though the harness and saddles were of the simplest design with little or no attempt at ornamentation, both man and horse were ready for work—and fighting, too.

The sun was high in the sky and beating down upon the column when Sergeant Beidler rode up alongside of Ian. The column had slowed to the snail's pace of the wagons. The soldiers sat lazily in their saddles, some half asleep, others joking with the teamsters, and a few were getting acquainted with the unmarried girls of the emigrant train.

Ian rode alone at some distance from the caravan, viewing the scenery, thinking occasionally of Louisa. He was enjoying the day and glad to be on the trail.

"Warming up a bit," Sergeant Beidler greeted Ian, wiping the sweat from his face with a bright red kerchief.

"Yes, but it feels good," Ian replied, thoroughly enjoying the warmth of the sun.

The two rode along together for a few moments, not saying anything, as if testing each other as to whether they both wanted to talk or not.

Finally, Ian broke the silence, "How did you get to come along on this expedition, Tom? I thought you were going back to St. Louis to pick up some recruits."

"Well, I was," replied Tom, who broke off a chew of "Yankee Girl" before continuing, "but the old man called me in. Said to come along."

He thought for a moment with a frown on his face, as if wondering whether he should ask a question that had been bothering him. He decided it was best to ask, "What's going on, Lieutenant?" Even though they had much friendship for each other, the military force of habit just naturally made Tom call Ian, Lieutenant. Tom continued without waiting for Ian to answer, "The Colonel said that I was supposed to be sure you and the good Father return okay. He said you didn't know too much about the Indians and I was to tell you all I could. So, whenever you feel like it, I'll be glad to tell you what I know."

"Why don't we start right now, Tom?" Ian suggested.

"Okay, Lieutenant," Tom replied, getting at ease in his saddle as the horses moved slowly along the easy prairie trail.

Sergeant Tom spit out a mouthful of tobacco juice, wiped the slobbers off his whiskers with a sweep of his arm, then slowly said, "This here," he waved his arm in a half circle, "is Kansa, Shawnee and Osage country. Not much trouble here. They're pretty well civilized."

"There," and he pointed to the south, "are the Cherokees and Creeks. They were relocated from your country, Lieutenant, from Georgia and the Carolinas."

"But ahead of us is a different story. There's the Cheyenne and the Gros Ventre to the north of the Arkansas River. Sometimes raiding parties of the Pawnee who normally stay up on the South Platte River stray this far."

"When we cross the Arkansas into Mexico, we go through Comanche and Kiowa country."

"The first wild Indians we will probably meet are the Gros Ventre of the Prairies. It's claimed this tribe got its name from the custom they had of running from one lodge to another to get something to eat—always having their bellies full—so were called 'Big Bellies.' The Gros Ventre claim that the whites gave them this name; they do not have larger abdomens than other Indians do. The tribe is called Gros Ventre of the Prairie to distinguish them from the Gros Ventre of the North, being an entirely distinct tribe, different in language, customs, and beliefs. These Indians are an outshoot from the Arapaho. When I first came out here in 1826, the Gros Ventre were living with the Blackfeet up north, and numbered some three or four hundred lodges. There are about two thousand lodges of Blackfeet, including the Bloods and Piegans."

"Last year smallpox broke out in the Gros Ventre camp and large numbers of them died. The other Indians were farther north, and did not have the disease. The old men of the Gros Ventre claim that they came from the far north, across some wide body of water. They worship the sun or a supreme power, which they locate in the sun. They used to sacrifice their bodies to this power. In 1829 they had very few ponies. When they left the Arapaho, they fought their way through the tribes. In this fighting they were stripped of all their property, including the ponies their kinsfolk, the Arapaho, had given them. At that time they were considered very brave and fought well. They do not keep an accurate account of individual ages and their traditions were not reliable for more than three generations, and are poor at that. They can give no reason for their separation from the Arapaho. Some old men claim the killing of the wife of one of their chiefs ruptured their pleasant relations. This led to war which has lasted since then."

The sergeant spit and then continued, "They have what they call a Sun Dance and hold the torture in high esteem. They claim they suffer to please the god in the sun, and also the white man's god. Among other dances, they have the Strong Dance for women, intended as a support to their chastity. They also have a Buffalo Dance that is a religious ceremony to appease the power, force, or god in the sun—a prayer for the sun to take pity on them and give them buffalo-bonnets or head-dresses. The Manhood Dance is also an annual dance held late in the summer when lodges are made. This is for young men old enough to take on the responsibility of a family."

"They bury their dead mostly in lodges (tepees) and believe that after death they go to the Lonesome Land north of the mountains. They said one died, probably fainted, went there, and came back and told them."

"In dress, the Prairie Gros Ventres resemble the Crow and Blackfeet. They are fond of the coarse fringe at the shoulders, wrists, and down the seams of their leggings. They have no particular style of dressing the hair, going through all the grades from the stiff, upright bang

Blackfoot Head Chief—Artist, George Catlin

ARMY DIGEST December 1967

of the Crow to the plain braid and scalp lock of the Cheyenne. Their women are lighter colored than the Arapaho women and dress like the Crow—short skirts and short leggings not reaching the knees. Their vocal language is Arapaho. They have a few myths and keep no pictorial history of the tribe."

"Their several Medicine Dances seem to look more to the sun as the seat of their god and they could be called sun worshippers."

Ian listened intently to Sergeant Beidler. He had learned one thing—get to know your enemy and friends. Know their weaknesses, their strengths, their peculiarities, their thinking, customs—everything that you can find out.

"What about the Cheyenne?" asked Ian as he remembered that the sergeant mentioned they would cross their territory.

"The Cheyenne are proud, war-loving, and tough. Believe me, tough! Don't ever under rate them, Lieutenant! They are not afraid of anything or anyone. They live to make war. The Gros Ventre will steal your horse, which is about all; once in a while they will accidentally kill you. But the Cheyenne will kill, rob, steal, maim, and plunder just for the fun of it and come back and do it all over again the next day. They can outsmart, outride, and outfight any ordinary white. That is why we cross their territory in caravans for protection. Last year they robbed and murdered lone traders of over $50,000 gold and silver bullion and 2,000 horses and mules."

"The Cheyenne speak an entirely different vocal language from any of the nations surrounding them. The word Cheyenne evidently came from the Sioux 'Sha-ey-la,' or 'Sha-en-na.' According to the Indian explanation, they first met a Cheyenne who wore a robe painted red and his body painted the same color. 'Sha' is the Sioux word for red, and 'la' simply a diminutive, sometimes used it would seem only for agreeable sound. In recent conversation with a missionary on this subject, he informed me that the Sioux called any language they understood a 'white' language, and anything they did not understand a 'red' language. Because the Sioux could not understand the Cheyenne language, they called them red-talkers (Sha-en-na)."

"It is also said that it came from the French word Chien, and because of the Cheyenne soldier being called dog-soldier. The Cheyenne call themselves 'Sa-Sis-tas,' and one claimed that this word meant 'the cut or slashed arms.' Some of their traditions and myths seem in a very faint way to point to their location as far east as Niagara Falls, but there is no evidence of migrations westward from any place beyond the headwaters of the Mississippi. I was at first inclined to think that the great prominence given to their myths and stories in regard to the first buffalo, some of them commencing with 'before we had buffalo,' indicated that it must have been at a comparatively recent date that they reached the buffalo country."

"Occupying the country at the headwaters of the Mississippi several hundred years ago, they were slowly forced westward by the Sioux and perhaps southward by the Mandans. The latter being driven from the north by the same power which pressed upon the Sioux—the great Algonquin family assisted in later years by French arms. It is more than probable that this migration was due to their search for game because the Sioux and the Cheyenne were never regularly at war, but had frequent misunderstandings and difficulties with each other. At any rate, they left the wooded country and drifted into the plains, where they were joined by the Arapaho and about two hundred or two hundred fifty years ago, reached the Missouri, and crossed near the mouth of the Cheyenne, or Good River, as they called it. A portion of the Arapaho refused to cross, and going to the northwest, joined the Blackfeet. Before commencing this movement, it would appear that they lived in permanent villages, contiguous to their cultivated fields, and went out for their annual hunts like the Pawnee, Mandans, and other tribes who lived in dirt lodges. It is impossible to locate the time when they first saw a white man. They never had many ponies until after they reached the Black Hills. The Crow then roamed near the head of the Little Missouri River, Powder, and Tongue River country. The Kiowas and Apaches were southwest of and near the Black Hills, while the Pawnee occupied the Lower Platte Valley. Some claim that the Arapaho first secured a pony, but others say that a Mexican gave a pony to one of their chiefs. Be that as it may, the Cheyennes, soon after their arrival near the Black Hills, heard of a tribe who had ponies and of the wild horses on the plains to the south. They gave up farming and apparently went into the business of driving the Crows, Kiowas, and Apaches out of the country, catching wild ponies, and stealing them from the tribes to the south and west who had them. They claim at this time to have had anywhere from three to five thousand lodges. Keeping in a northwesterly direction, they drove the Crows before them, took possession of the country, and roamed about near the headwaters of the Little Missouri, Powder, and Tongue Rivers. They sometimes ventured to the mouth of the Rosebud, not crossing the Yellowstone, except above the mouth of the Tongue River. They forced the Kiowas and Apaches south, between the Pawnees and numerous other tribes to the east, and the Utes to the west, until they joined the powerful nation of Comanches, here in the south. In the meantime, the Arapaho had separated from them (though always remaining friendly and frequently joining them in offensive and defensive warfare), and had gone farther into the mountains. Peace had been made and broken numerous times with the Sioux, but about sixty years ago a permanent and lasting peace was effected."

"About thirty years ago a partial separation of the tribe took place on a tributary of the Tongue River. This separation was largely due to a desire of a portion of the tribe to go with a trader who was with them and also to increase their supply of ponies by trade and theft from the tribes to the south. A permanent separation was not made until some twenty years later."

"Four chiefs formerly ruled the Cheyenne camp. They were selected for their bravery, wisdom, good judgment, and generosity to the poor. These four decided all matters of minor importance, and they usually selected one of their numbers to act as head chief. Any question of vital importance, such as declaring war or making peace is decided on in a general council. At the election, only a few prominent men from each of the soldier bands are pres-

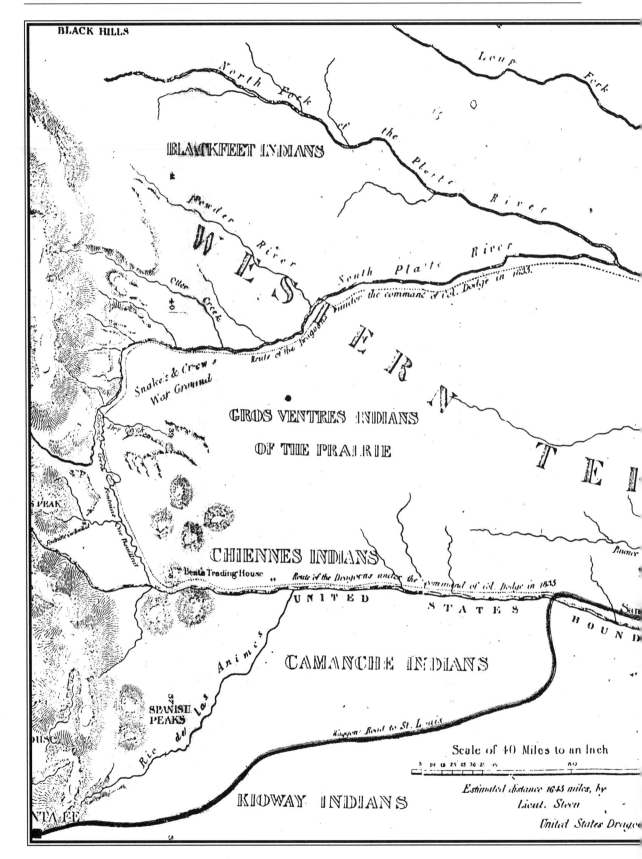

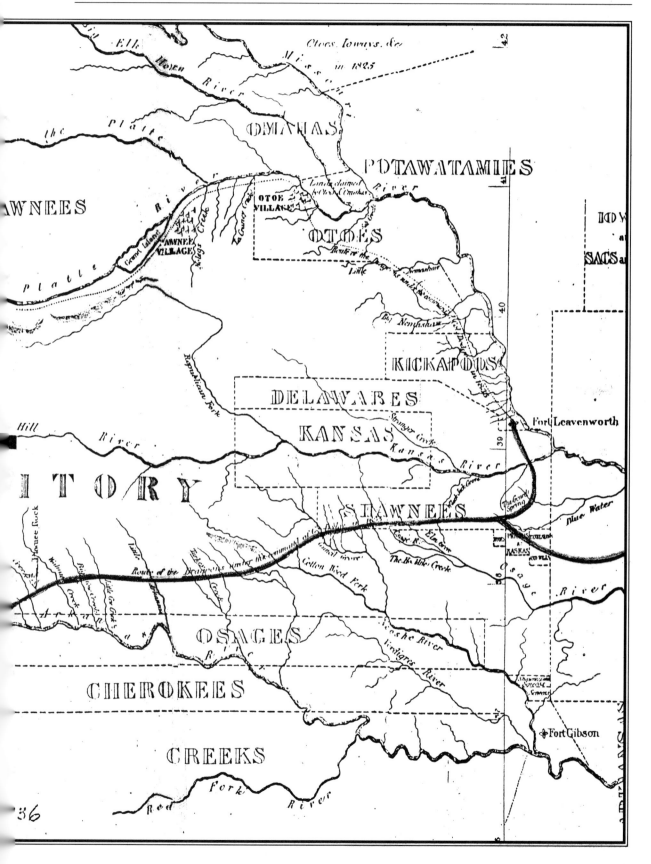

**Mandan
Second Chief—
Artist, George Catlin**

ARMY DIGEST
December 1967

ent; they had five such bands: Strong Heart (sometimes called Crazy Dog and Bow String), Dog, Fox, Smooth Elkhorn, and Swift's Tail."

"In dress and general appearance they differ but little from the Arapaho and Sioux. Their vocal language is difficult to acquire, and is noticeable for the rapidity with which orators can articulate in making their speeches and harangues. It literally flows forth a constant and swift stream. I have heard no Indian tongue that compares to it in this respect, except perhaps the Nez Perce."

136

*   *   *

It was getting late as Sergeant Beidler finished his summary of the Cheyenne and they rode on in silence for awhile, neither speaking. Ian broke the silence soon and galloped off to the head of the train to check on everything before nightfall.

It was three or four miles to the lead wagons and, by the time he finished his inspections and started back to the detachment, it was rapidly getting dark and the wagon train had stopped for the night. At the troopers' camp, the horses had already been curried, and set out to pasture an hour or so before dark.

The cooks had kept his meal warm for him and he ate alone as the rest of the men had already finished. As he made his way to his tent, which had been set up for him by an orderly, nightfall was upon him. Passing the sergeant's tent, he asked him to come over to his tent to continue the afternoon's discussion.

Sir Charles encamped close by, dropped in for a chat before retiring. Sitting on the ground before a small fire in front of the tent, the two talked of the day's march as Sergeant Tom joined them, sat down cross-legged, and bit a chunk off his ever present plug of tobacco.

During the course of conversation, Ian casually asked if the two had ever heard of saints or messiahs among the Indians.

Sir Charles spoke first, "They always have saints among them. They usually are called 'medicine-men.' The Indians use this word to indicate the mysterious and unknown. God is the Great Mystery rather than the Great Spirit, as it is usually translated. We have no word that can convey the meaning of 'medicine' as used by the Indians. Sometimes it means holiness, mystery, spirits, luck, visions, dreams, prophecies; at other times the concealed and obscure forces of nature which work for us—good or evil."

"When they first saw a pony, some tribes called it a 'medicine-dog' while 'medicine-iron' referred to a gun."

"They have medicine-men who claim to have visions, to prophesy, to cure the sick by remedies known only to themselves, and, which they insist, were learned from the whisperings of some animal to them while they were asleep. If success crowns their efforts, their medicine was good; and defeat, suffering, and death were all the legitimate fruits of 'bad medicine.'

"They live close to nature, and are impressed and awed by her wonders and mysteries; and anything which is beyond their comprehension they call medicine."

"Their faith in their medicine to secure their personal protection from physical harm, as well as to promote their general happiness, is simply marvelous."

"I remember a famous medicine-man among the Delaware from several years ago by the name of Kanuk." Sergeant Beidler recounted, "His people had been removed to

Missouri, close to Fort Leavenworth, in spite of his eloquent appeals in their behalf. For many years he had been recognized as the chief of his tribe, and as such exerted a most beneficial influence over the Delaware in restraining the introduction and use of liquor among them. At the same time he staunchly upheld the old Indian ideas and resisted every advance of the missionaries and civilization to the last. He was regarded as possessed with supernatural powers. He died of smallpox and in his last illness asserted that he would arise again three days after death. In expectation of the fulfillment of the prophecy, a number of his followers remained watching near the corpse until they too contracted the contagion and died likewise."

*   *   *

The next morning a light drizzling rain started long before sunrise and the caravan marched all day through the mud. As the day wore on, the rain became a steady downpour and the heavy wagons sank deep in the wet dirt of the Kansa River bottomlands.

Many creeks flowed into the Kansa River and they were now swollen to bankful. The grades to several of the creeks fell abruptly and the teamsters dragged with all their strength on the chains attached to the pole brakes of the hind-wheels as the heavy wagons slid down the steep inclines. The sure-footed mules, slipping over the loose stones and slimy mud, braced their feet and strained back against their collars. Near the bottom of the slope, the brakes were let go and the wagons and mules rushed through the waters; the momentum carried them halfway up the other side. Wagon after wagon followed the ruts until some of the mules were fetlock deep in the sticky mud. The mules strained and pulled, but the wheels sank deeper and deeper. Some of the mules gave up and quit pulling. Once a Missouri mule makes up his mind that it is useless to try anymore, no power on earth will make him try again, at least not in the desired direction. The team from a wagon already up the slope was unhitched and brought down to their aid. The lead mules were lashed with the leather reins, the whips cracked above their backs, and the air was blue with curses. They floundered and strained but another team had to be brought up. More cracking of whips, more cursing, more floundering and scattering about in the mud until the mules, teamsters and wagons were covered with it.

"Moll! Jack! Get in there! You long-eared, blue-nosed, lazy, good for nothing bastards!" was shouted at them.

The bearded teamsters held the long reins tightly in one fist and with the other slapped the loose rein end hard on the straining mule's backs and rumps. The sting of the leather made them step side to side nervously. Then they set their hind feet deep in the mud and strained their great leg and back muscles, and at last the wheels slowly moved, churning up masses of the brown gumbo. Another heave ahead by the three teams, another stop, some more profanity and cracking of whips across the heaving animals' rears, and little by little they pulled the wagon up to the high ground.

Panting, hot and sweating, worn out and wet, the teamsters and mules rested a spell before starting on the next wagon.

The rest of the train must follow and, as each wagon stirred up the mud, the trail became more difficult. There was only one thing to do; the wagons were relieved of part of their load because enough mules and oxen could not be hitched to a wagon to pull it through the muck. All hands pitched in. Teamsters and soldiers partially unpacked wagons; it was then pulled across the stream, the remainder of the load was taken off, and it was then driven back again for that which had been left, again dragged through the mud and reloaded. Hours passed in doing this and, when the last wagon was across and the march resumed, it was already late in the day and it was decided to make camp and wait for the rain to let up.

The tents were set up in the mud, and the troopers had hardly anything to eat because there was no dry wood to start a fire. The rain turned cold and a violent storm came up in the night. In the morning many of the cattle were gone. There had been a great deal of rain and the prairie was so muddy it would mire down a snipe, so the cattle didn't wander far. They were easy to follow, but it took most of the day to round them up. The rain continued for three days and the prairie became nearly impassable. The wagons had to be unloaded and the teams doubled at every stream crossing, this frequently being two or three times a day. Sleeping on the wet ground and clothes hardly ever dry, many wished they were back home in their snug, dry cabins. The wet blankets, with no chance to dry, became maggoty in two or three days. Some wagons became mired down and their tongues broke off as double teams tried to move them. Unable to get them out of the creek before dark, some wagons had to be left standing in the water. During the night the water rose and came very near running into the wagons. In the morning the broken tongues were fixed, and by emptying the wagons, they succeeded in getting them out.

After the heavily loaded trader wagons got across a particularly bad creek crossing, Ian and the troopers had to get their own supply wagons across the stream. The water was rising and there was not much time to lose, if all of the wagons were to get across before nightfall.

The mess wagon driver, worried about the rising water, went upstream a few yards from where the other wagons were crossing and whipped his small team through the sand bed at a gallop. The horses splashed out of the stream onto the far shore when the back wheels sank down to the axles and jerked to a stop. The driver hollered for help to get the wagon out of the water as the stream was already lapping into the rear of the wagon box. Everyone panicked, because much of the mess equipment and barrels of flour and sugar were in danger of being lost. All the teams were busy with the other loads so several troopers broke away at a gallop to get some extra teams out of the caballada. It would take some time and the wagon would probably be lost before they arrived back, but there wasn't much else that anybody could do.

While looking on in utter despair, Ian saw little Jamie Bill coming up in the drizzling rain with his team to help them out. Ian had seen a lot of mules before—blacks, sorrel, bluenose, and "rat" colored, but Jamie had about the prettiest team he had ever seen. They were big, red mules, weighing 1800 to 1900 pounds each. Mules, like people, have personalities, and you could tell they were proud and strong by the way their ears jerked with their gait, even in this godawful rain.

Jamie Bill had won the team in a poker game with Charlie Duncan, a rough muleskinner whose left ear had been bitten off in a fight with river boatmen.

"Want that wagon moved, Lieutenant?" Jamie Bill asked boastfully in his curiously feminine voice.

"Think your team can do the trick?" Ian asked in return.

"Unhook those horses and we'll see," Jamie replied confidently.

"Alright, men, let's give Jamie's mules a try."

The men weren't long in getting the exhausted horses unhitched; they wanted to save all that food and equipment. They knew they would be hurting for something to eat the next week or two if the wagon wasn't saved.

Jamie Bill, holding the bits and gently jerking back on them, backed the team into the load and held them still while a couple of troopers hitched them onto the wagon.

Jamie moved to the side of the team about ten feet and gently whipped the reins. The team was rough shod, with heavy spikes on their shoes, about five-eighths of an inch long so they could get good footing. The mules laid into the load, but the wagon was stuck fast. They tried once, twice . . . but no luck.

By this time Jamie was getting a good ribbing from the men. Many kidded him about the team and asked if he wanted to bet on the big reds to get the wagon out. Jamie took on about twenty dollars in bets that looked like a sure loser to the troopers, but Jamie had a trick the other men didn't know about. Picking up a heavy chain out of a nearby wagon, he returned to the team and picked up the reins again.

He slapped the rumps of the team, hollered a "get-up" and rattled the chain noisily. The mules jerked with all their muscles and the wagon came out of the hole. With much effort, it made it up the side of the ravine. The chain had done the trick.

Charlie Duncan had become insanely mad at the team a few weeks before when they refused to pull a load and in his anger had picked up a heavy log chain and laid it across their foreheads with all his might. The team went to their knees under the blow but when they got back up they were ready to pull the load and ever since that time all Charlie had to do was rattle a chain and they would pull with every muscle in them.

*   *   *

After a week of rain, it cleared off and the sun came out. A loud cheer rose from the caravan at the appearance of old Sol. The expedition had hoped to reach Council Grove in fifteen days at the most, but the rains added ten more days to the journey.

At Council Grove the caravan halted and rested for several days. It offered an irresistible argument to be lazy for awhile. The prairie was at its most handsome, with flowers sprinkled over the green meadows and groves of elm, willow, and hickory trees crowding the banks of the many small creeks. Council Grove Creek was luxuriously timbered with 150 acres of shaded land. The contrast to the prairie prompted open admiration from reticent men. A beautiful lawn of the wilderness—a Garden of Eden. And all who traversed this beautiful region, looked forward to the day when the Indian title to these lands would somehow be extinguished.

Beginning on the 10th day of August in 1825, the government commissioners had met with representatives of the powerful Osage nations under a giant, old "council oak" and made the treaty, which led to the establishment of the Santa Fe Trail and this crossing. It gave the name "Council Grove" to this historic spot. The United States commission received permission from the Osage to permit trade caravans to pass unmolested and to lend their aid to those engaged in trade, for which the Indians were paid eight hundred dollars in merchandise. That very same year an expedition under Major Sibley started the survey and for three years was engaged in formally laying out the Santa Fe highway and securing the proper concessions for its recognition. The first caravans to cross at this point before 1825 were composed of pack animals—Missouri mules. In 1824, a few wagons were successfully used and now many huge Conestoga freighters had increased the trade with the Mexicans a hundredfold.

Since 1825, Council Grove was frequently the meeting place between Indians and officials in authority to hold councils of peace. Although the Indians had promised peaceful passage, the trade caravans suffered frightfully at their hands. Murder and robberies were their regular occupation. The early traders, having but seldom experienced any molestation from the Indians, generally crossed the plains in detached bands, each individual rarely carrying more than two or three hundred dollars worth of stock. This peaceful season, however, did not last very long, and it is known that the traders were not always innocent of having instigated the Indians hostilities that ensued in these later years. Instead of cultivating feelings with those Indians who remained peaceful and honest, there was an occasional trader always disposed to kill, even in cold blood, every Indian that fell in their power, merely because some of the tribe had committed some outrage either against himself or his friends.

Since the commencement of this trade, returning parties had made the homeward journey across the plains with the proceeds of their enterprise, partly in coined money, and partly in furs, buffalo rugs and animals. Occasionally, these straggling bands would be set upon by marauding Indians, but if well armed and of resolute spirit, they found very little difficulty in persuading the Indians to let them pass unmolested. As the traders had learned, the Indians were always willing to compromise when they found they could not rob without losing the lives of their warriors. This they hardly ever risked, unless for revenge in open warfare.

*   *   *

The plains were horseman's country. A man's first thought, on reaching a prairie port, was to obtain an animal to carry him to Santa Fe.

English-speaking people had always been horsemen. Their primitive ancestors lived on horseflesh, and worshipped the white horse, as the Plains Indians worshipped the albino buffalo. The English language has more words for horse than for any other creature; the white horse was flaunted upon the banners of the Anglo-Saxons who came to settle Britain. Men of that breed felt only half-grown, half-alive, when afoot.

That tradition, that feeling, was even stronger in America, if only because of the distances to be covered here. A man born and bred on the plains was ashamed to be seen walking.

The great weakness of the horse lies in his feet, and the chief enemy of his feet is moisture. Keep a horse dry-shod, with plenty of forage, and the world is his paradise. Such a paradise was furnished ready-made for him on the high, grassy, semi-arid plains of the far west.

There, man and horse became one. The animal was no longer a tame creature of stall and barnyard, but the companion of his wandering master, a friend in need, indispensable in war or peace—something precious that a man must risk his own neck in guarding; something irresistible, worth a man's neck to steal or capture.

Many a man was hanged or shot for horse stealing on the plains; many a man perished miserably from famine or in prairie fires, or under the scalping-knife when left afoot. Many a man broke his neck in a tumble from the back of his horse. The saddle was, of all places, the most dangerous—yet also the happiest.

But, as with arms and clothing, the greenhorn found that he had everything to learn, when it came to buying a saddle animal.

Horses bred in the States did not stand up well under prairie conditions. With nothing but grass in summer and cottonwood bark in the winter to feed on, they lost flesh and spirit alarmingly. The first run after buffalo was likely to leave them stoved up. Rattlesnakes bit them, wolves nipped their heels, and mosquitoes drove them frantic. Their thin, silken coats left them unprotected against the chill rains and freezing blizzards on the open prairie. Their courage deserted them, and they fled back to the settlements and their familiar pastures, their comfortable stalls, at every opportunity.

The horses native to the plains were hardy breeds descended from the barbs brought over by the Spanish conquerors.

It used to be thought that the mustang was the progeny of animals, which had run away from the caballadas of the Spaniards; from Cortez or Coronado. But historical research has pretty well punctured that legend, since very few horses did get away, and wild horses were seldom found later in the regions where those few escaped. The fact seems to be that, principally during the twenty years following the Pueblo Revolt near the end of the seventeenth century, when all the Spaniards had been killed or driven away, the Indians of New Mexico took to trading horses to the nomads of the plains. Santa Fe, Taos, and other towns became horse-markets, and for many years thereafter supplied the Indians—sometimes by trade, often by theft—with the animals which multiplied like rabbits and spread all over the grasslands.

The greenhorn was apt to be disappointed on seeing his first Indian pony. The mustang was not, as a rule, a handsome, dashing steed like his Arab ancestor. He lacked the size, bone, and general conformation of an American saddler, or of the carefully bred Spanish horse of Northern Mexico, the slender legs, the long body, the white star and stockings.

The hardships of wild life had stunted and changed him; the severe winters had taken their toll. Indiscriminate coupling in Indian camps or wild bands had flared and blotched his hide fantastically with white and many colors. He was small, tough, deer-legged, big-barreled, with mulish hocks and slanting quarters.

His coat was thick and his mane fell to right and left indifferently and his tail was full of burrs. He was wary and self-sufficient as a coyote. Yet no stable-bred horse from the States could match him for sheer service.

Once broken, the mustang showed as much sense as a mule, as much endurance as the wolves that pestered him, and he had a hard stomach that enabled him to stand an incredible amount of riding, and to go without grass and water for long periods. He could dodge an angry buffalo or a man's snaring rope; he would buck and kick and bite.

He could go, and go, and go. When his white master had abandoned him as "used up," a Mexican would ride him all day and leave him for dead. Then an Indian would ride him for a week—clear into the Happy Hunting Grounds!

The greenhorn who bought him, merely because he looked western and bizarre, soon found that he had an animal with any number of good points —and a mind of its own.

There were those, of course, who preferred mules.

These were men who had lived much in the mountains, where mules were more sure-footed than horses, or men who had become accustomed to riding mules in Mexico, where most of the mules in use on the trail originally came from. Mexican scrub mules were unequal to the heavy work of drawing freight wagons, and in the attempt to replace them with bigger animals for the Santa Fe trade, the Missouri mule was bred. Those who rode mules lauded their staying qualities, the way they endured heat, and the certainty with which they gave warning when they whiffed Injuns. 'Mules,' they claimed, 'are knowin' crittters—next to human, if it comes to that.'

The United States Army once tried out camels as a means of transportation on the Great American Desert, but the notion never "took."

Americans either rode horses, or mules—or walked. A man on foot was little better than a captive or a slave, plodding wearily along the ruts, lugging his heavy arms and other plunder—plunder for which there was no room in the groaning wagons. The man on foot dared not wander from the trail; he could not hunt buffalo or antelope. He missed most of the fun and dangers of the trip and was almost a part of the wagons he accompanied. He was welcome since he might stand guard at night, help shoulder wagon wheels through the mire, fetch buffalo chips for the fire in his blanket, or carry water from the river. If his boot-soles did not become so slick from walking on grass that he went lame, he would eventually arrive at his destination. But nobody who could afford a saddle animal, nobody who had a carriage, or was free from the duty of driving a team, would walk of his own volition.

On the trail only hirelings walked, goading their sullen oxen, lashing their stubborn mules. Invalids and women and old men rode in Dearborn carriages or spring wagons. But free men, healthy men, rode horseback, or on mules.

Horse or mule, they had to have a saddle. And that saddle, by almost unanimous agreement, was the California, made by the cussed Spaniards across the mountains. It had no iron in its composition, but was tied together with buckskin strings, so that it was a simple matter to take it to pieces for mending or cleaning. The tree conformed to the animal's back, distributing the burden over a wide surface. It was covered with rawhide—put on green, and stitched—which, in drying, bound the whole thing tight together. The horn—a regular snubbing-post—was large as a saucer, but not very high, and the stirrup leathers hung so that the rider sat nearly erect, in a position to use his gun or control his horse. The whole saddle was covered by a large, thick sheet of sole-leather, with a hole in it for the pommel, and wide skirts to cover the animal's hips, and support saddlebags. In camp, this sheet could be spread down as a foundation for the blankets of a bed. The girth was a single cinch of hair six inches wide.

The stirrups, in those days, were uniformly of wood, broad and flat for the thin soles of moccasins, with huge *tapaderas* covering them.

With a California saddle, a hemp picket-rope (wolves gnawed ropes of leather), and hobbles, the horseman had only to buy his bridle, and his outfit was complete. A few also carried hair ropes, or rawhide ropes boiled in grease, or plaited leather lariats suppled with oil, for roping animals.

So equipped, the stranger rode out to the wagons which he was to accompany, and made friends with the men belonging to them.

There he would see Mexican ropers, in their tight-fitting leather costumes, performing miracles with graceful lariats, snaring a horse or a mule, in preparation for breaking them to harness. Once noosed, the mules would be snubbed up to a wagon wheel, choked down by the ruthless rope, while their labored breath came *whoof, whoof* through straining throats, tied there, with a bare two inches of rope, and left to starve for a day and a night, until they were subdued enough to endure the harness.

Then Markus, Snowd or Pedro would grab the ropes, lash the frightened team into lunging and rearing activity; the big wagon would roll and rumble behind them, scaring their eyes almost out of their heads as they lurched away; so, after an hour's exhausting flogging and yanking, the bewildered mules stopped kicking and plunging, and pulled the locked wheels after them in sober earnest. That done, they were pronounced 'broken to harness,' and ready for the Trail. It was an unflinching discipline.

Oxen were broken in a manner equally picturesque. The teamster would snare them with a rope, drag two of them to a snubbing post, yoke the pair, and tie the tails together. Then he released them and stood laughing as they charged toward the prairie or threshed through the brush. By this method, they soon became accustomed to the yoke and to moving together. Tying their tails together prevented them from breaking their necks.

Meanwhile, men had been greasing the axles with a mixture of tar, rosin, and tallow. And evening found them making camp under the shelter of wagon sheets stretched out from the side of a big Pennsylvania wagon. Invariably, while they could enjoy the shelter of such an improvised tent, the weather would continue fine!

There they spread down their bedding: the poor man, his single Mackinaw blanket; the canny stranger, his pair of them; the old-timer, his buffalo robe and Navaho rug, tattered, greasy, and burned with holes where sparks from campfires had lodged; the lover of luxury, his painted canvas sheet, his two blankets, comforter, pillow, and water-proof coverlet.

Little cook-fires sprang up, dancing in the twilight, as the men of each mess gathered about the camp—kettles, coffeepots, and spiders. Afterward, for a time, there would be only the sound of steady mastication, as, mess—pork and bread went into their gullets. Sighs of content followed, and the loosening of belts.

Then, when the old-timers had cleaned their knives by thrusting them into the earth a few times, and had cleaned the grease off their fingers, Indian-fashion, by wiping them on their long hair, could be heard the click of flint on steel, pipes began to glow, and there would be tales to tell.

Those tales, naturally enough, generally had to do with the cussed Injuns—a subject on which the greenhorns had a yawning curiosity to be satisfied. And the veterans of the Trail were ready to give them their bellyful . . .

'Nope. Injuns is sociable critters. Happen you see one, thar's allus another'n not far away—and more'n likely a dozen. Fact is, you ain't likely to see none atall, lessen they want you to see'em, and that means they figger they got everything their own way . . .'

'Sure, the Injuns air brave—accordin' to their lights. In a corner, they'll scrap like so many wildcats, and die to the last man afore they'll give in. But they don't aim to git in no corner; they aim to git you in one. And if they do, and know it, 'tain't no use shakin' hands and makin' peace with 'em. Might makes right with them every time.'

'Take Carafel—trader used to work with the Assiniboine. Him and a fellow named Ramsay was a-ridin' to camp, when all of a suddent, fifteen Sioux warriors came up over the hill, sprang in front of 'em. The Injuns cut loose all together, and Carafel caught it in three places. Down he went, and Ramsay lit out, tight as he could go.'

'When Carafel dropped, his horse dropped too, and his gun went under the horse. The horse was dead, and he couldn't git it out. So he was helpless to fight, and his foot was all shot to pieces, so he couldn't run nuther. Leastways, not fast.'

'He got up and tried, all right. But his lame foot made him clumsy, and he caught his toes in a tangle of grass and tumbled again. They war right on top of him then, and when he jumped up, one of 'em stuck his rifle in his face and pulled the trigger.'

'Howsomever, Carafel grabbed the muzzle and shoved it away, so it didn't kill him. But then the rest of the varmints war all around him, beating him down with the buttends of their rifles. Well, he thought he was gone then. So he says to them, "It sure takes a lot of you Sioux to kill one white man!" And down he goes. He thought he war done for. He could feel the prick of the scalp-knives on his yaller hair already. But lo and behold, they all quit then, and run off as if he'd had smallpox. Then he fainted dead away.

'When Carafel come to, the Sioux war clean gone. Nary one in sight no whars. So Carafel he crawled home to the fort in a pretty fix, all covered with blood, and his foot torn to pieces. He'll allus be lame, I reckon . . .'

'How come they didn't finish him? Why, when they heerd him say he was white, they seen his yaller hair and blue eyes, I reckon, and they knowed he warn't no Chippeway half-breed, like they thought he was. They thought he war dead, sabe? So they skipped, for fear somebody would find out they had killed him. You see, he war married to one of their women. Lucky for Carafel! Lucky for Ramsay, too. Ramsay war a half-breed Chippeway sure enough!'

'Wagh! Injuns are the most onsartainest varmints in all creation, and I reckon they're not more'n half human. For you never seed a human, after you'd fed him and treated him to the best fixin's in your lodge, jist turn around and steal all your horses, or ary other thing he could lay hands on. No, not adzackly. He would feel kinder grateful, and ask you to spread a blanket in his lodge if ever you passed that away. But the Injun don't keer shucks for you, and is ready to do you a heap of mischief as soon as he quits your feed..'

'Nope. It's not the right way to giv'em presents to buy peace. But if I was Governor of these yeer United States I'll tell you what I'd do. I'd invite'em all to a big feast, and make believe I wanted to have a big talk. And as soon as I got'em all together, I'd pitch in and sculp about half of 'em, and then t'other half would be mighty glad to make a peace that would stick. That's the way I'd make a treaty with the Indians; and as sure as you're born, that's the only way.

'Tain't no use to talk about honor with them, anyhow. They hain't got no sich thing in 'em, and they won't show fair fight, any ways you fix it. Don't they kill and sculp a white man when-ar they git the better of him? The varmints, they'll never behave theirselves until you give 'em a clean out and out lickin'. They can't understand white folks' ways, and they won't l'arn 'em; and if you treat 'em decent, they think you air afeard. Nope, you kin depend on it: the only way to treat Injuns is to thrash 'em plenty first. Then the balance will sorter take to you and behave theirselves . . .'

Then the old-timer would gravely put up his pipe, roll into his blankets, and cock one wary eye at his disturbed listener, waiting for the inevitable question. When it came, he had his answer ready.

'Wal, no. It's been some time since they cut up any right yereabouts. But you never kin tell . . . Sure I'm a-goin' to sleep. I'd ruther be sculped sleepin' than stay awake and be sculped anyhow. Happen you don't feel thataway, keep yore eyes peeled. That's all!'

Such the horror of Indians among greenhorns, that many a stranger, after hearing such yarns and opinions, valid as they might be on the high plains, found himself unable to sleep after hearing them, until the snores of the mountain men, drowning the hum of mosquitoes, made sleep impossible anyhow!

Yet it was close upon two hundred miles to the nearest Indians who could be called hostile.

The independent traders usually deferred the organizing until they reached Council Grove. Aspirants for the captaincy of the caravan presented themselves and the assembled traders debated and bickered, defended and denounced, until balloting settled the question. There was some honor in the captaincy but little money. The captain could direct the course of the march, select the night's campground and handle other matters of routine, expectant to being obeyed; but, in emergencies, any of the many members of this social compact was apt to renege. That is why the military was along, to be in charge and give orders when the occasion demanded it. Organization of the caravan in military fashion was the best protection against Indians and the greater danger of the pioneer's talent and tendency for kicking over the traces and going on their own.

The emigrants assembling in Council Grove were kept busy all day working on their wagons. Women sewed and patched clothes in preparation for the long journey, but the evenings were usually lively affairs.

After dinner the dancing commenced and the first figure was usually a "square four" set. With reels, square sets, and jigs, the dancing lasted until sunup many nights. Ladies could rest and gentlemen could drink, while other ladies and gentlemen kept the fiddler at his almost constant sawing; but, if any weary ones attempted to snatch a little sleep, they were hunted up, paraded onto the dance area, and the fiddler ordered to play.

The expedition was about ready to move out. They were only waiting for twenty wagons laden with flour and four ox-carts bearing camp equipage.

It was decided to "lay-in" some meat so Ian and Sergeant Beidler, with a buckboard, several pack mules, and sixteen troopers set out to do some hunting along the Arkansas River, eighty miles south. They were to travel straight south to the river, then follow the valley west and join the caravan at Pawnee Rock. There a mass of large blocks of sienite, towering to the height of several hundred feet where a clear spring flowed out of the rock, had become an overnight stop for most of the trains.

The little party rose early and commenced the march at five o'clock, halted at ten and at two on the side of a creek; their route having been all the time along its border. As the weather was hot, several men drank plentifully of the water, and were made so sick by it that camp was pitched for the day. The distance traveled was about eighteen miles. Three deer were killed.

The second day, the men being over their sickness, the march began at quarter past five with the sun shining very brightly, but in fifteen minutes it began to rain and continued to rain very hard until one o'clock. Four deer had been killed so the tents were pitched for the day, and the meat was dressed out. Soon one of the deer was roasting over the fire.

The next day a tremendous thunderstorm came up and it continued to blow and rain with thunder and lightning all day and night. The baggage was secured in a dry position and the little band remained encamped all day. The time was spent repairing their gear, singing the folk songs, and playing the mouth organ. Ian's thoughts turned to Louisa for a few minutes of mediation and he wondered what she was doing and how things were going for her. He would never forget her no matter how far away they were.

The next two days were clear and two turkeys and a bear were killed in the deep woods.

The following day after advancing fifteen miles, they camped on a fine stream, where they swam their horses, and bathed themselves. In the holes of the creek were many fish twelve to sixteen inches long, which, from the stripes on their bellies and their spots, were guessed to be trout or bass. A net was made and a number caught and cooked that evening.

The Neoshe and Verdigres Rivers were crossed and soon the Arkansas was sighted and crossed. The party followed the Red Fork River for twelve miles before turning back north to the Arkansas. Some of the best hunting was experienced with four deer and an elk killed. The fire dried the meat that evening.

Up to now, no Indians had been seen, although this was Osage and Pawnee country. The Pawnee are a large nation residing on the rivers Platte and Kansas and roaming over most of the plains from the Missouri to the Rocky Mountains.

Camp was pitched upon a beautiful hilltop, and with the eye glass Ian viewed the adjacent country. He observed a herd of horses on the prairie and Sergeant Tom and he went to examine them. When they were within about a quarter of a mile, they discovered the two men, and immediately approached, making the earth tremble under them like a charge of cavalry. The horses stopped and gave the men a chance to view them. Amongst them were some beautiful bays, blacks, and greys, in fact all colors. Upon returning to camp they decided to try to noose the wild horses. In the morning, six men on the fastest horses set out to catch several. The herd stood still until the troopers approached within forty yards, neighing and whinnying, then the chase began, which continued for two miles without success. Two of the mounted dragoons galloped up with the prairie ponies, but they could not take them.

Returning to camp, they laughed at their foolishness of trying to take the wild horses in that manner, which is scarcely ever attempted even with the fleetest animals and most expert ropers.

The next day they marched at the usual early hour. The riverbanks were entirely covered with woods on both sides, but no other species than cottonwood. Fresh signs of Indians were discovered having passed a camp where it appeared a party had remained some days to lay up meat. Nearing the Arkansas River from the south, one of the troopers saw a man on horseback. The small party followed cautiously and soon came upon an Indian encampment.

As they indicated friendly gestures, the troop rode into the camp. The sergeant said they were Wichita Indians, a member of the Pawnee nation. The entire population of the Wichita was only two hundred. Their permanent village lodge was made in a conical shape similar to the skin tepee, but larger, and thatched with willows and grass. On this account some tribes called them "the people of the dark lodge." In the fall, after they harvest their corn, they hunt after buffalo, and do not return until mid-winter. Their corn, beans, dried pumpkins, and personal effects were cached in huge cistern-like holes, and so much care was exercised in concealing the locations of these caches that no one ever thought of looking for them.

Many of the men wore white man's dress, with their hair cut squarely off round the neck. They possessed quite a number of old wagons, and by the strenuous efforts of the missionaries, had partially adopted the forms of worship of the Christian religion. They would gather together at their little church on Saturday evening bringing food and tents. Many remained until Monday morning, though the less enthusiastic left on Sunday afternoon. With their singing, preaching, and praying, they mix a great deal of feasting when food was plentiful.

About Christmas-time they have a sort of camp meeting service, which lasts about a week. In personal appearance they were of dark complexion, almost black, stout, and short in stature. They were conversant with the sign language.

During the hot summer months, such as was presently being experienced, women wore only a short bark shirt about the loins . . . nothing above their waist. The women painted or tattooed their face and painted rings around their bare breasts. The men did not tattoo any part or portion of their face or body.

Some of the women rubbed their faces, hands and feet black and stiff with dirt. Others rubbed themselves every morning with a composition of red and brown earth mixed with fish oil. Their hair, long and disheveled, served as a towel to wipe their hands on. Their garments were tattered, and stiff and shining with dust and grease.

The Indians had built a little church for the use of the missionary who visited them. Although the missionaries were hardworking, they remained in their primitive simplicity.

These people were being further degraded and every year the missionaries lost ground through the approach of the whites, the ease with which whisky—"fire water," so fatal to the Indians, could be obtained, and with it all the vices and excesses of modern civilization, especially as understood and practiced by the American pioneer.

Scattered all along the frontier there was the same sad spectacle. First robes, skins, and beadwork are sold, then the ponies; many thefts and murders are committed, either to secure whiskey or as the result of drinking it. The old Methodist missionary who was in the camp at the time complained bitterly of the government agents and the soldiers. They first deceived the Indians then they robbed them in the distribution of their yearly payment of money and supplies, and the others demoralized them by their indecent conduct. All last winter, they were slaves of a hard and cruel captain, who seemed to make it his business to torment these Indians. When the old women covered in rags with their starving babies came up to the camp to pick up the filthy garbage thrown out of the soldier's kitchen, they were shown no pity and driven off with scalding water thrown upon their wasted bodies, covered only with rags in the severest of the cold weather.

Their crop having failed, they were reduced to famine and the captain of the camp refused them all assistance. Reduced to the last extremity, they cried out to the Great Spirit in the name of their children, but no relief came from the white man's cruelties.

The kindly missionary, embracing two young and dirty tots holding onto his black robe, sadly commented, "These Indians are destined to disappear before the white man, and the only question is how it may best be done. This disappearance from our midst should be tempered with kindness so to produce to them the least amount of suffering and to us the least amount of cost."

All of this suffering and evil bothered Ian; he complained bitterly of the wickedness of other men. But he kept his world small and at a distance from their wickedness. He lived in a world of his own creation rather than in the one he had been placed in. As long as he kept his world—his sphere of activities—limited, confined, hemmed in, he had a much larger world out there to place the blame for all that he disliked. As long as he kept that big wicked world from his little one, he was safe. If the big world penetrated his, then he would have to share the blame for all that was wrong and all that was evil. He was not ready to confront the truth, but by ignoring it, he gave aid and encouragement to the cruelties and shameful injustice.

As the hunt had netted over nine hundred pounds of meat which had been sliced into strips and dried in the sun or over a fire to preserve it, the detachment headed north, not stopping for any further hunting except what was needed for the day's meal.

The next two days were without adventure, as the small detachment turned back to join the caravan, scarcely ever out of sight of the river, but the group was rather more cautious than usual and slower due to the heavy load of meat.

*   *   *

Back at the caravan campsite, the wagon corral became a scene of almost frantic activity the moment the captain of the caravan roused the sleeping men with his loud "Turn out!" Every man was on his feet rolling and tying his blankets, tossing them into the wagons. This was hardly done when they heard the second command, "Catch up! Catch up!" The men hurried after the animals, repeating the call up and down the valley, while others yipped and whooped in the enthusiasm and confusion of getting started. Every man went quickly to work throwing the harness on his mules, urging his oxen under the yoke, in the midst of a great clatter of bells, and rattle of yokes, and jingle of harness. Ropes uncoiled through the air; saddles were swung upon the backs of restless horses, the bustle of preparation was accented by good round oaths in French, Spanish and plain English. Each teamster fought to be first in getting ready, and within an incredibly short time, the first one straightened up and sang out, "All set!"

Some of the men had to hitch a team to the halter of an unusually stubborn mule, or ox, and drag him into position. But finally the teams were all hooked up, and the last sweating teamster reported himself ready. His call was echoed from every side, and the captain, rising in his stirrups, bellowed the final command, "Stretch out!"

It was an impressive sight to the greenhorns, the way that double file of great, hulking wagons rumbled away to the west behind the eight-mule teams and oxen. With them went the carriages and horsemen of the captain and his mess, the ponies of the Indian hunters, the mountaineers' saddle mules and pack animals, and the mob of spare animals shambling along behind. The boy who wrangled this herd of miscellaneous animals—lame oxen, extra saddle horses, sore-backed mules, broncos, mares with foals, and milch cows— no longer required the help of Mexican ropers to keep them moving. By the time the outbound train reached Council Grove, few of the animals cared any longer to attempt a run back to the settlements.

The first camp west of Council Grove was one of the best on the trail with a large spring that flowed into Otter Creek. The Government Survey of 1825 named the place 'the diamond of the plain,' but it was more commonly known as Diamond Springs. A generous fountain gushed out from the head of a hollow in the prairie from which game trails radiated. The spring supplied a large flow of clear water that was also really cold—a rare treat. Some benefactor of mankind had set out mint roots around the four-foot basin of the spring, and they provided a bountiful supply of leaves for all that passed that way. Old-timers always had mint juleps at Diamond Springs.

Nearby there was a gulch filled with the remains of stampeded oxen lost in a blizzard. Two miles east of the springs, in a gully, some nameless caravan came to its end. Whether by fire, Indians, or stampede, no man can say. Teamsters who needed chains, bolts, or wagon irons of any sort could find them there.

From Diamond Springs to the Big Bend of the Arkansas River (a distance of one hundred five miles), the trail crossed a series of small streams cutting the prairie from north to south, each one more difficult than the last. These creeks were narrow, but muddy with steep banks.

A march of fifteen miles from Diamond Springs brought caravans to uninviting Lost Springs, which had gained its name from the fact that it sometimes went dry. All that day and the next day's march, twelve miles to Cottonwood Creek, was over a level prairie covered with tall, rank grass. On this desolate portion of the trail, travelers observed zigzag strips of grass, denser and taller than the rest, which amateur natural philosophers explained as a result of lightning that, striking there, had made the earth more fertile. Some elaborated their guess into a scheme for irrigating the plains with electric fluid, by means of lightning rods or an iron forest!

On the way, the train was sure to be mired down at Mud Creek, otherwise known as the Devil's Hind Quarters. The teamsters cut grass to bridge the mud, but, even so, they lost half a day. Here the first antelope might be seen.

Cottonwood Creek, still worse with its deep mud and steep banks, was always a difficult crossing. It was hard to keep a wagon from turning over, as it slid down one bank on top of its team—in spite of the locked wheels and a yoke of oxen behind holding back. But, if getting down was bad, getting up again proved even worse. Moreover, this heavy labor came always at the end of the day, when everyone was tired, cross, and profane, for on the Santa Fe Trail, it was the rule to ford any stream before making camp. Otherwise, there might be a cloudburst during the night, filling the creek from bank to bank, and causing a delay of days or weeks.

The Cottonwood Fork, when not in flood, was clear and clean, and caravans sometimes halted here to wash their clothing.

This entire region was barren of trees; from the Cottonwood on, the vegetation changed. Cottonwood, elm, box elder, and willows took the place of ash, burr oak, black walnut, blackjack, sycamore, buckeye, pignut hickory, and maple. Wild plum was seen, and goldenrod abounded. Buffalo grass hugged the ground. Tall grass, except in the bottoms, was left behind. The crumbling bones of buffalo were seen occasionally.

At Turkey Creek, twenty-five miles beyond, men found good grass and water, but not a stick of timber, or even a twig as thick as a pipe stem. Here the traveler learned to gather the round, dry buffalo chips that were scattered in profusion over the prairie. When dry these burned easily, and quickly provided hot embers on which to cook. Wet, a chip fire was only a stinking smoke, into which a man was glad to stick his head at night, in the vain hope of snatching a few hours of rest from the torment of the mosquitoes. Without that smudge, a man soon learned why the Indians, in their sign language, dubbed the mosquito 'bites-through-blanket!' But wet or dry, a chip fire kept a man busy gathering fuel to keep it going.

In the three forks of Turkey Creek, fishermen caught sun perch and catfish. Along its banks, bright with scarlet flowers, they found pomme blanche, tumblebugs, and rattlesnakes! The bleaching bones of long-dead bison began to be seen more frequently now.

Seventeen more miles brought the caravan to the Little Arkansas at a point some ten miles below its source. Here the stranger had his first mass encounter with the buffalo gnat, which filled the air and drove human victims and their animals half-mad with pain and vexation.

The buffalo gnat was a small black insect. It attacked the bare face and hands, and even got under the clothing, fastened itself, and remained until sated. The bites caused intense irritation and swelling and soon made a man look as if he had smallpox.

Some travelers carried mosquito nets to sleep under and then found no sticks on which to prop them. Others wore green veils over their heads, running the risk of not being able to see where they were going, and so colliding with the business end of a mule! Men unprotected sometimes were ready to break down and cry from vexation. The gnat was worse than the mosquitoes, which were found chiefly along the streams. Men from the woodlands, used to making camp in valleys, had to learn that on the prairies the place to camp in summer was on the uplands.

Disused buffalo wallows, full of water, and ringed with golden coreopsis, scarlet mallow, and silver-edged euphorbia began to show themselves. The blow-fly was behind now, and blankets soon lost their maggots, even in the wet. Antelope were seen more often now, but the hunter's gun was so wet that his powder would not explode. Crows began to be replaced by ravens. The water-foul were everywhere and puffballs, large and white as so many human skulls, dotted the damp prairie. Purslane and lamb's quarter abounded, and the air was filled with swallows, doves, blue jays, kingfishers, and the whirring quail.

The Little Arkansas was only a small creek five or six yards wide, but its bed was so mire and its banks so steep that men were always sent ahead with axes, spades, and mattocks to dig down its banks and cut willows to bridge the quagmire. If the caravans crossed that stream without breaking a wagon-tongue or injuring draft animals, old-timers considered it a miracle.

Land turtles began to be a lively feature of the ruts, lizards darted about, and crawfish scuttled into the pools as the men advanced. In the distance Plumb Buttes showed themselves, crickets hopped about big anthills, and beyond Cow Creek a large village of prairie dogs studded the plain with mounded holes.

Cow Creek, twenty miles beyond the Little Arkansas, was even worse. After digging, bridging, and shouldering the wheels with the usual accompaniment of whooping, sweating, and cracking of whips, they got safely over and encamped in the valley beyond. All the streams in this part of the trail had slippery, treacherous crossings.

**Sauk Chief—
Artist, George Catlin**

ARMY DIGEST
December 1967

*   *   *

One morning, shortly after crossing Walnut Creek, which followed into the Arkansas, the men were firing off, cleaning, and reloading their guns because the bad rain had dampened them the night before. The journey was renewed but had not proceeded far before a man was seen on horseback climbing up a steep hill some distance away. Another and others at short intervals were seen until the butte was covered with Indians. The riding and loose animals were immediately corralled then the wagon mules and oxen were unhitched, corralled, and staked to the ground. Very soon every man was in line with the wagons, armed to receive the Indians, whether friends or enemies. The loud warning was often repeated by the old-timers, "Now boys don't be fooled. They'll say "Wazhazhe" but you've got to fight."

The friendly border Indians sometimes when out in the buffalo range would join the Commanche and have some fun and take some scalps, and return as friendly Indians, having won trophies and honors among their people, under the name of another nation at war with the whites. The friendly Osage (Wazhazhe) were frequently suspected of doing this.

It was arranged that if they appeared claiming to be friends, two of the traders who understood the Osage language would meet two of the Indians some distance away but under the protection of the caravan's guns.

Soon the Indians left the butte and came towards the train on a run, which appeared as if they meant war, but after the caravan made the sign for them to halt, they stopped. The sign was given them to send two men out to meet the two traders who advanced to meet them for a parley.

The first sound greeting the caravan was "Wazhazhe."

The fellow who had cautioned them before, again warned, "Yes! Damn Wazhazhe! Boys, don't be fooled by 'em. We've got to fight. They're butchering devils."

On the assurance that the caravan would not be fooled by them, but would be ready for them as friends or enemies, he quieted down.

The four men soon met and began to talk as well as they could by signs, when another Indian advanced from their line as if to take part in the negotiations. This, Captain Bellnap knew, was not in order, and to impress upon the minds of the Indian and his friends that the train would not permit it, he advanced twenty foot or so and signed for him to stop—which he did, but soon started again to advance. The captain cocked his gun, raised it to his shoulder, and aimed so the Indian could see that if he pulled the trigger he was sure to be hit. The Indian made no more moves to advance and all the men on both sides remained in their positions until the talk was closed.

The caravan was informed they were Osage on a buffalo hunt and the Sauk and Fox were encamped on the Arkansas below the Big Bend, and all were friendly to the whites. They said they would travel with them as far as Plumb Buttes and the whites would be convinced they were not deceiving them, and they would separate as friends. The captain consented, but on condition that they should not approach the wagons, but travel at a distance.

Everything arranged, the teams were hitched up and continued on the route and did not travel far before everything indicated that they were large parties of Indians on their summer hunt, as they had told them.

Many dead carcasses of buffalo were scattered over the prairie on each side of the road as far as they could see for several miles. Soon numbers of Sauk and Fox came from their camps on the Arkansas. The caravan soon felt assured that there were so many from the frontier tribes that they would not presume to attack them under the guise of hostile Comanche or Pawnee, and they were permitted nearer approach and greater familiarity. Between Plumb Buttes and Cow Creek they left the train, and no more Indians or buffalo were seen. Everyone breathed and felt a great relief.

While eating the evening meal, Ian heard some of the men, who seemed to have become convinced of Captain Bellnap's cowardice and incapacity as a fighter, say, "he did not see how so cautious and timid a man should ever venture upon the prairies."

Ian made no remark to indicate he had overheard them but Sergeant Tom told them that sensible judgement and caution on the prairie was the best way to keep their hair.

Ian noticed the oppressive heat was hard on Father Gregg. He was like a regular old man, full of infirmities; his head especially troubled him the most. The frontier life was a hard one and his health was very much undermined by the fatigues of the journey, but still more by the shocking heat. As he advanced in age, the heat became more and more unbearable. Many believed this would be the priest's last trip.

Very often, Ian thought he resembled a man whose end was near at hand; panting with open mouth with the thermometer ranging from 104 to 109 degrees in the shade and up to 130 degrees in the burning sun.

One night there was a heavy rain all night with thick fog and cold weather. Toward noon the sun came out and soon it was stifling hot. Even after the caravan had stopped for the day, it was still furnace hot with not even a slight breeze stirring.

Ian had finished eating and was resting against a tree near his tent when a most terrible scream from the priest's camp shattered the normal noise of camping. It was long and loud and mournful, as if all the troubles of the world were combined in one awful yell.

Ian ran over to see what was the trouble. Father Gregg was holding onto the sideboard of his wagon with all his strength and screaming from the pain of his old wounds. He screamed until he was out of breath, but it didn't ease the pain. By this time others had gathered around, but none knew what to do to comfort him.

Then in a blind fit, he tore his black shirt off and clawed at his chest. The scars had become raw from the sweat of the heat and blood oozed from the broad scars.

The deep cross scars burned into his chest by Major Moore's men bled profusely as he clawed at the pain. With wide eyes fixed with pain, he staggered around, reeling and turning trying to escape the pain.

Finally Ian grabbed one of his arms while a tough Missouri trooper grabbed the other to prevent him from tearing the flesh off his chest.

He struggled against the two men, lunging back and forth, screaming all the time, until completely exhausted. Finally, too weak to scream anymore, his shoulders sagged and his head dropped down until his chin rested on his blood smeared chest. In another few seconds he became unconscious from all his exertions and intense pain and fell to the ground.

His Indian housekeeper all this time was sobbing and helpless to ease the pain of her beloved priest. Ian and the soldier dragged him as gently as possible to a field cot and laid him on his back, as his chest was bleeding the worst. The old weeping woman began to gently rub a salve on the scars and the flow of blood began to stop the bleeding.

All this time the soldiers gathered around were quiet, not knowing what to say or do. On many of their faces the guilt that their kind had done this to this man showed plainly and many would have done anything, even die, to set right this terrible crime. But this was all past history and nothing much could be done, except show him a little sympathy. But the sympathy didn't help ease the pain.

The little group dispersed and Ian was left alone with the unconscious Father Gregg and Kalespel, his Indian woman servant. She was a hideously, repulsive old woman, which masked her true loving nature. Born to drudgery and exposure, sustained by the worst of food, most of her life, she had been a beast of burden. Abandoned by her people on the prairie because of her advanced age and infirmities, Father Gregg had doctored her back to health and her affection for him was of the character of the love which a wild beast has for its young.

As she cared for the priest, she chanted a prayer in slow monotone to her Great Spirit, all the time bobbing her head up and down in time with the chanting.

In a reflective mood, Ian thought of the misery and suffering that must be all around him that he didn't even know about, let alone do something about.

Here was Father Gregg, not over two hundred feet from his tent, in great pain and agony, and Ian didn't even know of it before; he had not even thought of it. Maybe he should step out of his little world and try to help correct some wrongs, stop some new injustices, and seek out those miseries hidden from the casual view.

Poor Father Gregg! How he must have suffered and yet he continued on with his priestly work. Devout, fired by a holy zeal, he left everything behind him and went forth to conquer darkness with light. Prompted by unselfish motives and sustained by faith, he met the difficulties in his journey as a real Christian soldier.

On the trails of an unexplored and unknown wilderness inhabited by heathen races and wild beasts, far from the supports of civilization with sickness and death meeting him on the way and continuing with him, he met every obstacle. He endured every sorrow and disappointment, and suffered untold hardships of every kind as he sought to teach the Indians. He unceasingly praised God for his mercies and constant care.

*   *   *

The trail from Independence, Missouri to Santa Fe, Mexico was over 780 miles long. Camps were set up by other detachments of the First United States Dragoons to protect the caravans. Blue Camp, Round Grove, Oregon Trail Junction, Black Jack Point and 110-mile Creek were well known points on the trail. Duty at these camps was unromantic but an interesting routine. It took about three weeks to travel from Council Grove to Chouteau's Island on the Upper Arkansas River. The camps on the road relieved the sameness of the prairie's landscape. Further stations were set up at Diamond Spring, Cottonwood Creek, Turkey Creek, and Cow Creek.

For about 130 miles the route lay along the Arkansas River. From the high sandy hills the troops gazed upon great moving herds of buffalo which furnished sport and food for the caravan.

From numerous hilltops, travelers and soldiers enjoyed the grand sight of perhaps ten thousand buffalo feeding on the plains below as far as the eye could see.

In shooting them the surest weapon was a short barreled shot-gun carrying a large ball, as they are the most easily managed. The fat of the buffalo was more oily than tallow and was better for cooking. In selecting an animal from the herd to kill, one had to look at the thickness through the hump, because the fattest are the broadest through the hump. For a mile or two they run almost as fast as a horse, and are then easily caught. Their hides are very thick and from the form of the animal they are well adapted to make skin boats.

Marches during the last weeks of summer offered pleasant scenery. Water from clear springs refreshed men and animals, and the evening encampments were surrounded by groves of cedar, elm, and cottonwood. Gypsum beds, salt rock, contorted mineral forms, and brackish streams which cut up the country into a multitude of little valleys, gave character to the surface. Buffalo were observed almost daily by the outriders, and elk at times timidly approached the dragoon camps. The dragoons would race the wild mustangs across the uneven plains.

Ian was kept busy killing buffalo for the train. He enjoyed the dangerous sport. Hunting was a pleasure and also a necessity; buffalo meat with a half ration of flour and salt was the daily fare. Terrified deer and antelopes sped away over the hot plains and the soldiers captured the swift rabbits in the rushes and tall grass.

Buffalo, wolves, rattlesnakes, and grasshoppers seemed to fill up the country.

One day Ian had not gone a mile, when the prairie in front was literally black with buffalo. Ian and the others put after them, driving them up the nearby hills. His horse brought him upon the rear of the large herd and in the clouds of dust he could scarcely see a yard; his horse, also almost blind, dashed into the midst of the dust cloud. The buffalo's rumps gradually became visible, but he could not urge his horse amongst them.

Suddenly down went buffalo after buffalo in dust and confusion into an invisible ravine some dozen feet deep, and down in the midst of them plunged Ian and his horse. Ian was almost thrown, but his big stallion scrambled up the opposite side. As the dust cleared, he fired and wounded a buffalo, which soon dropped behind. Ian shot him several times before the bull fell.

Wolf tracks were astonishingly numerous and at night the wolves set up a mournful and discordant howling which lasted all the night, feeding on the carcasses.

The troopers on several occasions saw small bands of Indians also hunting, but the parties always stayed a respectful distance apart. Many times the dragoons came across butchered carcasses strewed for miles of prairie as the Indians gathered their winter meat.

Pushing steadily on, the wagons reached the valley of the Arkansas River, the Grand Arkansas. The trail struck the stream at the top of the Big Bend, south of Cheyenne Bottoms, at a point some 265 miles from Independence. Thereafter, it followed the river 122 miles to the Cimarron Crossing, where the Desert Route turned southwest; if the mountain route was chosen; it was another 143 miles to Bent's Old Fort.

The Arkansas River, seldom less than a quarter of a mile in width between its low, barren banks, flowed shallow and turbid over broad bars of sand, which rose here and there into small, shifting islands set thick with stunted, short-lived cottonwoods. The banks were vertical, but the water ran only three or four feet below the level bottom, so that a careless man might almost walk into the stream before he saw it. No trees marked the banks, except here and there, where a lone elm or hackberry or a few cottonwoods had survived the prairie fires under the protection of some slough or sand dune. The hills on either side of the broad bottoms were equally bare. The river itself, often dividing into several winding streams, was seldom more than knee-deep.

For all that, the sight of the Grand Arkansas roused the heart in every man who came with the rolling wagons from the east. Everyone felt that, on reaching the river, he had emerged into a new region. Far behind were the gentle, fertile prairies, the luxuriant grasses, the gay flowers, and timbered creeks. Here began the Great Plains. Bright green in spring, the short grass turned a greenish gray in summer, browned to buffalo color as autumn came on, and showed faintly blue in winter, matching the delicate tint of the sky above.

This was the heart of buffalo country. Far and wide, on every hand, the sign of the majestic animals was to be seen at all seasons. Everywhere the short grass was dotted with dried buffalo chips. Everywhere the turf was crisscrossed by narrow trails leading to and from the river. Everywhere bleaching bones, broad skulls, and flaking horns marked the sites where Indian hunters or savage wolves had thrown their prey to earth. Everywhere the soil had been scooped into shallow, saucer-like depressions by wallowing bison.

These wallows were indestructible, unmistakable from their circular shape—though they varied in size from four to fifty feet across. In spring the rains filled them, and their round mirrors were ringed with lush greenery, haunted by snipe and killdeer, inhabited by small aquatic animals, offering water to man and beast, so that one could camp anywhere at that season. In summer the plants around the wallows withered, the blossoms of the wild mallow vanished, the water evaporated, and the mud cracked into hard, dry, geometrical plates. In autumn the wallows became miniature dust bowls, and in winter showed only as round depressions under the snow, or harbored a tilted drift under the northern rim. But in any season, those wallows were an unfailing sign that buffalo ranged the country. And now, as gray wolves were seen insolently trotting along the ridges, everyone knew that the herds could not be far off. Every man in the caravan felt his blood begin to heat with buffalo fever.

Many of those men had come west with no other ambition than to shoot buffalo. Most preferred the flesh of the bison to that of any other creature. And after long weeks of subsisting on salt sowbelly, all were eager to feast upon fresh meat, or, as the trappers called it, "fat cow!"

Those men's imaginations were filled with the buffalo; buffalo marching in long, majestic files to drink at the river; buffalo grazing as far as the eye could reach, covering the plains as with one great shaggy robe. Their minds imagined buffalo wallowing in the mud, smearing their ample shoulder with wet clay, an armor against their insect enemies on the fly. They imagined buffalo rolling in the dust in summer; buffalo blocking the trail, trampling down tents, oversetting wagons, stampeding mules, as they rushed furiously away; and buffalo rooting with bleeding noses for the grass beneath the crusted snow. The buffalo they dreamt of were cowering together in some snug canyon during a blizzard, or milling on the open plain, each one trying to force his way into the midst of the herd, out of the bitter wind. Their imaginations also filled with buffalo crossing a river on a mile wide front, so that the splashing of their headlong rush into the water made a sound like some gigantic waterfall. There were buffalo blinded in a prairie fire, to blunder and wander and all prey to merciless wolves; buffalo pacing round a grazing herd on sentry duty; and buffalo with heads down and tossing horns, forming a ring about their calves, shaking their red tongues lolling. And there were buffalo bawling and roaring in the rutting season; buffalo pawing up the earth, gouging the prairies with angry horns in savage, jealous rage; and buffalo fighting!

Summer was the season of their fury. And after the calves were big enough to travel with the herd, and the bulls had rejoined the cows, that fury knew no bounds. Hundreds of battles went on in the same herd, at the same time, and the prairie was rent and channeled, and showed like a plowed field, where those titanic struggles had taken place.

The bulls, fat and saucy with good living, stood and pawed the ground, shaking their heads, tossing tall plumes and banners of sand into the sky, so that bits of earth fell all around like hail. Then those mighty champions, each weighing a ton or more, standing above six feet tall at the top of their humps, charged, rushing together with a terrific impact and thud of broad foreheads. They stood braced and straining, thrusting hard, clashing their tough black horns, moving back and forwards with cracking sinews and foaming jaws until the muscles of their thighs stood out like huge welts. So they would struggle, their small, dark eyes rolling in their stubborn heads, until one gave way, pushed to his knees, and suddenly found himself across the other's horns, ripped open.

All during the season they raged, and every bull, so long as he remained in the herd, found, wherever he turned, a fight on his horns. But in the end, the younger, lustier bulls prevailed, and drove the old fellows, with their wrinkled, splintering horns, out of the herd. Hunters preferred cows, and bulls far outnumbered them. And each season as the disparity in numbers increased the fury of the bulls mounted.

The greenhorns had much to learn about the animals. There was time for the lesson as they eagerly approached the range: in the saddle by day with the crawling wagons; in the corral during the long noonday halt for breakfast; or, better still, sitting around the camp-fire at night listening to the tales of Indian hunters and mountain men.

Old-timers never tired of arguing about the number of bison on the plains. Some had very definite opinions, estimates for which they were ready to fight, if need be. Some said forty million, twenty million, or, as one insisted, exactly seventeen million—the precise number needed to maintain the species! But all agreed on the vast numbers they had seen. There were herds that took days and weeks to pass a given point and herds that blocked the trail, compelling men to corral their wagons about their excited livestock. There were herds that, grazing slowly forward, devoured every blade of grass in their path, so that oxen and mules were left without forage until they had cleared the trail of the buffalo— perhaps after a march of forty miles! Such a herd might be two hundred miles long, fifty broad. Where it had passed, the water was so fouled that men who tasted it sickened, and even oxen and mules refused to drink. The buffalo had a habit of standing and stalling in the water. After a man had to quench his thirst on such "buffalo tea" for a few days, he acquired a hatred for the animals—a grudge, which goes far to account for the wanton killing of the shaggy beasts.

A lone horseman, finding himself in such a herd, had to keep moving all night, or fell trees around his camp to fend off the buffalo. Then, all night long, he could hear the cease-less trampling of that marching multitude, feel the heavy logs about him shiver as the huge creatures rubbed past, and in the morning find his shelter brown with their shed wool.

There was always danger, in passing through a vast herd, of starting a stampede, in which wagons and teams might be injured or swept away. For the buffalo had an ingrained dislike for being headed off, and would not willingly cross a trail behind the wagons. If the herd was heading in somewhat the same direction as the caravan, it would insist on passing ahead of the lead wagons. As bulls in the rear had to run to catch up and pass the oxen, it was natural that the whole herd should get to running and start a stampede. Indian hunters sometimes took advantage of this peculiarity of the buffalo to guide a herd to a bluff, or even near their village. For the leaders of the herd would always incline towards any riders advancing on one flank in a parallel course, if not too close. Thus, by sending flankers riding on either side, alternately pressing forward and dropping back, the herd could be steered sometimes in the desired direction. This accounts for the fact that Indian medicine men were able to lure buffalo over the plains to the corral where they were to be destroyed.

If the wagons had already passed, the buffalo, on coming to the ruts, would often stop, snuff the trail, and then jump quickly over like sheep jumping over a stick. They did not like the odor of white men and cattle or the sound of Indian drums. The creatures had very definite traits and characteristics. And when disturbed, the bulls bravely turned and walked "into the wind," in order to avoid being approached from leeward. This fact saved many an old-timer's life on the plains. When he saw a buffalo, or a bunch of them, moving against the wind, contrary to the general direction of the migration, he knew that Indians had been after them, and took steps to protect his scalp. The lore of the buffalo was a matter of practical value to the frontiersman. His life might depend upon his observation of their habits. Besides, he had a natural curiosity, and watched the herds, hoping to see something of which his comrades were ignorant.

The plainsmen, who had hunted buffalo season after season, prided themselves upon their knowledge, and were as touchy as though the animals had been their own personal property. They were always ready to talk, and once a man started talking about buffalo, he never wanted to stop. The lore of the bison was without end.

The greenhorn, naturally enough, compared the bison with tame cattle in the settlements. His mentor soon showed him the superiority of the buffalo. They were, it seemed, altogether hardier and more enduring than domestic cattle. They did not drift in storms, nor have their tough horns split open, even by the cruelest frost. They ate less and fattened faster, seemed never to require salt, and were never known to eat locoweed, which was always to be seen standing, untouched, after they had passed. When they lay down, they never got wrong-end-to on the hillside; and when they got up, they got up front feet first like a horse—though they got up so swiftly that some old hunters swore that they sprang up on all fours, like a jack-in-the-box! They would fight anything in defense of their calves, and once started, would not turn aside for any danger. They would jump off a bluff that a horse or mule would wheel from. And in the spring, when the ice on the Stinking Water grew treacherous, they marched out upon it, following their leaders, crashing through, until the stream was clogged with their bloating bodies, and the whole country stunk to heaven for miles around. It was the same in bogs. Men had counted as many as seven thousand bulls mired on the banks of one river.

Yet, hunters did not consider them stupid. They were speedy, too, and had a wonderfully keen sense of smell, though not much for eyesight. They were long-lived because they had better teeth than a cow, more ribs, and could graze closer to the ground. They had a hump to store their fat and when a buffalo lay down, it tucked its feet up under it, where the heel-flies could not bother. As for the meat, there could be no comparison! Beginning with Cabeza de Vaca, every traveler in the southwest had declared that buffalo meat was finer and fatter than the flesh of cattle.

When it came to fighting qualities, the buffalo had backers galore. No Spanish bull could match him, so they said.

With every mile, more and more wolves were seen, trotting along the ridges, following the caravan in packs. The wolf was a clever creature, and much preferred devouring meat killed by hunters, both red and white, in order to share in the kill. In those days, they were called "white wolves," though a dirty gray in color, except in extreme old age. And as the men had opportunity, they shot at them.

In those days of muzzle-loaders, loading a gun was a slow process for most men, and as a result, they carried their weapons loaded. Teamsters, having their hands full with their long whips, and tiring of toting heavy weapons, commonly stowed them in the tail of the wagon, or under the tilt up front. And all too often, knowing that a gun resting on its barrel might damage the sights, they put the gun into the wagon butt first.

As a result, accidents were common, and almost every caravan had one or more men injured by gunshot wounds, such as an accident that befell a man named Broadus.

In his haste to bring down a particularly large wolf, which was making off over the prairie, Broadus ran to the tail of his moving wagon and began to pull his gun out by the muzzle as he ran. Somehow or other, the gun went off, and the ball shattered the bone of his forearm to bits.

The captain halted the train, and inquired if there was a surgeon in the caravan. There was none.

Then Charles Bent and the wagonmaster urged the injured man to let them amputate, telling him that otherwise it was only a question of days until he would be a dead man.

But the man with the broken arm would not consent. His nerve was shaken, and he refused point-blank to let green hands experiment upon him. And so they made room for him in one of the carriages, and the train moved on. They all regarded him as a dead man. The caravan moved slowly on, until Broadus himself knew that death stared him in the face.

The train halted for a day. Broadus was going to die, they agreed. His arm was so gangrened that spots had appeared well above the place where the amputation should have been performed. The poor fellow, who had suffered agonies as he jolted over the rough prairie trails, and hoping against hope, now began to plead with his mess mates to perform the operation which he had refused to permit before. It seemed no use to them. It would surely kill him outright, and they wanted no hand in his death. But he was so urgent, so persistent, that at last volunteers were called for.

Broadus lay on the buffalo grass, sick with terror and pain, begging the men not to let him die—arguing, crying, pleading—while they stood around and looked on, stirring uneasily, looking at each other, chafing at their inability to help—curious, pitiful, nervous. Kit Carson, then just a boy, was first to offer his services.

Following his lead, shamed out of their inaction, two or three of the men undertook to amputate the arm, assuring each other that they did so only to gratify the dying man. After that there was no delay.

A skinning knife was whetted to razor sharpness. One of the teamsters brought out an old rusty handsaw from his toolbox, and the back of this was filed to a fine set of teeth. A small fire was built, and the kingbolt of one of the wagons lay upon the coals to heat. When all was ready, they placed the patient on his back on the grass, and a dozen men held him fast while the amateur surgeons went about their terrible deed of mercy.

A tourniquet prevented bleeding. The whetted knife quickly opened the arm to the bone; the bone was immediately sawed off; the white-hot bolt seared the raw stump, taking up the arteries more swiftly than ligatures could have done had they had any. Then a coating of cool axle-grease was laid over the wound and covered with improvised bandages. The patient was carried to his bed in the shade of one of the wagons. Next day the caravan moved on. The arm healed rapidly, and long before they reached Santa Fe the patient was sound and well.

The operation was performed at Walnut Creek.

Next day about noon the men of the caravan heard confused, dull, and murmuring sounds, which seemed to come from a distance, and grew louder as they advanced. Not long after, dark masses showed on the plains ahead, and the cry of "Buffalo! Bison! Cibola!" rang out along the train.

Under the cracking of impatient whips, the wagons rolled along more swiftly, and swung into the circle of the corral for the midday halt. On every side, men were rounding up the loose animals, tightening their girths, reloading weapons, mounting, dashing away. Everywhere was bustle, shouting, and laughter. Now they were through with hard bread and salt sowbelly. Now they would feast upon dark red fresh meat, sweet fat, hump ribs, marrow, and tongue!

At that season the bulls were fatter than the cows, and much preferred, if not too old. They were sleek and lively, and in color were between a dark umber and a liver shining brown on the back of the hump and forward bushy with black manes and beards and frontlets. Having shed the wool behind, and retained their long hair before, they looked perfectly ferocious. But they could not run so fast as the cows, now lean and rangy.

As the hunters approached the herd, the nearest bull turned suddenly to face them. The others, too, raised their heads and stood motionless together, staring. Then, as if pricked with a knife, they whirled as one, and lunged away. Immediately, the fright was communicated to the others, and the whole herd was in motion. They rushed off in a mass, shouldering each other, moving in a curious rocking gallop, much like the frantic flight of a bunch of gigantic hogs.

To kill buffalo in the chase or "run meat," as the old-timers called it, a man had to have a trained buffalo horse, a sure seat, and skill in using weapons on horseback. An untrained horse would not willingly approach a bison, and, if he did, was likely to be caught unprepared, if a wounded bull jerked round to hook him. An animal unused to firearms might also take fright, jump, and destroy his rider's aim as the gun went off. Even a trained horse had to be swift and able to endure a run of miles. A speedy cow might lead a man a chase of ten or twenty miles before he could come up with her.

Many of the best buffalo-chasers were Indian trained, and old-timers preferred them. Their split ears could generally recognize them, a mark by which Indians distinguished such animals on the Southern Plains. These horses were rarely used for ordinary purposes, but were pampered and maintained only for hunting or war. Horses had no grain on the prairie, and their strength and spirit had to be conserved. Their master's dinner and even his life might depend upon their speed and agility.

In the hurly-burly of the chase, a sure seat was indispensable. And a sure seat meant more than the ability to stick to a saddle. Old-timers often unsaddled and rode bareback after buffalo, in order to make their horses as quick and agile as possible. They also dispensed with bridles, using only a halter, or a rope knotted about the lower jaw, with which to stop the horse. They had no need of reins to guide him, for a trained pony knew his work; such animals, when turned loose, would haze buffalo over the prairie for the fun of it, as a cow pony will haze cattle, even without a rider. Such control as was needed was exercised by the pressure of the horseman's knees, or by leaning his weight towards the side to which he wished the horse to go. Riding in that way, a man could anticipate the movements of his horse by the feel of his muscles, and the two became, in effect, one creature.

Such bareback riding at the dead run in a smothering cloud of dust, over unknown ground, among dog holes and across gullies, while loading and firing and anticipating the movements of the horse as it charged warily among the frantic bulls, was no past-time for

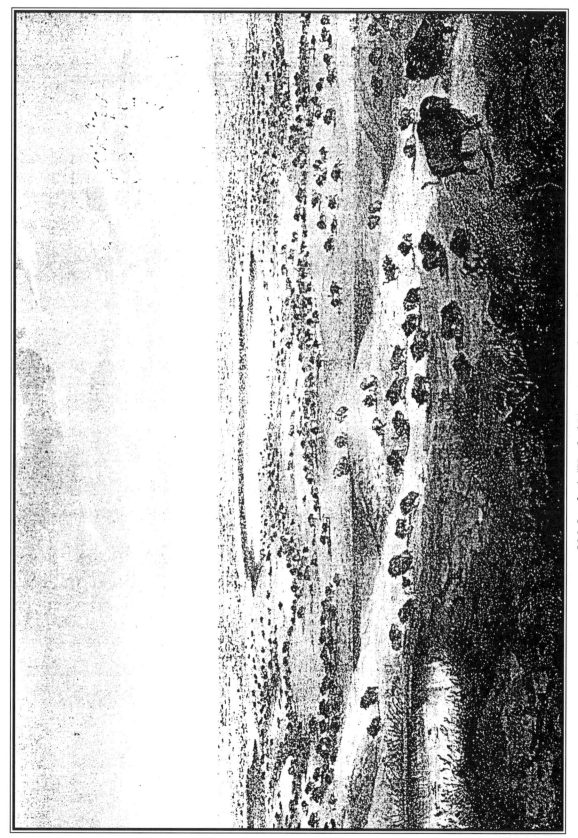

J.M. Stanley's "Herd of Bison, Near Lake Jessie"

amateurs. Jogging along the trail beside the wagons, or going for a canter in the park, proved poor training for the buffalo hunt. To run meat, a man had to be able to ride.

More, he had to handle weapons dexterously. For the buffalo, big as it was, was hard to kill, and unless hit in the heart or spine, seemed indifferent to bullets, as to weapons of any kind. The lance—a six-foot stave with a three-foot blade—was quicker, but demanded expert hands, a stout wrist and arm. The Mexicans preferred this weapon, which was always loaded.

The Indian's short bow was excellent for the purpose, and many white men, who had lived with Indians, used it on occasion. Made of horn, bois d'arc, or hickory, the bow was tough, strong, and short enough to be handled with ease in the saddle. Indians were incredibly quick, as anyone who had timed an old hunter killing buffalo or cattle can testify. A skilled hunter could loose an arrow once a second, for he had no need to aim at close range. The quiver was slung under his left arm, handy to his right-hand fingers, but he often grasped half a dozen arrows in his bow hand for greater speed. Good bowmen sometimes dropped a dozen buffalo before their horses were winded—and each with a single arrow!

White men generally used firearms: rifles, carbines, light weapons of choice, with large bore and short barrels for close work, throwing heavy slugs. Those who used muzzle-loaders never bothered with ramrods, but carried powder loose in their coat-pockets, and the bullets in their mouths. At such close range, the size of the charge did not count. So they poured in the powder by guess, dropped the wet bullets on top, and sent the charge home by striking the butt on the horn of the saddle. A wet bullet was supposed to stick to the powder, for the muzzle was not depressed until the moment of firing. A dry ball, however, would roll towards the muzzle, and if it did, an explosion followed, which might maim or kill the hunter or his horse. The famous mountain man, Fitzpatrick, earned his name Broken Hand in such an accident.

Thus, a seasoned hunter, tossing his hat off, and tying his long hair with a handkerchief around his head, would jump on his split-ear, and bending his knees, push them under the lariat tied loosely about the animal's barrel. In that position he was securely fastened to the bare back of the horse; yet, if he wished to dismount, or free himself in case of a fall, he had only to straighten his legs, and the rope released him instantly.

Riding so, or with shortened stirrups, and armed with a lance or rifle, he was ready to kill, and in one day could provide food for a whole wagon train. He and his horse were a team of trained acrobats, who thought and acted as one.

Giving rein, such a rider trusted his horse. The pony, with ears set back and long tail flagging the wind, knew his business perfectly. He soon laid his master alongside the racing buffalo, and held the pace—not ten feet distant—until the hunter, without aiming, and trusting only to his trained sense of direction, fired down and forward, trying to pierce the bull's heart, or smash his spine.

The buffalo was a vital creature, hard to kill, and even when shot through the heart might run on a hundred yards or more before he fell—records of the hunt are full of such cases. Therefore, the hunter had to know where his ball struck. Then, knowing he had made his kill, he could swing his weight slightly to one side, the pony would catch the signal and veer in that direction, bring his master alongside a new victim, and the two made another kill. Experienced men did not waste time, or get too near wounded animals, unless these required another shot to finish them. It was wise to kill quickly, before the horse tired—not merely to spare the animal, but because the moment a bull began to tire and lag, it was likely to turn and attack its tormentors.

The greenhorn might, or might not, be instructed in all this theory before he reached buffalo country. But theory and practice are two things. And when the novice asked the old-timer about hunting, and casually inquired as to the dangers of the sport, he was likely to be taken aback at the candid reply: "Runnin' meat dangerous? Wal, yes, I reckon it is, if you come right down to it. Specially if thar's a greenhorn along. Fact is, the greenhorns are more dangerous than the bulls!"

That statement was true, though the greenhorn himself might think it a joke. One day Will Comstock, the famous scout, was watching a flock of greenhorns chasing a lone bull along a crawling caravan, and proposed to a comrade that they join the chase and put the bull out of his misery—before the greenhorns scared him to death!

The greenhorns, galloping wildly over the prairie, and firing even more wildly from a distance of fifty yards behind, filled the air with their flying lead. Will's partner, watching this performance from the wagons, expressed the opinion that joining such a chase would be too dangerous.

Will snorted, "Wagh! Come on. The closer we are to the bull, the safer we'll be." He rode swiftly out, fired a single shot, and dropped the animal. The greenhorns, riding up, were amazed to learn that only one bullet could be found in the huge carcass, and spent the rest of the day arguing as to which one of them had fired it.

Too often, the greenhorn rode an untrained horse, and exhausted it before he reached the herd, instead of getting as near as possible at a walk, before spurring into a gallop. Even if trained, the horse would be nervous, uncertain what to make of the unfamiliar signals of its master, and excited by the nervousness of the man as well, to say nothing of being over-loaded with a heavy California tree and Spanish bridle. A horse unused to buffalo and the sound of firearms would never close on the buffalo, and long-range shooting was apt to prove ineffective.

Shooting from the saddle of a running horse at a moving, dodging mark was novel and hard for the beginner. The size of the buffalo offered such a broad target that he was apt to forget that his lead would be thrown away unless he placed his shots with care. The result was that he commonly dashed away the moment he saw a herd, with his horse in a trot and himself in a gallop, brandishing a deadly cocked pistol, a menace to every living thing within range—except the buffalo he was after!

Such men met with a variety of adventures.

One greenhorn blazed away, time after time, throwing his lead in to the huge bulk of a bull, astonished that it did not fall, unable to hit the vital spots. The greenhorn was naturally sensitive to ridicule, and he knew well how the men would laugh at him if he returned unsuccessful. He had traveled hundreds of miles to kill buffalo, and he intended to do it, now or never. And so he kept going, spurring his weary horse after the herd, mile after mile, until the pony, exhausted, overheated, and used up, played out completely, and stood covered with lather, heaving, utterly stove up. Too late the greenhorn realized that he had ruined his horse! Sadder, if not wiser, he would set out afoot to plod all those weary miles back to the trail, where he would be told that "the idee is to shoot buffalo, not run 'em down!" He would have time to ponder the lesson as he plodded all the way to Santa Fe.

Sometimes, of course, the greenhorn, though new to the plains, was nevertheless a shot and a horseman. Such a man would place his shots, and find his mark. Then, if not dropped in its tracks, the wounded bull might whirl, quick as lightning, and throwing its horns under the belly of the horse, toss him over and down, gore him, trample him, and his rider. The neck of a buffalo bull was strong enough to lift a horse in the air, and its horns were sharp and deadly. If the bull confined its fury to the horse, the man was lucky and lucky, too, if the falling horse, in its somersault, did not crush him. Sometimes he staggered to his feet, bruised and shaken, with a broken gun, and no cover, only to find himself on the horns of the furious buffalo. There could be only one end to such an incident.

Even the best of hunters had falls. Fremont tells how Kit Carson's horse fell headlong, but sprang up and joined the flying herd. Though considerably hurt, he had the good fortune to break no bones; and Maxwell, who was mounted on a fleet hunter, captured the runaway after a hard chase. He was on the point of shooting him, to avoid the loss of his bridle (a handsomely mounted Spanish one) when he found that his horse was able to come up with him. To avoid the loss of the horse, some adopted the custom of the Indian warrior, who tied one end of a lariat about the horse's neck. The other end would be tied about his own waist and carried the slack coiled and tucked up under his belt, where it would play out in case of a fall and stop the horse. Either way, when a horse went down, there was always a chance of smashing a thigh, or a pelvis—injuries for which there was no remedy on the plains.

But Kit Carson never found running buffalo half so dangerous as the greenhorns did. They were their own worst enemies. Ian witnessed some inexperienced hunters that had wounded a savage bull, which turned and charged one of the parties. The greenhorn's horse, without waiting for instructions, wheeled and raced away with the bull right at his heels. The wind caught at the brim of the greenhorn's hat. He felt it going. His left hand was busy with the bridle reins. In his right hand he held a cocked pistol. Instinctively, he put up his right hand to hold his hat. The pistol discharged. The hat went one way and the pistol the other. The horse jumped with fright and the rider tumbled forward upon the animal's neck and began slipping to the ground. In this predicament, tragedy was averted by one of the greenhorn's friends, who stopped the bull with a single shot. Fortunately, the pistol bullet had hit the hat, not the greenhorn's skull.

In the snow, running meat was even more hazardous. Palliser tells how he killed a cow and a bull, and then rode after an uncommonly fine fat cow. "She gave me an awful chase, turning and doubling incessantly. My little horse began to show symptoms of distress, but I could not manage to get a broadside shot. At last, making one more push, I got pretty close behind her, and raising myself in my stirrups, fired down upon her. The bullet broke her spine. My horse, unable to stop himself, rolled right over her, making a complete somersault, and sending me, gun and all, flying clean over both of them into a snowdrift. I leaped up, ran back to my horse, which I caught without much difficulty and was glad to find no more hurt than myself. My gun was filled with snow, of course, but otherwise I was uninjured."

But the greenhorn was not content with unavoidable adventures like these. He had a knack for putting himself afoot and regularly did it in a way of his own. The method seems strange, yet it was common, however surprising to the man who uses it. The greenhorn did not lose his horse—he shot it!

Wild with buffalo fever on his first chase, half-choked with dust, and half-blinded by the gravel and dirt flying into his face from the hells of the scurrying bison was too much to handle. At the same time trying to manage his frightened horse, keep his seat and his stirrups, watch the buffalo, take aim, fire, and remember all the advice he had been given, the poor fellow was overwhelmed.

Perhaps his horse stumbled, or dropped suddenly down the side of a gully, or scrambled up the other side. In either case, the greenhorn was thrown off balance. He felt himself slipping, and grabbed wildly at the mane, thinking only of hanging on, forgetting the cocked pistol in his hand. Without knowing how he did it, he pulled the trigger and blew out the brains of his horse.

With startling suddenness, the horse vanished from beneath him; he parted with his saddle, lost his gun, and sailed through the air. That moment of calm surprise ended abruptly as he felt himself mauled by a heavy blunt instrument—the earth. Looking up in amazement he might see a dead horse falling on him from the sky, and only escape by rolling his bruised body out of the way. If not killed, or seriously injured, he would get up then, and stand with shaking knees, watching the buffalo disappear over the horizon in a cloud of dust.

At length he came out of his daze, collected his wits, gathered up his pistol, hat, and bridle, and started on his walk back to camp. Perhaps he was able to recover his saddle as well, and lug it along. In that case, he might hope to buy another mount for the long trip to Santa Fe.

On reaching the wagons, worn out and shamefaced, he was sure to be gravely approached by a tall Santa Fe trader. Without batting an eye, the trader would courteously inquire whether the greenhorn had brought in any buffalo hides to sell.

Shamefaced, the greenhorn would answer, "No!"

"Too bad," the trader would reply. "You see, at present there is no demand for horse robes. Of course, there will be. There's bound to be if you stay on the plains long enough!"

The chorus of guffaws that followed taught the stranger something of the hearty, but not unfriendly, elaborate humor of the southwest.

Another common experience while running buffalo was to get lost. A man used to the woodlands found himself literally at sea on the plains. None of the rules for lost men applied. He could not follow the streams down to the river for no streams were visible. He could not look for moss on the north side of trees, and so determine the points of the compass, for there were no trees. He could not take his bearings from the landmarks, for no landmarks existed. He could not, as a rule, even follow the trail he had made in reaching his lost position for the grass and the wind left few traces to be seen. On the boundless flat plains of western Kansas, when a greenhorn was lost, he was lost!

On a cloudy day, or after night came on, his sense of direction would desert him, and he might wander in a circle during the hours of darkness. The level grassy plains curved regularly, like the sea, and a lone man could be seen for only a few miles in such country. Firing his gun seldom helped in a region where the wind was always blowing. His friends were far away and could not hear; while, in Indian country, his enemies might be nearer, within earshot. The grass might as well have been water. All around there was nothing—only the grass and sky—and, of course, the lost greenhorn.

If he had any friends, they generally found him. If he kept his head, he might remember whether he had ridden north, or south, from the trail, wait for sunrise, head back and find his wagons again. But sometimes he lost his head. Then, it might be, a tragedy followed. In the nature of things, the details of such tragedies are hard to come by. But, if nothing else happened to the beginner on his first hunt, he was almost sure to have a good scare! Running meat was a ticklish business.

The first attempts of a greenhorn to kill a buffalo are invariably unsuccessful. He sees before him a mass of flesh, nearly five feet in depth from the top of the hump to the brisket, and consequently imagines that, by planting his ball midway between these points, it must surely reach the vitals. Nothing, however, is more erroneous than the impression. To "throw a buffalo in his tracks," which is the phrase for making a clean shot, he must be struck but a few inches above the brisket behind the shoulder where alone, unless the spine be divided, a death shot will reach the vitals. Ian once shot a bull, the ball passing directly through the very center of the heart and tearing a hole sufficiently large to insert the finger. The bull which ran upwards of half a mile before it fell, and yet the ball had passed completely through the animal, cutting its heart almost in two. He also saw eighteen shots, and half of them muskets, deliberately fired into an old bull at six paces and some of them passing through the body—the poor animal standing the whole time and making feeble attempts to charge. The nineteenth shot, with the muzzle touching his body, brought him to the ground. The head of the buffalo bull is so thickly covered with coarse matted hair that a ball fired at half a dozen paces will not penetrate the skull through the shaggy frontlock. Ian had frequently attempted this with a rifle carrying twenty-five balls to the pound, but never once succeeded.

"Hard to kill"—those were the only words to describe a buffalo.

*   *   *

If already well supplied with meat, hunters were often content to take only the choicest cuts. Of these, the tongue was most easily butchered out. Since the buffalo's jaws were likely to be closed, and perhaps rigid, the proper method was to slash out the skin between the prongs of the jawbone, pull the tongue through the opening so made, and cut it off.

The hump might be taken by skinning down each side of the shoulders and cutting away the meat and chopping off the hump-ribs (vertical projections of the vertebrae above the spine) with a hatchet. The large bones containing marrow were very choice parts. And the *dépouille,* or 'back-fat,' a strip of fatty matter lying along the backbone from the shoulder blade on, was hardly less appetizing. This piece, if scalded for a few minutes in hot grease, would keep a long time, hanging on a wagon. Slices were cut off from time to time from this tasty 'Injun bread,' and it was never a long time between slices!

Men trained in Indian methods were likely to begin by opening the belly and getting out some of the warm, raw liver. On this they sprinkled a sauce squeezed from the gall-bladder, and refreshed themselves. Buffalo gall was something of a stimulant, and a man could get quite a glow, if he took it straight on an empty stomach. Buffalo-hunters did not wait for the liver to cool; their "idee was to eat it while it's hot!" If time permitted, they would take also the heart, kidneys, and intestines; first pulling these between their fingers to get rid of the contents, and knitting the long tubes into a floppy chain. This part of the butchering was likely to disgust the greenhorn. He was usually content with other portions.

Old-timers used to urge the novice to be sure and bring in the liver. A story was common on the plains about three greenhorns who cut open a cow and tried to find this organ—about the size of a saddlebag—but could not, and returned to camp without it!

If meat was needed, the hunters made a thorough job of butchering and having propped the cow on her belly by stretching out the legs front and back, cut the hide in two along the backbone, peeled down the hide on both sides, working rapidly and allowing much of the meat to remain on the hide itself, especially on the belly. These bits of meat, taken off with a dubber, made excellent soup, when dried looked rather like potato chips.

The hunters then cut away the outer blanket of flesh from the back and sides of the animal; this part was taken off in one piece, and called the 'fleece.' The front quarters were taken off next, the hind quarters removed at the hip joints, the hump removed, and the remaining meat stripped for the ribs. Having cut the ribs free all round, they were chopped off from the backbone in a slab with a hatchet, or broken off with one of the leg-bones used as a club. The insides were put into the paunch (turned wrong-side out) along with the fat. What little remained was left to the wolves. To the Indians, even the content of the stomach was not entirely useless; they used it as a poultice.

When the meat was brought to camp, it did not take long to have the fire ready. Then the men gathered round, and feasting was the order of the day. Tongues were boiled, hump-ribs and marrowbones roasted before the embers, the fat-covered *dépouille* took the place of bread and butter, and yard upon yard upon yard of *boudin* (the intestine containing the chyme) were sizzling on the coals like hissing snakes. Kidneys and tongues and hearts baked to delicious tenderness in the hot ashes. The other parts went to contribute their various flavors to make son-of-a-gun stew.

The fleece and muscles generally were not eaten fresh, but were jerked, or dried, in the sun and wind. This process was known as making meat. The flesh was cut into thin sheets and hung on the wagons to dry, like so much washing. Some of these sheets were no bigger than a man's hand; others—parts of the fleece, for example—might be big as a face towel, and stretched upon skewers of plum or willow a foot long and about the size of lead-pencils. Men who understood this art never cut the meat across the grain; they tried to keep the rich juices from escaping, letting them dry inside. On the high, dry plains, making meat did not take long; after a few days' travel the skewered sheets would be a dark brown, and stiff as a board. Then they would be stacked in a wagon, where they would be dry, and would keep indefinitely. But, if there was time, even this dried meat would be made into pemmican—roasted and pulverized with a stone hammer to brown dust, or fibrous shreds, mixed with dried, powdered cherries and melted tallow, and tightly packed in a rawhide case.

But on the evening of the buffalo hunt, such labors had to wait. Then every man was busy chawing on hump-ribs and succulent *boudin,* filling himself with incredible quantities of meat. The hard exercise, the fresh air, the tasty food made everyone cheerful and happy.

Buffalo fat, unlike the fat of cattle, could be devoured by the pound without any unpleasant effects. And it was a proverb on the plains that a man could eat his own weight of buffalo meat, and never have a bellyache!

But, as the feasting went on, other moods developed. Men full of fresh meat became touchy and combative as the bulls they had killed. Invariably, the night after the first buffalo hunt, the camp was the scene of several fights. The fury of the bison was somehow communicated to their slayers. Maybe there is something in the Indian's idea that the spirit of a creature slain enters into his killer. Certainly, on the Santa Fe Trail, buffalo and bloodshed went together.

When the campfires had died to ashes, and the gorged wayfarers lay in their blankets, they were conscious of other woes than their own, and forgot the snarling of the wolves in the distance. For the buffalo hunt had its note of pathetic, too.

Orphaned calves, left behind by the fleeing herd, would take up with the hunters who had shot their mother, and attaching themselves to the horses, faithfully follow them back to the wagons. These hungry little fellows, udderless and lonesome, blundered among the cattle in the darkness, bawling for their suppers.

*   *   *

Over swelling meadows whose waves became gentler as the days passed, the caravan moved toward the Arkansas. At evenings the wagons maneuvered into a rough quadrangle, within which the most valuable horses and oxen were put, and the rest of the stock staked or "hobbled" just outside. Among these animals, a night watch was kept; the guard crouched motionless for his two hours, vigilant for any moving shadow against the line of light around the lower edge of the horizon. 270 miles from Independence, Missouri, the caravan reached the valley of the Arkansas where Ian's hunting party rejoined them.

The country had an imposing appearance. Beneath a ledge of wave-like yellow sandy ridges and hillocks spreading far beyond, descended the majestic river bespeckled with islets covered with green vegetation, thickly set with cottonwood timber. But several days' march along the valley wore away the picturesque impression with desolate monotony. Only here and there was a tree, an occasional little grove of stunted cottonwoods, flat, grassy islands dividing the wide, shallow river, or high sandy hills at the edge of the valley. Meals were cooked over buffalo-chip fires now and hunters spread out into the buffalo herds. The outriders in advance of the main body of wagons kept popping away at rattlesnakes.

The buffalo range was Indian country. From Walnut Creek, the trail led southwestward up the left bank of the river over a level prairie usually teeming with buffalo. As each hour's march brought the caravan nearer to the hostile Indians, the greenhorns became more nervous.

Even though no Indian signs were discovered when the wagons corralled at the base of Pawnee Rock, all realized that they were now in the danger zone.

Pawnee Rock, sometimes called Painted Rock, or Rock Point, was the most famous land-mark on the Santa Fe Trail. It was a kind of promontory, projecting towards the river (two miles distant) from the high prairies to the north. Its soft sandstone face was abrupt and some forty feet high.

By day the meadowlarks cheered the plain with their confident singing, and the river bottoms were alive with yellow-headed blackbirds, cowbirds, and immense flocks of Baltimore orioles. The grass was brightened with prairie indigo clumps of plum and cherry bushes. At night a man could avoid pools, being warned by the shrill cries of the killdeer which haunted them. Such was the country about the Pawnee Rock. Various legends account for its name.

The Pawnee were great fighters and, in the early days of the Santa Fe trade, some-times attacked the caravans, and very possibly near this spot since their trail from their villages in Nebraska came down past the Blue Hills and Pawnee Rock to Oklahoma, the Texas Panhandle, and New Mexico. Quite possibly, the "Rock" takes its name from this fact. The Indians would naturally make camp at the "rock" beside the river on their way north or south.

In those days the Pawnee were very numerous and warlike, but they have been blamed for too many raids of which they were not guilty.

Perhaps, too, they were talked of more than other tribes, merely because their name was easy to pronounce!

Just beyond the "Rock," Ash Creek flowed towards the river, a stream on which Indian signs, such as discarded moccasins and smoking campfires, often gave proof that Indians were watching from the hills around.

From Pawnee Rock on almost to the Cimarron crossing, the caravans had a choice of routes. The longer followed the course of the river; the shorter, or dry route, ran over the hills and high prairie at a distance of some ten miles from the river.

Caravans hastened in order to reach the crossing of the Arkansas before the June freshet —caused by melting snows in the Rockies—could reach the trail.

Ash Creek, often dry in summer, offered little obstacle. But the Pawnee Ford was another matter altogether. If in flood, it was a difficult stream to cross, and sometimes horses and wag-ons were swept away or a man drowned in trying to ford. Then the water came pouring down, bank-full, half-submerging the trees along its margins, tumbling brush and logs in whirling eddies and sweeping the willow up and down by the force of the current until it looked as if a hurricane were blowing. Only the elms, box elders, and willows could hold the muddy banks from being washed away. It was the part of wisdom to wait until the stream went down.

In such a time, the men of the caravan might wander over the prairies, noting the prickly pear that studded them. They would identify the tea plant or the toothache tree, catch some of the enormous toads abounding there, or dig up the tubers of the prairie convolvulus, known to the Indians as badger's food. Sometimes that tuber was two feet long, twenty inches around. It had a sweetish taste, and was said to be a cure for fever. Swamp grasses abounded along the river, and in the damp spots, the sick gold of the twining dodder smothered the weeds in an inextricable tangle.

Lone wolves loafed around, serenading the camps at night. And a party of naked Indians with painted faces might appear to inspect the caravan. Then the men would form the wagons in a tight corral, picket their horses close on short ropes, and lie awake all night beside a wagon with the rifle ready across the wagon tongue.

Pawnee Fork, when not in flood, was a bold, limpid stream with a sparkle that promised a cool drink to the thirsty horseman. Because it afforded good water and fuel for fires, it was a favorite haunt of these Indians and of their allies the Comanche. Raids often were made there, particularly when caravans were numerous enough to attract hostiles.

Beyond the Pawnee Ford, the trail passed through a barren region, crossing two small creeks, known as Little Coon Creek and Big Coon Creek. This was the dangerous part of the trail, as there was no cover in case of an attack. Here, wild horses were often seen, as in the river bottom there was good grass for the animals. Elsewhere it was scanty, the soil consisting of granite sand, which was much cut up by washes, offering cover to marauding Indians.

Here, in summer, the heat was intense.

So, at last, the caravans approached the Cimarron Crossing, or Ford of the Arkansas, where the trail divided. The mountain route passed on up the river toward Bent's Fort and the Raton Pass; the other crossed the river to traverse the dreaded "Journada" and strike more directly towards the New Mexican settlements.

Near the Ford, caravans were likely to encounter the camps of the Arapaho Indians, if they fared no worse before crossing the river into Comanche territory. On this part of the trail, one of the regular stopping places was known as the Caches. It gained its name from an adventure of some traders who set out for Santa Fe in the fall of 1822. Their names were Samuel Chambers and James Baird. It was a small party with an assortment of merchandise. They reached the Arkansas River late in the season, and pushed up the stream toward the crossing. Shortly before they reached the ford, snow began to fall. It soon became too deep for travel, and they were forced to go into winter quarters. Fearing an attack by Indians, they made their camp on an island in the river, and somehow managed to keep themselves alive during three long months. Some of their animals perished in the snow, others strayed away. When the snow melted in the spring, they had no means of transport.

Knowing that the Indians would steal their property unless it was concealed, they decided to cache their goods until they could return and recover them.

Choosing a level bench of firm soil near the river, they went to work. First the sod was carefully cut out and laid on buffalo robes that were spread near. Then a bottle-shaped excavation was made, narrow at the top and much bigger below the surface of the ground. All the earth taken out was carefully placed upon the robes, carried to the river, and thrown into the water, so that not a clod remained to show that a hole had been dug. Then the hole was lined with branches and leaves put all round, and the tightly packed goods were stowed in it. A covering of poles, grass and earth tapped firm was added, and at last the sod was carefully replaced. When all was finished, no one would have supposed that the grass had been disturbed.

It was the custom to obliterate the marks of digging by tethering horses above the cache for a day or two, so that their restless feet would hide all signs of excavation. Sometimes a fire was built on the spot, which charred the space and left it covered with ashes. Unless some prowling Indian had watched their work, they knew that their goods were now in safety.

The men set out, reached Taos, and recovered their goods. For many years after, the holes left in the ground were still visible, and few travelers passed that way without visiting those mossy pits.

*　　*　　*

In the sultry hot days the dust from the wagons and teams became thick and covered everything and everyone. Combined with sweating, clothes soon became stinking and filthy. Camp was usually made alongside a stream so the men could wash, shave, and bathe. Some of the old bearded teamsters didn't want to be bothered, they figured they could bathe at the end of the journey and, besides, they stunk so badly nobody stayed around them much. But, this is what these men wanted—to be left alone with their mules and oxen.

Jamie Bill, being the same age as the younger soldiers and not so tough and stubborn as the regular wagoners, stayed close to the soldiers' column of march. Ian noticed him every so often, usually once a day, and usually in the evenings having fun with the dragoons.

One evening after camp had been pitched and he was walking down to the stream to clean up, he noticed four soldiers horseplaying around, trying to undress Jamie Bill. They were laughing, hollering and kidding. It seemed that Jamie Bill had not bathed as long as anyone could remember and his clothes were stiff from sweat and dust. Ian hadn't thought about it much but did recall only seeing him wash his face and hands.

Ian stripped his shirt off and finished washing his face and arms. Drying off, he noticed Jamie Bill was still struggling hard against the four soldiers. He was plainly mad now, scratching, biting, hitting hard with his fists, but even though he had a couple of them bested several times, four of them were too much and his shirt finally came off.

The four still couldn't remove his trousers and as they needed washing also he was thrown high into the air and out into the thigh-deep water.

Under he went and as he staggered to his feet, coughing out the water from his lungs, and struggling with both hands to keep his pants on, the tight bandage around his chest washed away, revealing two small, yet decidedly feminine breasts. Standing naked to the waist in the water with her adolescent breasts protruding, her incredible masquerade was discovered.

For a long moment, everyone within seeing distance was dumbfounded.

Embarrassed and feeling sympathy for her; she must be a deeply troubled girl; Ian waded over to her and offered her his shirt. She quickly slipped into it and Ian helped her to the shore as she struggled to keep her trousers on. By now all the other troopers had taken to the 'tall timber' and Ian and Jamie Bill were alone.

Totally worn out by the struggle and dunking, she flopped down against the nearest tree trunk.

Ian sat nearby but didn't say a word for a long while as he recalled that she really had not done any real masculine thing in the past, but more of a tomboy nature. She had never undressed in front of anyone, even when she sat on the bank and talked to the other naked dragoons swimming and bathing.

Ian didn't know what to do so he fell back on the 'good old army excuse,' "You know, I'm going to have to report this to the Captain, Jamie Bill."

"Yes, I know," she replied, looking at him with tearful eyes, as if her whole life had been destroyed.

Not wanting to be inquisitive but he sensed she wanted to talk about it, so he asked, "Why? Jamie Bill, why did you do this?"

"Because I'm a man," she replied, "I feel like a man."

"Must my life be ruined because nature gave me a female's organs?"

"Externally I'm a woman, but inside I'm a man."

"What make a woman a woman and a man a man?" she asked. "Which is the critical factor? How you look or how you feel? What determines femininity and masculinity? In the head or on the chest or what's below the belly?"

"Sure, I know what everyone says. Sex is merely a matter of what kind of equipment you are born with, but what you think you are is more important than what your organs say you are. The sole criterion of sex is not physical, is it?" she questioned.

"No, I guess not, Jamie," Ian replied, not knowing what else to say. He really hadn't thought about it much.

With all her pent up emotions overflowing, she poured out all of her thoughts to Ian. She insisted that she was a boy because she felt like one. She was deeply troubled and lived an extraordinarily complicated life. She had fought the feelings for a long time but finally the boy feelings inside her could not be quieted any longer. Unhappy and misunderstood, she adopted a boy's name. She had flattened her breasts with tight bandages and dressed and lived as a man. Now that he thought about it, Ian realized that it could happen. There probably is a sex center within the brain that directs people how to behave—as a male or female.

Something could go wrong at the moment of conception, during the long and complicated process that began when the egg and the sperm united new life. There could be a special breed; Jamie Bill was proof of that; who has the body of one sex but the mind of the other. She wasn't a homosexual. She said she had no sexual craving for members of her own sex.

She wasn't a transvestite because she didn't get any sexual pleasure from dressing in the clothes of the opposite sex.

Jamie Bill must have suffered terribly in her transformation. Ian knew children cross and recross the boy and girl life pattern many times. Girls, at times, enjoy baseball and boys play with dolls. Being a sissy or a tomboy is considered normal growing up. In fact, many parent's take pride in their daughter's tomboy antics. Most children like to put on Mom's or Dad's clothes, and it was smiled upon as long as it isn't an obsession.

But then girls are usually through with tomboy's ways at thirteen and acquire strongly feminine traits.

Something just went wrong with Jamie Bill's sex center and she just couldn't help it. It would be hard for many people to understand, but Ian did and he would try to explain to the others.

"You will have to live with one of the immigrant families, Jamie" Ian explained, "You can't camp with the teamsters or troopers now."

Jamie understood. She was going to find the going very difficult from now on.

Ian and Jamie rode over to the emigrant's camp and explained to his friend, the 'yaller' haired buxom country girl he had met back in Fort Leavenworth. She accepted Jamie Bill as a family member with her usual jolly and friendly readiness and she insisted that Ian set down for supper with them.

After a fine meal of wild meat, beans and hot corn bread, Ian returned to the army camp and informed the Captain of Jamie Bill's masquerade.

*   *   *

Beautiful prairies, unsoiled by plow or spade, sweetly scented with the blossoming of summer, had been around since time commenced. This was the theater of the Indian's bravery, of his hopes, joys, and sorrows. But these hopes and joys many a time ran to thoughts of stealing, and sometimes of bloody warfare.

Ian also found joy in the land. Many an evening before dark, he would retire from the noise of the camp and ride out to enjoy the country and the solitude of the big land. He seemed to collect inner strength from the quietness of nature. It was fine to be in the company of the others, but sometimes he enjoyed the loneness. He never gave a passing thought of the supposed dangers around him. He just absorbed the quietness of the prairie, the unfettered streams, the prairie dogs, the owl, squirrel and occasional deer or snake; most of all the unending sky and the majestic music of the gentle winds seemingly trying to tell him some secret. Here in the wilderness with no other human in view, he found happiness difficult to put into words. His soul was refreshed and everything seemed to fall in to place. After these moments, he found reason to live, if for no other reason than to enjoy future moments of silent nature. Here he became part of nature—of the trees, tall grass, and sky. Here he remembered the past joys of life, of memories of Louisa, of laughter with Annie, and the brawls of Rialto. . . . of all things good.

At other times in the solitude, he tried to figure out some of the absurdities of life, as the wind cleared the cobwebs of frustrations. The giant land seemed to manifest the power of nature, magnify its glory, goodness, beauty and freedom. He felt a strong bond uniting him to its mysterious power. Although unknown to him, these feelings and strengths were similar to those of the Great Plains Indians he felt. Here . . . in nature . . . was the beginnings of great religions.

He sensed the exhilaration of being very small, but at the same time a giant. He was part of the universe, part of the majesty of the sky, part of this immense land. If there was a Messiah, an oracle or whatever he was called, he would be here on these Great Plains.

One fine clear day, late in the afternoon, Ian rode out onto the prairie to enjoy the solitude. After five miles or so he started back to the train. His return journey was by a different route through some low hills. As he rounded a large rock mass he was suddenly confronted by a small band of Indians. Out in front of the others was a lone warrior, evidently the chief in command, who was of almost gigantic stature. Ian's natural instinct was to draw his pistol, but before he pulled his pistol from the holster, he noticed the warrior's lance was stuck in the ground beside his mount—a sign of peace.

The Indian was mounted on a large, fine-limbed chestnut stallion. He sat well forward on his bare-backed charger with his knees passing under a horse-hair lariat that twice loosely encircled the animal's body and his horse's bridle grasped in his left hand, which was also closely wound in its flowing mane. He was over six feet three inches tall, beautifully formed, and bare to the waist. He looked very intelligent and brave—a formidable foe. Perhaps a Cheyenne or a Sioux, Ian did not know for sure. He had not met a Sioux but Sergeant Tom had described them to him. His face was hideously painted and his breech-cloth, leggings, and moccasins were decorated with a long fringe and with beads.

His hair was cut off on only one side, with the other side worn long down to his shoulders in a braid and wrapped with a string of red cloth. An ornament of deer-hoofs, shells, and beads hung around his neck.

He was without movement for a short while sitting there in all his savage splendor, careful not to make any move that Ian might interpret as warlike.

After the initial shock was over for Ian, the warrior made the sign of peace—hands clasped in front of his body, with the back of the left hand down. Ian, not knowing what to do, gave the same sign.

With the sign returned to him, the huge Indian gently spurred his horse toward Ian as the rest of the party stayed their ground.

Having no idea what to do, Ian waited to see what would happen next. The savage approached to within twenty or so feet of Ian and stopped his mount.

Suddenly he spoke in broken English and with great dignity, "I am sent by the one you seek!"

Ian was startled, not only by the savage's ability to speak English, but he evidently knew of Ian's secret mission.

But Ian still said nothing, mainly because his mind was whirling with a hundred thoughts.

The Indian was the first to speak again, "The Great Hasunan wishes to inform you that "Keesh-she-la-mil-long-up' who thought us into being, has willed that you shall meet."

Ian was thoroughly dumb-struck and speechless although his mind was filled with intense excitement.

The red chieftain drew nearer, and stretching out his hand, offered a medallion to Ian, "Wear this, so you may journey safe."

Very impressed, Ian accepted the medal solemnly.

The warrior gave the common sign of friend of the northern tribes. He held his right hand in front of and back towards his neck, with index and second fingers extended and touching, pointing upwards and slightly to front with the others and thumb closed. He raised his hand moving it slightly to the front until the tips of the fingers were as high as the top of his head.

Although he did not understand, Ian gave the sign in return as the Indian turned and rode away. As he passed his lance, he pulled it from the ground and rode off with the others following.

Soon they were out of sight.

It all happened so quickly, Ian could have sworn it was all a dream, if he didn't have the medal. It was a large medallion, almost three inches across and of a bright yellow gold color. Hung from a substantial chain, it had strange hieroglyphics on both sides.

Ian stared at it for a long while, with questions racing through his brain.

"How did this so-called Hasanun know he was looking for him?"

"How did he know where to find Ian?"

"Maybe he was one of those truly uncommon geniuses which spring up occasionally to produce revolutions and overturn the established nature of things."

As he rode back to the train, Ian kept thinking of these questions and the only possible explanation was that this Hasanun was perhaps supernatural, capable of power and mystery and knowledge far beyond that of common men.

"If the promise was true, if they were to meet, the occasion would be interesting," Ian thought.

*   *   *

The safest course was to follow the Arkansas Valley as far as Chouteau's Island, four hundred miles from Santa Fe, and a small detachment of troops remained at Chouteau's Island during the summer when the caravans were most numerous.

Several years before, one of the first caravans was escorted there by Major Riley. The traders after receiving careful instructions from the major had resumed their march toward Santa Fe. A few hours later a horseman dashed into the major's camp bringing the news that the caravan had been attacked by a band of Indians and that a trader had been killed. Major Riley quickly broke camp and rejoined the traders with all speed. The Indians had escaped, but Major Riley continued to escort the traders many miles into Mexican territory. The suffering from heat and thirst grew intense, and after several days, thirteen yoke of oxen gave out. Three days later the escort returned to Chouteau's Island.

Nearly three months—from July to October—Major Riley's command remained near the island waiting for the caravan, which was to return from Santa Fe to the States. Indian alarms and attacks were frequent, and one day an Indian arrow killed a bugler. Hostile Indians nearly always surrounded the camp. For months, the men slept in pantaloons and moccasins, with pistols, and a loose woolen coat for a pillow; and with a sword stuck in the ground at the mouth of the tent, with their cap upon the hilt.

During the warm summer days, now that it was more peaceful, the troops stationed near Chouteau's Island fished, hunted, and made hundreds of buffalo powder horns. The more skilled troopers carved out of the horns such articles as spoons, cups, buttons, and wineglasses.

Here the caravans usually stopped and it was customary to cut extra axletrees and to make other repairs for the heavy Pittsburgh or Dearborn wagons. Oxen and mules, grazing in the lush grass, dotted the hills and valleys.

As the caravan rested for a few days, a Mexican caravan of Creoles, Spanish, Indians, and Frenchmen arrived at Chouteau's Island escorted by a strong detachment of Mexican troops.

Cheers, unearthly yells, and volleys of whipcracks from the swarthy Mexicans urged the overworked mules to an encampment about a mile below the American's camp.

Ian estimated the value of the traders' goods and their two thousand horses, mules, and jacks at about $200,000.

The officers exchanged compliments and dragoon detachment was reviewed and drilled for the edification of the Mexican officers. After military courtesies were exchanged, a feast was given in honor of the Mexican officials. Seated cross-legged around green blankets; the small party of troopers partook of bread, buffalo meat, and, as an extraordinary rarity, some salt pork; but to crown it all, were several large raw onions, for which they were indebted to the arrival of the Mexican guests. A tin cup of whiskey, which, like the pork, had been reserved for an unusual occasion, was passed around, followed by another of water.

Some of the Mexicans decided to trade their wares rather than proceed on to Independence. As a result of these transactions, some of the Americans realized a net profit of about forty-five per cent. Feeling well paid for their venture; they escorted the remainder of the Mexicans to Missouri, prepared to make a larger investment in the same business for the following year.

The next few days were vocal with the rude jests of the wagoners, farmers, and back-woodsmen, as well as the oaths of the Mexican drivers as they harnessed the animals or reloaded the merchandise of the caravan. Soon the motley line of dragoons and traders were moving again across the prairies to Missouri.

The safest course to Santa Fe did not happen to be the shortest course and the Mexicans returning to the city used the shorter route, as they were familiar with the country. Twenty miles above the island the banks of the Arkansas were very low on either side; here the Mexican caravan made its crossing to start on a long oblique march over unstable sands. As fuel was plentiful here at the island, the travelers baked bread enough to last them for the next hundred miles.

When the Arkansas was crossed for the direct route to Santa Fe, a weary waste extended as far as the eye could see and the "water scrape" began soon after. The Mexican caravan headed boldly into the desert between the Arkansas and the Cimarron, fifty miles away. The plain was hard, unmarked by ruts, and destitute of water. Every keg was filled before the wagons left the Arkansas, and the caravan tried to push through the distance in two days. And there was always the chance that the Cimarron would be dry.

The Arkansas River was treacherous to cross and could be accomplished only by a good deal of risk and hard work, so Ian and the troopers helped the Mexicans across. The stream was about a third to half a mile wide with a rapid current and quicksand bottom. The channel shifted from day to day, forming holes and bars, making necessary much crooking and

Indians shooting the rapids of the river

Mode of crossing rivers by Indians
From Mullan's Report

turning in the stream to avoid miring down so the water would not reach the bottoms on the wagons and wet the goods. On several of the heavy wagons, the load had to be raised by placing timbers on the bolsters as high as they dared and chanced that the loads wouldn't overturn.

A Mexican, who had made many trips before this, told Ian that on one or two occasions he found the water so high that they could find no place to ford. They had selected a wagon body best fitted for the purpose, caulked it as well as they could, and, stretching raw buffalo skins on the outside, made a boat to ferry over the goods. It was no small job to ferry across the stream seventy-five to one hundred tons of freight. The work sometimes delayed a train a week or ten days.

The river was in fair fordable condition and was crossed in one day by doubling teams. Twelve yoke of oxen or mules were used on each wagon with three or four drivers to a wagon. Plenty of men walked beside each wagon to lift at the sides in case of danger of turning over or to roll at the wheels in case of danger of miring down. The current was so rapid and the quicksand so treacherous that a wagon shook and rattled by the sand washing from under the wheels as much as it would going over the worst cobblestone pavement. And if the team stopped for a very few minutes, it would settle so deep that it would be almost impossible to get out.

The caravan with good luck could travel thirty miles, leaving encampment at four o'clock in the morning and traveling without making any stops until four o'clock in the afternoon. Without a drop of water for their horses or mules, many of them were nearly exhausted, as well as a number of the men. Many a time the dogs, which traveled with every caravan, would fall down and die, due to the extreme heat and suffering.

Fortunately for the Mexican caravan, at about four o'clock a small ravine was discovered and followed for a few miles. After digging in the sand at the bottom of it, water was procured in sufficient quantity to satisfy both man and horses, but not until after five or six wells were dug.

At the Cimarron it was the same story, water was remarkably bad and scarce, having to dig for it at every place they stopped. Past the Cimarron, nature offered no serious hazards, but only a little water, so the way was very rugged. On the summit of the ridge between the Cimarron and the Canadian, the travelers came into view of the Rockies. The march would perk up then and a party of runners would push forward in advance of the caravan for Santa Fe.

After all the wagons that were going south were safely across the river, the remainder of the wagons continued on up the Arkansas Valley. Everyone except the United States Government looked upon the Arkansas River as the border between Mexico and the United States and the Mexicans frowned upon too many American troops on their soil. President Jackson considered the Red River further to the south as the boundary.

As Indian signs were all around them, the American caravan decided to follow the river to the mountains to Bent's Fort and then turn south to Santa Fe. The route was much easier and innumerable buffalo were on either side of the wide, shallow stream and prairie dogs, rabbits, and wild horses appeared abundantly on the vast prairie.

Five miles march from Horse Creek brought the wagons to Bent's Old Fort, the most celebrated and for many years the only building between Westport and the Mexican settlements. The fur trade had always been big business in North America, and in the Old West was for a long time the biggest of all. In this trade only the Astor's rivaled the firm of Bent & St. Vrain, who were also interested in trade with Mexico. They had many posts: Fort St. Vrain, near Long's Peak in Colorado; Adobe Walls, on the Canadian River in the Panhandle of Texas; the Log Houses in the Big Timbers; and the several stockades above the mouth of Fountain Creek on the Arkansas. But the largest of all, and most permanent, was Bent's Old Fort, erected by William Bent, who made his home there and directed the trade with the Plains Indians. This fort was often called Fort William after him, and known to old-timers as Bent's Big Lodge on the Arkansas. It stood on a bench a little distance north of the river.

Coming up the valley, travelers were first aware of a large gray block on the treeless plains, with a flag flying above it. As the caravan crept nearer, the men found themselves facing an extensive gray wall, with loopholes piercing the top at intervals.

Bent's Fort had been built in 1833 by the Bent brothers and modeled after a medieval castle. The structure was a parallelogram one hundred fifty feet by one hundred feet, with adobe walls six or seven feet in thickness, and seventeen or eighteen feet in height. It was built of Santiago silt loam and San Joaquin black adobe, soils which are in the immediate vicinity and which were especially adapted to adobe construction.

The fort was built for trade, not war. It was the center of a large trading empire stretching from the Province of Texas into the middle of the Kansas Territory and one of the most important trading posts in the Far West. It was the headquarters of Bent, St. Vrain and Co., widely known by Indian traders, trappers, and Santa Fe traders.

Mountain men such as Kit Carson worked there, and Indians of all nations were free to come and go. Charles and William Bent enforced strict peace at the fort, and of them it was said, "They were mighty men, whose will was prairie law."

After three days of traveling, the train camped at Big Timber—a section of the river of about twenty-four miles in length on the island and banks of which more than the usual amount of cottonwood grew.

The next day the caravan arrived at the fort and met a hospitable reception. Three shots from the post's swivel gun sounded a noisy salute to the dragoons, emigrants, and traders. The proprietors, Charles Bent and Ceran St. Vrain, extended to everyone a hearty welcome at the sally port.

The main body of the caravan, camped a mile down the stream on a grassy meadow.

The commerce of the prairies gave to Bent's Fort a far-flung renown, which had been known to some of the traders for several years. Conestoga wagons from Missouri, six hundred miles away, brought hardware, calicoes, and dry goods, or continued on to Santa Fe. From the Mexican City of Taos, about 150 miles away, the post received sugar, flour, bread, and beans. Here furs and buffalo robes gathered by roving bands of Comanches and Cheyennes were collected and then laboriously transported to St. Louis. Prairie travelers appreciated the character of this trade as well as the hospitality of the post.

In the evening the dragoon officers and caravan leaders partook of an excellent dinner served in the hospitable quarters of Bent and St. Vrain.

Ceran St. Vrain had been born near St. Louis, Missouri, in 1798. He had come to New Mexico Province as early as 1826, when he participated in a trapping expedition to the Gila River. During the next few years, he engaged in the fur trade and in the Santa Fe trade. In 1830 he joined with Charles Bent to found the firm of Bent and St. Vrain, the predecessor of Bent, St. Vrain and Co. Though appointed United States Consul at Santa Fe, he never took over the duties of the office. Mr. St. Vrain was a gentleman in the true sense of the term. His French descent gave him an exquisite, indefinable degree of politeness, and, combined with the frankness of a straightforward mountain man, made him a likeable fellow traveler.

Charles Bent, well known throughout the West, was born in Charleston, Virginia, in 1799. He moved to St. Louis in 1806. As early as 1823, he traveled to the headwaters of the Mississippi River in the employ of the St. Louis, Missouri Fur Company. Making his first journey to New Mexico Province in 1829, he engaged in the Santa Fe trade, and shortly afterward, he settled in Taos.

*   *   *

The next morning, Ian was able to observe the organization and equipment of the wilderness post. Ranged about the enclosure, he saw the servants' quarters, the storehouses, the proprietor's lodgings, and the wagon house.

At the left end a hexagonal bastion towered up thirty feet high, showing portholes for cannons. At the right end, a second story rose equally high. Above the ironbound gate was a square blockhouse with windows through which a long brass telescope might be seen. Perched upon the gatehouse, a slatted, wooden belfry held two live eagles and a large brass bell. Near the gate, a few graves, protected by living cactus, sheltered the remains of members of the family who had died there.

The faces and figures offered great variety, for Bent's Fort was a large establishment, employing as many as a hundred men, traders, clerks, packers, teamsters, hunters, servants, and their families. In that gallery, one might see Americans, Indians, Mexicans, French, Germans, Negroes, and Kaneka. In summer, many of the men would be gone with Bent's caravan, heading for the States.

If Indians were about, the gates, covered with iron and studded with huge nails, would be closed with only a wicket being opened for purposes of trading and communication. But now these swing open, and the men from the east walk in through the deep, shady tunnel and find themselves within the "placita," or patio, of the fort. This hollow square was spacious and paved with gravel. In the middle stood the robe press, where folded hides were crushed flat and bound together for shipment. All around, the roofs on one-story rooms sloped inward, projecting to form a "portal," or primitive portico, supported at intervals by upright posts. At the back, a ladder was mounted to the roof, now crowded with men, women, and children. After the gloom of the entrance, men blinked against the glare from the whitewashed walls. From the rear came the clang of the blacksmith's hammer and the rasp of the carpenter's saw where wagons were being repaired and horses shod. A cock might be heard crowing, or the gabble of hens, with an occasional shriek of a peacock. If the traveler was fortunate, he might see the tame goat belonging to the establishment run up or down the ladder leading to the roof. Perhaps the bray of a jackass led the visitor to suspect a corral at the rear of the building.

Those who explored the fort found a large number of rooms with low-beamed ceilings and whitewashed walls of adobe, and felt their nostrils refreshed with the clean smell of earthen floors freshly sprinkled with water. These rooms on the ground floor were used for various purposes. There was a warehouse containing the goods needed for the Indian trade. Belts, buckles, finger rings, hawk's bells, tubular bone beads, steel brackets, hand axes, brass kettles, tin pans, awls, Green River knives, bags of Galena lead, powder-horns, beaver and bear traps, pins, thread, needles, combs, and looking glasses, all sorts of fofurraw ("fanfaron"), as the old-timers called such civilized trinkets.

Along with these were stored cases of imported edibles—bags of coffee, flour, sugar, raisins, boxes of water crackers, salt pork in barrels, spices of all sorts, and bottles of peppersaucer and "saleratus." On shelves would be stacked bales of domestic cotton, blue and scarlet strouding, flannel, calico, and three-point Northwest blankets, red as blood.

Then, too, there was hardware. There were frying pans, which the Indians desired in order to make arrow points, and axes, lanceheads, trade guns, horseshoes and ox shoes, spare parts for the wagons, and a number of kegs of Pass brandy, rum, and Taos Lightning. In the corner was a strong box, banded with heavy strips of iron, in which men suspected might be silver ingots, gold bullion, or bags of the curious slug coinage from the California mints. At certain seasons, bale of buffalo robes and packs of beaver were stacked high in a dark mound at one end, the swarthy wool matted with ticks and sand burrs. In the large parlor, with its polished central pillar, blankets and mattresses were stacked along the walls for seats, and a bucket of water with a gourd dipper stood on a bare deal table.

The fort contained twenty-two bedrooms, and in addition rooms used by the blacksmith, carpenter, barber, and clerk, two bastions in opposite corners where powder and ammunition were kept, and the walls hung with firearms and buffalo lances. There was a small store with a counter across the middle of the room so that visitors could not reach the shelves behind.

Best of all, to men hungry for civilized food, was the kitchen from whose window floated the welcome aroma of boiling coffee and bread baking. With the use of a little flattery, one might persuade Charlotte to part with a pie or some of her delicious biscuits, the only biscuits between Westport and California. Those who were fortunate enough to be invited to dinner enjoyed the unfamiliar luxury of putting their knives on a table covered with a white cloth and adorned with castors. There a man might remember how a fork was used, and eat from a tin plate like a gentleman.

William Bent and his brothers might wear frock coats and high beaver hats in St. Louis, but in this castle on the plains, they found it advantageous to dress like chiefs, in moccasins garnished with bright beads and porcupine quills, in fringed trousers of deerskin, and in handsome hunting shirts. William Bent, with eyes like augers and a jaw like a steel trap, was lavish in his hospitality. Being a thorough-going Yankee, he had an ice house on the river bank, and those whom he invited to climb the ladder and enter his private rooms on the second floor enjoyed mint juleps served by black Andrew over the bar there. Afterward, if time permitted, a game of billiards was in order on the only billiard table west of the Missouri. On the second floor also were the officers of the chief clerks and traders.

In the bastions were several small cannon. Beyond the fort proper, an extension of the walls equally large served as a corral for the stock. Here, the parapet was only eight feet high and three feet thick, topped with growing cactus to keep out horse thieves. A gate led from this corral into the main patio.

Nearly every man of importance in the region, at one time or another, was connected with the fort. Kit Carson was hunter; Lucien Maxwell was foreman; Old Bill Gary (William Guerrier) was trader. He had a habit of wearing a white blanket coat and fur cap like a typical voyageur. All trails in the southwest led to Bent's Fort. It was the house of refuge, the general store, the bank, and the home of hundreds. Indian women tripped around the battlements in glittering moccasins and long doeskin frocks. Traders and Indian chiefs sat in the shade of the portal, smoking the long red pipe, drawing the precious smoke—tobacco was four dollars a pound—into their lungs then blowing it out through their nostrils. Some sat eating jerked buffalo meat, bread made of coarse meal, and drinking black coffee. Sometimes, the notes of a flute might be heard or the tuneful scraping of the fiddle.

The Bents seemed never to have had much trouble with the Indians, though occasionally these staged a raid upon the caballada. This was hardly surprising, since in summer, the season for war parties, thousands of savages were within easy striking distance. For many years after the Bents established themselves on the Arkansas, the Kiowa and Comanche were at war with the Cheyenne. For this reason, the fort called Adobe Walls was built on the Canadian, so that the firm could trade with the southern tribes more readily.

*　　*　　*

Out of the foothills of the high mountains, which extended north all the way to Canada, four fine-looking, tall and well-formed Indians rode in.

They were the royalties of the plains, proud and uncorrupted by civilization. The small group rode through the crowded meadow straight to Father Gregg's tent-staff—a long pole with an old iron cross affixed to the top and a small flag of the holy name of Jesus fluttering below.

Sergeant Tom, watching the horsemen with Ian, asked a nearby Indian who they were and he replied in sign language. He extended his hands, with backs nearly up in front a little higher than, and slightly to the right, and left of his shoulders; then moved the hands simultaneously a little downwards, slightly outwards and a trifle to the right and left, indicating motion of wings.

"Crows!" said Tom, "from up north."

"They call themselves Absaraka, but the surrounding tribes and the whites call them Crows."

There were several explanations for the name. It was claimed by some of the Gros Ventres that soon after their separation from the Crows, they had a fight with their enemies, the Sioux, and some of the Crows being present sat on the hills nearby and would not come down. A warrior called out to them, and asked them why they sat up there like a lot of crows. Ever afterwards, they were called Crows.

Their dress was similar to that which all the mountain tribes wear. The men had on very long tunics of the skin of the antelope or bighorn; leggings of buckskin or doeskin; shoes of the same material, and a mantle of buffalo skin.

They had their hair cut squarely off round the forehead, leaving the bangs from four to six inches in length, which stood upright by a dressing of clay and a sticky substance made by boiling gummy weeds and brushes. Several of them had their side hair braided and the hair on the back of the head separated into several strips, which was held in place by glue placed at regular intervals. To give them the appearance of having very long hair, hair from their ponies' tails and manes was glued on to lengthen it out. On two of the savages, their hair trailed on the ground after they dismounted their horses. But Ian noticed they did not pull out their eyebrows or lashes as many Indians did.

All of them had at least one eagle feather in their long hair, the emblem of a warrior and which shows that the person has already distinguished himself in battle.

They had taken great pains in decorating their mounts. The animals' heads, chests, and flanks were covered with hangings of scarlet cloth, embroidered with ornaments of shell and bone and adorned with long fringes, to which they attached little bells.

Many considered the Crows as one of the noblest on the plains and mountains. They have a piercing eye, a nose like an eagle, and teeth of ivory whiteness. They were of a very high intellect, but their superstitious ideas and ceremonies dominated their movements and actions.

Unknown to Ian, Father Gregg had sent several notes into their country to announce his intention of visiting them.

Each was the bearer of a small charge of tobacco. The sending of tobacco is the same thing as a formal invitation, or the announcement of a desire to meet to confer upon important affairs. If the tobacco is accepted, it is a sure sign that you will be admitted among them; if on the contrary it is refused, you may understand that all communication is forbidden, and govern yourself accordingly.

All came and shook hands with the priest with special eagerness. After they had smoked the pipe of peace together—a first proof of their good will—they announced, in the name of the head chiefs of their camp, that the "Blackrobe's" tobacco had been favorably received. Entry into their camp was open to the Blackrobe and the wearer of the medallion. No other white man would get out of it with his scalp. They also said that the chiefs and warriors were awaiting them with impatience.

Upon being notified of this news, Father Gregg invited Ian to join in the circle and the offer was retold. Ian was puzzled by the offer, but remembering their superstitious ideas thought this would be a good chance to get some information on their imagined Hasanun —their supposedly great prophet, who spoke for their god.

The Indians left as quickly as they had appeared.

When Captain Bellnap learned of their intended journey, he was very much against it. He knew of the letter Ian carried but to risk Father Gregg's life amongst the warring northern tribes was another matter.

Ian was beginning to realize that Father Gregg was full of surprises and as the captain would not let up on his decision, the Jesuit priest produced a newly written letter.

Captain Bellnap read it slowly, then handed it to Ian.

Under the letterhead of Headquarters, Military Division of Mississippi, was written:

> All officers of the Army within this Military Division are required, and
> all citizens are requested to extend to the bearer of this letter, the
> Reverend Father, a Catholic priest, who has heretofore traveled much

among the Indians and is now enroute for missions under his control, all the assistance and protection they can to enable him to fulfill his benevolent and humane purposes.

Signed,

W. T. Sherman, Major General

An "agent extraordinary" of the government carried with it the military rank of major, strangely mated with that of a Jesuit priest.

Preparations for the journey did not take long and, before daylight the following day, the little band consisting of Father Gregg, his Indian woman servant Kalespel, Ian, and three packhorses started north.

They followed the foothills that separated the plains and the high mountains. The singing and warbling of numerous birds enlivened the silent march. At noon they dined on the banks of a little creek on a pigeon, snipe, and duck that Ian had shot during the morning's march.

The afternoon route was across the plains covered with a short but very nutritious grass called buffalo grass, which someday would support and fatten numerous domestic cattle herds. Beds of beautiful variegated flowers were seen especially in spots where the soil was light and sandy.

Everywhere, the pomme blanche was in abundance. It was a kind of wild potato, which an Indian, when pressed by hunger, would dismount from his horse and armed with a little pointed stick of hardwood, which he always carried when traveling, could pull out roots enough in ten minutes to satisfy him for the moment. This potato was starchy and could be eaten raw, boiled, or cooked with meat, and was a great remedy for scurvy, a sickness by which the Indians were hardly ever attacked.

For the evening meal Kalespel cooked some of the wild potatoes. Combined with the leftover meat from the noon meal, the stew was very tasty and filling.

After supper Father Gregg lit his pipe and warmed himself by the small campfire. After Ian had tethered the horses for the night, he joined him for a few quiet words.

Ian noticed that Father Gregg hadn't touched any whiskey since he had started out and in unpacking the animals had noticed he had not brought any with him. He also seemed in good spirits, and the march seemed to bother him less. He looked and acted half his age. Ian questioned their safety from the savages in this wilderness.

"We are quite safe," replied the priest. "Conscious of my own nothingness, I place myself confidently in the hands of the holy providence of the Lord and under the protection of our illustrious and good Mother, the Immaculate Virgin Mary. I pray that I may render myself worthy of their guidance and concern."

"I know," the priest continued, "that in time of war the most terrible and atrocious cruelties are practiced by the Indians. All their passions are let loose and they abandon themselves wholly to the spirit of vengeance against the whites for all the wrongs and injustices their race has suffered. It is always true that if the savage sin against the whites, it is because the whites have greatly sinned against them."

"I wish to be able to renew and continue my missions and travels among the Indian tribes of the Great Plains. They have need of being visited and receiving good advice. For the last two years, they have been making merciless war upon the whites, pushed to the limit of endurance by injustices and provocations. Hundreds of soldiers are on the point of leaving St. Louis to subjugate the warlike tribes and annihilate them if they can."

"Before this annihilation campaign starts, the Commissioner of the Indian Department in Washington has requested me to undertake this journey and to bring about, if possible, a peace among the hostiles."

Ian thought that it was a good idea to try to avoid sending 3,000 to 4,000 soldiers into the Great Plains. Little did he realize that the men in the Grand Conspiracy thought exactly the same thing!

Father Gregg continued, "Separation from the Indian gives me great heartache; but I hope to be able to work yet a little for the glory of God and the salvation of souls. This is the supernatural magnet that draws me so far away from my dear Belgium. I always miss something when I am not among my good Indians and their kindly welcome that I meet everywhere. I am conscious of a certain void wherever I go, until I come again to my dear plains. Then calm comes back to me, then only am I happy. You will someday understand. After having passed a good share of my life among the Indians, it is among them that I desire to finish the few years that are left me still. It is among them also, if it were the will of God that I desire to die. Ah! This would be my last and greatest happiness on earth."

*　　　*　　　*

In the morning they rose early. The fire was quickly lit again and water was heated. The coffee was drunk as they ate a slice of meat and biscuit. All of this took about three-quarters of an hour and by five o'clock they were on their journey again.

In the afternoon a forest fire was raging during their passage and had spread over a dozen miles of the mountain side and even to their highest parts. The smoke was very thick, and thousands of tree trunks, fallen one upon another in confusion, obstructed the path.

Camp was made early and Ian caught a string of fine spotted mountain trout for supper.

The next day the mountains were enveloped in a bluish fog and smoke from the forest fire they had passed. They traveled twenty-seven miles by pushing all day and following the prairie instead of the mountains. Game was scarcer here, but Ian killed a goose for supper.

A severe storm came up and they all spent a very disagreeable night, without shelter, and with but one blanket each.

The march was repetitious day after day, hills and valleys, prairies and buttes, and hot, dry weather. There seemed to be a drought in the region, and the further north they went, the dryer it became. The entire region was in its primitive condition, in possession of the Indians and it was the grazing ground for the numerous herds of wild animals that ranged it.

"We are nearing their lodges, Lieutenant," Father Gregg informed him on the afternoon of the sixth day.

As he looked over the immense prairies he continued, "One day soon the whites will take possession of this land of the Indians, then push them farther back into the wilderness or exterminate them."

"The grievances of the Indians against the whites are very numerous and the vengeance which they provoke are often most cruel and frightful. Nevertheless, one is compelled to admit that they are less guilty than the whites. Nine times out of ten, the provocations come from the whites, that is to say, from the scum of civilization, who bring to them the lowest and grossest vices, and none of the virtues of civilized men."

"They are for the most part victims of the misdeeds of the whites. When the warriors raise the hatchet or go on the warpath, it is because they are pushed to the limit of endurance and then the blows that they deal are hard, cruel, and terrible. It is their nature."

"I have seen enough Indians to convince me of this fact. They can never exist in contact with the whites and their only salvation is to be removed far from their presence. But they have been removed so often that there seems now no place left for their further migration. The waves of civilization have invaded their homes from both oceans, driving them year after year toward the Rocky Mountains. Now that we propose to invade this mountain solitude, to wrest from them their hidden wealth, where under heaven can the Indians go?"

"We can expect these people to make one desperate struggle in the fastness of the mountains for the maintenance of their last homes and the preservation of their lives."

At mid-morning the following day, a strong force of horsemen, composed of 200 to 300 warriors, rode toward them. Father Gregg raised his standard of peace and, as they surrounded them, they received the priest with unmistakable tokens of friendship and respect.

Four head chiefs acted as an escort, as a guard of honor and to prevent any treacherous attack by secret traitors who might be determined to take vengeance on the pale faces. By the penal code in force among the savages, every Indian who lost a member of his family at the hands of the whites is obliged to avenge himself on the first white man he meets —and there were a good many of them in this position.

They appeared rejoiced at Ian and Father Gregg's arrival, and manifested their joy by galloping around them several times. The two whites were then escorted to the Crow village.

The village was situated on a high prairie ridge, about two miles from a river, and overlooked the surrounding country for many miles. In front lay a green level valley with a broad stream running through the middle and the valley terminated on the opposite side by hills covered with groves of timber. In the rear nothing could be seen but an extension of the vast prairie until its smooth undulating surface became almost blended with the distant horizon. To the right and left the river could be seen for many miles wending its course though the valley, its broad shining surface here and there darkened by island groves of timber, the whole element combined forming the most beautiful landscape Ian had ever seen.

An old chief conducted them to his lodge, seated them around the fire, confirming strictly with the rules of etiquette, by giving Father Gregg the highest seat. He then set before them a large bowl of boiled deer meat, which they found to be very good.

The venerable old man, of remarkable stature but bowed beneath the weight of age, supported himself on a staff tipped with a bayonet. He wore upon his breast a copper cross, old and worn.

Father Gregg questioned him, eagerly to know from whom he had received the cross. After a moment's thought, and counting on his fingers, he answered, "It was you, Blackrobe, who gave me this cross. I have never laid it aside for twenty-six snows. The cross has raised me to the clouds among my people (meaning that it had made him great and respectable). I still walk on earth; it is the cross that I owe it."

"When I was younger, I loved whiskey to madness, and at every chance I would get drunk and commit excesses. It is now twenty-six snows since my last turbulent indulgence. I was stupid and sick from it. Then I had the good fortune to meet you and you made known to me that my behavior was against the will of the Master of Life and offended Him grievously. Since then I have often had opportunities; my friends have sometimes sought to induce me to join them in their illicit enjoyments, and often my old evil inclination would combat my good will, which desired to resist the temptation. Every time the cross has come to my help. I would take it between my hands, imploring the Great Spirit to give me strength, and your words, Blackrobe, would come to my mind. I have renounced drink, and have never tasted a drop since."

Armed with the grace of God, the good old man's strength of soul and his good will to resist temptation were really admirable. This simple-minded Indian, living among his pagan brothers, in the most hostile camp on the prairie, had little trouble in comprehending the loftiest things. He received the light of intelligence from on high and drew strength from the humble little cross.

Runners had been dispatched to the other villages to inform them of the arrival of Blackrobe so that the mothers could bring their children here to be baptized.

The council opened with songs and dances, noisy, joyful, and very wild, in which the warriors alone took part. Soaring Eagle, the principal chief, lighted his calumet of peace; he presented it first solemnly to the Great Spirit, offered it to the four cardinal points and to the sun and the earth, as witnesses to the action of the council.

Then he passed the pipe from mouth to mouth. Ian was the first to receive it after Father Gregg, and every chief was placed accordingly to the rank that he held in the tribe. Each one took a few puffs.

From an early hour, men and women had been busy preparing the spot where the council was to be held. The spot covered nearly a half-acre of ground. The whole place was surrounded by a series of tepees or Indian lodges, composed of twenty to twenty-four buffalo skins each, which were suspended on long pine poles. The banner of the Holy Virgin occupied the center and on one side a seat was prepared of fine buffalo robes.

When the ceremony of the pipe was finished, the head chief said, "Speak, Blackrobe, my ears are open to your words."

All this was done with the greatest gravity and amid a profound silence.

Rising to his feet and raising his hands to heaven, he made a prayer to the Great Spirit, imploring light and blessing from him and his help in this great meeting.

Father Gregg told the gathering that "they must put their faith in Christ and to embrace the crucifix with confidence. The Son of God descended from heaven and came upon earth to redeem us and deliver us from hell at the price of his own precious blood."

Soaring Eagle, six feet six inches in height addressed Father Gregg in reply, in fitting and well-chosen words, accompanied by a really remarkable oratorical bearing and gestures. The facility in speaking seems to be natural to the Indians of the plains.

Pipe in hand, and addressing his people, he said, "Lend an ear to my words."

Then he raised the pipe solemnly to heaven and lowered it to earth, thus invoking, by the Indian interpretation, heaven and earth as his witnesses.

Then he said in a loud voice, "The Blackrobe has made a long journey to come to us. His presence among us makes me very glad, and with all my heart I wish him welcome to our country."

"I can understand all the words that the Blackrobe has just said to us; they are good and filled with truth. I shall lay them up in my memory. Still, our hearts are sore; they have received deep wounds. These wounds have yet to be healed. A cruel war has desolated and impoverished our country. We did not kindle the torch of war. It was the Sioux east of us and the Cheyenne south of us who raised the war first, to revenge themselves for the white man's cruelties and injustice. We have been forced to take part, for we too have been victims of their wrongdoing. Today, when we ride over our plains, we find them spotted with blood; these are not the blood stains of buffalo and deer killed in the chase, but those of our own comrades or of white men, sacrificed to vengeance. The buffalo, the elk, the antelope, the bighorn, and the deer have quitted our immense plains. Against our will, the whites are interlacing our country with the ways of transportation and emigration; they build forts at various points and mount thunders upon them. They kill our animals—more than they need. They are cruel to our people. They massacre them without reason or for the slightest cause even when they are searching for food, for animals, and roots to nourish their wives and children. This soil is ours, and we are determined not to yield an inch of it. Here our fathers were born and are buried. We desire, like them, to live here and to be buried in this same soil. We have been forced to hate the whites; let them treat us like brothers and the war will cease. Let them stay at home; we will never go to trouble them."

Soaring Eagle then took his seat.

Yellow Hawk, Iron Heart, and Red Tail Wolf followed him. They all touched on the same matters as Soaring Eagle.

They all complained bitterly of the bad faith of the whites, of the commissioners and agents of the government always so prodigal of promises and always so slow in fulfilling them, if they ever do so. This conduct sticks in their minds; they propose to wait a while longer and see. In their speeches and in private conversation, they declared themselves favorable to peace with the whites and ready to call on their young warriors to bury the hatchet and withdraw from the fighting bands.

The council lasted nearly two hours and, at the moment of breaking up, the chief begged Father Gregg most earnestly to leave his great banner of peace with them as a souvenir of the great day of the council. Near the end of the council, they related that the Great Hasanun had visited the village two moons ago and had told them that the two white men were their friends and that they would help restore them to their original happy condition. These words were believed by the superstitious Crow people to be the direct voice from the other world.

Soaring Eagle had asked the messiah, "You who have such power, can you not also make a little rain come?"

The Crows were experiencing a drought. For weeks there had been no rain. The earth was parched and burnt and the heat had been intense—day after day the same cloudless sky. That evening as the sun, like a great ball of fire, was sinking in the west, the Hasanun told them that it would rain the next day. There was not a cloud to be seen, not a sign which indicated anything of the sort. They had been having the Medicine Dance for three days and that afternoon the Hasanun had assured them that their prayers had been heard and that it would rain the next day. And it did.

The sky clouded up for the first time in a long while and a gentle and abundant rain fell at intervals for about twenty-four hours. Several weeks later a second rain was granted, which did much good. These favors from on high made a deep impression on these nature-minded people.

Ian tried to find out more about the Hasunan, but they spoke no more of the messiah. However, they had confirmed one thing . . . there was a prophet.

Father Gregg gladly agreed to their wish. He presented the banner to them in sign of gratitude for the confidence with which they had inspired him in all their behavior toward him and the speeches that they had just uttered. He hoped that the banner, bearing the sweet name of Jesus and the lovely image of the Virgin, might be a gauge of future happiness and welfare to all the tribe.

There was a singing that roused the echoes of the hills and a dance that made the ground tremble. This was the end of the council. It closed tranquilly, in good order and harmony. Every man then went his way and Father Gregg and Ian were escorted to a large lodge and the principle Indians followed them.

A large number of children appeared, led by their mothers, who had also their babies in their arms. They crowded around him with a rare trustfulness, very unusual among Indian children, to offer him their little hands. The mothers were not satisfied until he had laid his hands upon the heads of all the babies and little ones around him, then they withdrew contented and happy.

A standard bearer was chosen from among the most distinguished warrior, named Gall. He was a very remarkable man, by reason of his sufferings and a wonderful escape from the bayonets of the American soldiers. He told the story of his troubles.

He had been arrested on a charge of stealing horses. It was in the dead of winter, and the ground was covered with snow. On the road to the prison at the fort, the soldiers feared that he intended to escape and they ran him through the body twice with bayonets. He fell, bathed in blood, but being still conscious, he counterfeited death. They trampled him and kicked him, covering him with bruises. To finish their cowardly and cruel work upon their prisoner, they thrust a third bayonet through his neck, and at last threw him into a deep ravine. Here he lay unconscious for quite a while, entirely naked, on a drifted snow. When he came to himself, it was already far into the night. He got up and walked about twenty miles. When he reached the timber, on the bank of the Missouri, he found a fire, at which he warmed his limbs, stiffened by the cold. The hope of life returned to him and he implored the Great Spirit to "take pity on him and preserve him." He then quenched his burning and feverish thirst and washed off from his body the clotted blood that covered it. In the hope of meeting someone, he continued to drag himself on, and after traveling some miles farther, he discovered an Indian lodge. It was that of old Peter Padanegricka, who treated him like a virtual Samaritan. When it was daylight, his host conveyed him on a stretcher to the main camp where he was received with all the honors of a great warrior. Upon hearing his tale of the soldiers' cruelty and seeing his wounds, the rage of the warriors knew no bounds, and a great number of unhappy whites fell victims to it. In less than a year, Gall himself set out on his war of vengeance, and returned to camp amid acclamations with seven white scalps on the end of his lance.

In the evening, while some busied themselves about the arrangement of their beds, composed of the small branches of willows and cottonwoods, others hastened to kindle fires, fill the kettles and arrange rows of roasts on sharpened sticks to satisfy their hunger.

The next day Father Gregg baptized seventy-four babies. He also baptized a great number of adults. They seemed to desire it ardently; but these desires were not yet sufficiently imbued with the true principles of religion. When the savages have received baptism, they believe they can conquer any enemy whatsoever. This explains why some wretches, who seek only to kill their neighbors, were the first to petition for baptism.

There was an earthquake in the land of the Blackfeet and directly a report was spread abroad that a blackrobe was the cause of the earth's trembling, and that this shock was an indication that the smallpox was about to return to the country. It was believed that this happened because the Indians did not give sufficient attention to the discourse of the blackrobe.

There did appear to be instances of sudden death of a dozen persons, stricken down either in their lodges or in war, but at the moment that they were straying most widely from the right path. One of these had robbed a blackrobe of three mules. When the others found out the deed, they took the mules from him and gave them back to the blackrobe, but he died on the day after.

There was at present a malady raging among the northern tribes said to be deadly and which indeed had proved fatal to a few persons. As this disease began in the ear, they thought the punishment arrived to them because their hardness of heart had prevented them from listening to the words of the blackrobe.

Thus, in one way or another, the Almighty Spirit was preparing the way for the conversion of these idolaters.

*   *   *

Ian and Father Gregg rose early the next morning, saddled up, loaded the packhorses and were on their way before the sun appeared over the horizon.

Ian's stallion was anxious for the journey, but Father Gregg and Kalespel's mules plodded their usual slow pace. Before sundown, they had journeyed over seventeen miles, as the plains were easy to cross. By late afternoon they had approached the foothills of the Rocky Mountains and Ian found a stream with a good supply of fish. Soon he found a cave-like washout in the hillside that afforded good protection from the drizzle that had started to fall.

Ian caught several nice size trout while Kalespel started a fire to cook them and Father Gregg read his Bible.

By the time supper was over, darkness had fallen. Ian was thankful for the comfortable cave out of the heavy rain that had set in.

Father Gregg wrote in his diary for a while, and then Kalespel rubbed some buffalo grease into his welts.

The fire had burned down and as Father Gregg seemed to be tired, Ian put several logs on the fire before bedding down.

Kalespel was already asleep and soon Father Gregg was sound asleep also. Ian stretched his arms and back to rid himself of the kinks in his body and sat down at the opening of the cave just inside of the drizzling rain and thought about many things that was bothering him. Of life . . . and the old man. . . .

They set out early the next morning and rode hard. After many days they arrived back at Bent's Fort. The fort was full of men of various races and complexions—all more or less drunk at the time. A company of Santa Fe traders had too many supplies for their trading. Therefore, a part had to be thrown away or sold at a great loss to the other traders, but they had determined to get rid of their very copious stock of Missouri whiskey by drinking it on the spot.

The party that evening was wild and loud. The fiddlers mounted a table, and the old hearty square dances filled the crowded room with dust up to the ceiling. Chipita, the enormously fat housekeeper, flopped about with colossal good humor. The Indian squaws pranced, giggling, without a trace of Indian stoicism, and Charlotte mimicked the fine ladies whom she had seen pass on their way to California. Women were so few that every one received the most flattering attentions.

Father Gregg had a high fever from the long and weary journey and his wounds continued to bleed, so much so that every morning his nightshirt was glued to his skin from the blood. He decided to return to Fort Leavenworth by a wagon train returning from Santa Fe.

Ian's troop was in Santa Fe and he had to join them. Two enterprising Santa Fe traders, by the names of Albert Speyer and Eugene Leitensdorfer were on their way to Santa Fe, so Ian joined them. Both were natives of Prussia and had migrated to the United States.

Speyer who seemed to run the outfit was a small, spare man with a wiry figure and thin, sharp visage, with sallow complexion and dark moustache. He had keen, clean set eyes and a nose so aquiline that he might pass for a woman. The firm compression of his thin lips, indicated strong determination of purpose. He was a man a great energy of character where nothing daunted his courageous spirit.

The two had purchased merchandise that had cost about $15,000 and it took six huge wagons to transport these goods.

Among the other things, the Prussian Jews were transporting two wagonloads of arms and ammunition to the governor of Chihuahua.

Leitensdorfer had been in the country several years and knew the officials well and understood the language thoroughly. The governor of Chihuahua selected him to represent his interest. Even though the American government considered the guns contraband, they had to put up with the business or else the Mexican authorities would strictly enforce the tariff laws. If the governor had enforced the stiff Mexican tariff laws, collecting the legal duties and prohibiting the introduction of contraband, the Santa Fe trade would have declined rapidly.

As Ian was a greenhorn on the trail, he asked the privilege of joining them, and after they had satisfied themselves that he would not question their dealings, he was permitted to do so, as another gun may be useful.

From the fort they traveled up the north side of the river about fifteen miles and crossed, thence without trail or track, taking the mountains as a guiding point to the Huerfano River, aiming to strike it below the canyon. In this, they were successful.

They crossed the river and on their way up overtook a party of Mexicans on their return from a trading expedition with the Indians.

Leitensdorfer began complaining of illness, and they decided to travel with the Mexicans for a time.

The next day, Leitensdorfer was so ill they were compelled to stop a day for rest. They camped in a beautiful grove of cottonwoods at the foot of the mountains. Being without a doctor or medicine, the prospect of a rapid journey was rather discouraging. They cut two poles and prepared a litter by tying a rope to the small ends and hanging it across the saddle and letting the other ends of the poles drag. They weaved lariats across behind the mule and spread blankets over for a bed, this forming a very easy and comfortable litter. Where the path was too narrow to permit its passage, the litter was doubled up and dragged with the sick man riding the mule.

The scenery of Huerfano Pass was beyond imagination. It was beautifully grand. This pass had been used by travelers and traders every since Spanish days.

Leitensdorfer's continued illness compelled the train to travel by short journeys across the mountains and down the valley on the west side of the mountains to Rio Colorado, the first settlement since Bent's Fort.

One day they camped on the Rio Culebra, a small stream running from the mountains into the Rio Grande, and in the early afternoon, three men approached the camp at a brisk gallop, each leading a horse. They dismounted, unsaddled, and in a few minutes had a fire kindled, and the coffeepot over the fire. They were old mountain men and acquaintances of several in the party. Kit Carson was one that Ian was acquainted with, having first met him several nights out of Fort Leavenworth on the train Ian was escorting to Santa Fe.

As soon as they got dinner cooking—coffee boiling, a prairie dog dressed and opened out on a stick before the fire—Carson came over to Ian's camp and talked for a few minutes. Carson had become dissatisfied with the train's slow rate of travel and left it to travel on to Santa Fe. He had met his two friends there and they were on their way to the mountains. They soon ate their dinner, saddled their horses, caught their led horse and were off. Kit galloping up to the trail rope, or lariat, of his led horse and stooping in his saddle, picked up the rope and was off without breaking a gallop, giving Ian a word of caution.

"Look out for your hair, boys! The Ute are plenty about here."

The train took about a day and a half getting to Rio Colorado, which was first settled in 1816. There, Ian took his first meal in a Mexican house, which consisted of baked pumpkin, wheat gordos, tortillas and atole.

The gordos were prepared by grinding the wheat on the metate—a hollowed oblong stone used as a grinding machine. The meal was then wetted with water sufficient to pat it into cakes about the size but rather thicker than our buckwheat cakes and then baked on a flat stone without the addition of soda or yeast and frequently without salt.

The atole was a thick gruel made of corn flour, somewhat similar to mush. Atole in the north is frequently called "el café de los Mexicano" (the coffee of the Mexicans).

The house had the usual accommodations of Mexican houses, using the floor for a table, and a jerga—a kind of coarse woolen cloth with a shaggy nap on one side—for a tablecloth. The tortillas were brought in on a napkin and the atole in earthen dishes made by the Indians. No spoons, forks, or knives, except the travelers' own knives, were used so they used fingers for forks and the tortillas for spoons.

Leitensdorfer, whose stomach was still uneasy, asked if he could get a chicken and make him some soup.

"Yes, sir," they replied, "but we have no money to buy it."

He gave the hostess some money, and she went out with her tinaja (water jar) and soon returned with a tinaja of water on her head, an old hen in one hand, and some onions in the other. Only these ingredients were used to make the soup with the addition of some salt; they all ate of it and, at the time, called it good.

They remained there the remainder of the day and night. Their beds were wool mattresses, with pillows of the same; there were no sheets but the common Mexican blanket.

The next morning they started for Turley's Mill and Distillery about six miles across a spur of mountains. They were met with a warm and cordial reception, and were entertained with the hospitality universal among the American residents in New Mexico on the arrival of the gringos (strangers), especially countrymen, at their houses. Their food was the usual dishes of chile colorado, beans, atole and tortillas Americanized by the addition of bacon, ham, coffee, and bread. Mr. Turley had a pen of some fifteen or twenty hogs, which he fed from the mill and distillery, and raised enough pork for his own family. There was no market for hog products outside of his own wants.

The chile colorado was a compound of red peppers and dried buffalo meat stewed together, flaming like a crater of Vesuvius. Sometimes it was called chile con carne.

The tortillas were thin cakes made of corn—a type of cornbread. The corn is boiled in water with a little lime. When it has been sufficiently softened so as to strip it of its skin, it is ground into paste upon the metate, and formed into a thin cake. This is afterwards spread on a small sheet of iron or copper, called comal (comalli, by the Indians), and placed over the fire, where in less than three minutes, it is baked and ready for use. The thinness of the tortilla is always a great test of skill of the maker and much rivalry ensues in the art of preparation.

The frijoles were a species of dark beans of large size, stewed or fried in mutton fat and not too highly seasoned. Frijoles wind up the substantial part of a dinner, breakfast, and supper. Seldom is this favorite and national dish omitted. A failure of the bean crop in Mexico would be looked upon as a national calamity. The frijoles sometimes are boiled a long time, and then fried in grease and flavored with onions and garlic.

The meal was topped off by a bottle of Taos whiskey.

The small party of traders and teamsters remained there for a couple of days, and although Leitensdorfer was still very weak, they proceeded to Taos and stopped at a friend of Speyer's house. He was a Canadian Frenchman who had settled in the country many years before, married a Mexican woman, and had a family of daughters.

San Fernandes de Taos was an adobe town situated in a beautiful valley. It was the official port of entry for New Mexico, though the customhouse was located at Santa Fe. Formerly, many of its residents had been engaged in the fur trade of the far southwest, but now that business was declining in importance.

After a two-day's stay in Taos, Speyer secured the services of a guide and started across the mountains without road or trail in the direction of the crossing of the Red River. The first night was spent in the mountains, not daring to make a fire for fear of attracting the attention of some Indians.

After passing the night among the spruce and aspen in chilly dreariness, they left camp at daylight and descended the mountain into a valley, where they surprised a prairie dog village. Ian succeeded in killing one, which was cooked at the noon rest and they dined on prairie dog and coffee without salt or sugar. In the afternoon they got to the foot of the mountain and camped but a short distance from the road leading to the Raton Mountain and Bent's Fort.

They slept without supper and started at daylight. They thought they were on the plains, but shortly, to their great surprise, they came to a bluff, which at first appeared impossible to descend. The mesa must have been at least three hundred feet higher than the plain below, and they descended at an angle of nearly forty-five degrees over a debris of trap rock formed by ages of decay and crumbling with no vegetation, path, or track. Every moment it seemed as if they might stumble and fall and go rolling and tumbling over the rocks to the bottom. In some places where there would be a perpendicular descent of four or five feet from one rock to another, they would jump down, give the mules their time and plenty of rope. After the mules' thoughtful and intelligent survey of the distance and landing place, they would make the jump and land upon all fours, their feet sometimes so close together that it seemed as though within a space not larger than a half bushel measure. After a long and patient effort, they landed on the plain below without accident to man or mule.

After a short rest they proceeded on their journey. It was not long before they discovered a band of antelope. The guide said he would kill one for dinner and brought one down at the first shot.

They skinned the animal and took the liver and meat, cutting it up so they could each take a portion on their horse tied to the saddleskirt. Soon after, they struck the wagon road in the valley about midway between the Red River and the Point of Rocks. This road was known as the Cimarron route. The "Rocks" was a prominent landmark, being a mass of large blocks of sienite, towering to the height of several hundred feet. A clear mountain spring flowed out of the rock.

Coming to a pool of water, they camped for a meal and had a feast of antelope meat, liver, and coffee. Traveling three or four miles further, they camped for the night with good water, plenty of grass, and a secluded camp. They rested well and arose early the next morning, refreshed and happy.

At early dawn they started. They expected to meet the soldiers at the Rio Colorado (Red River) as it had been the custom to send out a guard to the point to keep watch and see that no goods were sent off to other points. But they did not meet any soldiers until near Wagon Mound, and this but a small escort.

At Rio Moro, they passed a dugout, or cellar, dug in the ground and poles laid across, covered with grass and earth—only one room, which was occupied by an Englishman. He had a wife or housekeeper and four children.

Next morning, they started early and crossed Sapello Creek and thence over the mesa to Las Vegas, where they camped in the meadow in the valley of the Gallinas River at the foot of the mesa and a mile or so from the town. The camp was visited as usual by a numerous delegation of men, women, and children who came from curiosity to meet acquaintances, and to sell such

PLACES AND DISTANCES ON THE SANTA FE TRAIL
The encampment through Kansas, printed in italic.

FROM INDEPENDENCE TO	Miles.	Total.	FROM INDEPENDENCE TO	Miles.	Total.
Round Grove....	35	....	*Cimarron River (Lower Spring)*	8	445
Narrows	30	65	*Middle Spring (up Cimarron R.)*	36	481
110-Mile Creek....	30	95	*Willow Bar....*	26	507
Bridge Creek....	8	103	Upper Spring....	18	525
Big John Springs....	40	143	Cold Spring (leav'g Cimar. Riv.)	5	530
Council Grove	2	145	McNee's Creek	25	555
Diamond Spring..	15	160	Rabbit Ear Creek....	20	575
Lost Spring....	15	175	Round Mound....	8	583
Cotton Wood Creek	12	187	Rock Creek....	8	591
Turkey Creek....	25	212	Point of Rocks....	19	610
Little Arkansas	17	229	Rio Colorado....	20	630
Cow Creek...	20	249	Ocaté	6	636
Arkansas River....	16	265	Santa Clara Springs....	21	657
Walnut Creek (up Arkansas Riv.)	8	273	Rio Mora....	22	679
Ash Creek...	19	292	Rio Gallinas (vegas)....	20	699
Pawnee Fork....	6	298	Ojo de Bernal (spring)....	17	716
Coon Creek....	33	331	San Miguel....	6	722
Caches	36	367	Pecos Village	23	755
Ford of Arkansas	20	387	Santa Fé....	25	780
Sand Creek (leaving Arkansas R.)	50	437			

Places and distances on the Santa Fe Trail

•Round Grove, also called "Lone Elm" and "The Glenn," was on the headwaters of Cedar Creek, between Olathe and Gardner, Johnson County, Kansas.

articles in the way of provisions as they had to dispose of. The men were very anxious to indulge in the luxuries of raised bread, eggs, onions, and such which afforded them a lively market.

The next day the train passed through Las Vegas, at that time but a small town of not more than three or four hundred inhabitants, and no Americans. There was a large open space in the center of the town. The streets ran north and south, east and west. The houses were built of adobe. Through the midst of the town, there was a large canal for the purpose of supplying the town with water and of irrigating the fields.

The road through the mountains was the worst imaginable, to be called a road was questionable as no labor had been expended to keep it in repairs except such as was done by the traders to make it possible to get along. Tecolote Hill was a place always looked forward to with dread and apprehension. It was a very hard day's work to get up with a train of twenty or twenty-five wagons.

The next day they passed the old Pecos ruins of a Pueblo Indian village, which had become so reduced in numbers that they were unable to keep their irrigating ditches in repair. Having insufficient and necessary community labor and unable to support themselves in comfort, they had abandoned the home of their fathers and joined the Pueblo Jemez. The time of this abandonment must have been many years ago as the church was nearly in ruins—the walls and tower with a very small portion of the roof only remaining. The migration was made with great formality, the sacred fire not being allowed to be extinguished, but was kept burning and borne upon the shoulders of the old men who formerly had charge of it and who had directed the ceremonious worship of the Indians in the council chamber. The Pueblo Indians are good Catholics, each having a church and paying the parish priest his tithes and firstlings and the legal fees for marrying, baptizing, and burying. Yet, in each pueblo, the ancient mode of worship was maintained in the estufa (council chamber) in all its form as handed down by tradition. Seldom or ever was a Mexican permitted to enter the estufa even to gratify curiosity, much less to be present during the performances of any religious ceremonies.

A few miles further along, they entered a big canyon, where the road winds and turns, crossing steep pitches and ravines, over rocks, and around boulders, making short and difficult turns, with double teams to make an ascent. At other places the turns are so short that only two or three yoke of oxen can be allowed to pull the load from danger of turning over into the ravine. One of these difficult passes they called the "S," which required all the skill of the best drivers to get around. Often wagons would be turned over in spite of all the precautions they could use. Six or eight miles a day was considered good traveling.

From the big canyon, they crossed a spur of the mountain, not very high but steep and rough; so it was necessary to "double" to get up. Thence through heavy pine timber and by a very rough and winding road to Arroyo Hondo, six miles from Santa Fe, they camped for the night and made preparations to enter the long-sought end of their journey.

Ian had kept a journal on places and distances of the trail. The entire length of the traveled route was approximately 780 miles.

Travels Through Mexico

*T*he men had washed their faces and hands, and those that possessed the luxury would don a clean shirt. Those having no spare clothes would content themselves with fixing up shirts and trousers by substituting splinters for buttons and tying a handkerchief around their necks in such a way that it would cover the holes in their shirts as much as possible. But the most important preparation for the drivers was to put on new and broad crackers, so as to be able to announce their arrival by the cracking of their whips, which would nearly equal the reports made by the firing of so many pistols.

The next morning they started at early dawn and arrived on the loma (slopes) overlooking the town about ten o'clock. The customhouse officers met them and escorted them to the customhouse, where they were compelled, contrary to the custom under the administration of Governor Armijo, to unload and have their goods undergo inspection. Armijo had permitted the traders to unload their goods in their stores, and had allowed the introduction of all goods suitable for the market of New Mexico except clothing, boots, and shoes, tobacco, and some other goods which were manufactured in the low country and would interfere with that trade.

Speyer's stock of goods consisted of dry goods, notions, and hardware. The dry goods, which were the largest items, included: black cloth; striped, plaid, and black and white calicoes; white cambric; cotton, pongee (silk cloth), fancy and blue plaid handkerchiefs; bleached and plaid muslin's; blue and brown drillings; bleached sheeting; bonnet ribbons; plaid silk shawls; women's white cotton hose; hickory shirts; and satin jeans. Among the notions were: cotton thread, black sewing silk, hooks and eyes, ivory combs, coat buttons, plain and gilded vest buttons, needles, "London pins," and suspenders. Brass nails, iron spoons, scissors, pocketknives, butcher knives, saw files, padlocks, tacks, hoes, and spades comprised most of the hardware.

The leading politicians in Mexico, including the governor, would admit goods by the wagon load, receive nominal duties, and of these goods a comparatively few ever went to the low country. Previous to his administration, the general government had been compelled to send considerable sums to support the government in the territory, but by means of the duties received from the increase of trade through the course pursued by him, he never called upon the general government for a dollar. True, he would send trains of his own to the States, and introduce goods (paying no duties) and pay off the soldiers in goods with a small portion of money, thus making a profit for himself and savings to the government. The soldiers were regularly paid, and at least as well as the uncertain and frequently reduced pay in the low country.

Ian's trip to Santa Fe took seventy days, which at that time was not considered an especially long trip.

Santa Fe was situated along the banks of a small creek, which comes down from the mountains and runs west to the Rio del Norte. The length of the town on the creek was estimated at one mile, and it was but three streets in width. Its appearance from a distance, thought Ian, was like a fleet of flat bottom boats, such as are seen in the spring and fall seasons descending the Ohio river. There were two churches, the magnificence of whose steeples formed a striking contrast to the miserable appearance of the other buildings. On the north side of the town was a square of soldiers' houses, one hundred and twenty, or one hundred and forty on each flank. The public square was in the center of the town, on the north side of which was situated the palace, as they called it, or government house, with the quarters for guards. The clergy and public officers occupied the other side. In general, the houses have a shed before their front, some of which have a flooring of brick; this occasions the streets to be very narrow, being, in general, about twenty-five feet. The supposed population was four thousand five hundred souls.

Governor Pedro de Peralta founded Santa Fe, the capital of New Mexico, sometime between 1610 and 1614. Although an important northern outpost of the Spanish Empire in America, it was isolated and sluggish, unlike the lively mining towns to the south. Like other New Mexican towns, its houses were one-story high and built of adobes or large mud bricks dried in the sun. To many Americans entering Santa Fe for the first time, this method of construction gave the town the appearance of a group of brick kilns. The people were nearly all in extreme poverty, and there were absolutely none that could be classed as wealthy except by comparison. The Pinos and Ortizes were considered the ricos (wealthy), and those most respected as leaders in society and political influence. Idleness, gambling, and the Indians had made such inroads upon their means and influence that there was little left except the reputation of honorable descent from a wealthy and distinguished ancestry. Nearly all the houses were old and dilapidated, the streets narrow and filthy, and people, when in best attire, not half dressed. And even those who could occasionally afford a new and expensive dress would make it up in such a way that it would appear extravagantly ridiculous.

The northeast corner of the plaza was the government storehouse, or public granary, devoted in ancient times to the storage of corn by the government to sell to the poor and improvident in time of necessity. This year it was used as a government warehouse to store American goods while being examined by the customhouse officers.

From thence south was nearly all government offices, except on the southeast corner, which was a store occupied by Don Juan Sena as agent of Don Jose Chavez. This was the second best store in town—Mr. John Scolly having the best—and floored with plank, the only plank Ian had seen in New Mexico, except a store in Taos. Mr. Turley, at Turley's Mill, also had one or two rooms floored with plank.

On the southeast corner was the residence of one of the Pinos and only one or two stores, or tendajones (small rickety shops) until you came to the corner of the street leading to Rio Chiquito. This was a small stream where there was a store about fifteen feet square, which was rented and occupied by Messrs. Leitensdorfer and Speyer, with several back rooms for storage and housekeeping.

The west side of the plaza was filled with residences. Near the center was the post office where mail sometimes arrived from the south, and also the estanquillo, a shop licensed to sell cigars, where the government sold a limited amount of cigars and tobacco. There were but few houses on the rising ground south of the river. The principal one was owned and occupied by "Old Taosenian," and he gave a fandango once or more a week, according to the number of strangers visiting the city and the demand for amusement.

The Mexican fandango was quite a curiosity. The sala, or dancing hall, was from twenty to thirty feet long and fifteen to eighteen feet wide, sometimes with benches on the sides, but frequently without seats of any kind. It was usually packed full, only leaving sufficient space through the center for the couples to waltz through, up and down. When the dance began, the men would place themselves in line on one side, and when the line was complete, the women would begin to rise and take their positions opposite the men, almost always in regular order manifesting any choice of partners. When the numbers were equal, the music would strike up and the dance would proceed.

It was not uncommon or surprising to see the most elaborately dressed and aristocratic woman at the ball dancing with a peon dressed only in his shirt and trousers open from the hip down, with very wide and full drawers underneath, and frequently barefoot, but usually with moccasins. And such disparity of ages! On one occasion Ian saw an old man of eighty dancing with a child not over eight or ten. One could not help the reflection that it was a dance of the cradle and the grave. There were disorders and serious brawls in fandangos, but it was almost invariable where Americans and whiskey were found in profusion.

In New Mexico, a fandango was not a particular type of dance, but any ordinary assembly where dancing was the principal amusement. A baile, or ball, was a fandango attended chiefly by the better classes. Sometimes there was no clear distinction between a baile and a fandango.

The Americans called all dances or balls in Santa Fe fandangos. There was generally an extra apartment where sweetbreads, Pasa whiskey, and wine were sold at double prices, and this was the landlord or landlady's remuneration for the use of the ballroom. In the whole town there was but one house that had a boarded floor. This apartment with the boarded floor was the fashionable ballroom.

In compliment to the American strangers then in Santa Fe, Governor Alvarez gave a ball in this grand boarded saloon during Ian's visit. All the beauty and fashion attended, and also the entire rabble, for true to their republican principles, none can be refused admission. The night was warm, the windows were open, the Americans threw down their hats carelessly, and the Mexicans walked off with them cautiously. The governor's lady, Senora Alvarez, led off the dance with Ian, he being the handsomest and youngest of the American guests.

The only music was a guitar and violin, and the same instruments were used for sacred music in the churches. Although there was little elegance in their dances, yet about them there is wildness and novelty truly enchanting to such young enthusiasts as Ian was. With all this unrestrained freedom of manners, quarrels are generally seldom, and the harmony of an evening's amusement was seldom broken unless by some imprudent conduct of the Americans themselves. Scarcely an evening of the week passed without a fandango in one part of the town or another, and the same faces would be seen at every one. It would seem as if the people could not exist without the fandango.

Ian went to several of the dances in the company of Speyer and Leitensdorfer and was introduced to the governor. With so many people there, his meeting was brief and Ian thought the governor did not even remember his name. However, two days later Ian was requested to come to the government-house.

He was ushered in through various rooms; the floors all covered with the skins of buffalo, bear, or some other animal. He waited in a chamber for some time until His Excellency appeared.

As Ian rose to his feet, His Excellency asked in English, "Do you speak French?" evidently preferring to speak in a language he was more proficient in than English.

"No, sir," Ian replied.

The governor continued in English, "You come to reconnoiter our country?"

"No, sir, only to guard the wagon train from the Indians."

The Governor Manuel Alvarez was born in Spain about 1794. He had left his native land in 1818, and in the following year came to Mexico. In 1824 he journeyed from Missouri to New Mexico and began his career as a Santa Fe trader. Opening a store in Santa Fe, he continued in business there, building up one of the largest mercantile establishments in New Mexico.

He was naturally irritable and sometimes overbearing, but allowances should be made for his early opportunities. He was emphatically a self-made man, and rose from the position of sheep herder to that of governor by his own energies—without aid, counsel, or even sympathy from those who were born in a higher walk of life and had opportunities of superior instruction.

The governor offered Ian some mescal. It was spirituous liquor of great strength, much more so than the strongest American whiskey. It was obtained from the bulb or root of the maguey, or agave mexicana, and was the common alcoholic drink throughout the country.

As the two sipped the whiskey and talked small talk, Lieutenant Don Malgores, who Ian had met in Rialto, entered the room.

The lieutenant paid his respects to the governor and, after shaking hands with Ian, he told the governor he had met Ian in Kansas Territory.

Ian told him about his trip to Santa Fe and explained that the rest of the troop had started back already and, in spite of the fine hospitality, he must return to the States very soon.

Lieutenant Malgores mentioned that he was starting on an expedition to San Antonio in the Province of Texas and asked Ian if he would like to accompany his troop. Ian had heard talk of American and Mexican bad feelings against each other and he sensed that the offer was actually a diplomatic order; the Mexican authorities wanted him to be escorted and to be watched at all times while he was in Mexico. Although San Antonio was quite a bit out of the way from Leavenworth, it was in the same direction and he wanted to see Jamie Bill's Texas and also did not want to provoke the anger of the Mexican government.

Lieutenant Malgores, the officer selected to command the expedition, was a European, and his uncle was at that time one of the royal judges of His Catholic Majesty of Spain. He had distinguished himself in several long expeditions against the Apaches and other Indian nations, with whom the Mexicans were at war. Added to these circumstances, he was a man of immense fortune, and generous in its disposal, almost to profusion; he possessed a liberal education, a high sense of honor, and a disposition formed for military enterprise.

Ian, Lieutenant Malgores and twenty dragoons marched early two days later. The dragoons were the best calvaries to be found in all of Mexico, being the personal soldiers of the governor.

Their lances were fixed to the side of the saddle under the left thigh, and slanted about five feet above the horse. On the right the carbine was slung in a case to the front of the saddle (or pummel) crossways, the breech to the right hand, and on each side of the saddle behind the rider was a pistol. Below the breech of the carbine was slung the shield, which was made of sole leather trebled, sewn together with thongs, with a band on the inside to slip the left arm through; those of the privates were round and about two feet in diameter. The officers and non-commissioned officers had them of an oval bending on both sides, in order to permit the arrow to glance. There was gilt on the outside and various other devices, which added much to the elegance of their appearance on horseback, but were only calculated to be of service against wild Indians, who had no fire-arms. The dragoons of the President do not make use of the lance or shield, but are armed, equipped, and clothed after the modern manner, as are the dragoons of the eastern provinces. When they recently expected to be opposed by the American troops, they were deprived of their lance and shield and received the straight cutlass in their stead.

Their dress is a short blue coat with a red cape and cuff without facings, and leather or blue cotton velvet small clothes and waist-coat; the small clothes always open at the knee. The wrapping boot with the jackboot had permanent spurs over it; a broad-brimmed high-crowned wool hat was worn with a ribbon around it of various colors. This was usually received as a present from some female, which they wore as a badge of favor of the fair sex and mark of their gallantry.

Their horses are small and slender limbed, but very agile, and are capable of enduring great fatigue. The equipment of the horses is, to Ian's ideas, awkward, but he believed them superior to the English. They have the advantage over us, as to the skill of the rider as well as the quality of the horse. Their bridles have a strong curb, which gives them so great a mechanical force that he believed it almost practical with it to break the jaw of the horse. The saddle is made after the Persian model, with a high projecting pummel, or, as anciently termed, bow, and is likewise raised behind; this is merely the tree. It is then covered by two or three coats of carved leather, and embroidered workmanship, some with gold and silver in a very superb manner. The stirrups are of wood and closed in front, carved generally in the figure of a lion's head or some other beast; they are very heavy and present a very clumsy appearance. The horseman seated on his horse has a small bag tied behind him, his blankets either under him or lying with his cloak between his body and the bow, which makes him at his ease. Thus mounted, it is impossible for the most vicious animals to dismount them. They will catch another horse, when both are running nearly at full speed, with a noose and hair rope, with which they will soon choke down the animals they are pursuing. They are probably the most expert horsemen in the world.

*   *   *

Before leaving Santa Fe, the troops stocked up on supplies needed for the journey. At each fort is a store, where it was the original intention of the government that the soldiers should be supplied at a cheap rate with provisions, clothing, and arms. When a dragoon joins the service he receives five horses and two mules, and this number he is always obliged to keep good from his own pocket. But when he is discharged, the horses and mules receive the discharge mark and become his private property. They engage for five or ten years, at the option of the soldier, but in the bounty there is a very material difference. It is extremely easy to keep up the corps, as a private dragoon considers himself equal to most of the citizens, and infinitely superior to the lower class; it is not infrequent to see men of considerable fortune marrying the daughters of sergeants and corporals.

Although they rode very hard, by the afternoon they got only to the village of Agua Caliente or Warm Springs, which was about forty-five miles. The village of Agua Caliente was situated on the eastern branch of a creek of that name and, at a distance, presented to the eye a square enclosure of mud walls with houses forming the wall. They are flat on the top, or with extremely little slope to one side, where there are spouts to carry off the water of the rain when it falls. Ian was informed that this had not been the case but once in two years. Inside the enclosure were the different streets, formed of houses of the same fashion, all of one story; the doors narrow, the windows small, and in one or two houses, Ian observed talc lights, that is, from burning magnesium silicate.

The village had a mill near it on a little creek, which made very good flour. Here, they had a fandango that lasted most of the night. Ian got fairly drunk and showed the people the "stomp dance" he had learned from the river men, which he could do best when he was half drunk. He made friends with most of the dragoons that night, drinking and carousing with them.

As most of the men still felt the effects of the tequila, they marched late and passed several little mud-walled villages and settlements, all of which had round mud towers of the ancient shape and construction to defend the inhabitants from the intrusions of the Indians. Ian was this day shown the ruins of several old villages, which had been taken and destroyed by the Ietans.

Frequently, the women, who invited them into their houses to eat, stopped them on the march, and, in every place where they halted a moment, there was a contest of who should be their hosts.

They descended the creek of Agua Caliente about twelve miles to where it joined the river of Conejos from the west. This river was about thirty yards wide. From their junction, the distance was about five miles to the Rio del Norte (Rio Grande), on the eastern branch of which was situated the village of St. John's, which was the residence of the President Priest of the Province, who had dwelt there forty years.

The tops of the houses, as well as the streets, were crowded when the dragoons entered. At the door of the public quarters, the priest met them. Lieutenant Malgores, who commanded the escort, received him in the street and embraced him, and all poor creatures that stood around strove to kiss the ring or hand of the Holy Father. Ian saluted him in the usual style.

The men were conducted into the quarter and Ian and Lieutenant Malgores went to the house of the priest, where they were treated with politeness.

This was the first place where Ian had partaken of a good meal and wine. The house being too warm, and having perhaps rather an immoderate use of the refreshments, Ian was attacked by something like the cholera morbus, with vomiting, diarrhea and cramps. The escort stayed there for two days while Ian recuperated.

St. John's was enclosed with a mud wall, and probably contained one thousand souls. Its population consisted principally of civilized Indians, and indeed most of the villages of North Mexico were the same with the whites not forming but one-twentieth part.

They marched after breakfast the next morning and in about six miles came to a village containing more than two thousand people. Here they halted at the house of the priest, who, understanding that Ian would not kiss his hand, did not present it to him.

They arrived at two o'clock at the village of St. Domingo, which Ian apprehended to be nine miles to the eastward of the Rio del Norte. Its population may have been about one thousand natives, generally governed by their own chief. A cane with a silver head and black tassel distinguished the chiefs of the villages. On their arrival at the public house, Lieutenant Malgores waited on the governor, cap in hand, to receive his orders for furnishing them quarters, and with wood, water, provisions, etc., for the house contained nothing but bare walls, and small grated windows.

After Ian had refreshed himself a little, the lieutenant sent for the keys of the church. Ian was much astonished to find enclosed in mud brick walls many rich paintings, and the Saint Domingo as large as life, elegantly ornamented with gold and silver. Lieutenant Malgores made a slight inclination of his head, and intimated to Ian that this was the patron of the village. In an outside hall was placed another image of the Saint, less richly ornamented, where the populace retired daily and knelt to return thanks for benefactions received or to ask new favors.

Many young girls made choice of the time of Ian's visit to be on their knees before the holy patron. Ian noticed the girls were unusually beautiful with long hair falling to their shoulders and with flashing dark eyes. Like temptresses of the Bible, they would excite any man to foolishness. Ian tried to keep his mind off these things. Lieutenant Malgores motioned him to the roof of the church. From the flat roof, they had a delightful view of the village, the Rio del Norte on the west and the mountains of St. Dies to the south and the valley around the town on which were numerous herds of goats, sheep and asses. This was one of the finest views in New Mexico. Ian enjoyed the view and, including the girls leaving the church, and he thought a man might be happy here enjoying all of god's creations—the mountains, the warm climate, and quiet lazy living. Nothing more could be asked.

The next day they marched down the Rio del Norte, on the eastern side, passing large flocks of goats. At the village of St. Phillip they crossed a bridge of eight arches, constructed of pillars made of neat woodwork, something similar to a crate, and in the form of a keel boat, the sharp end (or bow) to the current. This crate or abutment was filled with stone in which the river had lodged sand and clay, until it had become of a tolerably firm consistence. On the top of the pillars pine logs were laid lengthways, squared on two sides, and, being joined pretty closely, made a tolerable bridge for horses, but would not have been very safe for carriages, as there were no hand rails.

On their arrival at the house of the priest, they were received in a very polite and friendly manner, and before their departure they seemed to have been friends for years. During the dinner, at which a variety of wines were served, they were entertained with music, consisting of bass drums, French horns, violins, and cymbals. The Father entered into a long and candid detail of the injustice done to the Creoles—Indians descended from the Spanish settlers by inter-marriage—where the Father neither spared the government nor its administrators. Both as to government and religion, he displayed a broad-minded opinion

Mexican Senorita

and a fund of knowledge, which astonished Ian. He showed Ian a statistical table on which he had in a regular manner taken the whole province of New Mexico by villages, beginning at Taos on the northwest, and ending with Balencia on the south and detailed much information: their latitude, longitude, population, whether Indians or Mexicans, civilized or hostile, Christians or pagans. He included numbers, name of the nation, when converted, how governed, military force, clergy, salary, etc. In short, a complete geographical and historical sketch of the province.

Ian wished to obtain a copy, but perceived that the lieutenant was somewhat surprised at the Father's having shown it to him, so Ian remembered as much as he could.

The priest explained that New Mexico was the most northern province of Mexico. It extended on the northwest into an undefined limit. The Americans who had purchased Louisiana, on the south by Biscay and Cogquilla and on the west bound it on the north and east by Senora and California. Its length is unknown; its breadth may be one hundred miles, but the inhabited part is not more than four hundred miles in length and fifty in breadth, lying along the River del Norte (Rio Grande). But in this space there is a desert of more than two hundred fifty miles.

No person accustomed to the temperate climate in the United States can form any idea of the piercing cold experienced in New Mexico. But the air is serene and subject to damps or fogs, as it rains but only once a year and some years not at all. It is mountainous country. The grand dividing ridges which separate the waters of the Rio del Norte from those of

California are covered in some places with eternal snows and gives a keenness to the air that would never be calculated on in a temperate zone.

The cotton-tree is the sole production of this province, except for some scrubby pines and cedars at the foot of the mountains; the former borders the banks of the Rio del Norte and its tributary streams. All the rest of the country presents to the eye a barren wild of poor land, scarcely to be improved by culture, and appears only capable of producing a scanty subsistence for the animals, which live on a few succulent plants and herbage.

There are no mines known in the province, except one of copper, situated in a mountain on the western side of the Rio del Norte. It is worked and produces twenty thousand mule loads of copper each year, furnishing that article for the manufacture of nearly all the internal provinces. It contains gold, but not quite in sufficient quantity to pay for its extraction; consequently, it has not been pursued. In some of the mountains near Santa Fe, there is a stratum of talc. It is so large and flexible as to admit of being subdivided into thin flakes of which the greatest proportion of the houses in Santa Fe, and all the villages to the north, have their window lights made.

The River del Norte takes its rise in the mountains, which gives birth to the head waters of California, the Platte, Pierre, Jaune of the Missouri, and Arkansas of the Mississippi. Its course from its source to the Gulf of Mexico may be by its meanders estimated at two thousand miles and passing through the Provinces of New Mexico, part of Biscay, Cogquilla and New San Andrea, where it falls into the Gulf. It cannot in any part of its course be termed a navigable stream, owing to sandbars in the flat country, and mountains in the upper part, with which its course is interrupted. Small boats might ascent as high as the Presido de Rio Grande in Cogquilla, and it might be navigable for canoes in various parts of its course. Even in the mountains above Santa Fe, it afforded amply sufficient water for that species of navigation, and more than appeared to be flowing in its bed in the plains. This must be attributed to the numerous canals and the dry sandy soil through which the river takes its course, and where much of the water that flows from the mountains is absorbed and lost. In the Province of New Mexico it is called the Rio del Norte; below it is termed the Rio Grande, but in no instance did Ian hear it called the Rio Bravo, as many of the ancient maps designated it. There are also, in the limits of the province to the west, the rivers: San Rafael, San Xavier, River de los Dolores, and de los Anamas or Nabajos. These all unite and form the Great Rio Colorado of California. The first two take their sources in the same mountains as the Rio del Norte, but on the western side.

The Rio Colorado by its meanders may be about one thousand miles in length from its sources to its entrance into the head of the Gulf of California. It had been represented to many men of research and information to be navigable for three hundred miles above the gulf for square-rigged vessels.

There are numerous and warlike nations of Indians on its banks. Through the whole of its course, its shores are entirely destitute of timber, and Ian was informed that for three hundred miles there was not a tree ten inches in diameter.

North Mexico produces deer, elk, buffalo, cabrie, black bear and wild horses. Its population is not far short of thirty thousand souls, one-twentieth of which may be Spaniards from Europe, four-twentieths Creoles, five-twentieths Mestis, and the others, half-civilized Indians.

New Mexico sends out annually about thirty thousand sheep, tobacco, dressed deer and cabrie (goat) skins, some fur, buffalo robes, salt, and wrought copper vessels of a superior quality. It receives dry goods, confectionery, arms, iron, steel, ammunition, and some choice European wines and liquors from the southern provinces. From Senora, they received gold, silver, and cheese. The following articles sell as stated in this province, which shows the cheapness of provision, and the extreme dearness of goods: flour at two dollars per pound; salt—five dollars a mule load; sheep—one dollar each; pork—twenty-five dollars per hundred; beeves—five dollars each; wine Del Passo—fifteen dollars per barrel; horses—eleven dollars each; mules—thirty dollars each; superfine clothes—twenty-five dollars per yard; fine cloths—twenty dollars; linen—four dollars; and all other dry goods in proportion.

The journey with loaded mules from Santa Fe to Mexico City and returning takes five months. They manufacture rough leather, cigars, a vast variety and quantity of potter's ware, cotton, some coarse woolen cloths, and blankets of a superior quality. The civilized Indians carry on all these manufactures, as the Mexicans think it more honorable to be agriculturists than mechanics. The Indians likewise far exceed their conquerors in the quality and variety of genius in all mechanical operations.

New Mexico had the exclusive right of cultivating tobacco. About two miles above the town of Passo del Norte was a bridge over the river, where the road passes to the western side. At this place is a large canal that takes out an ample supply of water for the purpose of cultivation, which is carried on at the place in as great perfection as at any Ian visited in the province. There was a wall bordering the canal the entire way on both sides to protect it from animals, and when it arrives at the village, it is distributed in such a manner that each person has his field watered in succession. At this place were as finely cultivated fields of wheat and other small grain as Ian ever saw. There were also numerous vineyards from which were produced the finest wine ever drank in the country, which was celebrated throughout all the provinces, and was the only wine used on the table of the commanding general.

They cultivated corn, wheat, rye, barley, rice, and all the common plants of the same latitude in the United States. But they were at least a century behind the eastern United States in the art of cultivation. For even though there were numerous herds of cattle and horses, Ian saw them frequently breaking up whole fields with the hoe. Their oxen draw by the horns after the French mode. Their carts are extremely awkward and clumsily made. During the whole of the time Ian was in Mexico, he never saw one horse pulling a vehicle of any description, as mules were made use of in carriages as well as for the purpose of labor.

On the River St. Francis, a large branch of the Gila, which leads near the copper mines of New Mexico, discharges itself into the Red River of California. Here are the remains of old walls and houses, which were established to be vestiges of the Mexicans on their route of emigration from the northwest to the plains of Mexico, where they finally established themselves. Those walls are of black cement, which increases in stability with age and bids defiance to the war of time; the secret of its composition is now entirely lost. There are also found at this place many broken pieces of earthenware which still possessed glazing as perfect as when first put on.

The government of New Mexico could be termed military in the pure sense of the word. Although they have their inferior officers, their judgments are subject to a reversion by the military commandants of districts. The whole male population is subject to military duties, without pay, and are obliged to find their own horses, arms, and provisions. The only thing furnished by their government is ammunition, and it is extraordinary with what subordination they act when turned out on military service. A strong proof of this was exhibited in the expedition of Malgores to the Pawnees—his command consisting of one hundred dragoons of the regular service and five hundred drafts from the province. He had continued down the Red River until their provisions began to be short. They then demanded of the lieutenant where he was bound and his intention. To this he haughtily replied, "wherever his horse carried him." A few mornings after, he was presented with a petition, signed by two hundred of the militia, to return home. He halted immediately, and caused his dragoons to erect gallows. He then beat to arms, and the troops fell in; he separated the petitioners from the others, took the man who had presented him the petition, tied him up, gave him fifty lashes, and threatened to put to death on the gallows any man who should dare to murmur. This effectually silenced them and crushed the rising spirit of rebellion.

The country being a frontier, and the people cut off from the more populated parts of the republic, together with their continual wars with some of the savage nations who surround them, make them brave and most hardy subjects. They are generally armed and know the use of their weapons. Their want of gold and silver makes them work hard, and their isolated and remote situation causes them to exhibit in a superior degree, the heaven-like qualities of hospitality and kindness. These they appear to endeavor to fulfill the commands of the Bible, which enjoins us to feed the hungry, clothe the naked, and give comfort to the oppressed.

There seemed but one troop of dragoons in all New Mexico, of the regular force, which was stationed at Santa Fe, and was one thousand strong. Of this the governor is always the captain, styling himself captain of the troop of Santa Fe dragoons; but they are commanded by a first lieutenant, who is by honorary rank a captain without captain's pay. The men capable of bearing arms may be estimated at five thousand. Of those, probably one thousand are completely armed—one thousand badly, and the rest not at all.

The Catholic religion is well known and, with all others, tolerated in the United States. It is practiced after the same manner in all the provinces, but the clergy in this province are much more liberal than those nearer the presidency, where the terrors of the inquisition keep them in awe. In Ian's presence, they and the officers used to laugh openly at the terror and superstition in which the common people held by them. Many of them were generous and friendly, and Ian certainly felt himself indebted to them for their polite and hospitable treatment.

The next day they marched at nine o'clock, through a country better cultivated and inhabited than any Ian had yet seen. They arrived at Albuquerque, a village on the eastern side of Rio del Norte. They were received by Father Ambrosia Guerra in a very flattering manner, and led into his hall. From thence, after taking some refreshment into an inner apartment, he ordered his adopted female children to appear, when they came in by turns. They were Indians of various nations—Spanish, French, and finally two young girls who, from their complexion, Ian conceived to be English. On perceiving Ian's reaction, the priest ordered the rest to retire many of whom were beautiful, and directed the two to sit down on the sofa beside Ian. Thus situated, he told Ian that they had been taken to the east by the Ietans, passed from one nation to the other until he purchased them, at the time infants, but they could recollect neither names nor language. Concluding they were Ian's countrywomen, he ordered them to embrace Ian as a mark of their friendship, which they did with no reluctance. They then sat down to dinner, which consisted of various dishes and excellent wines. To crown all, they were waited upon by a half a dozen of those beautiful girls.

Both above and below Albuquerque, the citizens were beginning to open the canals to let in the water of the river to fertilize the plains and fields, which border its banks on both sides. Ian saw men, women, and children of all ages and both sexes at the joyful labor, which was to crown with rich abundance their future harvest, and insures them plenty for the ensuing year. These scenes brought to Ian's recollection the opening of the canals of Egypt. The cultivation of the fields was beautiful and everything appeared to give life and gaiety to the surrounding scenery.

The plough in universal use is that that was used two thousand years ago neither more nor less than a wooden wedge, without a particle of iron attached to it. The hoe is a wooden staff with an iron spike in the end. What is still more remarkable is that the only animal used in ploughing is the ox. A planter, with twenty thousand horses and mules (by no means an unusual number), will only use his oxen on the plough.

They crossed the Rio del Norte, a little below the village of Albuquerque, where it was four hundred yards wide, but not more than three feet deep, and excellent fording. Malgores, perceiving Ian did not find himself at ease, took every means in his power to banish his reserve. Malgores possessed none of the haughty Castilian pride, but much of the courtesies of the Frenchmen and the loyalty of his new country. He had the mind to plan, the heart to feel, and the hands to carry the responsibility to build a great and important country out of the state wrestled back from the Spanish usurpers.

In the afternoon a friend of Malgores wrote the following notification to the several surrounding villages: "Send this evening six or eight of your handsomest young girls to the village of St. Fernandez, where I propose giving a fandango, for the entertainment of the American officer arrived to-day."

This order was punctually obeyed and that evening, when the company arrived, the ball began after the usual manner, and there was really a handsome display of beauty.

The next day the troops marched about ten o'clock with Ian leaving with a fond memory of the beautiful girls. They passed a village called St. Thomas, one-mile distance from the camp. As hostile Indians had been reported, the camp was formed in an ellipse, the two long sides presenting a breastwork, composed of the saddles and loads of the mules. At the end of ellipse was a small opening to pass through. In the center was the commandant's tent. Thus, in case of an attack upon the camp, there were ready-formed works to fight from.

Malgores' manner of living was superior to anything in the United States Army, having eight mules loaded with his common camp equipage, wines, confections, etc. The discipline of the Mexican troops is very different from the Americans. They relieve their guards at night, and, as soon as they halt, the new guard is formed on foot with their carbines. They then march before the commandant's tent, where the commanding officer of the guard cries the invocation of the Holy Virgin three times. The commanding officer replies, "It is well." They then retire and mount their horses. Some go to act as guards of the horses, as calvary; others as guards of the camp, as infantry. The old guard are then paraded and relieved, and the new sentinels take post. The sentinels are singing half their time, and it is no uncommon thing for them to quit their post to come to the fire or go for water. In fact, after the officer is in bed, frequently the whole guard comes in; yet Ian never knew any man punished for these breaches of military duty.

From the physical as well as moral properties of the inhabitants of New Mexico, Ian believed they were capable of being made the best troops in the world, possessing sobriety, enterprise, great physical force, docility, and a conception equally quick and penetrating.

As the small band was now in an area where the Indians roamed and plundered continuously, Lieutenant Malgores briefed Ian on the various tribes in New Mexico.

Sitting on blankets around the campfire, Malgores related that the Kiowa wander on the sources of the Platte and are supposed to be one thousand men strong. They possess immense herds of horses, and were at war with both the Pawnees and Ietan, as well as with the Sioux. They were armed with bows, arrows, and lances and follow the buffalo. This nation, the Ietan, and the Utah spoke the same language.

The Utah wanders on the sources of the Rio del Norte; they are supposed to be two thousand warriors strong, are armed in the same manner, and pursue the same game as the Kiowa. They are a little more civilized, having more connection with the Mexicans, with whom however they are frequently at war. They were at this time at peace with them, but waging war with Ietans.

The Nanahaws are situated to the northwest of Santa Fe, and are frequently at war with the Mexicans. They are supposed to be two thousand warriors strong, and are armed in the same manner as the other Indians. This nation, as well as all the others to the west of them bordering on California, speak the language of the Apaches and Lee Panis, who are in a line with them to the Atlantic.

The Apache are a nation of Indians who extend from the Black Mountains in New Mexico to the border of Cogquilla. They keep the frontiers of these three provinces in a continual state of alarm and ready and employing nearly two thousand dragoons to escort the caravans, protect the villages, and revenge the various attacks they are continually making on the subjects of presidency. They formerly extended from the entrance of the Rio Grande to the Gulf of California, and they have waged a continual warfare with the exception of short truces, with the Spaniards. It is extremely difficult to say what their numbers are at the present day, but they must be extremely reduced by their long constant hostilities. The wandering life they lead on the mountains is so injurious to an increase of population, and they are often extremely pinched by famine.

At the commencement of their warfare, the Spaniards used to take their prisoners and make slaves of them, but finding that their unconquerable attachment to liberty made them surmount every difficulty and danger to return to their mountains, they adopted the practice of sending them to Cuba. The Apache no sooner learned this than they refused to give or receive quarter. In no instance have there been any taken since that period, except when surprised asleep, or knocked down and overpowered.

Their arms are the bow and arrow and the lance. The bow forms two semicircles, with a shoulder in the middle; the back of it is entirely covered with sinew, which are laid on in so nice a manner by the use of some glutinous substance, as to be almost imperceptible. This gives great force to the elasticity of the weapon. Their arrows are more than a cloth yard of English, being three and a half feet long, the upper part consisting of some light rush or cane into which is inserted a shaft of about one foot. The shaft is made of some hard seasoned lightwood; the point is of iron, cane, or stone. When the arrow enters the body, in attempting to extract it, the shaft comes out of its socket and remains in the wound. With this weapon they shoot with such force as to go through the body of a man at a distance of one hundred yards. An officer told Ian that in an engagement with them one of their arrows struck his shield and dismounted him in an instant.

Their other weapon of offense is a lance of fifteen feet in length, which with both hands they charge over their heads, managing the horse principally with their knees. They all have the shield. Some few are armed with guns and ammunition taken from the Mexicans. These, as well as the archers, generally march to war on foot, but the lance men are always mounted.

Numerous were the stories relating to their personal bravery and the spirit of their fighting. Not long before Ian passed through, a cornet (calvary officer of the lowest rank) with sixty-three dragoons were passing between New Mexico and Chihuahua. About two hundred Apache's infantry surrounded them. Instead of charging through them, as it occurred on the plains, the officer ordered his dragoons to dismount and fight with their carbines, by which means he and his whole party fell a sacrifice. Lieutenant Malgores related an instance when he was marching with one hundred forty men and was attacked by a party of Apaches, both on horse and foot, who continued the fight for four hours. Whenever the dragoons made a general charge, the Apache's cavalry would retreat behind their infantry, who met the dragoons with a shower of arrows, on which they immediately retreated. Even gallant Malgores spoke of his cavalry breaking their infantry as a thing not to be thought of. Malgores assured Ian that if the men had seconded the efforts and bravery of the Indian chieftain, they would have been defeated. In various instances, he rallied his men and brought them up to the charge, and when they flew, retired indignantly in the rear. Seeing Malgores very actively engaged in forming and bringing up the men, he rode out ahead of his party and challenged him to single combat with his lance. This Ian's friend refused as he said the chief was one of the stoutest men he knew, carried a remarkably heavy lance, and rode a very fine charger. One of his corporals enraged to see them thus braved by the Indian, begged permission to meet the "infidel." Malgores refused his request, and ordered him to keep his ranks; but he reiterated his request and Malgores in passion told him to go.

The Indian chief had turned his horse to join his party, but seeing his enemy advancing, turned, and giving a shout, met him at full speed. The dragoon thought to parry the lance of his antagonist, which he in part effected by not throwing it quite high enough and it entered his neck in front and came out at the nape. When he fell dead to the ground, his victorious enemy gave a shout of victory in which all his followers joined him. This enraged the dragoons to such a degree that they made a general charge in which the Indian cavalry retreated again, ignoring the shouts of their gallant leader.

In another instance a small billow of smoke was discovered on the prairie, and one hundred dragoons surrounded three Indians. They were ordered to lay down their arms. They smiled at the officer's demand and asked him if he could suppose that men who had arms in their hands would ever consent to become slaves? He being loathed to kill them held a conference for an hour and, when finding that his threats had as little effect as his requests, he ordered his men to attack them at a distance, keeping out of the reach of their arrows and firing at them with their carbines. This they did with the Indians never ceasing to resist as long as life remained.

In a truce that was once held, a captain was ordered to meet with some of the bands; he received their deputies with disdainfulness, and they could not come to terms. The truce was broken and the Indians retreated to their fastness in the mountains. In a day or two this same officer pursued them. They were in the place called the Door in the Mountains through which Ian had passed in his journey, where only two or three dragoons could enter at a time, and there were rocks and caves on the flanks. The Indians secreted themselves until a number of the Mexicans had come in. When the Indians sounded a trumpet, the attack began and continued on the side of the Apache, until the captain fell. The Indian chief then ordered the firing to cease, saying that "the man who had so haughtily spurned the proffered peace was now dead." They made prisoner of a young officer, who during the peace had treated them with great kindness, and sent him home safe and unhurt.

Some of the bands made temporary truces with the Mexicans and received from them twenty-five cents per day each. These people hang around the fortifications of the country — drink, shoot, and waste their time. They are arrogant and independent, and great jealousy exists between them and the Mexicans. An officer was under trial when Ian was in the country, for anticipating an attack on his fortress, by attacking the chiefs of the supposed conspiracy, and putting them to death before they had time to mature and carry their plan into operation. Ian never learned the decision of his case; but, those Indians who had been for some time around the forts and villages, become by far the most dangerous enemies the Mexicans have when hostile. They acquire the Mexican language, manners, and habits; and, passing through the populated parts under the disguise of the civilized and friendly Indians, commit murders and robberies without being suspected. There is in the province of Cogquilla an Apache by the name of Ralph, who, it is calculated, had killed more than three hundred persons. He comes into the town under the disguise of a peasant, buys provisions, goes to the gambling tables and to mass, and before he leaves the village is sure to kill some person, or carry off a woman, which he has frequently done. Sometimes he joins travelers on the road, insinuates himself into their confidence, and takes his opportunity to assassinate them. He has only six followers, and from their knowledge of the country, their activity, and cunning, he keeps about three hundred dragoons continually employed. The government has offered one thousand dollars for his head.

The civilized Indians of the province of New Mexico consist of what were formerly twenty-four different bands, several names which Ian was not able to learn, but the Keres were one of the most powerful. They formed at present the population of St. Domingo, St. Philip's and Deis, and one or two other towns. They were men of large stature, round, full visage, fine teeth, and appeared to be of a gentle, easy disposition. They resemble the Osage more than any other nation. Although they are not the servants of individuals, they may properly be termed slaves of the state. They are compelled to do military duty, drive mules, carry loads or, in fact, perform any other act of duty or bondage at the will of the commandant of the district, or any passing military tyrant.

Ian was himself eye-witness to a scene that made his heart bleed for the poor wretches. At the same time it excited his indignation and contempt that they should suffer themselves with arms in their hands to be beaten and knocked about by beings no way their superiors, unless a tint of complexion could be supposed to give that superiority. One night as they rested near one of the villages where resided the families of two of their horsemen, they took the liberty to pay them a visit in the night. The next morning the whole escort was called up, and because they refused to testify against their imprudent companions, the dragoons knocked down several from their horses with the butt end of their lances. With the blood streaking down their faces, and bows in their hands, they stood cool and quiet! Not a frown, neither discontent, nor painful cry escaped their lips. Yet, what must have been the boiling indignation of their souls, at the insults offered by the soldiers, clothed with a little brief authority?

The next morning they marched at eleven o'clock, went twelve miles and encamped, the troops having preceded Ian and the lieutenant. The village at which they passed in the night, being the last of the inhabited country, they entered the wilderness, and the road became rough, with small hills running into the river forming valleys, but the bottoms appeared richer than those to the north.

The habitations (for houses they were not) which were seen on the trailside at distances of fifteen and twenty miles from each other resembled chicken coops rather than the abodes of human beings. They were constructed of canes about ten feet long, the large end resting on the ground, standing upright, wickered together in one or two places, and covered with straw.

In the villages the houses were generally small hovels ten or twelve feet square, built with unburned bricks with a small enclosure, in which the chili (red pepper), and a small patch of Indian corn for tortillas was cultivated.

Each hour the little band established the probability that they were following on the heels of a large body of Indians who could not be far ahead. Here and there they dropped tent-poles, pieces of half-dried buffalo meat. Now and then little articles of clothing, and old moccasins, a worn-out basket, and various odds and ends that attested their rapid movement was discarded. Furthermore, no game had been seen for two days, an indication that it had been hunted away; so the little band moved slowly and cautiously, fearing an ambush or a sudden attack.

A dead and mutilated express-rider was passed at early morning, surrounded by fragments of cut-up and destroyed mail.

That evening the campfire was not lit for fear of ambush, and the dragoons went to sleep without a thing for supper.

The traveling food of the dragoons in New Mexico consisted of a very excellent species of wheat biscuit and shaved meat well dried with a vast quantity of red pepper, of which they make a bouillon and then pour it on their broken biscuit. When it becomes soft, it is excellent eating. Farther south they use great quantities of parched corn meal and sugar, as practiced by our hunters, each dragoon having a small bag. They thus live, when on command, on an allowance which our troops would conceive little better than starving, never except at night attempting to eat anything like a meal, but biting a piece of biscuit or drinking some parched meal and sugar with water during the day.

As day was breaking, a band of Indians numbering forty active young warriors attacked a village about fifteen miles ahead of the dragoons. The warriors were armed with bows and arrows, lances, war clubs and some had short flintlock muskets. The warriors had surprised the poor fellows at a time when least expected—just before the dawn of day. Some were killed while lying in their beds. The men had not even time to seize their rifles.

Yell after yell reverberated through the village as the marauders leaped upon the hapless group before them.

They had some horses and mules, but not many, and they were prone to use them for food in times of scarcity. The lance was a weapon used by them, but their arms mainly were bows, arrows, and clubs.

It is simply a stick cut from a kind of live oak that grows in the mountains—one of the few species of woods that will sink in water after it has been seasoned.

The Indians were naked except for their small breechcloths.

One woman clasped to her bosom her youngest child, a boy of two years. The marauding warriors dashed upon her with tiger bounds, pounding out the life of mother and child at once, while her screams for help were mockingly thrown back from the bleak hills.

A little girl was seized by the hair and beaten until she was dead. Another small girl, less than four years old, was killed with one blow. Her older brother was the last to fall of those that died. He had stood farthest away. He saw the others killed and stood nerveless, overcome with horror. As the warriors came upon him, he gave one piercing shriek, and a moment later was struggling in unconscious convulsion under the stroke of the club.

They found the headman of the village and decided to put him to death slowly.

The chieftain became incensed and he seized his gun, and a ball from it passed through the brave fellow's heart and ended his frightful sufferings.

After all the villagers they could find were killed, the work of plunder began—the rifles, the clothing of the dead—taking what they wanted and strewing the rest over the ground.

As they came upon the middle-aged man named Lorenzo who showed some sign of life, they removed his scalp and shoes. Two of them seized him by the feet, dragged him to the edge of the bluff, and hurled him over. Down, twenty feet, he fell. Down, over the ragged rocks, he rolled. During part of this time he had a dim consciousness of his surroundings, but no power of motion. He heard the shrieks of his children and despairing cry of his wife, but the blow on the back of his head left him helpless and half-alive. He had felt the Indians searching him and felt the terrible pain, as his scalp was half cut off, half tore off, and knew they were dragging him over the ground. Then came the weird feeling of a wandering consciousness. At one moment he seemed to move between great rows of pictures hung in distant air. At another, the din of unearthly and discordant noises shocked his senses. Again, he was lulled by strains of heavenly music that soothed him into overwhelming rest. At the same time, he was conscious that he lay on the rocky slope in the bright sun with blood flowing from his ears and nose. Then darkness came.

As the route of the dragoons lay through a broken and rugged country, well suited for ambush, the small band rode cautiously toward the village. As they neared the scene of the massacre, their gallop was checked by the ghastly sight of a grinning head elevated on a small pyre, baked and blackened, surrounded by fragments of the unfortunate rider—first mutilated and, afterwards, torn and partially devoured by wolves. The devilish attempt to burn the head of the slaughtered man, an old dragoon soldier, so incensed the lieutenant that he vowed that if he caught the "rag-tailed rascals," their skins would pay the penalty of the deed.

While the dragoons were scooping out a shallow grave and gathering together the fragments of the cut-up and torn-up mail, the guides were seeking for the trail of the murderers. After the murder, they had taken every precaution to obliterate it and to throw pursuers at fault. They had burned the grounds in the vicinity and up to the margin of a small stream that ran by the spot, and then taken to the water, some up the stream and some down. The lure was intended for the dragoons; it was too shallow for Uchee and Tony, the red and black guides. The first moccasin track discovered leaving the stream was followed up, and the trail was soon added to by the joining in of others, until it became sufficiently marked and plain to enable the guides to follow it at a lope. Their camp of the night before was soon reached, but as the fires were out, it was plain that they had made an early start and were then probably hours ahead of their pursuers. The close observations of the guides, marking the tracks of each Indian as he joined the main trail, made out the number of warriors to be around forty.

Uchee pulled up short, slid off his mount, and bent over a clump of grass.

"This blade of grass," he remarked, holding it up, "was trod on this morning; you see it is crushed. The sun or the light of day has not shone upon it. Had either, it would have wilted. You see it is green, but crushed. Here are more. There is the print of a foot!"

A sixteen-year-old girl was seized at the outset and dragged to a cross that was in the town plaza and they crucified her. She was raised to the crossbeam, about eight feet above the ground, and her hands fastened by driving coarse wooden pegs through them. Similar pegs were driven through the bones of her feet. Her head was tied to the upright by strings of bark stuck full of thorns.

For two hours the unfortunate lived, screaming all the time, the marauders shooting her with arrows and mangling her body with burning brands.

Her screams were heard faintly in the distance and Lieutenant Malgores knew the warriors were still in the village ahead. In their glee of murder and pillaging, they had thrown all caution to the winds, and even their lookouts had joined in the slaughter.

With lance firmly grasped in one hand, shield in the other and their broad-brimmed hats on their shoulders, the dragoons charged the murderers.

"Charge!" was the dread sound that startled the Indians in the village. The rush of fierce men and mad horses, the snapping of the brush, and the jingling of spurs—what a change of scene from the moment before!

Their attack was without regularity or concert, shouting, hollering, they charged with their lances. They threw themselves to avoid the dragoons getting a dead aim at them; but, they succeeded and six of the warriors fell with mortal wounds.

In the close quarters of the alleys, they were forced to draw their sabers. The sword is the legitimate weapon of cavalry. Without a practical knowledge of its use, the dragoons would be no better than mounted infantry would. These men were well mounted and trained and all capable of wielding the sword.

In a few minutes six more warriors were dead. Every man's skull was literally split open with the sabers of the horsemen, and they lay stretched upon the ground in ghastly groups.

There was one large Indian amongst them who seemed to be their leader and who had a gun. Ian picked him for his man, as he was the nearest to him and rode up to about forty feet of him. Ian gave him a shot from his revolver while he was in the act of firing at another man. Ian's ball entered his thigh and did not come out. He went down on one hand, but recovered, and started running away.

Ian fired again and missed him; but just as Ian could see where the ball struck, just behind him, one of the dragoons shot him with his musket, and he fell supposedly dead upon the ground.

Ian had already fired four shots from his pistol and had only one more left. As he saw another savage making for the plains with no one after him, Ian thought he could do no better with his last shot than to give him the loan of it. Ian at once gave his fine horse the spur and started after him, passing within about six feet of the one Ian supposed to be dead. "Bang" went the grounded Indian's gun—and the ball entered near the center of Ian's right shoulder. The ball passed clear through and came out in front, just touching the bone. Ian thought the fellow would die anyway without further assistance and kept up the chase. He got up to about fifteen yards of the man he was after. Ian raised his pistol and brought it down on a level for him and was just ready to pull the trigger when he found his hand kept falling and that he had not sufficient strength in his arm to hold up the pistol. He was forced to return it to the holster; still, Ian had the satisfaction of seeing the warrior shot by a dragoon who was between the Indian and open country.

Another hostile, who had a lance, ran at Lieutenant Malgores. He knocked the lance aside with his saber, and the point entered his horse's breast, but did not seriously injure him.

At the same moment, the Indian attempted to run under his horse to save himself from the saber; but Malgores was too quick for him and took off nearly all one side of his head just as he was in the act of stooping.

Ian looked around to see how the first Indian he had shot was getting on and found him upon his feet again and loading his gun. Ian was not able to finish him, but there was another dragoon now at hand who gave him a shot from his carbine, which dropped him to rise no more.

Malgores little party, although they numbered half of the Indian force, had the advantage of being mounted. The dragoons, incensed by the slaughter of their countrymen and women, fought savagely, whooping and yelling, until the shrill voices of the Indians were lost in the repeated imitations and shouts of the soldiers.

A few of the warriors escaped on their mules and horses, but most of them had been killed. Four were badly wounded; no prisoners were taken. Malgores himself, being a swordmaster and at the head of the little band, had dashed at the enemy, cut down three, and wounded two others. This ferocity of the dragoons caused the rest to fly in confusion. The enemy had been routed with only one loss to the dragoons, although three were wounded, including Ian. One was wounded in the right arm, another below the shoulder with an arrow, and Ian in the shoulder joint with a pistol ball. The body of their dead comrade was mangled in a most shocking manner.

While a man was busy bandaging Ian's shoulder, another man of the detachment came riding up and said, "I am shot in the head," but said it in such an unconcerned manner that they did not think he was much hurt and took little notice of him. In about five minutes, he fell from his horse, apparently dead.

About this time the fight was over and all hands assembled around to do what they could for the wounded.

After examination, it was found that a dragoon by the name of Carlos had received a wound in his head from an arrow, the point of which—two and a half inches in length—was still buried in his head. It struck him directly over the right ear and went through the skull-bone with about one-half of an inch sticking out. One of the dragoons got hold of it with his teeth, but could not move it. Another, who had seen a great deal of Indian fighting, tried it with his knife, but did not succeed.

It happened that one of the men, who was a saddler, had a pair of pliers, which answered the purpose and was the means of saving the man's life. They did not expect the man to live fifteen minutes, but they could not leave him here.

The men took a number of their blankets and cut holes in them, through which they ran rope and made a kind of litter between two mules; the man was so raving, it was impossible to keep him on it.

When Lorenzo gained consciousness the mid-day sun was beating upon his face. His head throbbed with a maddening pain. He tried to open his eyes, but could not. As his mind cleared, he rubbed away the clotted blood that locked his eyelids and looked about him. His clothing was in shreds. He put his hand to his head, felt his scalp torn from his skull, and stiffened like parchment. Up the slope he saw the stains of blood that had marked his fall and realized how he had reached his present place. His thoughts wandered back to the tragedy enacted on the mesa above. An uncontrollable impulse came upon him to look again on the faces of the kindred who lay there; it was so short a distance and yet how great. Faint and dizzy, he crawled up the rock slope. His strength failed; he fainted. His consciousness returned; he crept on—up and up and up—a full fifty feet he struggled, and then, crawled and stumbled toward the square. The full horror of the murder scene was brought back to him. His desire to look on the features of the dead was now gone. With eyesight hampered with blood, he stumbled into the cross where he looked up into the tortured face of his dead daughter.

He held onto her battered legs for several minutes, sobbing pitifully, then died also.

The villagers that had escaped the massacre began to come in from all directions, singly and in small parties, so changed as to be hardly recognizable by the others. The few men who had been in the fields or down by the river in the early morning, whose families had all been killed, when Malgores spoke to them and expressed sympathy for them, were obliged to turn away unable to speak and too proud to show their grief. The women whose children had been killed were convulsed with sadness and looked upon Malgores as though he was their last hope on earth.

Children, who yesterday had been full of fun and frolic, kept at a distance, expressing wondering horror. The dragoons did what they could, talked to them, and listened to their accounts. Two women who had escaped death were badly wounded. One was shot through the left lung and one had a shattered arm.

But there were enough men to care for the wounded and bury the dead, and even though it was hard to leave them, Lieutenant Malgores knew he must pursue the marauding warriors who had escaped.

There was now no way to take the wounded Carlos along with them, except to pack him across a saddle with a dragoon to ride behind him and hold him on. This they did.

One of the men came up to Ian and made him a present of the scalp-lock of the Indian who shot him, which he kept as he did not wish to forget his particular friends. They left the dead where they lay.

The braves would not move too fast—one was seen with his thigh broken and being dragged away by another wounded Indian. They saw another getting among the rocks with his leg broken and another get into the brush wounded, which made twenty-two who would never steal mules or murder again. If the dragoons had pursued them, they could probably have killed them all, but they stopped to help the wounded villagers.

Ian's wound had bled freely before being taken care of, so much so that his clothes from his shoulder to his knees were completely glued to his skin.

In the afternoon, comparatively fresh horse manure was seen on the trail, but not a warrior had been seen. That they had seen the little band of soldiers, Ian felt convinced. There were nearly out of supplies, save salt and coffee. The Indian was an unknown quantity, and from indications was likely to prove rather a larger unknown quantity than expected. Ian, like Lieutenant Malgores, felt the necessity of fighting them and decided to do so, even though he doubted their force to be strong enough to do more than partially cripple them for the time being.

It was about four o'clock in the afternoon as they followed the curving, crooked trail at a little distance from the bank of the stream as it wound in and out among wild-plum thickets, alder bushes, and swamp willows, that a bend in the river appeared. As they passed through a little gorge, the trail opened out upon a small well-grassed valley of perhaps a mile in length and nearly the same in width.

From their side of the water, the land sloped slowly down to the stream from the rolling plain while on the other side it receded from the water at almost a dead level for nearly three-quarters of a mile. It then terminated in a line of low hills or bluffs varying from forty to fifty feet in height.

As the horses and pack mules had to subsist upon such grazing as they could find, they decided to go into camp, graze the animals, rest the men, and take the trail again early in the morning. They were convinced that before the close of another day they would catch up with the hostiles.

They dismounted in the middle of the valley and rested on the bank of a stream opposite the center of a small island. The island had been formed in the sand in the middle of the bed of the stream at which point the water divided and gently rippled along each side until it again united about two hundred and fifty feet below. It made a pretty break in the landscape, lying out in the bed of the main stream.

All, or nearly all, of these streams are peculiar in one thing. In the spring and early summer when the snows melt in the hills and mountains, they are deep, wide, and even majestic rivers. Late in the summer they dwindle to almost the merest thread of water. This stream formed no exception to the rule and the little island in the center of its bed was fully seventy yards from the bank on either side. It was raised about a foot above the water at its head while on either side of it flowed a stream of fifteen feet in width and with an average depth of less than five inches. This came together at the foot of the island, which here sloped down to the level of the bed of the main stream. Long sage-grass grew on its head, and a thicket of alder and willows shot up four of five feet in height about the center.

Suddenly the soft thud of galloping hooves came to their ears. Out of everywhere, the warriors came. The ground literally seemed to sprout Indians. They apparently jumped from the sod itself and over the rolling hills, out of the thickets, from the bed of the stream, along the opposite bank, and out of the long grass on every side, hundreds of Indians—with shrill cries of hatred—rushed down upon the dragoons.

Shouting insults, hollering, and nude except for a breechcloth, their bodies were painted scarlet and the scalps and other trophies from the villagers decorated the foremost warriors.

With the savages attacking in from the valley and others lining the opposite shore of the stream, the only way out of the situation was to flee down the stream. Several hundred yards downstream, the river entered a small gorge with steep walls. Immediately, Ian and Lieutenant Malgores realized if there were more Indians in the party than they had seen and the trail had clearly indicated a larger force, then the canyon ridge would be covered with Indians just waiting to rain down a deadly fire of arrows, lances, and bullets. Probably no one would get through the canyon, so this was to be the desperate battleground of the troopers.

One look at the island told the lieutenant that, once established on the island, there was no direction from which they could take them unaware during daylight.

Three of their best men remained temporarily in the long grass on the bank of the river, covering the north end of the island, thereby holding in check any unusually adventurous warriors who might be inclined to attempt to crawl up that way through the river-bottom. Scarcely were the horses tied in a circle when the men threw themselves on the ground and began firing from beneath the animals. Suddenly, it seemed to dawn upon the savages that they had been outgeneraled, for as the dragoons started towards the island, judging by their actions in signaling their comrades on the opposite bank, they fully expected that they would cross the stream. Now they saw their error and also realized, too late, the mistake they had made in not occupying the island themselves. Apparently infuriated at their blunder and almost instantly seeing the advantage the dragoons would have should they fortify themselves, they made a desperate onslaught upon the troopers. Various Indians began riding rapidly around just outside of musket range and impetuously urging their dismounted warriors to close in upon the little band from all sides. Many of the mounted warriors sprang from their horses also and, running forward, they lined both banks of the river. From the reeds and long grass poured in a steady and galling fire upon them. A few of the dragoons were hit, one killed, and several more badly wounded; several horses and mules were being shot down. The poor animals plunged and reared at their tethers, and added their cries to the wild shouts of the Indians and the steady crack of the guns and whistling of arrows on every side. At the height of the crisis, one of the dragoons shouted, "Let's don't stay here and be shot down like dogs! Will any man try for the opposite bank with me?"

"I will," answered someone from the opposite of the circle.

"Stay where you are, men. It's our only chance," Malgores shouted as he stood in the center of the command, pistol in hand. "I'll shoot down any man who attempts to leave the island."

"You addle-headed fools, have you no sense?" called out a sergeant whose every shot was as carefully and coolly aimed as though he were shooting at a target.

"Steady, men! Steady, now! Aim low! Don't throw away a shot," was Malgores oft-repeated command, which was seconded by the sergeants.

"Get down to your work men. Don't shoot unless you can see something to hit. Don't waste your ammunition for our lives may depend on how we ration it."

This was constantly the repeated command for the first ten minutes of the attack. Then discipline began to tell. Many a warrior had fallen to the rear badly wounded and some had been carried back dead, judging from the wild wails of their comrades. The scouts had made it so hot for the Indians close in on the river's bank that they had crawled back out of short range, evidently satisfied that it was safer, as far as they were concerned, to send their bullets and arrows from a longer distance. During this lull in the fight, the men were not idle. With their knives to cut the sod and their tin plates to throw up the sand, most of them had already scooped out a hole the length of their body and eighteen inches to two feet in depth. They piled up the sand on the side facing the enemy, which provided ample cover against bullets and arrows.

Malgores still stood upright, walking from man to man, but from every side came appeals for him to lie down. As they were now in fairly good shape and the men cool and determined, he did so.

Scarcely had he lain down when he received a shot in the fore part of the right thigh, the bullet ranging upward remained embedded in the flesh. It was by far the most painful wound he had ever received. For a moment he could not speak, so intense was the pain. Several of the men, knowing he was hit, called out to hear if he still lived, but it was at least a full minute before he could command his voice and assure them that he was not mortally hurt.

In the meantime, one or two Indians had crawled up on the lower end of the island and, hidden by a few bushes, were annoying the troopers very much. However, a dragoon who had temporarily taken a position close upon the bank of the river, saw the flash of their rifles from the center of a little bush. The next instant a bullet from his carbine went through the very middle of the bush and crashed into the brave's brain; a wild half-smothered shriek told them there was one less enemy. As nothing was heard from the other one, it was concluded that he dared not again risk exposing his position.

As Ian was now about the only man of the command unprotected by a rifle-pit, a sergeant suggested enlarging his pit to accommodate them both. Several of the men promptly went to his assistance in enlarging and deepening it. While they were doing so, in leaning over to caution one of the men who he thought was firing a little too fast for really good shooting, he was obliged to draw up his left leg as he lay prone on the earth. Unfortunately for him, one of the Indians sent a bullet through it, breaking and shattering the bone badly about midway between the knee and ankle.

The braves who, as one of the men expressed it, were fairly frothing at the mouth at their unexpected resistance kept up a steady fire. Two years ago they had annihilated a detachment of seventy-four soldiers in forty minutes. The determined defense of this much smaller and rather worn party, in the very heart of their own country, was exasperating to them.

The sergeant with his leg broken, gradually worked himself to one end of the pit on his elbows. Dragging his body along with intense pain, he was able to partially sit up and, by resting on his elbows against and upon the fresh earth, craned his head forward so as to obtain a clear view of the field.

Ian in the meantime had scooped out a pit for his horse and the animal laid in it, although he shook and tried to run several times. But after a while, the horse laid quietly, obeying his master's commands.

A glance over the command was most reassuring for Ian. Each man was fairly well sheltered in a rifle-pit of his own construction, generally two men in a pit, and the various pits were in an irregular circle about six feet apart. These pits were fortified by an embankment of sand fully eighteen inches in thickness both front and rear, for the enemy's bullets and arrows came from all points of the compass. Some of the wounded men, with bandages around their heads, were as active and alert as their more fortunate companions were.

Several horses and pack mules lay dead; a few of them, badly wounded, still plunged and moaned and strained at their lariats.

Cover of any kind found on the island, such as reeds, long grass, trees, turf, plum thickets, and, in some places, small piles of stones and sand was thrown up hastily.

Riding around just out of range of their carbines was a dozen or so mounted warriors. Charging here and there, shouting, waving their guns and lances over their heads, they apparently were half-frenzied at the thought of the blunder they had made in permitting the troop to obtain possession of the island.

A steady volley of arrows and rifle shots was kept up constantly by the enemy, but only returned by the troopers when they saw an opportunity to effectively use their cartridges. The Indians began to realize this, for as it was, they were playing a losing game.

The dragoons were now better protected than they were, and they were also better shots. The consequence was that many a badly wounded brave fell to the rear, while very few of the dragoons were being hurt.

There must have been some Mexican renegade in their ranks, for twice since the opening of the engagement, Ian had distinctly heard the notes of an artillery bugle. Leaning too far forward to get a better view of the mounted warriors, who seemed to be moving towards the canyon below them, Ian rather rashly exposed his head, and one of the Indian riflemen promptly sent an excellent line shot towards him. The bullet struck Ian just on top of his soft felt hat; but having a high crown that was fortunately doubled down, it glanced off, cutting through several thickness of felt. It nevertheless knocked him almost senseless to the bottom of his rifle-pit. It was some seconds before he could completely recover and crawl back into his sitting position. He thought little of it at the time it occurred. Of course, a large lump swelled up at once, but as the skin was hardly broken and he then had so many other things to occupy his attention, Ian took little heed of the intense headache that for a short time half-blinded him.

About this time several of the mounted Indians, for some cause that Ian was not able to determine, dashed up within rifle range, and from their horses took a sort of pot-shot at Ian and the sergeant sharing the pit with him. The sergeant, who had been closely watching their approach as they careened around the island, gradually lessening their distance, watched his opportunity and shot one of them through the head. As the brave fell dead from his horse, the sergeant remarked, "That rascally redskin will not trouble us again." Almost immediately afterwards Ian heard the peculiar thud that tells the breaking of bone by a bullet. Turning to the sergeant, Ian saw him put his hand to his head, saying, "I'm hit," as his head at the same time fell forward on the sand. Crawling to him, Ian pulled his body down into the pit and turned him upon his back, but Ian saw at once that there was no hope. A bullet had entered his forehead just over the eye and the wound was mortal. He never spoke another rational word, but lingered the next day before dying. During the rest of the day's fight, the sergeant lay on his back opposite Ian at the other end of the rifle-pit. Several times during the day, he partially revived, and then, probably in order to see if Ian was in the pit and that he was not abandoned, he would push his body forward and kick out with his foot, a half-unconscious proceeding on his part that caused Ian much pain. He could neither see nor hear, and yet he was evidently able in a dim way to reason regarding the situation.

Once more placing his back against the side of the rifle-pit, and again raising himself upon his elbows, Ian peered over the little earthwork with rather more caution than before. Looking towards the opposite bank and down the stream, Ian saw that most of the mounted warriors had disappeared. Those who remained were slowly trotting towards the little gorge. Ian again distinctly heard the clear notes of an artillery bugle. Others of the mounted warriors now moved towards the gorge, and it flashed upon him that they were forming for a charge just around the bend of the river, out of sight, and beyond rifle range.

Ian called out his revelation to Lieutenant Malgores who was near the head of the island. "I believe you are right," was his reply.

"Men, get ready," was Malgores order. Accordingly each carbine and pistol was loaded. The guns of the dead and mortally wounded were also loaded and laid close at hand, as were the sabers and lances.

Word was passed not to attempt to return the fire of the dismounted Indians in case a mounted charge was made; but the men were told to turn towards the quarter from where the charge came and to commence firing at the word of command only. In the meantime the fire of the warriors lying around them had slackened and almost ceased. This confirmed their anticipation, and word was again passed cautioning the men to lie close until the fire of the dismounted Indians slackened.

Ian laid his new fast-firing Hall's rifle beside him. He would have to find out if the rifle was as good as Senator Clark said it was. He hoped he could fire fifteen rounds in four and one-half minutes. He was especially glad his father had sent him the Paterson Colts. He had practiced quite a bit and could handle them very well now. The .40-caliber, five-shot, repeating pistols with the extra cylinder would be quite a surprise to the enemy. With a rifled barrel they were quite accurate close up, and the pair gave him twenty shots in less than forty seconds.

He had not long to wait. A peal of the artillery bugle and at a slow trot the mounted warriors came partially into view in an apparently solid mass at the foot of the valley, halting just by the mouth of the canyon.

Ian was on the tip of the island and was the foremost man in the defense. He placed his back firmly against his little earthwork, laid his rifle across his chest, his revolvers on the sand beside him, and his saber close by, if it came to that.

Speaking to his horse to calm it, he figured he would take a few with him when he went. Closely watching the mounted warriors, Ian saw their chief facing his command and, by his gestures, evidently addressing them in a few impassioned words. Then waving his hand in their direction, he turned his horse's head toward them, and at the word of command, they broke at once into full gallop heading straight for the foot of the island. Ian was right in his surmise; they were to be annihilated by being shot down as they rode over them. As they dashed forward and swept into the open at the head of his command, the leader was the very ideal of an Indian chief. Mounted on a large, clean-limbed chestnut horse, he sat well forward on his barebacked charger, his knees passing under a horsehair lariat that twice encircled the animal's body. His horse's bridle was grasped in his left hand, which was also closely wound in its flowing mane, and at the same time, he clutched his rifle at the guard. The butt of the rifle lay partially upon and across the animal's neck, while its barrel, crossing diagonally in front of his body, rested slightly against the hollow of his left arm, leaving his right arm free to direct the course of his men. He was a man over six feet three inches in height, beautifully formed and, except for a crimson silk sash knotted around his waist and the moccasins on his feet, he was perfectly naked. His face was hideously painted in alternate lines of red and black, and his head was crowned with a magnificent war-bonnet from which, just above his temples and curving slightly forward, stood up two short black buffalo horns. While its ample length of eagles' feathers and herons' plumes trailed wildly on the wind behind him, he came swiftly on at the head of his charging warriors in all his barbaric strength and grandeur. He proudly rode that day—the most perfect type of a warrior it was Ian's lot to see.

He raised his right arm and waved his hand with a royal gesture in answer to the wild cries of rage and encouragement of his warriors on either side of the stream as he and his command swept down upon the dragoons. Again facing squarely towards where Ian lay, he twirled his heavy rifle around his head as if it were a wisp of straw.

He recklessly led the charge with a bravery that could only be equaled but not excelled, while their medicine-man, an equally brave but older chief, rode slightly in advance to the left of the charging column. To say that Ian was surprised at their splendid exhibition of pluck and discipline is to put it mildly. For an instant or two Ian was fairly lost in admiration of the glorious charge as it was far beyond anything he had heard of, read about, or even imagined regarding Indian warfare.

A quick backward glance at the men was most reassuring. Each dragoon had turned in his rifle-pit towards the direction from which the charge was coming. Crouching low and leaning forward with their knees well under them, they grasped their rifles with a grip of steel in their brown sinewy hands. Their chests heaving with excitement, their teeth set hard, their nostrils aquiver, their bronzed faces fairly aflame, and their eyes flashing fire, they grimly lay waiting the word of command, as brave and gallant a little company of men as ever yet upheld the reputation of Mexican courage. No sooner were the charging warriors fairly under way than a withering fire of the Indians who lay in ambush around them suddenly poured fire in upon the troopers. This group of Indians intently watched their every movement in the vain hope that they might sufficiently cow the troops to protect their charging column against their rifles. Ian had expected this action, but he well knew that once their horsemen came within a certain radius that their fire must cease. For eight or ten seconds it seemed to rain bullets and arrows, and then came a sudden lull.

Sitting upright in his pit as best as he was able and leaning backward on his elbows, Ian shouted, "Now!"—and "Now!" was echoed by Malgores.

Instantly the troopers were on their knees, with their rifles at their shoulders. A quick flash of their eyes along the barrels and sixteen good men sent their first of seven successive volleys into the ranks of the charging warriors.

Crash!

On they came, answering back the first volley with a ringing war whoop.

Crash!

And now Ian began to see fallen warriors; yes, and horses too; but still they swept forward with yet wilder yells.

Crash!

They seem to be falling over each other; both men and horses were down in heaps. The wild shrieks from the braves on either side of the stream proclaimed that they too could see the slaughter of their comrades; but still they came.

Crash!

They had ceased to yell but yet came bravely on. No! Yes, down goes their medicine man; but the leading chief still recklessly led the column. Now Ian could see great gaps in their ranks, showing that their bullets tolled heavily among them.

Crash!

Ian couldn't believe his eyes. The chief is down! He and his horse lie dead together on the sand, and for an instant the column shakes; but a hundred yards more and they would have been upon the troopers.

Crash!

They stagger! They half draw rein! They hesitate! They are breaking!

Crash!

And like an angry wave that hurls itself upon a mighty rock and breaks upon its rugged front, the Indians divide to each side of the breastwork and through themselves almost beneath the off side of their chargers. With hoarse cries of rage and anguish, they break for either bank of the river and scatter wildly in every direction as the dragoons spring to their feet with a ringing cheer and pour in volley after volley from their carbines almost in the very face of their now demoralized and retreating enemy.

Ian's devastating fire from his twin Colts accounted for over a dozen deaths.

"Down, men! Lie down!" Ian fairly shrieked, "Get down for your lives!"

And the men, hurling bitter taunts and curses after the retreating warriors, threw themselves, panting, flat on their faces inside their rifle-pits just in time to escape a scorching volley of arrows from the Indians still lying in ambush around them, who had been anxiously watching the charge and naturally enough were wildly enraged at its failure.

Ian craned his head forward for a view of the battlefield. Close to the pits—so close that the men by leaning forward could touch their bodies with their short muskets—lay eight dead warriors. Just beyond these lay several more. For six or seven hundred yards in the direction from which the charge had been made, the ground was strewn here and there by dead Indians and horses, singly and in little groups, showing clearly the effect of each one of the seven volleys the dragoons had poured into the charging column.

Malgores worked his way over to Ian and, as he surveyed the view with Ian, he said, "I have been on the plains as man and boy for more than fifteen years, and I never saw anything like that before. I think they have done their best."

Ian had little fear that the Indians would again assault them, and he knew that water within the pits could be had for the digging. In fact, one corporal had already dug a small well at the bottom of his rifle-pit, and, with a shout, announced that the water was rapidly seeping through the sand.

The dead horses and mules would furnish food for some days, if they could keep the meat from putrefying, and Ian believed they could rely upon some of the men to steal through the Indian lines and make their way to the nearest station.

Orders were given by Malgores to strengthen and connect all the rifle-pits, and to unsaddle the dead horses and use the saddles to help build up the parapet. He also ordered to dig out and fortify a place for the wounded and dress their wounds as well as could be done under the adverse circumstances. The men were to deepen the well, to cut off a large quantity of steaks from the dead horses and mules, and to bury all the meat that they did not immediately need in the sand.

Ian saw a large and very fleshy warrior, having placed himself just out of range, taunting and insulting the troopers in every possible way. He was perfectly naked, and his gestures especially were exceedingly exasperating. Not being in a particularly happy frame of mind, the man's actions annoyed Ian excessively. Now would be a good time to test the new Hall's rifle, which he knew would carry several hundred yards farther than the regular army issue. Ian sighted it at its limit and aimed well over the sight to see if by some chance he might stop the antics of this outrageously insulting warrior.

At the crack of the rifle the warrior sprang into the air with a yell of seemingly both surprise and anguish and fell over, stone dead, while the Indians in his vicinity scattered in every direction. This almost unexpected result of luck was a matter of intense satisfaction to everyone.

The men worked with a will and soon they were in very good shape. Now came a time of weary waiting and comparative inaction that was hard to bear and, under their peculiar circumstances, well nigh intolerable.

Night came slowly down and, as darkness overshadowed the land, it began to rain; never was night or rain more welcome, for during the day the sun had been intensely hot, blisteringly so, and their fight had been from early morning without water or food of any kind. They were well spent with the work and excitement of the day. As the Indians never attack at night, they were comparatively safe until morning; so, as soon as they had obtained water from the stream and quenched their thirst, Malgores asked for a list of the killed and wounded. In a few moments he had the result of the day's fighting. Considering the fact that his command only numbered twenty-four men including Ian, Lieutenant Malgores, and the two scouts, the list was somewhat dismal.

Five were dead or dying, two others lay mortally wounded, the sergeant still lived, also Carlos who had been struck by the arrow back at the village, three severely wounded and two others slightly. As for Ian with the wound in his shoulder and an inconvenient scalp wound that gave him an intense headache, he was not feeling too good.

Malgores with the bullet still in his right thigh could hardly get around. As the ball in his thigh had begun to pain him excessively, he decided to extract it. He appealed to several of the men to cut it out, but as soon as they saw how closely it lay to the artery, they declined in doing so, alleging the risk was too great. However, he was determined it should come out, as he feared it would move and then the artery would probably break in any event. So Ian took his razor from his saddle-pocket, and getting two of the men to press the adjacent flesh back and draw it taut, he managed to cut it out without disturbing the artery, greatly to Malgores almost immediate relief.

Both Ian and Malgores were proud of the individual heroism of the men. It was worthy of all praise. A young corporal, shot through the shoulder, fought straight through the day's fighting, never speaking of his condition until the list of casualties was called for. Another lost one of his eyes by a bullet that lodged just behind it, but he wrapped a handkerchief around his head and fought on steadily.

One of the oldest dragoons, a lifer in his early fifties, though mortally wounded, lay on one side and fought through the entire day's fight. Another man, with an arrow-point lodged squarely in his frontal bone, never ceased to bear his full share in the fray. When a bullet ploughed across his forehead and dislodged the arrow-head, the two falling together to the ground, he wrapped a rag around his head and, though covered with blood, fought to the very close of the days' fighting.

Five young troopers never once mentioned the fact they were wounded until after nightfall. Both Malgores and Ian thought that by moving out at night and keeping together they could make Passo del Norte, and, even if attacked, they had plenty of ammunition left with which to defend them. They believed that no ordinary scouting party of Indians would dare to attack them after their recent experience with them. Furthermore, they did not believe that any Indians, other than those whom they had fought, were in the vicinity, and they doubted if those who might still be watching them were in any great numbers; but they decided to wait a day or so, so the wounded could recover somewhat. Maybe relief would come. If not, they were soldiers and knew how to meet their fate.

After Ian ate a few mouthfuls of raw mule flesh, drank nearly a canteen of water, dressed his wounds as well as he could with wet dressings, and, having seen a strong guard mounted, he rested away until nearly daylight.

All night long they could hear Indians stealthily removing the dead bodies of their slain, and their camp resounded with the beat of drums and the death-wail of the mourners.

Malgores had cautioned the men to lie close and not to fire until the Indians were fairly upon them, as he thought they would make a rush on them at the first flush of dawn. However, he was mistaken; they had evidently left under cover of night.

As the sun rose higher in the sky, the wounded suffered very much. The nights here were really cold, but in the sheltered valleys, the clear sunny days were intensely hot, and already the bodies of the dead horses and mules lying around began to swell and decompose.

The sergeant who had been wounded in the head was senseless and slowly dying.

It became very hot; the mule meat became rotten and some of the wounded were delirious. The stench from the dead horses lying close around was almost intolerable.

No Indian was seen all day so in the late afternoon a little party crossed the stream and let their horses graze on the lush green grass near the water.

Things were not getting any better on the island so they decided to move out at daybreak and take their chances on the trail rather than to waste away on the island.

The following day they marched at seven o'clock and passed on the western side of the mountains of Magdalena and the Black Mountains on the east.

The little band moved slowly as nearly all the horses and mules were dead, and the wounded rode on available animals. Ian walked so two severely wounded men could ride on his fine horse who had come through the battle miraculously unharmed.

Late in the afternoon they came upon the encampment of a caravan going out with about fifteen thousand sheep for the other provinces for which they bring back merchandise. The expedition consisted of about three hundred men, chiefly citizens, escorted by an officer and thirty-five or forty troops. A doctor with the caravan treated the wounded and they all slept better that night. They killed and roasted three sheep for the survivors of the fight. This large caravan must have scared the Indians away from the island or else it may have been the terrible number of casualties that they had suffered.

Further along the next day, they met a caravan of fifty men and probably two hundred horses loaded with traffic for New Mexico. They obtained horses for everyone from the herd. They halted at twelve o'clock so the men could rest then continued the march at three. Lieutenant Malgores showed Ian the place where he had been in two affrays with the Indians—in the first one a Mexican was killed and eight wounded and ten Indians made prisoners; in the latter, fifty-two Indians were wounded and seventeen killed, they being surprised in the night. Malgores killed two and had two horses killed under him.

They traveled the next three days through mountains, crossed several rivers, and arrived at Passo del Norte by a road leading through a hilly mountainous country. They put up at the house of Don Francisco Garcia who was a merchant and a planter. He possessed twenty thousand sheep and one thousand cows in the vicinity to town. They were received in a most hospitable manner by the lieutenant governor and Father Joseph Prado, the vicar of the place. This was by far the most flourishing town they had been in.

Carlos, remarkable as it may seem, still lived and was doing very well, even though the arrowhead had gone two and a half inches into his head. They had carried him for eighty miles across the saddle with a trooper behind him.

While recuperating at the town, one of the horses threw a young woman and ran off, as was the habit of all the Mexican horses, if by chance they threw their rider. Many of the dragoons and Malgores himself pursued him. Ian being mounted on his elegant horse, joined in the chase, and, notwithstanding their superior horsemanship, overtook the horse, caught his bridle and stopped him when both the horses were nearly at full speed. This act procured Ian the applause of the dragoons, but it opened up the shoulder wound again.

Two days journey found them in St. Eleasaro. Malgores and Ian took up quarters at the house of the captain in charge. The captain was then at Chihuahua, but his lady and sister entertained them in a very elegant hospitable manner. To allow their wounds to heal, they rested at the hacienda and began playing cards, which continued until late in the third day. Malgores, who won considerably, would frequently send fifteen or twenty dollars from the table to the lady of the house, her sisters, and others, and beg their acceptance of them, in order that fortune might still continue favorable; in this manner he distributed five hundred dollars.

During breaks in the card playing, Malgores and Ian would ride in the vicinity for exercise. During their rides, Ian noticed the system of servitude that prevailed in Mexico. He thought the system was immeasurably worse for the slave, in every aspect, than the slavery in the United States.

It seemed all laborers in Mexico were Indian and all the proprietors Spaniards, or have mixed blood. There were a few exceptions, but there were very few of either. So of the army—the higher officers are all white men, or have mixed blood—the soldiers all Indians.

Everywhere Ian journeyed, he was treated, although somewhat coldly by the officer corps and the church, always by the other classes with the most perfect respect. Ian recognized that the higher classes of all countries are very much alike, but he doubted whether there was any other country where the military and lower classes were so generally courteous and polite. There is no country where kindness and courtesy are more certain to meet with a proper return. It may be that three hundred years of vassalage to their Spanish masters may have given the Indian population a habitual deference and respect for a race which they have always regarded as a superior one.

Composed of six or seven million people, Mexico was subjected to the intrigues of six or seven thousand officers and priests; and this beautiful country, so prosperous and so rich when it was called New Spain, is now crushed beneath tyranny.

The country had more than two hundred generals, most of them without commands. Every officer who commanded a regiment had the title of general and was distinguished from generals who had no commands by the addition of "general effectivo."

The northern departments of Mexico contain all the mines, and more of the wealth of the country than any others, and they all hang very loosely to the confederacy; they receive no benefit from the central government, which in truth they only know in its excessive demands and taxation. All the money collected from them is spent in Mexico City or elsewhere, and they have not even the satisfaction of knowing that it is beneficially or even honestly used.

The only inhabitants that rebelled at this were the "Texians," that is the ones that came from Missouri, Kentucky, Tennessee and Louisiana.

The biggest obstacle for a breakaway of the Province of Texas from the central government was the influence of the priesthood. The priests were well aware that such an action might be fatal, not only to their own supremacy, but to that of the Catholic religion also. Ian had heard intelligent men express the opinion that one-fourth of the property of the country was in the hands of the priesthood and, instead of diminishing, it was constantly increasing. This estimate, large as it was, was undoubtedly too small. No one pretended to know the value of the coin, jewels, and ornaments belonging to the various churches, which had been accumulating ever since the establishment of the Catholic religion. They owned very many of the finest houses in Mexico City and other cities besides valuable real estate all over the Republic. Their rents were enormous. Almost every person leaves a bequest in his will for masses for his soul, which constitute an encumbrance upon the estate, and thus nearly all the estates of the small proprietors were mortgaged to the church. The property held by the church is estimated at fifty million.

Mexico is the only country where the church property remains in its untouched entirety. Some small amounts had been realized from the sale of the estates of the banished Jesuits; but, with that exception, no president, however hard pressed (and there is no day in the year that they are not hard pressed), has ever dared to encroach upon that which is regarded as consecrated property.

Malgores, noting that Ian had seen the magnificent works of fortification erected at great cost by the Spaniards but falling into ruins, commented on the state of his country.

"Many politicians of the world are in the habit of believing and preaching that no people ought to be free till they are fit to use their freedom," he said. "That is like saying a man should not go into the water until he has learned to swim. If men are to wait for liberty, until they become wise and good in slavery, they will indeed wait forever. Nowhere is there greater enthusiasm for the mere words 'liberty and republic' than here, but the true meaning of which they have very little conception."

"It has been the apology of tyrants and usurpers in all times, that the people were not capable of governing themselves. Indeed, it is said that no people are. If the people of Mexico are not now prepared for a republican government, when will they be? If a European Prince should in mercy be sent them, or some military chieftain of their own should again usurp supreme power, will they then be taught the great principles of civil liberty and the rights of man, so that at some future day they will be prepared to receive free institutions? I borrow from an elegant writer the best reply to all such arguments."

"There is only one cure for the evils which newly acquired freedom produces—and that cure is freedom! When a prisoner leaves his cell, he cannot bear the light of day. He is unable to discriminate colors or recognize faces; the remedy is not to remand him into his dungeon, but rather to accustom him to the rays of the sun. The blaze of truth and liberty may at first dazzle and bewilder nations which have become half blind in the house of bondage, but let them gaze on, and they will soon be able to bear it. In a few years, men learn to reason; the extreme violence of opinion subsides; hostile theories correct each other; the scattered elements of truth cease to conflict and begin to coalesce. At length, a system of justice and order is educed out of the chaos."

"It may be that different provinces may slough off, and each form a separate government for a time with some military chieftain of their own, but he must be a man of high qualities."

"The destiny of Mexico is in her own hands; the present state of things cannot last much longer; no people can long endure such misrule, tumult, and anarchy. There must be a change. The present forms may continue for a time, but it will only be a lingering agony. The path of liberty is thorny and steep, not without much toil and many trials. Have any people obtained the summit to which it leads that Mexico may do so?"

Ian had not realized Lieutenant Malgores concern of the sad tyranny rampant throughout Mexico. Most people seemed to ignore the true state of affairs and looked the other way, and Ian had thought Malgores was with them. He now saw the terrible pain that Malgores felt and longed for true freedom in his native land. The journey to freedom would be long and sad.

Around this fort were a great number of Indians who were on a treaty with the Mexicans. These people appeared to be perfectly independent in their manners and were the only Indians Ian saw in the Mexican dominions whose spirit was not humbled and whose neck was not bound to the yoke of the government.

Malgores was popular with the peasants and Ian believed he sought popularity with them and with all the common people, for there was no man so poor or so humble under whose roof he would not enter. When he walked out, Ian had seen him put a handful of pesos in his pocket and give them all to the old men, women, and children before he returned to his quarters; but to his equals he was haughty and overbearing. This conduct he pursued through the whole province of North Mexico. But Ian could plainly perceive he was cautious of his conduct as he approached the capitol.

The weather turned very bad so divine service was performed in the morning at the garrison, at which all the troops attended under arms. At one part of their mass they presented arms; at another, sank on one knee and rested the muzzle of the gun on the ground in signification of their mission to their Divine Master. At one o'clock, they bade adieu to their friendly hostess, who was one of the finest women Ian had seen in Mexico.

On Thursday they marched early, and in a little over four hours arrived at Guaxequillo, situated on the River Florida, where they met Malgores friend Captain Barelo. He was a Mexican by birth, born near the capital, and entered as a cadet at Guaxequillo nearly twenty years past. By his extraordinary merits (being a Creole) had been promoted to the rank of captain, which was even by himself considered as his ultimate promotion. He was a gentleman in his manners, generous, and frank—a good soldier.

The captain gave a ball for Malgores, at which appeared at least sixty women, ten or so who were very beautiful.

With mountains on each side, the next day they marched twenty-eight miles. They marched through a gap in the mountain, then turned south to a river about twenty feet wide with high steep banks. It was now dry, except in holes.

The next day they did not march until half past four o'clock, and at about nine o'clock an officer arrived from Station Roas with twenty-four men and two Indians in irons; they were noble looking fellows of large stature and appeared by no means cast down by their misfortunes.

The dust and dryness of the road obliged them to march in the night, when they proceeded fifteen miles and encamped without water.

After four hours rest they marched early and passed a hollow with a pit dug in it, which afforded a poor pittance of muddy water for themselves. Here they were again obliged to remain all day in order to travel in the night, as their horses could now enjoy the benefit of water. They left the place a little after five and proceeded fifteen miles by eleven o'clock, when they encamped without water or food for their horses. The next day was ninety-nine degrees and the soil burnt up. They marched two hours and arrived at a miserable house, where they drew water from a well for all their horses and ate.

The inn consisted of one low dirty room, about fifteen feet square, which served for dining room and kitchen. The only furniture was some wooden forks stuck in the ground upon which two or three rough planks were placed for a table. There was a rough bench on each side and some earthen pans in which the food was cooked. As to knives and forks, they were a modern luxury, which Ian did not suppose that the old Indian hostess had ever even heard. The meal consisted of a thick stew of meat and vegetables—a hodgepodge of pork, beef, mutton, turkey, fowl, cabbage, Irish potatoes, carrots, squash, beans, onions, tomatoes, and red peppers were all boiled together. It made very little difference what was selected from the stew, for everything tasted alike.

They rested the remainder of the day, marched in the evening, and made fifteen miles further. The small party proceeded to the Hacienda of Polloss early the next morning before the sun had risen very far. It was a handsome place and the Marquis de San Miguel frequently spent his summer there, coming out from Mexico City in his coach in ten days.

The Hacienda of Polloss was a square enclosure of about three hundred feet, the building being one story high, but some of the apartments were very elegantly furnished. In the center of the square was a fountain, which cast forth water from eight spouts, extended from a colossal female form. From this fountain all the population procured their supply of water. The Marquis had likewise a very handsome church, which, with its ornaments, cost him at least twenty thousand dollars. To officiate in this, he maintained a little stiff superstitious priest. In the rear of the palace, for so it might be called, was a fishpond furnished with immense numbers of fine fish. The population was about two thousand souls.

This was the nearest point to the City of Mexico, for they turned northeast. The Marquis maintained fifteen hundred troops to protect his vassals and property from the Indians. They were all cavalry and were as well dressed and armed as the president, but were treated by the latter as if vastly their inferior.

A number of days later the small party arrived at the Province of Texas, the mosquitoes had become very troublesome. During the day they saw some wild horses on the open plains, but there was no water. After sixteen miles they stopped at a pond and dined.

The next morning they crossed a river and lost two horses in ferrying. They continued their route and passed two herds of wild horses, which merely left the road for them to pass by. At noon Ian saw his first oak since he entered Mexico, and this was of the scrub kind.

They met several parties of troops returning from the Texas and United States border, where they had been sent to reinforce, when American troops were near the line. Ian observed immense numbers of cross roads made by the wild horses. Ian killed a wild hog, which upon examination found to be very different from the tame breed, being smaller, of a brown color, with long hair and short legs. They were to be found in all parts between Red River and the Mexican settlements. In the afternoon they struck the woodland, which was the first they had been in from the time they had left the nation months before.

Several days later they arrived at the River Mariana—the line between Texas and Cogquilla—a pretty little stream and from thence in the afternoon to San Antonio.

They halted at the mission of St. Joseph and were received in a friendly manner by the priest of the mission and others. Governors' Cordero and Herrara met them in a coach about three miles out of town. Ian and Lieutenant Malgores were shown their quarters, where they were received like children. Governor Cordero informed Ian that he had discretionary orders as to the manner of Ian's leaving the country. He, therefore, wished Ian to chose his own time for leaving and that a sum of money Ian might want was at his service. In the meantime, Ian would make the governor's quarters his residence. He also had caused to be vacated a house immediately opposite for Lieutenant Malgores.

A crowd of officers and priests attended the dinner that evening. After the meal they all went to the public square, where the governors joined in a dance with people who in the daytime would approach them with reverence and awe. Here Ian was introduced to the sister of Lieutenant Malgores' wife, who was one of the finest women Ian saw. She was married to a captain.

For hospitality, generosity, docility, and sobriety, the people of Mexico exceed any nation perhaps on the globe; but in national energy, or patriotism, enterprise of character, and independence of soul, they appeared perhaps the most deficient. Yet there were men who had displayed bravery to a surprising degree and the Europeans who are there cherish with delight the idea of their gallant ancestry.

Their women have black eyes and hair. Ian met but one exception to this rule at Chihuahua. She was a fair lady and, by way of distinction, was called the girl with light hair. They are all inclining a little to en bon point, but few are elegant figures. Their dress is generally short jackets and petticoats and high-heel shoes, without any headdress; over this they have a silk wrapper which they always wear. When in the presence of men, they bring this wrap over their faces; but as Ian approached the Atlantic and the United States frontiers, he saw several ladies who wore the gowns of the United States women, which they conceive to be more elegant than their ancient costume. The lower class of the men are generally dressed in broad-brimmed hats, short coats, large waistcoats always open at the knees owing, Ian supposed, to the greater freedom it gave to the limb on horseback. They also wore a kind of leather boot or wrapper bound round the leg, somewhat in the manner of our frontier men's leggings and gartered on. The boot is of a soft pliable leather, but not colored. In the eastern provinces, the dragoons wear over this wrapper a sort of jack-boot made of seal leather, to which are fastened the spurs by a rivet, the gaffs of which are sometimes near an inch in length. But the spurs of the gentlemen and officers, although clumsy to our ideas, are frequently ornamented with raised silver work on the shoulders, and the strap embroidered with silver and gold thread. They are always ready to mount their horses, on which the inhabitants of the internal provinces spend nearly half the day. This description will generally apply for the dress of all the lower class men of the provinces. But, in the towns, amongst the more fashionable ranks, they dress after the European or United States mode with no more distinction than we see in our cities from one six months to another. Both men and women have remarkable fine hair and pride themselves in the display of it.

Their amusements are music, singing, dancing, and gambling; the latter is strictly prohibited, but the prohibition is not much attended to. There is a dance performed by one man and two women who beat time to the music, which is soft and voluptuous, but sometimes changes to a lively gay air, while the dancers occasionally exhibit the most indelicate gestures. The whole of this dance impressed Ian with the idea of an isolated society of once civilized beings, but now degenerated into a medium state between the improved world and the children of nature. The fandango is danced in various figures and numbers; the minuet is still danced by the superior class only. The music made use of the guitar, violin, and singers whom, in the first described dance, accompany the music with their hands and voices. There are always some words adapted to the music, which are generally of such a tendency, as would in the United States, occasion every lady to leave the room.

Their games are cards, billiards, horseracing, and cock fighting, the first and last of which are carried to the most extravagant length, the parties losing and winning immense sums. The commandant-general was very severe with his officers in these respects, frequently sending them to some frontier post in confinement for a month for no other fault than having lost large sums at play.

At every town of consequence is a public walk where the ladies and gentlemen meet and sing songs, which are always on the subject of love or the social board. The females have fine voices and sing in French, Italian, and Spanish with the whole company joining in the chorus. In their houses the ladies play on the guitar and generally accompany it with their voices. They either sit down on the carpet cross-legged or loll on a sofa. To sit upright in a chair appeared to put them to a great inconvenience, and although the better class would sometimes do it on their first introduction, they soon demanded liberty to follow their old habits. In their eating and drinking they are remarkably temperate. Early in the morning you receive a dish of chocolate and a cake; at twelve you dine on several dishes of meat, fowls, and fish after which you have a variety of confectioneries, and indeed an elegant dessert. Then you drink a few glasses of wine, sing a few songs, and retire to take the siesta, or afternoon nap, which is done by rich and poor. Then, at about two o'clock, the windows and doors are all closed, the streets deserted, and the stillness of midnight reigns throughout. About four o'clock they rise, wash, dress, and prepare for the dissipation of the night. About eleven o'clock some refreshments are offered, but few take any except a little wine and water and a little candied sugar.

The next evening a large party dined at Governor Cordero's, who gave the first toast to the President of the United States. Ian returned the compliment by toasting His Excellency; these were followed by toasting Ian's safe and happy arrival in his own country and the continuation of the good understanding which existed between the two countries. In conversations with the two governors, they exhibited an astonishing knowledge of the political character of the United States government, the local interests of the different parts of the union, the military disposition of the Army of the West, and the disputes between the two governments on the frontiers.

Governor Don Antonio Cordero was fifty years of age, about five feet ten inches in height, fair complexion, and blue eyes. He wore his hair turned back and, in every part of his dress, was eligibly written "the soldier." He yet possessed an excellent constitution, and a body that appeared to be neither impaired by the fatigues of the various campaigns he had made nor disfigured by the numerous wounds received from his enemies. He was universally beloved and respected, and by far the most popular man in the internal provinces. He spoke the Latin and French languages well, and he was generous, gallant, brave, and sincerely attached to his country. These numerous qualifications had advanced him to the rank of colonel of cavalry, and Governor of the Provinces of Boquilla and Texas. His usual residence was Montelovez, which he had greatly embellished; but since the Americans took possession of Louisiana, he had moved to San Antonio in order to be nearer the frontier, to be able to apply the remedy to any evil which might arise from the collision of the border.

Governor Don Simon de Herrara was about five feet eleven inches tall, had sparkling black eyes, and dark complexion and hair. He was born in the Canary Islands, served in the infantry in France, Spain, and Flanders, and spoke the French language well and a little of the English. He was engaging in his conversation with his equals. He was polite and obliging to his inferiors and, in all his actions, one of the most gallant and accomplished men. He possessed a great knowledge of mankind from his experience in various countries and societies, and he knew how to employ the genius of each of his subordinates to advantage. He had been in the United States several times and was now a lieutenant colonel of infantry and Governor of the Province of New Leon. His seat of government was Monterrey and probably if ever his people adored a chief it was Herrara. When his time expired last, he immediately journeyed to Mexico City attended by three hundred of the most respectable people of his district, who carried with them the sighs, tears, and prayers of thousands that he might be continued in that government. The president thought proper to accede to their wishes. During his one-year absence, the citizens of rank in Monterrey had no marriages or baptisms take place in any of their families, waiting until their common father could be there to consent and give joy to the occasion by his presence. What greater proof could be given of their esteem and love? In drawing a parallel between the two friends, it should be said, that Cordero was the man of the greatest reading, Herrara of the world. Cordero had lived all his life a bachelor; Herrara married an English lady in early youth that, by graceful manners, made her as much beloved and esteemed by the ladies as her noble husband was by the men. By her he had several children, one now an officer in the service of his country. But the two friends agreed perfectly on one point—a secret determination never to see that flourishing part of the New World subject to any European lord. Their honor and loyalty bound them to defend this determination with their lives and fortunes.

San Antonio, the capital of the Texas province, was situated on the head waters of the river of that name, and perhaps contained two thousand souls, most of whom resided in miserable mud-wall houses, covered with thatch grass roofs. The town was laid out on a very grand plan. To the east of it, on the other side of the river, is the station of the troops. About two, three, and four miles from San Antonio are three missions, formerly flourishing and prosperous. These buildings for solidity, accommodations, and majesty were surpassed by few that Ian met with in Mexico. The resident priest treated them with the greatest hospitality, and was respected and beloved by all that knew him. He made a singular observation relative to the Indians, who had formerly formed the population of these establishments under the charge of the monks. Ian asked him what had become of the natives. He replied that it appeared to him that they could not exist under the shadow of the whites. As the nations who formed these missions had been nurtured and put on the same footing as the Mexicans; yet they had, notwithstanding, dwindled away until the other two had become entirely depopulated. The one where he resided had no more than sufficient to perform his household labor. From this he had formed an idea that God never intended them to form one people, but that they should always remain distinct and separate.

There were in Texas, at the time Ian came through, nine hundred and eighty-eight men. The actual returns of the troops were as follows: three hundred eighty-eight at San Antonio; four hundred at cantonment on the Trinity; one hundred at the Trinity, and one hundred at Nacogdoches. The rabble militia were made the more respectable by a few American

Arthur Schott's "Military Plaza—San Antonio, Texas" (1853?)
Engraved by James D. Smillie. Emory's Boundary Survey Report

riflemen, who were incorporated among them; they are about three hundred in number, including bow and arrow men.

Sending out recruiting detachments into the mountains, where they hunt the Indians in their dens and caverns, and bring them in chains to Mexico City, generally collected this militia. There was scarcely a day that droves of these miserable and more than half-naked wretches were seen thus chained together and marching through the streets to the barracks. There they were scoured, and then dressed in a uniform made of linen cloth or of serge, and are occasionally drilled. The drilling consisted mainly in teaching them to march in column through the streets. Their military bands were good, and the men learned to march indifferently well, but only indifferently well; they put their feet down as if they were feeling for the place and did not step with the erect and graceful air that is so beautiful in well-drilled troops. As to the wheeling of well-trained dragoons, or the prompt and exact execution of other evolutions, they know nothing about them. There were not one in ten of these soldiers who had ever seen a gun, nor one in a hundred who had ever fired one before he was brought into the barracks. It was in this way that the ranks of the army were generally filled up. In particular emergencies, the prisons were thrown open, which always contained more prisoners than the army numbers. These felons became soldiers and some of them officers. Their arms, too, were generally worthless English muskets, which had been condemned and thrown aside, and were purchased at a low rate by the Mexican government. Their powder was equally bad. In the last battle between Santa Anna and Bustamente, which lasted the whole day, not one cannon ball in a thousand reached the enemy; they generally fell about halfway between the opposing armies.

However, the Rancheros were a different story. They formed an important part of the Mexican cavalry. "Rancheros" is a name derived from their occupation and mode of life, and is common to a similar class of men who subsist on the pampas of South America, half Indian and half Spanish. In their extraction, gaunt, shriveled, though muscular in their frames, dark and swarthy- visaged as they are, these men are the Arabs of the American continent. Living half of the time in the saddle, for they are unrivalled horsemen with lasso in hand, they traverse the vast plains in search of the buffalo and wild horse that roam in countless herds. The killing of these animals, and the preparation and sale of their hides, is their sole means of livelihood, other than occasionally lending a helping hand to some of the partisans in the civil wars that are being continually waged around them. Their costume generally consists of a pair of tough hide leggings with sandals of the same material bound together with leather thongs. Over this a blanket is worn that has a hole in the center large enough to allow the head to be thrust out and which falls gracefully over their shoulders, leaving ample room for the play of their arms. Add to this a broad straw sombrero, and the lasso hanging at his saddle-pummel, and you have the Ranchero as he appears in time of peace, or in the pursuit of his occupation. Join to this a long lance with a sharp spear head ornamented with a strip of red bunting on a horse as savage and unmanageable as himself with his belt plentifully supplied with pistols and knives, and you have the Ranchero as a member of the troop of bandido, or as a soldier in a body of cavalry. In a conflict among the chaparrals of Mexico or in an ambuscade, they are indeed a formidable enemy. Their power of enduring fatigue is almost inexhaustible, and a scanty meal each day of jerked beef is enough for months.

Such are the Rancheros, and under disciplined control, they would be the best light troops in the world. These are the men who comprise the great body of the Mexican cavalry. They are to the armies of this nation what the Cossacks are to the Russians—ever on the alert, never to be surprised, and untiring in the pursuit of the foe when plunder, no matter how trifling, is to be obtained.

Such is the condition and character of the Mexican army; but notwithstanding the materials of which it is composed; it contained some men as brave as ever fought upon a battlefield.

*   *   *

That evening there was another large party at the governor's hacienda in honor of Presidente Santa Anna. The dinner was elegant, and the general presided with great dignity. He was joyous and hilarious, but had the appearance and manners of a gentleman. Ian and Malgores sat near him and his aides-de-camp, who were not seated at the table, would occasionally come to his seat and say some playful thing to him. Ian was struck with the style of the intercourse between them; marked by an affectionate kindness on his part, and the utmost respect, but at the same time freedom from restraint, upon theirs.

The ball was well attended. The company was by no means select. In fact, Ian saw there were very few of the ladies belonging to the aristocracy; but many others who had no business there. This, however, was unavoidable in a revolutionary country like Mexico. Every general and politician holds his power by no other tenure than the caprice of the army, and he is forced, therefore, to conciliate it.

The ladies at the ball were perfect, as most ladies of Mexico are. In the great attributes of the heart, affection, kindness, and benevolence in all their forms, they have no superiors. They are eminently graceful in everything.

Ian was in the mood for more intimacy with a lady, so he and Malgores left the ball as soon as they could. The ladies of the higher class never walked the streets alone, but the streets were always swarming with women of the middle and lower classes. The only articles of dress worn by these were a one-piece dress and petticoat, satin slippers, but no stockings, and a rebozo; a long shawl improperly called by the American ladies, a mantilla. This they wear over the head and wrapped close around the chin thrown over the left shoulder. Whatever they may be in private, no people can be more proper in public. One could probably walk the streets of Mexico for a year and not see a wanton gesture or look on the part of a female of any description, with the single exception, that if you meet a woman with a fine bust, which they are very apt to have, she finds some reason to adjust her rebozo, and throws it open for a second. This rebozo answers all the purposes of shawl, bonnet, and frockbody (a loose outer garment).

After visiting several taverns and enjoying the wild dancing, drinking and conversation with a particularly striking wild beauty, Ian and Malgores decided to go to a cock-fight to round out the evening's entertainment. The fighting did not start until about twelve o'clock. Every human creature in Mexico, high and low, old and young, who can get there, is certain to go to cockfights.

When they entered the cockpit with a girl on his arm, Ian noticed that Santa Anna and a fellow general with a large number of the most distinguished men in Mexico, and quite a large number of ladies of the highest circles, were already there.

The master of ceremonies on the occasion walked into the pit, and exclaimed two or three times, "Ava Maria purissima los gallos vienen"—"Hail, most pure Mary, the chicken-cocks are coming." Whereupon a cock was brought in covered, and a challenge was proclaimed, to all comers, which was very soon accepted. The fowls were then uncovered, and allowed to walk about the pit that the spectators could see them and select the one on which they choose to risk their money. Those in the seats called some of the numerous brokers, who were in attendance, gave them whatever sum of money they desired to bet, and designated their favorite cock. It was genteel to bet nothing but gold.

Before the fight commences, the broker returns and informs the person whose money he has received whether his bet has been taken. If he loses, he sees no more of the broker; but if he wins, he is perfectly sure to get his money. A small gratification is expected by the broker, but never asked for, if it is not voluntarily given. Ian was surprised to see these fellows, who are often entrusted with the money of a dozen different persons, never make a mistake as to the person for whom the bet was made, nor the amount of it. And it is another evidence as to the honesty of that class of Mexicans that they never attempt to go off with the money, which they could so easily do. It would be as impossible for a stranger to identify one of these Indians, as it would be to select a particular crow out of a flock of a hundred.

Presidente Santa Anna was a national hero and much beloved. Whenever Santa Anna's fowl lost his fight, there was always the loudest shouting.

As soon as the cock fighting was over, the gambling at Monte commenced. There were great many public tables and some private ones; Santa Anna only played at the private tables. There were many tables where nothing but gold was bet—others where there was nothing but silver and other tables again for copper. The game was a perfectly fair one, and one at which cheating was impossible.

There was some very small advantage in the game in favor of the bank. If the bet was decided in favor of the better on the first turn, there was a very small deduction from the amount paid—an eighth, or perhaps a fourth. But there was another, and a much more important advantage to the bank. In this, as in all of these public games, men always double and bet high when they have won; generally speaking, if the bank wins one bet in three, the bettor has lost in the end. Ian had not seen one of these public games for a few years until he went to Mexico, and only saw it twice there.

Ian was much struck with one thing he noticed. He was sure he saw fifty thousand dollars on the tables at once, probably in fifty different piles, and belonging to as many different bettors, and yet he never witnessed a dispute of any sort as to the ownership of any one of the piles. Ian had seen a sum that the persons who bet had omitted to take up when he had won; no one claimed it until it had increased to quite a large sum by winning double every time. When it would be asked whose bet it was, and thus announced that it was forgotten, even then no one would claim it.

The gravity and propriety of Spanish manners are never wanting, even at the gaming table. Ian saw men in the humbler walks of life lose several thousand dollars, perhaps the last that they possessed, without a frown or the slightest sign of emotion of any sort. Greatly habit forming as is the practice of gaming everywhere, and in all its forms, it was nowhere so much so as in Mexico. Many people of the mining countries are characteristically thriftless and fail to provide for the future, but no where more than in Mexico. There are few instances in Mexico of men who have an idea of that certain competency which is the reward of industry in any employment—the savings of even small earnings. Whereby the small gains of one year swell those of the next, which is so well expressed in the maxim of Dr. Franklin "that the second hundred dollars is much easier made than the first, the first assisting to make the second."

While they habitually postpone everything hasta manana (until tomorrow), they never think of making any provision for that tomorrow. If they ever do lay up money, it is for the purpose of attending the feast of San Augustine and with the hope of winning a fortune with it. They hear of some one, perhaps, who had so won, but they do not think of the thousands who have lost.

Sometimes an evening is passed in playing at monte for four pences, when not more than three or four dollars were lost by any one.

Ian had heard much said of the gambling of priests and ladies in Mexico, but he never saw either doing it.

The more Ian saw the Presidente the more intriguing he became. He knew the American Texians hated the man, for probably very good reasons, as he rejected their attempts to set up an independent state. But, if the man was to be an enemy of the Texians and possibly the United States, it would be wise to know him.

He was about five feet ten inches high, with a finely proportioned person. His complexion was of an olive cast, but not indicating any mixture of blood, although Ian believed he was not of pure Spanish lineage. Ian had never seen a more striking and finely formed head and face. Ian remembered having heard a distinguished American statesman remark when Santa Anna was in Washington that he had rarely seen a face indicative in a higher degree of talent, firmness, and kindness.

To be popular with the Texians, Ian sensed he should dislike this man, but he did not let others prejudice his thinking, not even the fabulous Texians. His rule of conduct was to know people, friends and enemies, try to understand them, why they did things, why they did not do things, in addition to how they thought and why. This made life more exciting and full— to really know people. And after all, Santa Anna was tolerating Ian, an American, in his country, so Ian figured he should at least tolerate Santa Anna. Ian could understand why Santa Anna and the Texians did not see things eye to eye. After all, they were trying to break away from the rest of Mexico. If some of the American states tried to break away from the Union, Ian figured the President of the United States would be very angry, to say the least.

Ian was particularly struck with his high bearing and polished manners; the grace, ease, naturalness of his manners, and the thoughtfulness and repose which were so striking in his facial expression.

Ian had seen no countenance except that of General Jackson, whose range of expression was so great, where there was so great a difference between the quiet expression of the face when at rest and in a gentle mood, and its terrible ferocity when highly excited. The mildness of the lamb and fierceness of the enraged tiger would not too strongly express this difference. Such was his character, by nature kind and affectionate, but subject to bursts of passion fiery and fierce. He was a Spaniard; a race which, with its noble traits of character, is everywhere regarded as more than ordinarily bloodthirsty; perhaps not more so by nature than others. The Spaniards had been from the earliest period engaged in civil wars, and much bloodshed and murder everywhere accompany civil wars. That war between the Goths and the Moors lasted for eight hundred years, and there were elements in that protracted contest that exceeded the characteristic ferocity of civil wars. It was a religious war, and more than that, it was a war of races. The civil war between the mother country and Mexico, in which Santa Anna was bred, was not the best possible school for lessons of clemency and mercy. No leniency was generally the law of that war, at least on the part of Spain, and almost the only law that Spain respected. It would be strange indeed, if one brought up in such a school should not have committed some acts not strictly conformable to American notions.

General Santa Anna had for the last quarter of a century played so conspicuous a part in the drama of Mexican politics and civil war as to have attracted the attention of the world and to have made his name in some degree historic. No history of his country for that period could be written without the constant mention of his name; indeed, he was regarded more than any other man, the author and finisher of the last and successful struggle of Mexico for independence and a republican form of government.

Ian was no prophet, but he clearly saw that a full-scale war was not to be avoided.

*　　*　　*

The next day was spent in preparing to march. The following morning Ian and the escort marched at seven o'clock, with Governor Cordero taking Ian and Lieutenant Malgores out in his coach about five miles. They took friendly adieu of the governor and started north on the trip back to Fort Leavenworth.

When Ian left San Antonio, everything appeared to be in a flourishing and improving state. This owing to the examples and encouragement given to industry, politeness, and civilization by their excellent Governor Cordero and his colleague Herrara; also due to the large body of troops maintained at that place because of the differences existing between the Texians and Mexico.

Ian liked this Texas country. The province was large, bordered on the north by Louisiana, on the east by the Territory of Orleans, on the west by Cogquilla and New Mexico, and on the south by New San Andrea. Its greatest length from north to south may be five hundred miles, and breadth from east to west three hundred fifty.

The population of Texas was estimated at seven thousand; these were principally Spanish Creoles, some French, some Americans, and a few civilized Indians and half-breeds.

This province traded with Mexico City, by Monterrey and Monclova for merchandise, and with New Orleans by Nacogdoches, but the latter being contraband was liable to great damage and risk; they gave in return horses and mules.

The American emigrants were introducing some spirit of agriculture near to Nacogdoches and the Trinity, but the oppression and suspicions they labor under prevented their proceeding with that vigor that was necessary to give success to the establishment of a new country.

The religion of the province of Texas was Catholic, but much relaxed.

By the evening campfire, Ian tried to sum up the future of Mexico. The main difference from the United States was the insecurity of life and property that prevailed in Mexico. This alone accounted for not bringing the republic up to the standards of civilized lands. The country was infested with robbers; there was little law and order. The stagecoaches that ran in the more populated areas were held up regularly, sometimes at several places on the trip.

The highwaymen who came last would take from passengers even their underwear, though with inborn chivalry they allowed the ladies to keep their dresses. The unfortunate travelers would arrive at their destination gowned in newspapers and the curtains of the coach. Whenever the curtains were not seen to be in their proper places, it was at once understood in the town what had happened.

For three days the little band proceeded north out of San Antonio. There were signs of a killing drought everywhere. Through the clouds of dust and scorching heat, the perspiring men and animals pushed on. The scarcity of water and the swarms of flies caused both men and animals to suffer.

At early evening they usually camped to their horses, and the soldiers then lounged about the camp, smoking their pipes or cigars. Ian would ride out of camp occasionally to view the surrounding country at a leisurely pace.

Four days of hard riding and they left the desert far behind although the temperatures were still very great. They had crossed the Red River, which was considered by the United States the boundary between Mexico and United States. A little later they crossed the Canadian.

There they met General Leavenworth's expedition returning from the Pawnee Pict villages. Many of the dragoons were sick and unable to ride and were carried on litters between two horses. Nearly every tent belonging to the officers had been converted to hospitals for the sick; sighs and groaning were heard in all directions. From the Comanche village to this place, the country had been entirely prairie and most of the way high, dry ground without water for which they sometimes suffered very much. From day to day the expedition had moved on, exposed to the hot and burning rays of the sun, without a cloud to relieve the sun's intensity, or a bush to shade them, or anything to cast a shadow except the bodies of their horses. The grass for a great part of the way was very dried up, scarcely affording a bite for their horses. Sometimes for the distance of many miles, the only water they could find was in stagnant pools, lying on the highest ground in which the buffaloes had been lying and wallowing like hogs in a mud puddle. They had frequently come to these dirty pools from which they had driven the herds of wallowing buffalo, and into which their poor and almost dying horses irresistibly ran and plunged their noses, sucking up the dirty and poisonous draught until, in some instances, they fell dead in their tracks. The men also sprang from their horses and laded up and drank to almost fatal excess the disgusting and tepid draught, and with it filled their canteens, which were slung to their sides, and from which they were sucking the bilious contents during the day.

The expedition was snugly encamped on a beautiful plain, and in the midst of countless numbers of buffaloes had halted a few days to rest the horses and men and dry meat to last the remainder of their journey back to Fort Gibson.

*   *   *

Ian was happy to see his fellow officer, Lt. Philip St. George Cooke. They had shared several experiences together. Both had fought the arbitrary military regulations about short hair. A general order was issued that the hair had to be short, or what was generally termed "cropped." Whiskers were ordered not to extend below the lower tip of the ear, and a line thence with the curve of the mouth. Moustaches could not be worn by officers or men on any pretense whatsoever. The order stated that the non-observance of the regulation would be no longer permitted, and it was enjoined upon all officers to observe and enforce the regulation, by order of the Secretary of War. Ian and Cooke refused to cut their hair or moustaches and carried their fight all the way to the Secretary. They told the Secretary that a host of resignations would follow the order! The modern military will give up many things, do much for his country, sacrifice his comfort, his health, his friends, his fortune—perhaps, his life—certainly; but his moustache—NEVER!

The order was changed. The cavalry regiments were exempted!

Philip St. George Cooke was by now thoroughly tired of the dubious glories of the expedition. Ian longed for Fort Leavenworth—the girls, the parties—and especially wanted to see Louisa again.

The dragoons were out on the prairies because Secretary of War Cass had ordered the First United States Dragoons to impress upon the Pawnee Pict and Comanche Indians the power of the United States. Somewhere on the Red River about two hundred fifty miles to the west of Fort Gibson, Arkansas Territory, lay the villages of the restless Comanche and Pawnee Picts, between the Missouri and Arkansas frontiers and the Rocky Mountains, but beyond the reach of infantry forces; so nine companies of about five hundred men were sent on a summer campaign.

With the arrival of spring, General Leavenworth took command of the Western Division in preparation for the projected expedition. It was the intended policy of the government to impress the plains Indians with its strength and to treaty with them for the safety of emigrants and the eastern Indians who were to be settled near the plains. It was hoped that the appearance of the entire dragoon regiment on the plains would persuade the tribes to send treaty parties to Fort Gibson.

Preparations for the expedition began with the arrival of General Henry Leavenworth at Fort Gibson on April 23. Trails to the False Washita River, the site of an advance base, were laid out. The campaign orders called for a march to the swamps of the Red River, returning down the Arkansas to Fort Gibson. The False Washita was so called to distinguish it from the "true" Washita of Arkansas and Louisiana.

Leavenworth detached a dragoon officer to Franklin, Missouri, to arrange for an escort of the Santa Fe caravan; Clifton Wharton's A Company was detailed for this mission.

Leavenworth then sent Sumner's B Company to the unfriendly Osage villages, where they were instructed to seize two Pawnee squaws held captive by the Osage, for he intended to use them in recovering a Ranger, George B. Abbey, and a boy, Matthew Wright Martin, who were thought to be held by the Pawnee. On April 31, 1834, Leavenworth reviewed dragoons and the 7th Infantry detachment from the fort.

The following day, he praised the commands by adding that he had heard with "surprise and regret that some of the enlisted men have deserted." This brought smiles to the faces of the national elite, especially after it was learned that on the night after Leavenworth's speech, four more men had taken "leg-bail."

Although they should have marched before the first of May, Leavenworth was forced to await the arrival of the dragoon companies that had been enlisted during the winter. Company F, composed of Bostonians, and Company G, of Hoosiers, arrived shortly after the review, but the remaining three did not put in an appearance before June 12, all of them not drilled and unready for service.

Civilians gathered their paraphernalia for the departure: Indian Commissioner Montford Strokes; George Catlin, the artist; and the Prussian botanist, Carl Beyrich. With his strength at nearly five hundred men, Colonel Dodge left Camp Jackson on June 15, moving the regiment across the Arkansas about twenty miles to Camp Rendezvous, where it was assembled for the first time.

It had been an imposing cavalcade. The tramp of horses on the prairie was mingled with the commands of the officers; the proud and manly deportment of the young men indicated the cheerful hope and gay spirit of the regiment. A company of white horses made a striking contrast to another of blacks, while sorrels and bays gave added color. To the rear of the companies the lumbering movements of the baggage-wagons were seen and heard.

The regiment waited until June 21 for its Indian guides and interpreters, eleven Osage, eight Cherokee, six Delaware, and seven Seneca. As soon as they appeared Dodge immediately moved out along the south bank of the Arkansas, then left the regiment with forty men and headed south to the False Washita.

Long, forced marches were made during the sultry June days. Springs and streams provided a bountiful supply of water and the prairies furnished ample pasture for the horses.

But the pleasures soon petered out as the recruits quickly succumbed to the hardships of the trail and the heat.

The column followed with increasing difficulty, for the temperature was over 105 degrees in the shade, and twenty-three men, before the march even started, had to be sent back to Fort Gibson as unfit. Catlin noted that the younger officers "generally want to fight the Indians first and make peace later," but as the troops began to lengthen the distance between themselves and Fort Gibson, this attitude changed. Martial ardor quickly evaporated when faced with bad water, stubborn resistant wagons, and the rays of an unprecedented hot summer sun.

Five days after the start of the expedition, forty-five men and three officers were sick from the excessive heat. Each day more and more fell ill and had to be left to recuperate. Several days later the casualties were so numerous the regiment had to be reorganized. Six companies of forty-two men each continued on the campaign. One hundred and nine were left at the makeshift camp with eighty-six of the men sick and disabled. The baggage-wagons had been abandoned. Each man was furnished ten days rations, and eighty rounds of cartridges and the march began again.

Day after day through the month of July the command continued its march over the rolling prairies. Now and then a stray band of Indians was seen. Once again the heat and the strenuous forced marches prostrated the men and animals. About eight hundred lodges were visited and the Indians properly impressed, but by July 19 the command had been reduced to 103 men. Seventy-five, over one-half of whom were sick, had to be left behind. Desertions had also reduced the band. For a month the soldiers had been without a piece of bread, and they became so hungry they ate their dying and suffering horses. Many deer were seen but few were killed because they marched too fast to hunt much on the road.

Colonel Dodge ordered preparations to be made for a move to the head of the Canadian River, a distance of a hundred or more miles, where immense herds of buffalo might be found; a place where they could get enough to eat, and by lying by awhile could restore the sick, who were now occupying a great number of litters. Catlin was scarcely idle under such circumstances as these, where so many subjects for his brush and his pen were gathered about him.

The dragoons brought home a prisoner. He was smart and a very intelligent boy of nine years of age. When he came in he was entirely naked, as the Indians keep their own boys of that age.

The little boy was brought in the whole distance to Fort Gibson, in the arms of the dragoons, who took turns carrying him, and after the command arrived there, he was transmitted to the Red River by an officer who had the enviable satisfaction of delivering him into the arms of his disconsolate and half-distracted mother.

The Pawnee Picts, as well as the Comanches, were generally an ordinary looking set of men, when on their feet; but, being fine horsemen, are equally improved in appearance as soon as they mount upon their horses' backs.

Amongst the women of this tribe, there were many that were exceedingly pretty in feature and in form, and also in expression. The dress of the men of this tribe, as amongst the Comanches, consisted generally of leggings of dressed skins and moccasins, with a flap or breechcloth, made also of dressed skins or furs, and often very beautifully ornamented with shells. Above the waist they seldom wear any drapery, owing to the warmth of the climate, which will rarely justify it; their heads are generally covered with a headdress.

The woman of the Comanches and Pawnee Picts are always decently and comfortable clad, being covered generally with a gown or slip that reaches from the chin quite down to the ankles, made of deer or elk skins. They are often garnished very prettily and ornamented with long fringe of elk's teeth, which are fastened on them in rows, and more highly valued than any other ornament they can put upon them.

The head chief of the Kiowas, whose name was Teh-toot-sah, was found to be a very gentlemanly and high-minded man, who treated the dragoons and officers with great kindness while in his country. His long hair was ornamented with great many silver broaches, extended almost to his knees. This distinguished man, as well as several others of his tribe, had agreed to join the troop on the march to Fort Gibson.

All the above chiefs and braves, and many others, forming a very picturesque cavalcade, would move off in a day or two with the troop on their way back to Fort Gibson, where it was hoped the dragoons could arrive more happy than they were in their present jaded and sickly condition.

On the return journey, over one hundred miles were marched in the first week with twenty-one of the Kiowa, Comanche, Pawnee and Wacoah chiefs accompanying the dragoons back to Fort Gibson. The overpowering heat and the number of sick greatly slowed the speed of the dragoons, but time was taken out to hunt buffalo for the hungry command. Now and then a day of rest would be ordered for the jaded horses, and many times men were lost in hunting buffalo. Prairie fires at times threatened the command.

The plains, for many miles, seem actually speckled in distance, and for several days, the officers and men had been indulged in a general license to gratify their sporting propensities—a scene of bustle and cruel slaughter it had been, to be sure! From morning till night, the camp has been daily almost deserted; the men had dispersed in little squads in all directions, and were dealing death to these poor creatures to a most cruel and wanton extent, merely for the pleasure of destroying, generally without stopping to cut out the meat. During two-days, several hundreds were killed, and not so much as the flesh of half a dozen used. Such immense swarms of them were spread over this tract of country; and so divided and terrified have they become, finding their enemies in all directions where they run, that the poor beasts seem completely bewildered—running here and there. As often as otherwise, they come singly advancing to the horsemen as if to join them for their company and are easily shot down. In the turmoil and confusion, when their assailants have been pushing them forward, they have galloped though the encampment, jumping over the fires, upsetting pots and kettles, driving horses from their fastenings, and throwing the whole encampment into the greatest instant consternation and alarm. The hunting fever will be satiated in a few days amongst the young men, who are well enough to take part in the chase; the bilious fever, it is to be hoped, will be abated in a short time amongst those who are invalid, and enough meat was dried to last them to Fort Gibson, when they shall be on the march again, and winding their way towards that garrison.

General Leavenworth had ordered a halt hoping that it could help the regiment, for only half of his men were still on their feet. This did no good; Leavenworth, ill himself after being pitched off his horse during a buffalo hunt, then ordered Dodge to take the healthy men and press on to the Pawnee country.

George Catlin, the renowned English artist, wrote letters to his dear wife in England that very day.

He entered into his journal, "I am in much good company and amusement. Though I have an order from the Secretary at War to the commanding officer to protect and supply me, I shall ask but for their protection; as I have, with my friend Joe, laid in our own supplies for the campaign, not putting the government to any expense on my account, in pursuit of my own private object."

"I am writing this under General Leavenworth's tent, where he has generously invited me to take up my quarters during our encampment here, and he promises to send it by his express. At the time I am writing, the general lies pallid and emaciated before me on his couch with a dragoon fanning him, whilst he breathes forty or fifty breaths a minute and writhes under a burning fever, although he is yet unwilling even to admit that he is sick."

"In my last letter I have a brief account of a buffalo chase, where General Leavenworth and Colonel Dodge took part and met with pleasing success. The next day while on the march, and a mile or so in advance of the regiment, and two days before we reached this place, General Leavenworth, Colonel Dodge, Lieutenant Wheelock and myself were jogging along, all in turn complaining of the lameness of our bones from the chase on the former day, when the general, who had long ago had his surfeit of pleasure of this kind on the Upper Missouri, remonstrated against further indulgence, in the following manner: 'Well, Colonel, this running for buffaloes is bad business for us; we are getting too old, and should leave such amusements to the young men. I have had enough of this fun in my life, and I am determined not to hazard my limbs or weary my horse any more with it. It is the height of folly for us, but will do well enough for boys.' Colonel Dodge assented at once to his resolves, and approved them; whilst I, who had tried it in every form (and I had thought, to my hearts content), on the Upper Missouri, joined my assent to the folly of our destroying our horses, which had a long journey to perform, and agreed that I would join no more in the buffalo chase, however near and inviting they might come to me."

"In the midst of this conversation, and these mutual declarations (or rather just at the end of them), as we were jogging along in 'Indian file' and General Leavenworth taking the lead, and just rising to the tip of a little hill over which it seems he had had an instant peep, he dropped himself suddenly upon the side of his horse and wheeled back and rapidly informed us with an agitated whisper, and an exceeding game contraction of the eye, that a snug little band of buffalo were quietly grazing just over the knoll in a beautiful meadow for running, and that if I would take to the left and Lieutenant Wheelock to the right, then let him and the Colonel dash right into the midst of them, we could play the devil with them! One half of this at least was said after he had got upon his feet and taken off his portmanteau and valise, in which we had all followed suit, and were mounting for the start! I am almost sure nothing else was said, and if it had been, I should not have heard it for I was too far off and too rapidly dashed over the waving grass! Also, I was too eagerly gazing and plying the whip to hear or to see anything but the trampling hoofs! the blackened throng! the darting steeds! and the flashing guns! until I crossed the beautiful lawn and the limb of a tree! As my horse was darting into the timber, it had crossed by horse's back and had scraped me into the grass, from which I soon raised my head—and all was silent! All was out of sight save the dragoon regiment, which I could see in distance creeping along on the top of a high hill. I found my legs under me in a few moments and put them in their accustomed positions, none of which would for some time answer the usual purpose; but I at last got them to work."

"No buffalo was harmed in this furious assault, not horse nor rider. Colonel Dodge and Lieutenant Wheelock had joined the regiment, and General Leavenworth joined me, with too much game expression yet in his eye to allow him more time than to say, 'I'll have that calf before I quit!' and away he sailed, 'up hill and down dale,' in pursuit of a fine calf that had been hidden on the ground during the chase and was now making its way over the prairies in pursuit of the herd. I rode to the top of a little hill to witness the success of the general's second effort. After he had come close upon the little affrighted animal, it dodged about in such a manner as evidently to baffle his skill and perplex his horse, which at last fell in a hole, and both were instantly out of my sight. I ran my horse with all possible speed to the spot and found him on his hands and knees, endeavoring to get up. I dismounted and raised him onto his feet. When I asked him if he was hurt, to which he replies, 'no, but I might have been,' when he instantly fainted, and I laid him on the grass. I had left my canteen with my portmanteau, and had nothing to administer to him, nor was there water near us. I took my lancet from my pocket and was tying his arm to open a vein, when he recovered, and objected to the operation, assuring me that he was not in the least injured. I caught his horse and soon got him mounted again, when we rode on together, and after two or three hours were able to join the regiment."

"From that hour to the present, I think I have seen a decided change in the general's face; he has looked pale and feeble, and been continually troubled with a violent cough. I have rode by his side from day to day, and he has several times told me that he was fearful he was badly hurt. He looks very feeble now, and I very much fear the result of the fever that has set in upon him."

"We take up the line of march at bugle-call in the morning, and it may be a long time before I can send a letter again, as there are no men well enough for courier duty."

Lieutenant Cooke, who rode and ate everyday with the general after the hour of his fall, saw a different expression in his face from that which he naturally wore. When riding by his side two or three days after his fall, Cooke observed to him, "General, you have a very bad cough."

"Yes," he replied, "I have killed myself in running that devilish calf, and it was a very lucky thing that Catlin painted the portrait of me before we started, for it is all that my dear wife will ever see of me."

*   *   *

Although Ian and the Mexicans had suffered from the heat, they were in much better shape than the American dragoons were and, as Lieutenant Cooke was ill from the fever, General Leavenworth ordered Ian to join his expedition as he was in dire need of officers. So Ian bid fond farewell to Don Malgores as his little band continued on northward to Fort Leavenworth.

Lieutenant Cooke, riding at the head of the raw recruits of G Company, found it more difficult with every dawn to climb into the saddle. In the officers' mess tent at night he complained wearily about discipline problems and the injustice of having to surrender the command of G Company, which he handled for six months.

The lieutenant finally gave up and placed himself on sick report. One look was sufficient for the surgeon; Cooke was too ill to go on.

Ian was put in command of G Company. Composed of rawest recruits, he had to make incessant efforts to discipline the men.

In the march, they found many deep ravines, in the bottoms of which there were the marks of wild and powerful streams. But in this season of drought, they were all dried up, except an occasional one, where they found them dashing along in the coolest and clearest manner. On trail, to their great agony, they were so salty that even their horses could not drink from them; so occasionally they had the tantalizing pleasure of hearing the roar of them and looking into the clearest and most sparkling streams, but unable to drink. Out of dire necessity, they occasionally drank from stagnant pools, which lay from month to month exposed to the rays of the sun, until their waters become so poisonous and heavy, that they were neither diminished by absorption, nor taken into the atmosphere by evaporation.

This poisonous and indigestible water, with the intense rays of the sun in the hottest part of the summer, was the cause of the unexampled sickness of the horses and men. Both appeared to be suffering and dying with the same disease, a slow and distressing bilious fever, which seemed to terminate in a most frightful and fatal affection of the liver.

In these several cruel days of march, George Catlin suffered severely, having a distracting fever. His friend, Joe, constantly rode at his side, dismounting and filling his canteen for him, picked up minerals or fossils, which Catlin's jaundiced eyes were able to discover as they were passing over them, and did other kind offices for him. Joe helped him into the saddle when Catlin was too weak to mount his horse without help.

During the march over the dry and parched plains, Catlin and Joe picked up many curious things of the fossil and mineral kind.

Colonel Dodge and the two hundred fifty men who accompanied him suffered severely. They abandoned their baggage train, established a sick camp, leaving many men behind, and rode on.

The men with Dodge continued to topple off their horses; his back trail was marked by a succession of pathetic brushwood huts occupied by sick and dying dragoons. Although the temptation to call off the expedition pressed hard upon the weakening Leavenworth, Cooke's judgment of him as "hare-brained" was too severe. Had Dodge been ordered to turn back, the loss of face with both the Indians and the nation would have been unpardonable. Realizing, perhaps, that no excuses are valid for military failure, General Henry Leavenworth issued no such order.

Catlin was now carried upon a litter, unable to mount a horse. He had a horrid fever which daily took his strength, and almost, at times, his senses.

With only one hundred fifty men left in his column, Dodge passed north through a mountain defile to approach the Toyash (Wichita) villages of the Pawnee Picts on the North Fork of the Red River. Here in the bottle-shaped wattle huts of the Indians, Dodge, Commissioner Montford Stokes, and Indian Agent William Armstrong met the Pawnee chieftains in council. The chief objective of the negotiations, other than preparing the ground for peace treaties, was to arrange for the release of Ranger Abbey and the Martin boy. Ranger Abbey had been missing since last summer from Boone's Ranger Company. The Martin boy's father, Judge Gabriel N. Martin of Miller County, Arkansas, had been killed while adventuring on the plains with his son. The Pawnee denied all knowledge of either; but when Dodge produced their redeemed women, the boy was removed from a hiding place in a cornfield and turned over to the dragoons. Of Abbey, there was no trace; his captors had killed him. The three white leaders were gratified to observe that the Pawnees, like the Comanches, were greatly impressed by the mounted regiment. For the "walk-a-heaps" (infantry) who moved on foot like squaws, the Indians had only scorn; perhaps they now realized that they would have to deal in the future with soldiers of a different species, for a deputation of chiefs went back to Fort Gibson with Dodge.

On July 28, the dragoon regiment broke its camp, which lay six miles from the Pawnee villages, and crossing the Canadian, began its return march by a more northerly route. The heat was still great during the days, but the nights were relatively cool, affording some relief to the sick and weary men. On August 7, the column came to Cross Timbers and the dragoons learned of Leavenworth's death.

An express arrived from the encampment which the party had left at the mouth of False Washita, with the melancholy tidings of the death of General Leavenworth, Lieutenant McClure, and ten or fifteen of the men left at that place! This cast a gloom over the little encampment, and seemed to be received as a fatal foreboding by those who were sick with the same disease; and many of them, poor fellows, with scarce a hope left now for their recovery.

A week later, the main party marched into Fort Gibson, and by August 23, the Cross-Timbers contingent came in under Kearny with men and horses in very bad shape.

When the column reached Fort Gibson, not more than ten horses were in good condition out of the five hundred that started out. One hundred horses had died or broke down from the excessive heat. Of the five hundred men who marched from Fort Gibson only 190 men reached the Pawnee Pict villages. All the rest were left behind sick or attending the sick.

Lieutenant George W. McClure was dead; so were Beyrich the botanist, and over one hundred enlisted men of the dragoon and infantry columns. Eleven officers of the dragoon's thirty were too ill to be moved. Twice decimated, once by desertion, and again by death, the regiment had been roughly initiated.

Thereafter, there were many loose ends to be gathered. Dodge attempted to salvage some profit from the campaign, on his return sending runners to all the neighboring tribes, calling for a grand council, which met at Fort Gibson for several days in early September. Regimental reorganization was essential and was left to Kearny even though he, too, was sick. This activity was carried on despite the continuing sickness, which took an additional two of seven officers, a physician, and seventy-five dragoons.

Ian somehow had escaped the worst of the ordeal, and everyday he visited George Catlin, Lieutenant Cooke, and Captain Wharton. All three were quartered in a room in misery.

Captain Wharton of the dragoons, who came in from the prairies in a condition very similar to them, was laid in a bed in the opposite corner of the room. The three laid for several weeks, like grim ghosts, rolling their glaring and staring eyeballs upon each other, when they were totally unable to hold converse, other than that which was exchanged through the expressive language of their hollow, bilious, and sunken eyes.

The captain had been sent with a company of dragoons to escort the Santa Fe traders through the country of the Comanche and Pawnees. He had returned from a rapid and bold foray into the country with many of his men sick and himself attacked with the epidemic of the country. The captain was a gentleman of high and noble bearing, of one of the most respected families in Philadelphia, with a fine and chivalrous feeling; but with scarce physical stamina sufficient to bear him up under the rough vicissitudes of his wild and arduous sort of life in frontier country.

Surgeons clarified their flesh and bones with calomel, brought their pulses to beat calmly, their tongues to ply gently, and their stomachs to digest moderately. They soon began to feel pleasure exquisitely in their convalescence and drew amusement from mutual relations of scenes and adventures they had witnessed on their several marches.

Catlin, wanted to let his wife know of his adventures, but being still to weak to write, Ian offered to pen the letter for him.

The message read, "The last letter was written from my tent, and out upon the wild prairies, when I was shaken and terrified by a burning fever, with home and my dear wife and little one, two thousand miles ahead of me, whom I was despairing of ever embracing again. I am now scarcely better off, except that I am in comfortable quarters, with kind attendance, and friends about me. I am yet sick and very feeble, having been for several weeks upon my back since I was brought in from the prairie. I am slowly recovering, and for the first time since I wrote from the Canadian, able to use my brush."

"We drew off from that slaughtering ground a few days after my last letter was written. With a great number sick, carried upon litters with horses giving out and dying by the way, our progress was much impeded over the long and tedious route that laid between us and Fort Gibson. Fifteen days, however, of constant toil and fatigue brought us here, but in a most crippled condition. Many of the sick were left by the way with attendants to take care of them, others were buried from their litters on which they breathed their last while traveling, and many others were brought in to this place merely to die and get the privilege of a decent burial."

"Since the very day of our start into that country, the men have been constantly failing sick, and on their return, of those who are alive, there are not enough well ones to take care of the sick. Many are yet left out upon the prairies. Of those that have been brought in and quartered in the hospital with the soldiers of the infantry regiment stationed here, four or five are buried daily. As an equal number from the 9th regiment are falling by the same disease, I have the mournful sound of "Roslin Castle" with muffled drums passing six or eight times a day under my window to the burying ground. It is but a little distance in front of my room where I can lay in my bed and see every poor fellow lowered down into his silent and peaceful grave. During the day before yesterday, no less than eight solemn processions visited that insatiable ground, and amongst them was carried the corpse of my intimate and much-loved friend Lieutenant West. He was aid-de-camp to General Leavenworth on this disastrous campaign, and he has left in this place, a worthy and distracted widow with her little ones to mourn for his untimely end. On the same day was buried the Prussian botanist, a most excellent and scientific gentleman, who had obtained an order from the Secretary at War to accompany the expedition for scientific purposes. In St. Louis he purchased a very comfortable Dearborn wagon and a snug span of little horses to convey himself and his servant over the prairies with his collection of plants. In this he traveled in company with the regiment from St. Louis to Fort Gibson, some five or six hundred miles, and from that to the False Washita, and the Cross Timbers and back again. In this tour he had made an immense, and no doubt, very valuable collection of plants. He had been for some weeks indefatigably engaged in changing and drying them and, at last, fell a victim to the disease of the country, which seemed to have made an easy conquest of him from the very feeble and enervated state he was evidently in—hat of pulmonary consumption. This fine, gentlemanly and urbane, excellent man to whom I became very much attached, was lodged in a room adjoining to mine, where he died, as he had lived, peaceably and smiling, and that when nobody knew that his life was in immediate danger. The surgeon, Dr. Wright, who was attending me, was sitting at my bedside during his morning call at my room. A Negro boy, who alone had been left in the room with him, came into my apartment and said Mr. Beyrich was dying. We instantly stepped into his room and found him, not in the agonies of death, but quietly breathing his last, without a word or a struggle, as he had laid himself upon his bed with his clothes and his boots on. In this way perished this worthy man, who had no one here of kindred friends to drop tears for him; and on the day previous to his misfortune, died also, and much in the same way, his devoted and faithful servant, a young man, a native of Germany. Their bodies were buried by the side of each other, and a general feeling of deep grief was manifested by the officers and citizens of the post, in the respect that was paid to their remains in the appropriate and decent committal of them to the grave."

Catlin was exhausted so the letter was continued the next day.

"After leaving the head waters of the Canadian, my illness continually increased, and losing strength every day, I soon got so reduced that I was necessarily lifted on to and off of my horse. Eventually, I could not ride at all. I was then put into a baggage-wagon, which was going back empty, except with several soldiers sick. In this condition I rode eight days, most of the time in a delirious state, lying on the hard planks of the wagon, and made still harder by the jarring and jolting, until the skin from my elbows and knees was literally worn through, and I almost "wore-out"; when at length I reached this post. I was taken to a bed in comfortable quarters, where I have had the skillful attendance of my friend and old schoolmate Dr. Wright, under whose hands, thank God, I have been restored, and am now recovering my flesh and usual strength."

"The experiment has thus been made of sending an army of men from the north into this southern and warm climate in the hottest months of the year of July and August; and from this sad experiment I am sure a secret will be learned that will be of value on future occasions."

"Of the 450 fine fellows who started from this place four months since, about one-third have already died, and I believe many more there are whose fates are sealed and will fall victims to the deadly diseases contracted in that fatal country. About this post it seems to be almost equally unhealthy, and generally so during this season all over this region, which is probably owing to an unusual drought which has been visited on the country and unknown heretofore to the oldest inhabitants."

"Since we came in from the prairies, and the sickness has a little abated, we have had a bustling time with the Indians at this place. Colonel Dodge sent runners to the chiefs of all the contiguous tribes of Indians, with an invitation to meet the Pawnees in council, at his place. Seven or eight tribes flocked to us, in great numbers on the first day of the month, when the council commenced; it continued for several days, and gave these semi-civilized sons of the forest a fair opportunity of shaking the hands of their wild and untamed red brethren of the west of embracing them in their arms, with expressions of friendship, and of smoking the calumet together, as the solemn pledge of lasting peace and friendship."

"Colonel Dodge, Major Armstrong (the Indian agent), and General Stokes (the Indian commissioner), presided at this council, and I cannot name a scene more interesting and entertaining than it was; where, for several days in seccession, free vent was given to the feelings of men civilized, half-civilized, and wild; where the three stages of men were fearlessly asserting their rights, their happiness, and friendship for each other. The vain orations of the half-polished (and half-breed) Cherokees and Chocktaws, with all their finery and art, found their match in the brief and jarring gutturals of the wild and naked man."

"After the council had adjourned, and the fumes of the peace-making calumet had vanished away, and Colonel Dodge had made them additional presents, they made preparations for their departure, and on the next day started, with an escort of dragoons, for their own country. This movement is much to be regretted; for it would have been exceedingly gratifying to the people of the east to have seen so wild a group, and it would have been of great service to them to have visited Washington—a journey, though, which they could not be prevailed upon to make."

"We brought with us to this place, three of the principal chiefs of the Pawnees, fifteen Kiowas, one Comanche and one Wico chief. The group was undoubtedly one of the most interesting that ever visited our frontier; and I have taken the utmost pains in painting the portraits of all of them, as well as seven of the Comanche chiefs, who came part of the way with us and turned back. These portraits, together with other paintings which I have made, descriptions of their manners and customs, views of their villages, landscapes of the country, etc., will soon be laid before the amateurs of the east, and, I trust, will be found to be very interesting."

"Although the achievement has been a handsome one, of bringing these unknown people to an acquaintance, and a general peace; and at first sight would appear to be of great benefit to them—yet I have my strong doubts whether it will better their condition, unless with the exercised aid of the strong arm of the government, they can be protected in the rights which, by nature, they are entitled to."

"I have traveled too much among Indian tribes, and seen too much, not to know the evil consequences of such a system. Goods are sold at such exorbitant prices that the Indians get a mere shadow for their peltries. The Indians see no white people but traders and sellers of whisky; and of course, judge us all by them—they consequently hold us, and always will, in contempt; as inferior to themselves, as they have reason to do—and they neither fear nor respect us. When, on the contrary, if the government would promptly prohibit such establishments, and invite these Indians to our frontier posts, they would bring in their furs, their robes, horses, mules, etc., to his place, where there is a good market for them all—where there are several stores of goods—where there is an honorable competition, and where they would get four or five times as much for their articles of trade, as they would get from a trader in the village, out of reach of competition, and out of sight of the civilized world."

"At the same time, as they would be continually coming where they would see good and polished society, they would be gradually adopting our modes of living—introducing to their country our vegetables, our domestic animals, poultry, etc., and at length, our arts and manufactures; they would see and estimate our military strength, and advantages, and would be led to fear and respect us. In short, it would undoubtedly be the quickest and surest way to a general acquaintance—to friendship and peace, and at last, to civilization. If there is a law in existence for such protection of the Indian tribes, which many have been waived in the case of those nations with which we have long traded, it is a great pity that it should not be rigidly enforced in this new and important acquaintance, which we have just made with thirty or forty thousand strangers to the civilized world; yet (as we have learned from their unaffected hospitality when in their villages), with hearts of human mold, susceptible of all the noble feelings belonging to civilized man."

"This acquaintance has cost the United States a vast sum of money as well as the lives of several valuable and esteemed officers, and more than one hundred of the dragoons; and for the honor of the American name, I think we ought, in forming an acquaintance with these numerous tribes, to adopt and enforce some different system from that which has been generally practiced on and beyond our frontiers heretofore."

"We sometimes rode day after day, without a tree to shade us from the burning rays of tropical sun, or a breath of wind to regale us or cheer our hearts—and with mouths continually parched with thirst, we dipped our drink from stagnant pools that were heated by the sun, and kept in fermentation by the wallowing herds of buffalo that resort to them. In this way we dragged on, sometimes passing picturesque and broken country, with fine springs and streams, affording us the luxury of a refreshing shade and a cool draught of water."

Although the letter was long and detailed, Ian enjoyed writing it as it gave him a rare insight upon the expedition, devoid of all army thought.

The army was much indebted for the history of its labor in the early West to men of science and art, those who traveled in search of knowledge through the vast western domain. In those early times the army was, in many instances, the sole "inhabitant" of the new country, the advance guard of the civilization that was to build an empire. The homes of its officers and men were conducted on the "open door" plan where hospitality was dispensed to travelers with a freedom surpassed by none and so thoroughly characteristic of army men and women.

The next day the letter was continued.

"During my illness while I have been at this post, my friend Joe has been almost constantly by my bedside; evincing, as he did when we were creeping over the vast prairies, the most sincere and intense anxiety for my recovery, whilst he had administered like a brother every aid and every comfort that lay in his power to bring. Such tried friendship as this I shall ever recollect; and it will long hence and often lead my mind back to retrace at least the first part of our campaign, which was fully pleasant; many of its incidents have formed pleasing impressions on my memory, which I would preserve to the end of my life."

"When we started, we were fresh and ardent for the incidents that were before us. Our little packhorse carried our bedding and culinary articles, amongst which we had a coffeepot and a frying pan and coffee and sugar in good store. Wherever we spread our bearskin, and kindled our fire in the grass, we were sure to take by ourselves a delightful repast and a refreshing sleep. During the march, as we were subject to no military subordination, we galloped about wherever we were disposed, popping away at whatever we chose to spend ammunition upon and running our noses into every wild nook and crevice, as we saw fit. In this way we traveled happily, until our coffee was gone and our bread; and even then we were happy upon meat alone, until at last each one in his turn, like every other moving thing about us, both man and beast, were vomiting and fainting under the poisonous influence of some latent enemy that was floating in the air and threatening our destruction. Then came the "tug of war," and, instead of catering for our amusements, everyone seemed desperately studying the means that were to support him on his feet and bring him safe home again to the bosoms of his friends. In our start, our feelings were buoyant and light, and we had the luxuries of life—the green prairies spotted with wild flowers and the clear blue sky were an earthly paradise to us, until fatigue and disease and, at last, despair made them tiresome and painful to our jaundiced eyes."

"On our way, and while we were in good heart, my friend Joe and I had picked up many minerals and fossils of an interesting nature, which we put in our portmanteaux and carried for weeks with much pain, until the time when our ardor and our spirits lagged and then threw them away."

"One of the most curious places we met in all our route was a mountain ridge of fossil shells, from which a great number of mineral and fossil specimens were taken. During our second day's march from the mouth of the False Washita, we were astonished to find ourselves traveling over a bed of clam and oyster shells, which were all in a complete state of petrifaction. This ridge, which seemed to run from northeast to southwest, was several hundred feet high and varying from a quarter to half a mile in breadth, and seemed to be composed of nothing but a concretion of shells, which, on the surface, exposed to the weather for the depth of eight or ten inches, were entirely separated from the cementing material which had held them together. They were lying on the surface—sometimes for acres together—without a particle of soil or grass upon them and with the color, shapes and appearance exactly of the natural shells, lying loosely together, into which our horses' feet were sinking above their fetter locks at every step. These I consider the most extraordinary petrifaction I ever beheld. In any way they could be seen, individually or in the mass together, they seemed to be nothing but the pure shells themselves, both in color and in shape. In many instances we picked them up in their entirety, never having been opened and, taking our knives out, and splitting them open as we would an oyster, the fish was seen petrified in perfect form. By dipping it into water, it showed all the colors and freshness of an oyster just opened and lay on a plate to be eaten. Joe and I had carefully tied up many of these, with which we felt quite sure we could deceive our oyster-eating friends when we got back to the east. Yet like many other things we collected, they shared the fate that I have mentioned, without our bringing home one of them, though we brought many of them several hundreds of miles and at last threw them away. This remarkable ridge is in some parts covered with grass, but generally with mere scattering bunches for miles together, partially covering this compact mass of shells, forming (in my opinion) one of the greatest geological curiosities now to be seen in this country, as it lies evident some hundreds of feet above the level of the ocean and seven or eight hundred miles from the nearest point on the sea-coast."

"In another section of the country, lying between Fort Gibson and the Washita, we passed over a ridge for several miles running parallel to this where much of the way there was no earth or grass under foot, but our horses were traveling on a solid rock, which had on its surface a reddish or oxidized appearance; and on getting down from my horse and striking it with my hatchet, I found it to contain sixty or eighty percent of solid iron, which produced a ringing noise and a rebounding of the hatchet, as if it were struck upon an anvil."

"In other parts, and farther west, between the Comanche village and the Canadian, we passed over a similar surface for many miles denuded with the exception of here and there little bunches of grass and wild sage, a level and exposed surface of solid gypsum, of a dark gray color, and through it, occasionally as far as the eye could discover, to the east and the west, streaks of three and five inches of snowy gypsum, which was literally as white as the drifted snow."

"Of saltpetre (potassium and sodium nitrate), and salt there are also endless supplies; so it will be seen that the mineral resources of this wilderness country are inexhaustible and rich, and that the idle savage who never converts them to his use, must soon yield them to the occupation of lightened and cultivating man."

"In the vicinity of this post there are an immense number of Indians, most of whom have been removed to their present locations by the government, from their eastern original positions, within a few years past; and previous to my starting with the dragoons, I had two months at my leisure in this section of the country, which I used in traveling about with my canvass and notebook, and visiting all of them in their villages. I have made many paintings amongst them, and have a curious notebook to open at a future day. The tribes whom I thus visited, and of whom my notebook will yet speak are the Cherokee, Choctaw, Creeks, Seminole, Chickasawa, Quapaw, Seneca, Delaware, and several others, whose customs are interesting, and whose history, from their proximity to, and dealings with the civilized community, is one of great interest and of some importance to the enlightened world. Adieu."

Orders to Des Moines

More orders began to arrive; the regiment was divided into battalions and was to be stationed at three different posts: Fort Leavenworth, Fort Gibson, and Fort Des Moines. The last of these, the quarters still had to be built by the weary men of Companies B, H, and I (Sumner, Boone, and Brown).

Ian was to travel to Jefferson Barracks in St. Louis and pick up some new recruits then continue on to Des Moines, stopping at Fort Leavenworth to pick up more men, to replace the dragoons who had died on the Pawnee Pict expedition.

Ian found St. Louis enjoyable after the life on the plains. Men clad in buckskin and carrying rifles in their hands elbowed representatives of first families attired in the fashions that came from Paris via New Orleans or consorted with Indians in paint and feathers.

St. Louis was founded by Pierre Laclede Liguest and a few companions, all French voyagers, in 1764—at least it was in that year that Laclede's lieutenant, Auguste Chouteau, cleared away the site of the present city. Laclede Liguest, or as he is sometimes known, Liguest Laclede, a merchant of New Orleans, had from the French Government a monopoly of the fur trade in the Missouri River country. He left New Orleans with his family and a small party in August, 1763, with the intention of founding a town near the confluence of the Missouri and Mississippi Rivers.

The emporium of the fur trade was St. Louis. Travelers to the Far West generally came through that town. There they assembled; there they often outfitted; there they formed companies since no man dared to cross the Plains alone. They had to buy their supplies from men trained in the traditions of the business in which Lisa and Robidoux made their fortunes. They had to keep their eyes peeled and get up early in the morning to get the best of traders in St. Louis. The merchants in Missouri in those days were experts in skins and skinning.

From the start that business had been monopolistic. Rival companies and rival traders left little undone in their competition for the furs. Beyond the frontier there was no law, and regulation of business was hardly dreamed of then, even in the States. Some of the men engaged in the trade resorted to slander, bribery, smuggling, bootlegging, intimidation, theft, and even murder in their lust for fur. The profits were enormous; a fortune could be gained in a single good season. Some of these men set up as dictators in their lonely posts and ruled all comers with floggings, fines, and killings from ambush.

They advised the greenhorns that they would find prices much, much higher farther west at Franklin, Independence, or Westport.

Most travelers reached St. Louis by water—down river from the Falls or down the Ohio from Cincinnati or up river from New Orleans. Fleets of steamboats lay tier on tier alongside the narrow wharves of that busy little city, then the growing metropolis of the West.

Disembarking, the stranger fought his way through a mob of hotel runners, put his baggage into safe hands, then went into the town to enter his name on the books of the principal hotel, the Planter's House.

A few hours sufficed to explore the city, to inspect the shot towers, to wander through the shabby lanes of the French town Carondelet or to prowl along a back street past the open windows of the Rocky Mountain House, the rendezvous of the trappers.

There a fandango was likely to be in full blast. The greenhorn could watch shaggy, long-haired mountain men in blackened elk skins prancing with French belles to the scraping of fiddles and twanging banjo and introducing steps learned in far off Cheyenne camps, while some extremely loud mountaineer roared out an Indian chorus, thumping his belly to jerk out the vocals more forcibly.

There the stranger might match his skill at Old Sledge, with men whose leggings were fringed with Comanche hair, squatting on a buffalo robe over a greasy deck of cards and an old wool hat full of silver coins. There, over horns of potent Monongahela, he might fill his ears with tall tales of glass mountains and man-eating buffalo, or hear profane yarns of hard scrapes, coups, scalps, and "fixes"—yarns spiced with half-comprehended words of French, Spanish, Indian, and mountain-American lingo.

Though the residents of St. Louis numbered scarcely more than two thousand, there was a large floating population of many races and types. Sallow French Canadian voyageurs with a gay, joyous liveliness of mood and living freely without thought of the future and lank Missouri teamsters in homespuns and checkered woolen shirts filled the streets. There were dark Spaniards under tall peaked sombreros, rich merchants in high beaver hats and ruffled shirts, sturdy emigrant farmers in their blue jeans, and self-reliant Delaware hunters, blanketed squaws, naked brown children and Negroes. Packers, wagonmasters, bull-whackers, soldiers, mule-skinners, roustabouts from the steamboats, and keelboatmen swarmed up and down the muddy streets in the summer sunlight. Among them strode sun-browned trappers in worn buckskins, and the Santa Fe traders in frock coats of black broadcloth, which showed the creases of long disuse beyond the frontier.

From these, or from the pages of some manual of the trails like Captain Marcy's "Prairie Traveler," the greenhorn learned what he required for his long cruise across the sea of grass.

He went about the purchase of his equipment with serious purpose, for there was no place on the Trail where he could be sure of obtaining supplies, once he had left the last settlement behind him.

Accordingly, the greenhorn traded for arms, clothing, provisions, and medicines. He also traded for saddlery, cutlery, and kitchenware and for ammunition, harness, wagons, carts, bedding and animals, and sometimes for tents, carriage, and camp furniture. His health, his comfort, even his life might depend upon the right choice of the proper outfit.

All his notions of armament he found brushed aside as of no account. The long rifle of the woodsman, with its light charge and small bore, was rated no good in a country where buffalo and grizzly b'ar took the place of deer and turkeys; flintlocks gave way to percussion caps. Double-barreled fowling pieces were loaded with buckshot, ready to do heavy execution in a night attack. Breechloaders, first used on American soil by the British in the Revolutionary War, were gaining ground. Single-shot weapons were steadily losing it.

He was impressed by the respect shown by old-timers for the Indian's short buffalo bow with which the Indian could fire so rapidly. The muzzle velocity of the bow was also incredibly greater than that of most guns and he had heard tales of how the Indians had been known to shoot entirely through two bison.

Veterans of the beaver stream pinned their faith to the muzzle-loading rifle, with which their gnarled hands had made a heap of Indians dead. The greenhorn who bowed to their experience let the new models alone, went straight to Hawkins' gunstore and bought a regular mountain rifle, a piece of very heavy metal carrying thirty-two balls to the pound, stocked to the muzzle, and mounted with brass. Its only ornament was a buffalo bull, looking exceedingly ferocious, which was not very artistically engraved upon the trap in the stock. With such a weapon, he was told that a practiced hand could pour, load, ram, and fire five times a minute by the clock. With it, he could acquire an extra wiping stick of hickory, a supply of fine glazed DuPont powder and Galena lead, patches, and bullet mould. Give an old-timer his Hawkins and powderhorn filled with sure-fire powder 'to make her crack,' and with a Green River blade at his belt, he was ready for Indians galore.

The most fashionable costume for the prairies was a fustian coat furnished with a multitude of pockets in which to carry extra tackling. Backwoodsmen clung to a linsey or buckskin hunting shirt; teamsters wore flannel-sleeve vests over hickory shirts. Horsemen bought short, stout coats and boots big enough to contain the trouser-let for riding. Those who intended to walk looked for shoes with broad, heavy soles, in which the toes had free play. Broad-brimmed, low-crowned hats of soft felt, sometimes gaily painted against the rain, were popular. Calico and liner shirts gave way to blue or red flannel.

Greenhorns generally inclined to buy buckskins for the Trail. Most greenhorns had a secret craving to wear that historic costume of the frontier—colorful, fringed, and heroic.

Buckskins, they argued, would turn sharp winds, and nothing else would break the sharp bill of those big Plains mosquitoes. Caravans started, as a rule, as soon as the grass was high enough to feed the stock in spring—and that was the wet season on the prairies. Mosquitoes were bound to be bad; buckskins would be just the thing!

But the old-timers, who wore trousers of thick, soft woolen goods reinforced inside the leg with leather, shook their shaggy beards. "Buckskins in the rainy season? Wal, I reckon the green will rub off afore long."

Heavy cotton drawers, woolen undershirts, cotton and woolen socks, colored handkerchiefs, and extra shoes with perhaps a waterproof poncho, completed the outfit. The fastidious also carried razors, towels, comb and brush, toothbrush, Castile bar soap, and a whetstone for their shining belt-knives.

Caution dictated the purchase of a "housewife"—a small, waterproof package containing strong needles, stout linen thread, a bit of beeswax, extra buttons, a paper of pins, and a thimble. But veterans of the Trail got along with a bundle of buckskins, a sharp awl, and a few shreds of dried sinew for the mending of moccasins and hunting shirts.

His trading completed, the greenhorn was likely to go straight back to his room at the Planters' House tired and excited, but happy. There he divested himself of polished boots, high hat, and frock of broadcloth, packing those away in his trunk, to be held against his return—in case he did return!

After that, he would stand before his mirror as if by accident and somewhat self-consciously pull on his red flannel shirt, his "leather-stocking," and his beaded moccasins. Then, although he might never have killed anything more dangerous than a chicken, he buckled a belt, heavy with long sheath-knife and pistol, around his hips. Over his shirt, he put on the long-skirted buckskin hunting-coat, dripping fringes with beads and decorated in small black diapers of velvet running in horizontal bands all around—a swagger garment. Then he faced the mirror squarely to knot the silk scarf about his neck and tilt the broad-brimmed low felt hat jauntily across his sleek soap-lock. With powderhorn and shot-pouch slung over his shoulder and a new rifle in the crook of his arm, he felt at once manly—and embarrassed!

It was all a little theatrical acting. Yet adventure and the heavy drag of the weapons at his belt, seemed to justify a masculine love for fine feathers. Vaguely, he sensed the instinct of his sex; that a young man of spirit should go handsome and debonair to his rendezvous with death. Then as now, the West seemed to demand something colorful, romantic, and bizarre. The vastness of the country compelled a man to assert himself and make himself visible. Though now he felt uncomfortably conspicuous, he took comfort in the thought that every man on the Plains frontier had inevitably been in the beginning a greenhorn, tenderfoot, or dude.

It was only later, after some experience of the Trail, that the greenhorn discovered that his fantastic outfit was, in reality, devised on strictly practical lines. For the present, he took a deep breath, threw out his chest and went downstairs, looking every man straight in the eye, daring him to laugh.

Having sent his baggage to the wharf, the stranger hurried to the levee, crossed the landing-stage to the boat, located his cabin and then took his place at the rail, puffing a long Havana in affected nonchalance.

On the boat were Santa Fe traders, professional gamblers, adventurers of many kinds. The deck below was jammed with a motley, polyglot crowd of emigrants bound for Oregon or California, with mountain men and blanket Indians. Some were heading west to make a fortune, acquire free land, or merely to seek excitement. Some went out of curiosity or sheer restless love of travel. Others, non-talkative and watchful, were fugitives from justice, deserters from the army, or misfits who could no longer endure conditions in the States. There were also pioneers who found new settlements crowding around their familiar clearings and had moved on to be rid of unwelcome pressure. Writers and artists looking for new worlds to conquer, explorers; runaway boys heading west to kill Indians and embezzlers, thieves, murderers, and madmen.

In the cabins were always a few invalids afflicted with chronic liver complaint, dyspepsia, lung fever, rheumatism, or fleeing from epidemics of yellow jack, smallpox, or Asiatic cholera. Men, who having been given up as hopeless by the doctors at home, preferred to meet death suddenly under the scalping knife of the Indians rather than endure the slow tortures of incurable disease. Life on the prairies was said to effect remarkable cures.

With these were a sprinkling of foreign sportsmen in white shooting jackets of dandy cut, trousers of shepherd's plaid, and Panama hats, who had crossed the Atlantic to enter what was then a hunter's paradise.

The steamboat was so heavily loaded that water broke over her guards continually. Her upper deck was completely covered with big Pittsburgh and Conestoga wagons with blue beds and bright red wheels, all laden with precious goods for the trade with Mexico. Below was a band of horses, mules, oxen, and stacks of saddlery, harness, boxes, bales, trunks, bedrolls, carts and carriages, and assorted packages of every kind. At last everyone was aboard.

At the third tolling of the bell and in obedience to the signals of the high and mighty pilot, the steamboat swung away from the levee and was soon stemming the yellow waters of the Mississippi.

A few miles brought the craft to the mouth of the Missouri, where undercurrents projected the muddy waters of the swifter stream far out, to boil up to the surface of the more transparent river in surprising eddies. The steamboat nosed into the Missouri River. Then the greenhorn drew a long breath of satisfaction. He was on his way.

The trip up-river might occupy a week or more, and half the time the steamboat was sure to be hard aground on a sandbar somewhere in the shifting channel of the fickle stream. Everywhere were boiling eddies and hidden bars. Travelers did not find the journey dull.

The first travelers to follow the Trail made Franklin, county seat of Boone's Lick County, their jumping-off place. Founded in 1816, only five years before Captain William Becknell opened the Santa Fe Trail, Franklin was soon the second town in the Territory with a booming trade and a land-office. Local boosters bragged that "the public square contained two acres and that the principle streets were eighty-two and a half feet wide and nearly as deep in mud;" the town afforded "an agreeable and polished society"—a society from which the boy Kit Carson gladly ran away on September 1, 1826, two years before the town site was washed into the river.

After Franklin vanished, Independence, with its toy courthouse and four clanging blacksmith shops, became the prairie port, as steamboats gradually learned their way farther up the river to Fort Osage, Blue Mills, Ducker's Ferry, and on to Independence. First begun in 1827, the town took first place in 1832.

Many from Tennessee and Kentucky made their homes there and from that town thousands started for the West.

From Independence to Fort Leavenworth, a distance of 65 miles, the river passed between a long series of bluffs and hills.

Independence had its disadvantages, especially in the rainy season when most travelers set out. Then the prairies to the west were swampy and the Blue River was hard to ford or ferry. When the steamboats found a good landing above Blue River (now Kansas City), Westport sprang up nearby and won most of the outfitting trade from Independence. There were good reasons!

Westport had plenty of good grass for teams, a fine spring, groves ample enough to provide shelter, and fuel for any number of wagon trains. There was also a rocky ledge near the landing which supplied abundant building stone. Besides, sandbars had formed downriver which made landing at Independence difficult.

But whatever town the traveler made his starting-place, he found much the same life, much the same scenes, and the same people.

The Trail to Santa Fe led from Missouri almost a thousand miles across the Great Plains to the Spanish settlements at the foot of the Rocky Mountains.

Those plains were like the ocean—a region of magnificent distances, of desolate and barren wastes—strange, solitary, unexplored. Sometimes that ocean was a sea of grassy hillocks; sometimes it was level with the flatness of dead calm. Oftener it rolled in long swells to the far-off horizon—green, tumultuous, tossing its waves of grass under the driving winds and changing shape and color as swift cloud shadows sped over the uneven surface.

Like the sea, those plains were swept by masses of living things: vast shoals of shaggy bison, antelope, and other game, which appeared and disappeared without warning. Birds, sometimes even gulls, flapped and soared above it. And like the sea, the plains were subject to violent storms, sudden variations of temperature, terrific gales, cruel frosts, tornadoes, and drenching cloudbursts. Here and there that empty sea was broken by buttes like islands of sterile promontories.

The emptiness, the loneliness, the pathetic solemnity of the region oppressed some men, and all women, to the verge of madness. Many, on first emerging from their familiar woodlands, became physically sick. Even Coronado's hard-boiled Spanish troopers were terrified by a country where one could see the sky under a horse's belly.

But for those hardy tempers who could love great spaces, where one spot was no more important than another, experience of the sea of grass was glorifying. On the Great Plains, a man of strong identity stood always at the center of his world—a king of infinite space.

Wagons creaked up long prairie slopes; wagons rolled down hills; wagons grinded through heavy sand, were sucked through sticky mud, and swished through tall grass. Wagons with locked wheels plunged down steep river-banks; wagons snaked through clinging quicksands, or jiggled over ribbed sandbars rough as cobblestones; wagons hauled yard by painful yard up the forbidding rocks of the Raton Pass, two slow miles a day; and wagons corralled against the attacks of Indians. Wagons broke down, abandoned, and stranded by the loss of animals stolen by raiding warriors; wagons burned in prairie fires; and wagons were warped and shrunken by the heat and drought. Wagons were crammed with rich furs, Mexican silver, and gold bullion.

But in the old days, travelers on those plains spoke habitually of "making port," and urged Congress to enact navigation laws for the "prairie ocean." Their covered wagons, appropriately dubbed "prairie schooners," were in fact watertight boats mounted on wheels, rising high at prow and stern. They thought of the plains in terms of seafaring and felt the glamour of them as a magic of the sea. They named the jumping-off place in Missouri, Westport!

The Great Plains of the West were man's country. Women and weaklings shrank from the vastness and the sameness, where there was nothing to give shelter; there were no bower of trees, no security, no nest. The women either persuaded their men to halt and build at the edge of their familiar woodlands or scuttled fearfully across the prairies to the snug forests of Oregon or the cozy valleys of California. Even later, when those plains were settled and lone nesters dotted the grass with sod houses and dugouts, women still hated the lonesome, wind-bitten land. Everything there was different, strange, and frightening. Many a settler's wife went crazy on the plains.

But not the men. Not men of the old North European stock—hard-drinking, hard-fighting warriors, and wanderers, gamblers and explorers. They loved those plains and delighted in the vague, receding horizons, and in the loneliness, the sand, and the silence. They loved the independence and chancy emergencies of that romantic country. This was Valhalla come to earth, a region where men might do impromptu battle and ride away to fight again some other day. The moods of the plains were moods of violence and the men who loved them shared that moodiness. Not since the day of the Vikings had the virile white man found a country so congenial to his heart's desire.

*   *   *

In the bright summer morning while the children of the newly arrived officers and sergeants played on the parade grounds of Fort Leavenworth, there came a strange new sound. All listened a moment in awe and then was heard shouting from many voices, "The steamboat is coming! The steamboat is coming!" And look! There is smoke curling through the trees. Listen! to the puffing of the steam!

It had been talked of and expected for a long time. The children felt in listening to their elders that something great was about to happen. They ran down to the landing as fast as their legs could carry them.

The steamboat rounded the point and came into full view. They stood on tiptoe to see the exciting boat, but could not see all they longed to. One of the private's swung up his favorite little girl and held her on his shoulders. She clapped her hands and almost cried with delight for there it was, just landing, in all her pride and beauty, as if she knew she would become historic.

Officers and soldiers, women and other children, were hurrying down the hill.

Warm and heartfelt greetings and congratulations were exchanged. Speedily the mail was opened and papers and letters were distributed. All searched for news from home, and some joy turned into grief for the private who had lifted up little Susan. He had learned, by the very boat whose coming he hailed with so much pleasure, that he was fatherless. All his fellow dragoon's sympathized deeply with him. Few know how closely drawn together are the occupants of a frontier post, but the common joy, although dampened, was not destroyed, and civilities were tendered to the captain and officers of the boat, who were real gentlemen, and became great favorites at the fort as their pleasant excursion parties on the boat relieved the monotony of fort life.

The steamboat was the topic of conversation for a long time. The day of its arrival became a delightful and great event. It brought Fort Leavenworth into more direct and easy communication with the world, and small wonder that the steamboat should have caused excitement and rejoicing to those who had been receiving their mails at intervals of months instead of weeks. To the children it meant a sight never before witnessed—something heard of and seen in pictures, but never realized.

And there, on the platform, Ian saw Louisa and he looked for a new life of gaiety with her, sergeant, Annie, and a few other of his close friends. Her dark eyes were tearfully bright and her dainty figure excited upon seeing Ian. As the boat docked, he gave a war whoop, jumped over the boat railing, pushed through the crowd, and embraced her for a long moment. At first they talked little—that could wait; these moments were precious, like a string of jewels dropped one by one.

Ian was here with her again and she could feel his heart beating stoutly within him as she put her head on his broad chest. Ian pushed her at arms length and looked at her. She was beautiful in that little pink dress with the light jacket and the pretty hat.

"I am so glad to see you, Louisa," he whispered to her in so low and choking a voice that she scarcely heard.

On the trail up from the platform to the main parade, Ian plucked a wild rose and placed it in her hair. For the most part they said little. Then at the top of the incline, they sat down under one of the towering elms, and they talked quietly to each other. Louisa could not move her eyes from his face. Something there seemed to hold them as by some magic, and she could not conceal her trembling.

She laid her hand on his arm and the smile she lifted to him was suddenly vivid and tender and a valiant confession of unsuspected things.

"Ian," she whispered quietly, "I am carrying our child."

Ian contemplated on the thought for a moment. Tears of sheer nervousness trembled into her eyes, not knowing what Ian's reaction would be. But his thoughts, as always, were of her happiness. Perhaps it was a little dangerous to get so completely wrapped up in one person. These fellow dragoons and Mexican lancers had been all that was necessary to make his life pleasant, but now they had been displaced by a woman. One woman for thirty friends. Would the exchange be one that he would ever regret?

He, the blase Ian, the man who had thought rather lightly of his friends when they had fallen in love, was doing just what they had done. He was sure he loved her greatly, but then he wasn't alone in this; all the men of his set admitted that she was an angel and made him feel rather strange to think that she was interesting to some of them.

There were tears in her eyes, but they were unseen for her face was dark in its own shadow. Once or twice she opened her lips to speak again, but did not.

Marriage did not appeal to him at this time although he loved her. He was going through that period in vagabond life when cramped instinct shrinks from the human eye and shuffles past humanity with averted face. He kept away from others of his class, not from a lack of sociability, but because his tastes were more in harmony with the life that lay directly behind him—a life which was quite foreign to his compatriots of the army. His intellect leaned toward that higher atmosphere which the thinkers delight to cultivate.

But in the early month of August, in the cool shade of the trees, when the scent of the blossoms mingles with the fragrance of the new mown hay, a downward path to marriage taken through the open air was not an unpleasant one.

Louisa, as if reading his mind, reassured him as she had done when the child was conceived, "I still feel you will have greatness thrust upon you and we must forget marriage. This love-child is all I need. I will not destroy your destiny for as surely as the sun rises and sets, greatness will come to you."

Ian could see that her words caused her intense suffering. The beautiful high features were like a white marble mask, but she never broke down in any way. She showed herself to the world, in her carriage, as if she were happy. She knew how to bear suffering for she had borne much in her early life.

But that they belonged to each other made it much easier to bear trouble and grief and sadness together. Possibly, though he did not know it, he looked to her in his anxiety quite as much as she looked at him. It would have been hard to say for where there is such sympathy, such trust, and such love, there is also a sort of community of courage and of strength and of endurance for a joint suffering.

He opened his lips to speak, but could not find wise words for he believed that she had guessed the truth by some extraordinary and supernormal process of intuition of his search of meaning of himself and answers to absurdities of life. He wished to be something more than nothing.

She met his eyes for a moment, and her head sank on his chest as though she was very tired.

"A life together for us is not meant to be, love," she said and he could but just hear the words.

"It shall be, whether it is meant or not," he answered, bending down to her little ear.

She shook her head against his shirt, hiding her face, "No! No!"

She roused herself and laid her hands upon his shoulders, looking up suddenly into his face with wide, searching eyes, "I love you so—and yet—oh, Ian, Ian! How will it all end?"

She rocked herself a little, to and fro, her forehead against his shirt again and her hand twisted painfully upon his, but there were no tears in her voice for she had shed all she had in the lonely nights since she had seen him last.

"Nothing shall take you from me," Ian said, his arms going round her and holding her to him. "Nothing."

She was silent for a moment and the mirage of happiness rose in her eyes.

"But it is not possible."

"Do not talk of it, love."

He pressed her head gently backwards and his lips met hers.

A little shiver ran to her small hands and her eyelids dropped till they closed, and still he kissed her long and passionately. The color rose slowly in her cheeks. When her pulse beat again, for it had stopped for a moment, she then hid the scarlet blush of love against his shirt and heard the heavy, mysterious beating of his heart through flesh, bone, and cloth—the strong deep sound which no woman forgets who has heard it and has known that it was for her.

An hour later Ian entered the post commander's office. The latter looked up from his writing and it seemed to him that upon Ian's face there was a stronger and a nobler cast. With a word of greeting, the colonel came forward and laid his hands upon Ian's shoulders—none of that military etiquette here between friends.

"Ian," he said, "I am happy to see you again. Set down and tell me of your trip."

Ian gave him a quick resume of what had happened. He told him of his journey with Father Gregg to the Blackfoot nation, his travels through New Mexico and Texas with Lieutenant Malgares, and showed him the medallion he had received from the Indian stranger.

Colonel Williams examined it for a long while then said, "We had reports that the Great Hasanun is in the north country. All of the Indian prophets seem to originate in that territory for some reason."

"You know Tecumtha and Pontiac came from the north. We must find this new prophet before the entire frontier is engaged in a holy war."

"What am I to do, if I find this so-called prophet," Ian asked.

Colonel Williams thought for a moment before answering.

"First, we must verify there is a new prophet, then find out what he is preaching. Perhaps he is advocating peace. We must do these things. That is your mission."

"We have a detachment going up to Fort Des Moines in ten days. You accompany them and look for the Hasanun in that territory."

*   *   *

In a room at the Planters' House in St. Louis, four men were gathered about a table. On a heap of blankets in the corner, a grossly fat Mexican lay snoring in drunken slumber. Since they had doubts of his power of discretion, it was better so, especially as the game involved treason and bribery as well. They were quietly negotiating the transfer of an empire.

The four were curiously assorted; there were two lean-faced professional soldiers, a soberly clad man who might have been a merchant, and a flamboyantly-uniformed person of a more political stripe. As the conversation proceeded by the light of a few candles, it was apparent that the main issues had reached accommodation. All that remained was to settle details. Even so, the conversation was not proceeding smoothly. The dark-faced colonel burst into a rapid spate of Spanish which the merchant easily translated to the captain who sat beside him.

A pause followed, broken by snores from the corner, while the two Americans conferred. The merchant replied briefly and faces cleared; the objecting colonel withdrew satisfied from the talk. Shaking hands all around, the politician-general picked up his candle and made ready to leave. At that instant, the Grand Conspiracy of the West had reached final agreement to form an empire of the Southwest with His Catholic Majesty of Spain as titular head!

The merchant quickly carried his few possessions from the room, for his was a business that permitted no delays, and he marched even more swiftly in darkness. Only the hard-faced captain was left at last to keep condescending vigil over the rumbling bulk of the sleeper. The captain spent little time musing over the extraordinary conversation in which he had just participated, for he was not a man given to long-range speculation of that sort. He had merely been assigned a mission and had discharged it to the best of his considerable ability; now it was done and, like all soldiers, he valued his rest.

He wondered idly as he blew out the candle what he was doing so far from the blue foothills of the Shenandoahs where he was born. He turned over in his mind a fragment of an Indian legend he had once heard and hoped to write down someday, but he was soon asleep.

Early in the morning, Ian and George Catlin were astounded at the arrival of Captain Wharton. After Catlin had seen him, restoratives had brought back his strength and some days later, he ordered Claggett, his man servant, to bring his clothes and put them on, and have him placed in a wagon to go with a party starting for the Fort towards which he had been journeying. Remonstrances on account of his extreme weakness were unavailing. Wharton had peremptorily repeated his orders to Claggett, was placed in the wagon, and reached the Fort. His brother officers were shocked when he rose, tall and emaciated, his own ghost as they thought for a moment, for he had been reported dead and his successor congratulated on his promotion.

The captain was quickly taken to the small hospital, already overflowing with cholera patients. The sickness that had weakened and killed many of General Leavenworth's men followed the dragoons to the Fort. In their weakened condition, many fell victim to cholera.

Although cholera had raged in epidemic form on the frontier for many years, exacting heavy toll from the ranks of the army, and almost wiping out several Indians tribes in the vicinity of Fort Leavenworth, its garrison escaped those demands until now.

When Indian agent Dougherty returned from a visit to several Pawnee villages north of the post, he reported that their misery defied description. They had ceased to bury their dead whose bodies were to be seen in every direction—lying in the river, lodged on the sand bars, in the weeds around the villages, and in their old corn caches (excavations in the earth in which corn had been placed). Others again were dragged off by the hungry dogs into the prairies where they were torn to pieces by the more hungry wolves and buzzards.

That the Fort Leavenworth garrison escaped the ravages of this cholera scourge raging close by, using the polluted river water, was nothing less than a miracle. However, the post did experience other deadly diseases for a number of years. In the spring of 1829, many men were prostrated with malaria fever and a number of cases proved fatal. The Secretary of War, in his annual report for 1828, advised the President that "The garrison at Fort Leavenworth on the Missouri has suffered most severely from this cause. It is situated on dry and elevated ground selected with special regard to health, but the rich bottoms in its vicinity occasion the sickness, and it is doubtful whether a change of location to any other point high up the Missouri could escape or even diminish the cause of the evil."

Frontier conditions in the fall of 1829 improved very much as the malaria subsided.

In 1832, troops engaged in the Black Hawk War, some of which were furnished by Fort Leavenworth, fell victims to the disease. Over two hundred men died there from out of a total of 1500. That is the report of the Secretary of War.

Jefferson Barracks was the initial point from which the cholera was spread. Cholera broke out on the steamer Arabia carrying infantry on an expedition to the upper Missouri. Fifty-two cases and nine deaths were reported. The disease also appeared in the 6th Infantry. Twenty-four cases and fourteen deaths were reported by the surgeon, who stated that the soldiers had been exceedingly intemperate while at Jefferson Barracks.

It had been reported that two hundred recruits at Jefferson Barracks were crowded on a single boat with only one medical officer. The frightful disease broke out among the troops on the first day of their departure and spread with fearful rapidity. Nearly every man in the command was taken sick with it, in some of its stages, before their arrival at Fort Leavenworth. The captain of the boat was requested to push on to Fort Leavenworth as fast as steam could carry him and to stop for wood as seldom as possible. Whenever he did make a landing, the commissioned officers had to stand guard, pistol and sword in hand, to prevent a general desertion of such of the recruits as were able to be on their feet.

They placed the sick in the most comfortable part of the vessel, reserving other cabin passengers barely room for the dining table. Although the officers escaped the scourge, the groans of its victims were anything but sedative to their nerves. They had all been in the Black Hawk War where one of them was badly wounded. Yet, they acknowledged that they would far rather be under fire where the stimuli of the din of battle and military renown keep off fear, than to be spectators of the silent though deadly onslaught of the Asiatic cholera.

The Indians adjoining the area around the post were sent word not to come in, but they had no other place to go for food, as the severe drought had destroyed almost everything

Jefferson Barracks

edible. As the result, they were swept away. The atmosphere for miles was poisoned by the stench of the hundreds of carcasses unburied. The women and children wondered in groups, without food.

No matter how bad the conditions were on the frontier, the officers' ladies continued with the social affairs. There were balls and parties without number and many pretty ladies from Westport, Leavenworth, Liberty, and other places. There was a wedding party that Ian was ordered to attend. A large landowner in Liberty had married a captain's daughter, and everyone had to go to the wedding party to pay their respects. Catlin was there so Ian could visit with him again.

Among the wedding party was a young Indian woman of great personal attraction who danced in her Indian style with much grace. There was a new lieutenant by the name of Jeff Davis who Ian had met several times. His figure was very soldier-like and rather robust, his step springy, resembling the tread of an Indian brave on the warpath. Lieutenant Davis became fascinated with her charms and danced with her in almost every set. He would do many remarkable things, sometimes changing the order of the dance to suit his fancy. When quadrilles were danced, he would change into a waltz, so he could have his arms around the waist of the young woman. Then again, freeing himself from her, he would dance with all his might, causing his tall form to jerk and wiggle as it swayed to and fro. Sometimes he jumped up and down in quick succession and yelled at the top of his voice in imitation of the Indians at the door.

Colonel Taylor and Captain Thomas took no part in the dance, but set in one corner of the room looking on and almost splitting their sides with laughter.

The young woman, hearing the laughter, felt herself insulted in the presence of the company. She became indignant and informed her brother of it. Her brother, a tall, athletic Indian, was very angry and felt determined to punish the offender. Being quite drunk, his brain frenzied by whisky, selected Lieutenant Davis to vent his anger on and in bad English accused him of insulting his sister, at the same time pulling the lieutenant's nose. Davis, who never lacked courage, pushed the Indian from him and drew forth a pistol. The Indian with a fiendish smile drew from its scabbard a long scalping knife and was prepared to meet his antagonist in a death combat. The dance stopped, the women screamed, and all was confusion and alarm; everyone expected to see the death of one or both. But in an instant Colonel Taylor sprang between the combatants and thereby prevented the effusion of blood.

After the excitement died down and the lieutenant left for the barracks to sleep off the effects of the whisky, Ian noticed a young lady who appeared to be Colonel Taylor's daughter, Sarah. Ian danced with her several times. She was a girl of 20 or 21, graceful, rather small and dark, and danced well, so well indeed she was said to be one of the best dancers in Kentucky where she came from.

She was in the bloom of her girlish loveliness. Some men would say she was very beautiful. She was slight, with wavy brown hair and clear gray eyes, very lovely and livable and a young woman of decided spirit. The large eyes were trusting, innocent, and intelligent. The mouth was small and prettily modeled—the nose slightly tip-tilted. Her wavy brown hair was parted in the middle and divided into four graceful curls, which hung to her bosom. The pink dress was daintily and sparingly trimmed in white lace. Over her left forearm and wrist was draped a filmy scarf.

In mentioning the incident earlier in the evening, she related that the lieutenant and her were engaged but Colonel Taylor preferred Lieutenant Davis as junior officer to a son-in-law and had refused his consent to the marriage. Tonight it appeared Lieutenant Davis had danced himself out of a bride.

Two days later a court martial was ordered with Taylor as president; the other members were Major Tom Smith—between he and Taylor there was a bitter feud. Davis and Ian who had just reported for duty and who, when the Court assembled, appeared in citizen's dress, explained that his uniform had not been forwarded from St. Louis, his last station. Lack of uniform was a common occurrence, as the army's budget was usually expended before the purchase of uniform priority came to the top of the list of purchases.

Ian wore a hunting shirt, or hunting smock (a "wamus," as it was sometimes called) of a mountain man. It was not a coat in any sense, but a loose tunic that was slipped over the head. Close fitting sleeves were attached to it, and it was slit open for a little distance down the chest and laced together with buckskin thongs. It was cut to reach just above the knees. The seams of the sleeve and the bottom edges of the shirt were decorated by fringing the leather. It was made of soft buckskin, carefully tanned. This was a material, which was not only readily available, but it was light and resisted both water and wind. The wamus hung loosely from the shoulders without any effort to shape it to the body and was confined at the waist by a broad leather belt. A long hunting knife in its leather scabbard hung from the belt on the left side.

His leggings were much like those of the Indian. They were gartered in below the knee to prevent dragging and hampering the movements of the wearer. As in the case of the hunting shirt, the out seams were lined with fringe. At the bottom of the leggings, the seam was opened a bit to permit the easy passage of the foot. His footwear was the Indian moccasin. It fitted his foot snugly but not tightly. His long hair was tied behind in a rude pigtail. He had gotten used to these clothes on the long Santa Fe march and the Mexican expedition. Although it bothered the garrison desk officers, Ian and Lt. Phillip St. George Cook had appealed to Washington, and they had relented on wearing this dress in the field.

Taylor, a stickler for customs and rules, was unwilling to go on with the cases until Ian could take his seat in uniform with sword at his side. An angry discussion at once broke out between him and Smith over the question of proceeding and, to the Colonel's surprise and disgust, Davis voted with Smith to go on with the trial. A sharp exchange of words at once took place between Taylor and Davis. It was ended by the colonel letting fly an oath in which he shared with his fellow Army and Navy officers a fairly strong vocabulary that any man who would vote with Tom Smith on a question of that kind would never, never marry one of his daughters. He then forbade Davis from ever entering his house.

Ian had not entered the argument but, as he listened to the group, he wondered how many young officers of this day, engaged as Davis was to the colonel's daughter, would have voted against him? Not one in a hundred, Ian ventured a guess. Tom Smith would have been outvoted, and the court adjourned till the careless Ian could appear properly in full uniform, epaulettes, sash, and sword.

In this mood, the court progressed slowly and a good deal was told in evidence.

When Lieutenant Davis voted against the colonel's wishes, the friction between the two men increased. The colonel assailed him harshly.

Then Davis became angry. In the end, Taylor forbade Davis to enter his house and swore, "by the Eternal," that he should never become a member of his family. The "code" was not yet dead on the frontier, and Davis' irritation now drove him to the determination to challenge the colonel. He accordingly approached Captain McRee with the request that he act as his "second," only to be told how absurd it was to plan the death of the man whom he wished as a father-in-law. Mrs. McRee was called into council, seconded her husband's refusal, and declared that if Davis would master his temper, she could manage to bring him, at times, into Miss Taylor's company and facilitate his romance.

Two days later the fierceness of the cholera took fifteen men in one day. What added to the plight of the unfortunate population was the desertion of its only physician. Every one of the many young physicians then practicing in the city of Leavenworth declined this service, except one. He was paid less than forty dollars for this professional work, though the commander's inclinations to pay him a much larger sum—it was all he had at his disposal.

Ian had heard Sergeant Beidler's Annie was sick with cholera. He was impatient all day due to the slow proceedings of the court martial. When he finally arrived at the clearing it was late afternoon. He had intended to start much earlier but did not get out of the court martial until late. He had the best horse in the stable and he rode him hard.

There were several men at the sergeant's place. The peculiarities of the appearance of his companions were chiefly in their faces and expressions. Most of them had a sinister, unchanging smile with something contemptuous in it, which so often characterizes adventurers both within the pale of society and beyond its bounds. Such men do not laugh easily. They were mostly from what might be called the backwoods of Kentucky; they had some very crude notions of the world at large, but they were fine men to have on your side when the going got tough, and you were able to count them as friends.

Sergeant Tom met him at the door, plainly worried. Annie was in bed with wet towels across her head to try to lower the fever. Louisa was there, worn and haggard, trying her best to care for Annie and the children and cook for the men.

Her dress was typical of frontier women. Their dress had neither the picturesquesness nor the individuality of masculine attire.

Her bodice was of leather cut loosely to the body and laced in front. Under it was worn a coarse linen without a collar.

Her skirt was cut full but without an excessive amount of material. It fell in rather straight folds from under the bodice and hung to her ankles. Being warm weather, she was barefooted. Her usual coiffured hair now hung loose and disheveled around her shoulders, but in all her drabness, love showed through. . . . love for Big Annie, the children, Ian, and all of humanity.

Annie, though burning up with fever, welcomed Ian with a "How-d'y." Ian pulled up a low stool beside the bed, took her hand in his, and through her fevered eyes her affection for him showed through. The fever had exhausted her strength and made her very nearly helpless, it would seem almost beyond belief that she should survive. But her wonderfully hopeful disposition, unfailing courage and firm trust in God, helped her endure this heavy trial. The new surgeon of the regiment, who had arrived to replace the deserter, was a man of science and great skill in his profession, but an inveterate drunkard. He was so stupefied with liquor that the men had to souse him in cold water before he could get back on his horse when he left.

The next day Sergeant Tom had to leave on an expedition, and Annie got worse. Her youngest child, a boy of three years, was taken that night at midnight. Annie, when told that her end was approaching, asked Louisa to take down her last request to her children and absent husband. The sickness of her children had kindly been concealed from her by Louisa, who had managed by the aid of a soldier to attend to them all. Three died the next morning. The boy preceded and the girl followed Annie by about an hour. Sergeant Beidler had marched with his company, but only proceeded thirty miles when overtaken by a messenger. He returned in the night stripped of nearly everyone he loved; he found Annie and three children dead.

In the morning, the bodies were laid in the same grave and Sergeant Tom started for his camp with tears streaming down his face into his handlebar moustache, carrying his two remaining children, Ollie and Else, with him. A soldier has a hard life and but little consideration.

*   *   *

Ian sent Louisa on the next stage to St. Louis. Louisa was to go to Washington, DC. Sir Arthur had asked her to come back to his house to await the arrival of the baby. He had taken a fond liking to both Ian and Louisa and treated them as his children, as he had none of his own.

Sarah Knox Taylor, the girl Ian had met at the wedding party, was to accompany her. It was hard for both Davis and Taylor to bear the strained atmosphere between them, and the colonel sought to have the lieutenant transferred to another command and his daughter sent back to Kentucky under the pretext of the cholera epidemic.

Sarah had again asked her father for permission to marry Lieutenant Davis. The old soldier remained obstinate.

"Some day," she insisted, "you will see his rare qualities as I do." Then she declared with Taylor-like determination that she would marry Jefferson Davis, with or without parental consent. Her decision was a rash one for the times. Even young men in the 1830's hesitated to marry in the face of a father's strong disapproval.

So Sarah was to be sent to her Aunt Elizabeth's home three miles from Louisville.

Disappointed, but undaunted, Knox, as Davis called her, and Jeff became secretly engaged, and delayed plans for their marriage until some more opportune time. When he boarded the steamboat, like any young man in love, he carried away a flower Knox had given him as a keepsake and reminder. It was a wild pansy known sentimentally by the name "heartsease."

Only a brief rest was allowed the dragoons after their fatiguing expedition. Three companies of about one hundred and thirteen men set out for Fort Des Moines. An order of the previous May from the War Department had directed companies to take up their winter quarters "on the right bank of the Mississippi, within the Indian country near the mouth of the Des Moines." Company B was under the command of Captain Sumner, H under Captain Boone, and I under Captain Jesse B. Browne.

Lieutenant Colonel Kearny commanded all three companies. He set out from Fort Gibson. Ian and Davis were to take the steamer back down to St. Louis and pick up provisions for the fort and Fort Snelling, further up the Mississippi.

On the second day of the journey, several of the troopers became sick and Captain Brown became too ill to proceed. Soon they arrived at an Osage mission where several Indian families resided. These "subsist principally on fish and the chase with a few vegetables they raise themselves in poorly cultivated fields or rather patches." A dragoon in his journal recorded that "they are a race, naturally of a robust constitution."

Daily advances averaging about twenty miles were made during the three weeks march. Prairies, oak barrens, good timber, and thickly settled areas were traversed in turn during the journey across the State of Missouri. The dust atmosphere was cleared a few days later by a heavy rain which saturated the ground. The Missouri River was crossed at Boonville and the dragoons observed a country covered with farm houses and plantations. Six days later after steady advances, the command arrived at the mouth of the Des Moines River.

*   *   *

The boat trip to St. Louis was without special event. Ian and Jeff loitered about on deck. To pass the hours away, they would clean their pistols and relate their past lives.

Jefferson Davis said he was born in Georgia, the same state Ian was born, in 1808, and as a youth his parents moved to Mississippi.

At the school Davis found himself associated with a body of undergraduates—many of whom were destined to high positions in the life of the nation. He enjoyed the friendship of Henry Clay, a trustee of the university, already a commanding figure in national politics, and whose son was Davis' fellow student, and congenial comrade.

He remained in college until the end of his junior year, enjoying the life and beauty of surroundings, which made the Blue Grass region famous. He was always gay and brimful of buoyant spirits, but without the smallest tendency toward vice or immorality.

His father's cotton-field experiment, of making him work all day in the fields, had worked a real conversion for he no longer desired to escape the machinery of education. He studied with special diligence the Greek and Latin classics and developed a love of political philosophy and of history, which was his favorite diversion.

It had been Davis' intention to finish his course and enter the University of Virginia, but at this point his brother Joseph, a prominent member of the Mississippi bar, secured for him an appointment as a cadet at West Point. His mother protested saying boys there are "trained for vice and the army," and his academic life came to a sudden end.

The National Military Academy of West Point held a high reputation as a place of scientific education. Cadets, then under the direct control of the President, were the objects of keen competition, although the selection depended upon presidential favor rather than competitive examination, and there were, it was said, at least thirty applicants for every available appointment.

But somehow, on March 11, 1824, John C. Calhoun, Secretary of War, made out a cadet's commission for Davis and President Monroe signed it.

He graduated in 1828, and then, in accordance with the custom of cadets entered service with the rank of lieutenant. His first station was Jefferson Barracks, St. Louis, where he was a brevet Second Lieutenant of the First Regular Infantry. Soon, however, he was assigned to duty at Fort Crawford, in the Indian Country, far to the north, and better known to later generations as Prairie du Chien. It stood near the junction of the Wisconsin and Mississippi, commanding a wilderness occupied by Indians, and was thus the frontier guardian of civilization, upon the northern border of the Illinois tribes and the starting point of their raids against the Iroquois.

This was a drab beginning for a young and ardent West Pointer, with a proper idea of the dignity of his profession, though highly characteristic of the life of a frontier camp of the early nineteenth century.

Although he understood the Indians, what Davis didn't know were the frost and cold of these northern forests.

It is a cold of its own up through the North country, and the exposure—the contrast of the warmth and glow of his Southland where he had spent more than half of his twenty years—ended in sharp illness.

Young Davis had never concerned himself with care of his health. Though he possessed a highly sensitive nervous system, he had been remarkably well all of his life. Heedless of health hazards and the admonitions of James Pemberton, his body servant, he often got soaked to the skin while directing the sawmill construction. At last he came down with a virulent case of pneumonia.

Without benefit of a physician and with only the rudest camp fare for diet, Jeff lay at the verge of death. Except for the vigilant ministrations of Pemberton, he probably would have died. It was the heartening devotion of James Pemberton that kept the breath of life in him. Delegating much authority to James, he entrusted him with his weapons, his money, and his reports. Through the colored man, during his semidelirious illness, the lieutenant tried to direct the construction work. When he began to convalesce, he had lost so much weight and was so weak that James would pick the tall young man up in his arms like a child. Sometimes he would carry Davis to the window to glimpse the thrilling beauty of the whitened landscape. Jim Pemberton scorned to take advantage of the ordinance which made a slave in the Northwest free.

He owed his life to the care of James Pemberton, who had come with him from "The Hurricane," when he left there after his furlough following graduation from West Point. This young slave had been with Davis since both were boys, and Davis loved him as a brother.

The years at Fort Winnebago were soon gone and he was back at Fort Crawford and reporting to a new commanding officer, Colonel Zachary Taylor. It was the beginning of a connection that reached far on the long arm of consequence.

Brevet Colonel Zachary Taylor had been observing young Davis' conduct and abilities with special interest even before he took temporary command at Fort Crawford because of the illness of Colonel Willoughby Morgan. In 1832, he made Davis his aide.

Though the colonel's father, Richard Taylor, was a pioneer in Kentucky, Zachary was Virginia-born (in Orange County), and brought to Louisville in a saddlebag when he was eight weeks old. On both sides, his family were gentry.

Davis had studied his chances of promotion, even to the rank of captain, and had found them far from encouraging. Few vacancies were likely to occur, and the probability of new posts being created was slight. The West Point graduates found no vacant posts and they had to be attached as brevet (officers without official commands) second lieutenants to the companies to which they were assigned. One hundred seventeen of Davis' fellow officers had resigned chiefly because of the discouraging outlook for promotion.

But what bothered Davis mostly was that in the exciting year of 1832, in which he met his first love, Jefferson faced another decision—whether he should obey a Federal command or be true to what he regarded as the sacred constitutional principle of liberty and State Rights.

South Carolina was seriously threatening to "nullify" what the South considered an unjust tariff decreed to protect New England industries. The matter had been brewing since the year of Jefferson's graduation from West Point, in 1828, when John C. Calhoun had expounded his theory of nullification. As presented in his famous "Exposition," the South Carolinian argued that: (1) the tariff was ruinous to the South; (2) "protection" for privately owned industry was unconstitutional; and (3) when an act was both unconstitutional and injurious, any state had a constitutional right peacefully to nullify the law within her borders until Congress should appeal to the States and be sustained by a vote of three-fourths of them.

Though President Andrew Jackson was supposed to disapproved of the tariff, at the Jefferson Day banquet in Washington in 1830, he had significantly proposed the toast: "Our Federal Union, it must be preserved." And he had taken occasion several times after that night to declare openly he would meet nullification with force. In the fall of 1832, when South Carolina called for a state convention to adopt an Ordinance of Nullification, President Jackson promptly increased the Federal garrison at Charleston's Fort Moultrie.

On November 24, 1832, by a majority of 136 to 26, South Carolina declared the tariff laws void in the state and promised armed resistance if the Federal Government should try to enforce them. Jackson warned the South Carolinians that the laws would be enforced by bayonets, if necessary. But, at the same time, he urged Congress to make a further revision of the tariff.

Jefferson Davis had been brought up on the Jeffersonian principle of State Rights, and though he could not bring himself to agree with Calhoun's nullification as the right solution of the tariff controversy, he determined to resign his army commission if ordered to march against South Carolina to enforce execution of the laws. For months the tension in Washington and Charleston was discussed in the far-off northern military posts. Rumors circulated that the regiment to which Davis belonged would be among those sent to subdue South Carolina. "By education, by association, and by preference," he told Ian, "I am a soldier, regarding this profession as my vocation in life. Yet, looking the issue squarely in the face, I must choose the alternative of abandoning my profession rather than be employed in the subjugation or coercion of a State of the Union. . . . The Compromise of 1833 prevented the threatened calamity, but the sorrowful issue will arise one day, which will force upon me the determination of the question of State Sovereignty or Federal supremacy—of independence or submission to usurpation."

In the same spring of 1833, when bloodshed had been avoided in South Carolina and Lieutenant Davis had not had to resign his commission, he accepted a promotion to a first lieutenancy in a newly created regiment of dragoons. He went to Kentucky on recruiting duty.

While there, Jefferson requested a brief furlough to talk over everything with his brother Joseph.

When Jefferson arrived at Hurricane and bared his heart to his brother, he found Joseph had changed his mind about an army career since his July, 1832, letter. Now he confessed he could not see much future for an army officer, since so many West Point graduates in the past two years were without assignments. Besides, he argued, the United States was an isolated nation, far removed from European quarrels. He felt that the Americans were eager to develop the resources of their new country and to steer clear from entanglements with Europe. Their remoteness made it possible for them to stick to such policy. Jeff was convinced that if he stayed in the army there would be few opportunities for him except in fighting Indians, with whom he had a certain sympathy. His recent experiences in the Northwest had taught him that there were many disillusions and few rewards in that kind of army life.

* * *

Night had fallen and the two went below decks to their cabins. The next morning the steamboat had docked at St. Louis and Ian was supervising the loading of supplies when he saw Louisa and Sarah drive up in a buggy. A Negro boy carried their baggage onto the boat. Ian's question was quickly answered. The two had decided to go up to Fort Des Moines with Jeff and him.

Ian tried to explain that the comforts of home were not in the North country. She would be in the midst of Indians, deprived of almost everything that makes life dear to a woman.

Ian took Louisa to his heart, and, holding her close, exclaimed, "How can I refuse!" The thought of a few months together cleared away all anxieties and filled them with happiness.

Over the evening meal future plans were cheerfully discussed, dangers and difficulties were looked bravely in the face, and feeling that, with undying love for each other, they could meet and conquer whatever lay in their way. And they rested peacefully together during the night and looked forward to many other days and nights together enjoying each other's bodies and love.

In the morning, Ian lolled in front of the recruiting office, waiting the departure of their steamer. It was delayed by a steamboat, with its flag flying, coming down the river. As it rounded to the wharf, Ian noticed that the deck was crowded with Negroes, and he heard them singing some of their camp meeting hymns in a way to touch all hearts. The strain was in a minor key, and, as the poor creatures swayed their bodies back and forth and clapped their hands at intervals, he was strangely moved; and when, the landing being effected, and the gang-plank arranged, they came off, chained in pairs, and were marched, still singing, to a shed prepared for them. The overseer, a great strong man, cracking his "blacksnake" from time to time, to enforce authority.

Like cattle, they were penned for the night, and were to be kept there for a day or two, till another boat should take them to New Orleans to be sold for the cane brake and the cotton field. They had been bought by the dealer in men and women, who had them in charge at the slave pen in Washington, the capital of the United States.

A bright mulatto woman surprised Ian, begging him to purchase her, at the risk of being beaten. How she had enough courage to do it, Ian did not know, but she begged on her knees, pleading most earnestly, said she was not with her master's family where she was born and raised, and had been sold, "because massa died, and de family was too poor to keep me; I'se a fustrate cook, and'd sarve you faithful; and, oh, mistis," turning to Louisa, "I'se lef little chillun in de ole Virginny home, and if you buys me, may be I might see 'um again sometime."

Louisa could not keep back the tears, Ian knew this was wrong and he felt a strong indignation but there was little he could do. It was a cruel, dreadful reality but perhaps one day it would not be so.

But it could not be now, and the poor sorrowing mother would go back to the gang, whose breaking hearts were pining for home and dear ones they could never again behold. And on tomorrow morning they would be driven onto another boat, and sing as they sailed down the river to their doom, "swing low, sweet chariot."

The thought came to Ian as he listened to the woman and he cursed himself silently, "You stand here with supposedly good intentions and pity, but you do nothing," he told himself, "you talk and think good thoughts but you do nothing."

"Action, that is what moves the world."

"Action must be taken to change these injustices. And you are doing nothing. You are worse than most. You think about these terrible wrongs, but you do nothing," he kept telling himself.

"Do something! Do some little thing to change things."

"Besides Louisa will need help with the baby on the way!" So it came to pass that Ian finally did one more deed to bring more love into the world . . . and bought Clara's freedom, that being the slave's name. He told her he would pay her for helping Louisa. Clara again fell to her knees thanking Ian; time after time.

Louisa kissed Ian on the cheek tenderly and thanked him also, then turned to Clara and gently raised her to her feet, and hugged her as they both walked up the gang plank.

The steamer to Fort Des Moines had a single wheel at the stern. It carried 450 tons; 900,000 pounds; drew 30 inches of water when lightly loaded and had three boilers which consumed eighteen to twenty cords of wood daily. A cord being eight feet in length of four in height and four in depth and sold on the Mississippi for $4.00 to $8.00 per cord.

It had engines of 132 horsepower. The constant service in which the boats were kept on the great rivers of the West, where commerce and transportation were very considerable and much varied used them up in a very few years. They had to contend with impetuous currents, to ascend rapids, to cross banks or bars of sand or mud, where the full power of the windlasses had to be exerted to get them over.

Going against the current, the Pioneer made five to six miles an hour; with the current fifteen to eighteen miles. Her crew consisted of a captain, two clerks, two pilots, and an assistant, two engineers, two mates, a steward, two watchmen, one head cook and two assistants, one barkeeper, seven cabin boys, a porter or baggage man, eight white deckhands, four firemen, nineteen Negroes for all the work of the boat and one chambermaid.

The main cabin complex consisted of thirty staterooms, seven feet long by six wide, and with two berths each. There were thirty-two first class passengers; fifteen gentlemen, twelve ladies, and five children. There were among these some ten Catholics, Protestants of diverse shadings, free thinkers or infidels and a few Jews.

The long days were passed in social conversations, sometimes political, sometimes scientific or religious. Storytellers or jokers were never lacking in an assemblage of American travelers. Some read, others played at cards or dice, or checkers or other games of chance.

The Mississippi, or Muddy River, had an ordinary width of one to three miles. It went winding down over 2,546 miles often changing its channel, thus necessitating very watchful and expert pilots, who judge the depths of water by the appearance of the surface and in spots where the water spreads out over a wide expanse they had recourse to the lead depth finder.

When the boat stopped to cut and load wood, which took ordinarily one to two hours, some passengers would busy themselves fishing or hunting, while the greater number went walking over the adjacent hills or through the forests along the river, making bouquets of the flowers of the wilderness or picking up shells or petrifications of various varieties.

On another day, Louisa and Ian struck up a conversation with two Jesuit priests. They had lived amongst the Indians for neigh on fifteen years and had studied whence they came, of many tribes but all of one race, who once possessed this whole vast country from the Atlantic to the Pacific.

We needed a villain in the American saga and, inevitably, the Indian was given the role. We had to believe him wholly a devil to justify our own course, and there was enough devil in him to make this easy. He waged war as the warrior wages it, and so dreadful was he in war that the specter of him still haunts our racial memory. It is time now to admit that not only was the Indian fighting for his native land against an invader to whom treaties were scraps of paper, and the solemn pledges of statesmen merely a means of gaining an end, but also that every barbarity practiced by the Indian in war was practiced by the white man who fought him, including scalping, the slaughter of women and children, and the torturing of prisoners. Confronted by Indians in our advance across America, we reverted to savagery. The morals of it may be argued, but the fact is an essential part of the Indian's story.

Its end, perhaps, was inevitable; a people still living in the Stone Age could not withhold a vast continent from what we call (a little doubtfully at times) "the uses of civilization." When the sun rose upon the first band of white men, night was at hand for the Indian, and slowly the darkness engulfed them. If we, who took their country from them, were fighting the battle of progress and enlightenment, all the more reason why we should be fair to a conquered people's memory. Every few miles is written down in imperishable record, as a spot where the scanty, scattered tribes made a stand for justice and their own rights. Instead of searing it over with infamy, the future will recognize it as glorious record of a race that never melted out and never died away, but stood up manfully, man by man, foot by foot, and fought it out, for the land God gave him, against the world, which seemed to be poured out over him. There is much truth in that eulogy. The Indian, too much an individualist for his own good, nevertheless fought a good fight, the best fight that any race has ever made against the Colossus called Civilization. He was a terrible foeman, but it is questionable whether the methods he employed were more terrible than those used against him. The pioneers who faced and fought him in his wilderness-were a valiant breed, but they were not, in the circumstances they could not be, knightly or chivalrous foemen. Both were pawns in the hands of Destiny. Whether Destiny and God are always one and the same is a question for which the story of the Indian provides no satisfactory answer.

*   *   *

The steamer made slow headway against the current but finally reached the Des Moines River. It was only a short time later until they arrived at the rapids.

The rapids were about fourteen miles long, and at the top of them was the military post called Fort Des Moines. This site appeared to Ian to have been chosen with singularly bad judgment; it was low, unhealthy, and quite unimportant in a military point of view.

Ian and Louisa managed to get a cabin as did Jeff and Sarah, although many soldiers wondered, nothing was said. Out here men did not stick their noses into other people's business. In this north country where a man could be dead tomorrow, they did not concern themselves with gossip or the like. They all lived like they wanted to. That is why many deserted for a better life.

The cabin was uncomfortable but it had a roof. Louisa put down a carpet brought from St. Louis and Ian chinked the cabin and daubed and banked his private stable preparing for the coming winter as the soldiers had told him the sufferings of those stationed there in the wilderness last winter.

Unlike the majority of such in the West in the early days, this outpost at the "forks of the Raccoon" was not established to protect the whites from the Indians. On the contrary,

Fort Des Moines was founded to guard the Sac and Fox Indians, to secure them in the peaceful possession of their hunting-grounds and to protect them against rapacious land agents, the encroachments of the whites and the Sioux. And the event was typical of the relation of the national government with Indian tribes of Iowa.

When Iowa became known to the people of the East the tide of emigration soon began to run high and strong toward the Mississippi. It is not extravagant to say that never have more beautiful lands been opened for human settlement than lay beyond the "Father of Water's" in the hunting-grounds of the Sacs and Foxes. The wonderful stories related to the marvelous fertility of the soil and the attractiveness of nature in this country gave a tremendous impetus to emigration. But the national government firmly held back the tide. The Mississippi was patrolled by troops to prevent the settlers from invading the land. Colonel Zachary Taylor and Lieutenant Davis, were among those who guarded the rights of the Iowa Indians and ejected overzealous frontiersmen and squatters.

But the pressure of population westward was irresistible; and small pretexts were sufficient to break down the barriers. The war with the Sacs and Foxes under their great leader, Black Hawk, came on and by the treaty of 1832, known as the "Black Hawk Purchase," negotiated by General Winfield Scott, a tract along the Mississippi fifty miles wide was opened for settlement. This strip was rapidly being populated as this was some of the best land on the continent.

Ian and Louisa knew nothing of care and sorrow. And when the sight of the flag, run up, each morning, to the roll of the drum, and the sentinel's call, each night, "All's well around," made them feel secure and at home, even in this wilderness. There were many pleasant scenes. The country around the fort was beautiful, the climate invigorating, and in spite of the inconveniences and annoyances experienced by the pioneer regiment they were not without their enjoyments and recreations. With their delightful rides and rambles together, theirs was a happy life. But the most charming of all the recreations was the rapids. With the white water rushing through the rocks; they listened to the joyous liquid music of the laughing water. The picture was a gem of beauty. There was no saloon there then, no fences, no tables and benches cut up and disfigured with names and nonsense, no noisy railroad, no hotel, it was just pure rapids with its graceful ferns, its bright flowers, its bird music and its lovely little waterfalls.

Children rambled on the banks, and gathered pretty fragrant things fresh from their Maker's hand. There was some love-making going on in the cozy nooks and corners on the hill side or under the green trees. Ian and Louisa would come upon groups of two, scattered here and there in those same places, who looked like lovers. That enchanting spot, so dainty in its loveliness, was hallowed by a thousand tender associations. Standing there beside the river in all its purity, just as God made it, made their eyes full of unshed tears and its smoothly flowing ceaseless song seemed pleading to be saved from the vandalism which would surely come as civilization came along.

*   *   *

The delightful sojourn with Louisa came to an end, as Ian was ordered to take supplies up to Fort Crawford and Snelling in the Sioux country near the headwaters of the Mississippi.

When all was in readiness the expedition went southward on the Des Moines until it joined the Mississippi then turned northward and began the ascent to Fort Crawford. The flotilla was made up of bateaux (a flat-bottomed boat with raked bow and stern, flaring sides, strong shear, and rockered bottom used especially on rivers by lumbermen) and keel-boats, the latter having been fitted up as comfortable as possible for the women and children.

Notwithstanding the inconveniences of such a mode of traveling, the hope that the change might benefit all, and the fact that they were making the last stage of a very wearisome journey, inspired them with fresh courage, and a general cheerfulness prevailed throughout the command.

Of the difficulties and delays of such a journey up the Mississippi, few could form clear conception if they had not went through such an ordeal.

The perfect safety of this mode of travel commends itself to those who are in no hurry, and desire to learn all about the windings of the river and the geological and floral attractions along its banks.

At night the boats were tied up, camp-fires were lighted, tents pitched, sentinels posted and everything made ready, in case of an irruption of Indians.

The expedition finally arrived at Fort Crawford (Prairie du Chien), after a very trying journey, the troops worn out and exhausted. So instead of pushing on to Fort Snelling, it was decided to remain at this point several days for the rest of renewal of strength, before making the final plunge into the unknown wilderness, into the very midst of Indians, who might resist their progress and cause them much trouble.

The transportation of their supplies had been attended with so much difficulty that, notwithstanding all possible care, the pork barrels leaked badly and the contents were rusty; the flour had been so exposed to dampness that for the depth of three inches or more it was solid blue mould, and there was no choice between this wretched fare and starvation, for the miserable country about the fort afforded no supplies.

A long time would elapse before the provisions could have been officially condemned and fresh supplies sent from St. Louis, the nearest military base for supplies, for red tape was perplexing and entangling.

So Ian decided to deal with the problem in his own way. There was a fair sized village to the west situated on the Great Lakes which Ian thought he could pick up some supplies.

Two days later, Ian started well armed and escorted by five troopers. The little band arrived at Chicago with no incident. The little town had struggled for survival amid dismal prophecies that a city would never rise on this unfavorable swamp. There was for some years, because of the quagmire conditions of streets and the frequent inundation from the lake and river, Chicago was termed the "amphibious town." By filling in the land the city was literally lifting itself out of the mud. It was plain that the founders had come to build it into a center of trade and population. Encouraging progress was being made on the Illinois and Michigan Canal, the population of the town was increasing, neighboring prairies were being tilled, and the water carriers who drove their carts into the lake, filled their barrels, and then distributed water by the bucketful.

Ian bought the supplies he needed and started back to Fort Crawford immediately.

A change had come over the face of the land. The bright summer flowers had disappeared, a growth of yellow and blue ones, the harbingers of the departing year, supplies their places. Here and there a red flower, the survivor of those which had flourished in the summer, shot up its head amid clusters of golden-hued blossoms. The deep green of the trees had disappeared, and the brown tinge of autumn was creeping among the leaves. The bright, soft green of the prairie grass was giving place to a color of greenish brown. The geese and pelicans had left their lives of solitude, and in large flocks were winging their way to the south; the wind swept over the rustling grass with a moaning sound that spoke strongly of the approach of winter.

* * *

As Ian sat on the porch of the visiting officer's quarters next to Captain Clark's cabin, he heard a little girl and boy talking excitedly, "Oh! Malcolm, look at that little boy on the steps of our house; who can he be? Where did he come from?"

"Oh, sister, do you think he can be the little brother we have been praying God to send us? Let's ask mother about it."

The two little children had just been dismissed from the fort school house, and were going home to dinner. The sun shone very brightly that day. The dinner drum was beating, the soldiers, by companies, were in line before their quarters for roll-call, and the dear old flag floated gracefully in front of headquarters.

The little son and daughter of Captain Clark, hastened to their home with their eyes all the while fixed on the little fair-haired stranger, who stood on the porch of their cabin, the first in the row of officers' quarters as you entered the fort by the front gate, and just beyond the steps leading down to the commissary's store.

When they reached their goal, there stood the pretty blue-eyed boy, looking about with wonder at all he saw, and smiling at them as they came up to him, and laid their hands on him gently, to assure themselves that he was real. Just inside the door stood their mother, with a bright happy look, enjoying their surprise, and the children, with one voice, exclaimed: "Mother, who is this little boy? Where did he come from? Is he going to stay with us always?" As soon as they gave her a chance to reply she said: "Don't you know that every night when you say your prayers, you always say, 'please, God, give us a little brother!' How do you know but God has heard your prayers, and sent you this little brother?" They were very quiet then, and tried to take it all in, but before they had succeeded to their satisfaction in fully comprehending it, their father came from roll-call, and taking them by the hand, said: "Come to dinner now, mother will lead little Andrew to his place and we will tell you all about it."

Ian was invited to their dinner table and he listened to the story told to the children.

"A few weeks ago, the colonel heard from some hunters, who had been far out west, that there were two little white boys held captive by a band of Sioux; he sent out some troops, who rescued the children, and they reached the Fort this morning with the boys; the oldest one, John, is at the colonel's, and this is the other, 'Andrew Tully;' shall we keep him with us?"

"Oh, yes! Father, we want him for our little brother;" and he became one of them.

Later that evening after the children were asleep, Captain Clark said they had learned from John, who was a bright boy, and from the rescuing party, who had heard some particulars, that Mr. Davis Tully, a Scotchman, had been living three years at the Selkirk settlement, where the crops had been so poor, from various causes, notably from the grasshoppers and the ravages of innumerable blackbirds, that a famine was threatened, and he, becoming discouraged, had started, with his wife and children, two boys and an infant daughter, to come to the fort, hoping in some way to continue his journey from there to the white settlements, and find work to enable him to live and support his family comfortably.

After traveling for many days, they were overtaken by a party of Sioux, who, returning from an unsuccessful hunt were in a very bad humor, and attacking Mr. Tully, demanded such provisions as he had. He refused, of course, to give up that, without which his family must perish, and they fell upon him, soon disabled him, and seizing the little baby, dashed its brains out on the ice, then mortally wounded his wife, and with a blow of a hatchet, one of the party finished them both. John said he remembers seeing his father, who had broken through the ice, struggling to save his mother and the baby, but that when they knew there was no hope left, his parents told him to take his little brother and hide in the bushes, and try in every way to get to the settlements. Then, with their dying breath, they besought God to take care of their little boys, and their freed spirits went beyond the reach of pain and suffering. The little fellows obeyed them, and ran for safety to some hazel brush near by, where, of course, the Indians soon found them, but their thirst for blood being somewhat allayed, and their object attained, they contented themselves with cutting off a piece of John's scalp, tearing it most brutally from the quivering flesh, when the women from some teepees nearby, hearing his heart-rendering screams, came to the rescue, and begged that they might keep the children. And there they had remained, receiving such care as the Indian women give their own papooses, and making friends of all in the wigwam. When the troops came to the rescue, the Indian women were unwilling to give them up; they had taken a special fancy to Andrew, who was very fair, and of a sweet, gentle disposition. He was not quite three years old, and, of course, could not so well understand the dreadful loss they had sustained as John, who was two years older, and who never recovered from the shock of the tragedy, and from the injury done his nervous system by the cruel scalping-knife.

Ian was asked by the commanding colonel to take John to Fort Leavenworth where he could get better treatment in overcoming his terrible injury.

A keel-boat was fitted up nicely for the trip down to Fort Des Moines, and in addition to the soldiers in the crew, they had as fellow travelers Captain Leonard, his wife and two children, and John, making quite a large party.

There were the good-byes from those who stood on shore, and as the boat progressed slowly as it was poled along by the crew, it was not without a quiver of sadness that they turned the point where they lost sight of the flag. The wife and children of Captain Leonard felt then that they were away from home and all seemed very strange, but there was much to interest them, and they soon became accustomed to their new experiences. The ceaseless walking to and fro of the men who propelled them along was an accompaniment to all their daily amusements and they went to sleep lulled by their regular footfalls.

And so they journeyed on, day after day, until they made Fort Des Moines.

Ian was glad to be reunited with his friends, especially Louisa, Sarah and Jeff. Although John would hardly talk to anyone, including Ian, he readily became attracted to Louisa. Her kindness was felt by the little boy whose scalp was half gone. The red scar made Ian sick with compassion every time he looked at the pitifully wounded little boy. Without uttering a word, he would help Louisa set the table, wash the dishes and helped her do all the other household chores. John clung to her gentleness as if it was the last thing on earth. Several days later, noticing that she needed some firewood, John tried to cut the wood and the axe glanced off a hard knot and he received a severe cut. Although the doctor had done all he could, John was taken with lock-jaw.

The little boy was very suddenly seized with fever in its most violent form, and for hours seemed in mortal agony. They had no efficient remedies though, and Ian and Louisa fought all night with the fearful disease, using all the external remedies within their reach, cupping the dear child with inexperienced hands, but Louisa's prayerful heart, leaning entirely upon God, who, when she cried unto him in her distress, heard and mercifully regarded her cries. The acute and agonizing symptoms of the attack were subdued, but the fever remained for a week and the dear boy lay very near death. His form wasted, his hands became almost translucent, and they could only watch and pray, and use all the means in their power to alleviate his sufferings.

During his illness he raved of the Indians, who killed his dear ones, begged them to spare the baby, and not hurt his mother; then he would seem to be hurrying Andrew out of the way of the murderers, and hiding him as well as he could.

During this trying time, the stock of candles was nearly exhausted and their weary watchings were only lighted by a sense of God's presence. So with her hand on the dear sufferer, and her ear attentive to his breathing, Louisa and Ian sat beside him, lighting the candle only when absolutely necessary. Louisa prayed during the night, never slumbering or sleeping, but a change for the worst came, and he died in a fever in the early morning.

He suffered terrible mental agony, but he had been carefully taught by his mother and Louisa, whom he learned to love very dearly, and, reason returning before he died, he gave clear evidence that he loved the Savior, and felt sure that he would take him to heaven, where his father and mother, and precious little sister were awaiting him.

A detail of soldiers from Ian's own "Company C" gave their encoffined form little John a full military funeral; to them the greatest tribute they could do for him. The funeral was a mournful occasion. The bearers with their burden; the long procession of soldiers with trailed arms; the commissioned officers each in his appropriate place, all keeping time and step to the muffled drum as it rolled out its requiem on the winter air, in the strains of Pleyel's heart-melting hymn; the weeping of Louisa and Sarah in the sleigh—all passing out the gate to the lone graveyard. And the precious burden was lowered, and at its head stood Surgeon Lyman, and in a voice trembling with emotion, read the words; "I am the Resurrection and the Life, saith the Lord."

After the burial service came the last salute, and leaving there that which was so dear to them, Ian and Louisa went back to the empty quarters, bowed down heavily, as those who mourn for one inexpressibly dear.

Ian's worrying about Louisa's health became worse so when the last steamboat of the season came with supplies, Ian insisted Louisa go back to St. Louis to have the baby in civilization.

The evening before the departure of the boat, Sarah and Jeff came over to talk about their future plans also.

Daily, Jefferson had become more and more disturbed about violations of states' rights by the government in Washington, D.C. and his ability to provide for Sarah on his army salary. Also, with the winter hardly started, the cold already bothered him and weakness like he experienced several years ago had him near pneumonia.

All these situations plus worrying about Sarah had made him decide to resign his commission, marry Sarah even thou against her father's wishes, and move to "The Hurricane," his brother's plantation.

Ian said his good-byes to Louisa, Sarah, Jeff, Clara and James Pemberton in the cold of a snow storm. The captain was anxious to start back before the ice filled the river, so the farewells did not last long.

He would miss Louisa but he was happy that she would have their baby in a civilized place. She was going back to Washington to stay with Sir Arthur during her last months.

Louisa seemed worn and harassed, he thought, and much less pretty than a few months ago. There was a nervous restlessness about her, and she was unable to sit still for a moment without moving her hands, or her feet, or her shoulders, to look around, when there was nothing to look at. Her gentle, young face still wore a smile but Ian knew she was in great discomfort, her stomach now protruding quite a bit and the weight of the unborn child stretched her skin and ruptured the veins.

He held her close and kissed her gently. He loved her more than anything else in the world.

A little shiver ran through her as she clung to him and her hand twisted painfully upon his, and there were tears in her voice. Both knew what they were doing had to be, but it did not make the parting any easier. Louisa was still the same, fashioned for masculine adoration, even though heavy with child.

The steamer captain hurried Ian off and the boat and Louisa was soon lost from sight. The last thing Ian saw was Sarah and Jeff standing together, totally happy with their new life. Little did Jeff know that his life would be full of great sadness and controversy; people would worship him, others hate him; he would be called a hero and a traitor. Every man must take life on the terms on which it is offered to him.

Early in December, winter came upon Fort Des Moines in earnest; snow fell to such a depth that they were fairly shut out from the whole world, and so suddenly as to find them unprepared. It was difficult and almost impossible, on account of the deep snow, to procure wood sufficient to keep up the constant fires necessary on account of the intense cold. They had no mail, no telegraph, no news from their supplies.

The winter was full of monotonous barracks life and drills followed; nor was it surprising that there was much card-playing after pay day. Drinking was considerable. Brightly dressed young soldiers would sometimes cross the river to Commerce where James White had a hospitable stone house and pretty daughters. And there with partners on a smooth floor amid the strains of tortured cat-gut, the young soldiers forgot the irksome duties of barracks life at Fort Des Moines.

The weather took a turn for the better; most of the snow melted and temperature hovered slightly below freezing. The commander of Fort Des Moines decided it would be a good time to take some wagons out to the logging outposts and bring back some timber to build a few more cabins.

Ian took a party of twelve dragoons and four wagons to pick up the logs. When they arrived at the logging camp, the cold had been so bad and some of the men were too sick to work so they had no lumber. Ian decided to leave the men there to help cut timber and he would go on back to Fort Des Moines.

Ian and a trooper by the name of Schuler started back in a small wagon that would be faster than the lumber wagons with the running gear.

They drove at a good speed in order to reach the creek before darkness set in, as absence of light always multiplies danger. They arrived at the stream about five o'clock and found it rushing madly over its banks, carrying driftwood of logs, trees, and brush so that their resolution gave way and they thought of returning to the station to spend the night.

About a mile downstream they found a likely-looking ford and pushed the horses out into the stream. Prospects were bright for the moment, when suddenly the wagon floated, spun around and very nearly tipped over—before they could shift their cuds of tobacco—and Ian and Schuler tumbled into the water. It so happened that the water, where the wagon spun and tilted, was not more than four feet deep, and they were able to keep their feet. Schuler's first act was to grab the horses by their bridles, while Ian seized the wagon and kept it righted, by skillful and instantaneous action they prevented the horses from becoming tangled, and soon had the satisfaction of getting on shore with no other inconvenience than wet clothing.

But their more serious difficulty was yet to come, for it had grown quite dark as it was still threatening rain. They had landed and were on solid earth, but their surroundings were something like the jungles of Central Africa. There was no semblance of a road leading out of the swampy, brush-grown place, nor did they have so much as a match to light their way. But, figuratively speaking, shutting their eyes and trusting to providence, they started the horses along in the direction they supposed the road lay. After about one hour or more of this delightful picnicking excursion in the garden of the gods, they found themselves lost. Ian had a compass in his pocket, but it might as well have been on top of the north-pole, for having neither a light nor the eyes of a nocturnal varmint, he couldn't see the point. But as if dissatisfied with their circumstances, the Lord pulled out the stop-cocks of heaven and deluged them with a rain of nearly six hours duration, while the frogs, between dashes of rain, croaked all manner of requiems around them.

Nothing could be done except face the artillery of misfortune, so they unhitched the horses and made them fast to their vehicle. Then came the rub of standing round and taking turns in saying such words as a distressed soul may be inspired to utter under the circumstances.

Morning broke at last, but such a morning as would shame creation, for the rain still poured down, until what wasn't mud was water. Frozen and drowned though they were, there was still enough aggravation left in their natures to stimulate them to renewed endeavors to get out of the woods, or hell, which was a more appropriate term.

So confused were they by the desperate experience undergone that wretched night that it was late in the afternoon before they found the trail again, and when they did find it there was nothing to make them proud except the realization that they still lived. Through mud up to the axles they plodded along, hungry, exhausted, wet, mad and intensely miserable, until twelve o'clock the following night before reaching the next logging camp. So thoroughly worn out was Ian that upon entering the station he threw himself upon a bench and did not stir again until morning, though the sergeant tried every way to arouse and direct him to a comfortable bed. The opiate of exhaustion was so powerful, in fact, that he no longer felt the wet clothes that were on him, or took the time to wish he was in dear Fort Leavenworth.

Renewing their journey about noon, the sun came out again, and they gradually forgot the miseries through which they had passed and began to find, one by one, some little pleasures in life. The trail also gradually became more tolerable, the weather turned cold, freezing the wet ground, and a heavy snow began to fall. The snow soon covered the ground, obscuring the trail, but Ian anticipated no difficulty in the return trip safely and speedily. Their horses had been chilled by standing so long in the raw atmosphere, and when they started them they broke away in a run which threatened destruction to their wagon and injury to themselves. They got them checked finally and were bowling along in a hilarious spirit until, reaching the apex of a hill. Ian looked out over the glinting landscape, and was upon the point of making some observation on the beautiful scene, when he spied three black objects nearly two hundred yards distant, which he thought were dogs. But Schuler was too old a traveler in this country to be deceived, and immediately upon seeing them he exclaimed, "Wolves! Get your pistol ready, for we may be in for it tonight."

His remark excited some fear in Ian, for with it the stories he had read of travelers being chased and eaten by the voracious beasts, came back to him with colorful exaggeration. This partially subsided when he saw the wolves making off from them, and to facilitate their retreat Ian fired two shots at them, but without effect. However, they had not proceeded more that two miles further when Ian saw standing in the way they were going two more wolves, which were so bold that he shot one of them not more than twenty feet from their wagon, while the other trodded off slowly, notwithstanding the shots fired at it. They had twelve miles to go before arriving at the fort and with Schuler driving they had calculated to reach the fort before night set in, as they never fancied driving on a lonely trail even in the moonlight.

Ian carried his trusty rifle but unfortunately on this occasion, he failed to provide himself with the usual complement of cartridges, taking less than twenty when he generally carried not less than fifty.

To ward off the cold, Schuler had drank a good quantity of whiskey. Late in the afternoon Schuler became so confused by the corn whiskey, he had intemperately indulged, that in the snow covering the ground, he left the trail and ran the wagon over a log, upsetting it in a bank of snow, but they both escaped injury. The vehicle was so badly damaged that they stopped nearly two hours making repairs, and after going only a short distance further they again broke down, their trouble being a broken shaft and tug, which was caused by the unruly capers of one of the horses.

It was nearly six o'clock in the afternoon when Ian heard the prolonged howl of a wolf, which was directly answered by several others in different directions. These sounds, however, did not alarm him in the least, for he had heard them too frequently; but it was not long before Ian saw crossing the trail ahead of them packs of five and six wolves, while others trotted along behind them in a sneaking manner. He knew these were the skirmishing forces and refrained from shooting, knowing full well that if he should kill one the others would devour him, and once tasting blood and flesh they would seek to finish their meal on them.

Schuler kept the horses in a brisk gallop, realizing more than Ian of the danger which now threatened. Growing more bold each minute as their numbers increased the wolves appeared on every side, some coming up within a few feet of their wagon and then stopping suddenly to stare at the men. Such howling Ian never before heard, the forest being apparently full of the hateful brutes, and every howl seeming to multiply the number. At length they grew so fearless that several would run out quickly and snap at the horses and then dart back again. Ian now saw that it was full time for action, as each moment served to embolden them, and once they would attack their horses little chance would remain for escape. Bringing his gun up, he shot one of the wolves, and scarcely did his blood stain the snow before not less than fifty piled on the wounded animal and tore him limb from limb almost instantly. Ian then fired two other shots into the pack and wounded several others. Looking back to observe the effects of his shots he could see a myriad of wolves running to where the others were feasting, until they were like flies in summer time swarming over a putrefying carcass.

It was only a few minutes after Ian had shot, and before they got out of sight of the pack, when every vestige of the wounded wolves had disappeared in the voracious stomachs of their comrades, and the latter were again soon howling after the two men.

The rest which their horses had by reason of the accidents was very advantageous to them for they were now put to their full speed without showing any suffering; but this speed could not avail against the wolves, which gained on them so rapidly that before they had gone three miles from where he fired his first shot they were upon them again. When they reached the wagon and were ready to spring in, Ian shot two more, which were immediately pounced upon by the entire pack, so they made another gain of a mile before they left this second feast and were upon them again.

Ian had every reason for husbanding his shots, for their escape lay in keeping the wolves from them by killing one of their number at a time, so as to distract the pack. Ian therefore continued this desultory warfare until his last cartridge had been fired, and they were nearly five miles from the fort. Ian had caused the death of perhaps twenty or more wolves, but there was no apparent diminuation in number, nor were there any manifestations of abandoning the attack on the part of those that had survived. Their horses had now become badly jaded, Schuler almost lost his reason through fright. Ian did not permit himself to lapse into a reflective mood, however, for the hungry, carnivorous, blood-loving wolves came after them on lightning feet, their red tongues lolling out between vicious fangs which sometimes snapped together as though they felt his flesh already between their teeth. Ian's gun was not useless, but he carried it in his muffled robes until the wolves' came so near that they tried to leap upon him; then he wielded it as a bludgeon with excellent effect, hitting three, or wounding them so that they were fallen upon and quickly devoured. But this successful way of repelling their attacks did not avail Ian long, for while he combated with more than a score, nearly that number ran ahead and attacked the horses. Ian now felt that it was time to abandon hope, but their poor horses battled so nobly for life that Ian was encouraged by their acts. The team ran on at full speed for nearly half a mile, while wolves were hanging at their haunches and throats or cutting great gashes in their legs and sides. Ian was astonished to see the horses survive so long, but when one fell at length the other could go no further, and here their last efforts were made to protect their lives. Schuler, having nothing with which to defend himself, was despite Ian's exertions, dragged from his seat by three strong wolves, and as he fell upon the snow his cries for aid almost set Ian wild. Oh, how the poor fellow prayed and called to him while the ferocious beasts stripped the flesh from his bones until death ended the torture he endured. The horses shared Schuler's fate, while with almost superhuman strength Ian wielded his rifle and scattered about him nearly twenty of the wolves that had attacked him and the driver. How could he come out of that fiery furnace alive it was impossible for him to hope, for he fought for many minutes, which seemed an age, before assistance came in the person of two Indians who bravely seized clubs and rushed to his aid. They were almost at the outskirts of the fort, and the noise created by their terrible encounter soon brought the soldiers to the scene of action. Ian's escape was chiefly due to the successful attack on the horses and driver, their bodies serving to draw away from him all the pack. But when relieved at last, upon examination he found

that his clothes were literally in shreds, and on his hands and legs were several scratches which, in his excited condition, had not before discovered.

The wolves were driven away by shooting and beating, but not until the horses had been almost entirely devoured, and of Schuler there only remained a grinning skull of flesh, the half of one hand, and a portion of his back and pelvic bone; his limbs had been torn asunder and carried off by the greedy members of the pack to some place where they could munch the bones undisturbed. Of his rifle there remained only the barrel, the stock having been broken and lost.

The Indians had fought back to back with Ian and when the fight was over no word was uttered between them, but Ian owed his life to them and his opinion of Indians improved quite a bit after the saddest experience and adventure in all his life.

With sign gestures they asked for some of the bodies of the wolves as if that was the only reason for fighting along with Ian. But Ian was to be eternally grateful for saving his life and gladly offered all they could carry on their horses. They each tied four carcasses over their horses backs and disappeared into the snow storm as silently as they had appeared.

*   *   *

It was a feeble garrison that remained during the winter. Many of the soldiers had been stricken with intermittent fever. The roofs of some of the buildings were leaky, the health of the garrison was unnecessarily bad, and the hospital facilities were very inadequate. Yet they survived and made the best of the situation. But day by day the temporary supplies lessened, and with all the faith they could call to their aid, the troopers could not but feel somewhat anxious. A supply of wheat had been stored unthreshed in some of the empty buildings, and this, at last, came to be their only dependence. The mill on the property had, of course, been frozen up, and only after hours of hard work could the soldiers clear it of ice, as to succeed in making flour. The wheat was very smutty, and having no machinery to remedy this evil, all efforts to cleanse it proved unsatisfactory, but the compound prepared from it which they called bread, was so rarely obtainable, as to be looked upon as a luxury. The daily "staff of life" was unground wheat.

A large number of Chippewa Indians were encamped about the fort most of the time, and not being able to hunt successfully, on account of the very deep snow, were driven to great extremity, and sometimes acting on the well established principle, that "self-preservation is the first law of nature," broke in the windows of the granaries, and helped themselves to grain. They were welcome to it under the circumstances, but in obtaining it they had broken in the windows, and had mixed glass with it to such an extent that it was unsafe for food until they had picked it all over, grain by grain. This process was a daily occupation and amusement. All available members of the command would set around a long pine table with a little pile of wheat before each, replenished from time to time from the large heap in the center, working away industriously, conversing cheerfully, telling interesting and amusing stories, singing songs, never complaining, but all manifesting a feeling of gratitude that they still saw before them what would support life, for, at least, a while longer; and taking heart and strength to endure, in the hope that before this, their last resource was exhausted, they should receive the long expected supplies, which were somewhere on the way to them. The wheat was boiled and eaten with salt, the only seasoning of any kind they had; no butter, no milk, no meat, nothing. But all ate it with intense relish.

Kansas Ghost Woman

The long hard winter told upon everyone and especially some of the children became feeble and sick. During the bitter wind and blinding snow storm, some snow birds took refuge in a wood-shed and were caught by the Indian boys. At the suggestion of the oldest son of Captain Clark, who had read somewhere the story of a sick child and her canaries, these little refugees were brought into the nursery and soon became perfectly tame, flying all about their sick boy's head, lighting on his hands, and amusing and resting him wonderfully. For several days the storm continued, and they sheltered the little creatures, with the invalid growing better so rapidly as to excite their surprise. But at last there came a mild bright day, and they returned them out to find their companions. They flew only a few rods and then fell dead. To the family it seemed that these little winged messengers had been driven to them in their extremity by the fury of the storm as healing agents, and had given their lives for the child's. The question then arose, where could they find suitable food for their convalescent? There seemed no possible help, but they believed it would come. One morning as they sat wondering how this would be brought about, the older brother came in and handed his mother a fresh laid egg, saying: "I did not know there was chicken on the place, but it seems that an old hen, who had lived in the wheat all winter has suddenly been aroused to a sense of her duty, and this is the result." The egg he had found was of priceless value, and she received it gratefully as a gift from God. It furnished a whole day's nourishment for their exhausted, feeble little boy, and for three days he was supplied in the same way; then, just as he was more hungry than ever, and when it was evident he never could regain his strength without nourishment, the supply ceased. The family waited and trusted, and in a day or two Ian found a fine pheasant, which had evidently lost its way, sitting in the snow, wondering perhaps, where all its companions were, and why the berries were all gone. Where it came from they never would know, but they knew that there never was so delicious a bird eaten. It was reserved for the sick child, but a small piece was given to each of the other children, and not one of them would ever forget the taste of that precious morsel. By the time the nutritious supply was exhausted, the invalid was so much better as to be able to do his share of picking over wheat, and of eating this simple but healthful diet.

The Peace Council

*I*n due time the days grew longer and warmer; the snow melted. Large flocks of wild geese passing northward over the fort assured everyone with their unmusical but most welcome notes, that the long winter was over and gone.

In the spring, fleas invaded the camp. Of the seventy-six men remaining the terms of enlistment of fifty-eight would expire during the winter or the ensuing spring. In early spring, the colonel received orders for the summer campaign, which was intended as a means of discipline and instruction for the soldiers who were no doubt weary of barrack duties.

The fort would be abandoned and the squadron would march for Fort Leavenworth. It was delayed until the grass was sufficiently high to afford grazing for the horses. And so the day came when eighteen dragoons, the remnants of companies H and I, bade hearty farewell to the hardships and joys of the rather inglorious post.

Soon the camp became a scene of hurried activity as men, horses, mules, provisions and tents were prepared for the journey.

In the midst of all this activity, Father Gregg arrived.

He rode a small pony, with a stiff mane and legs so short that when his long legs dangled down on each side, they were so near the ground that it was a matter of doubt which set of legs did the traveling. With him was George Catlin, the artist. Catlin was clad in a buck-skin coat with high boots and soft broad-brimmed white hat, which turned up all round and assumed any shape he might wish.

He road a small mule named Kitty Keero, upon whom he lavished various terms of endearment.

Their bedding, baggage, and camp furniture were in two light wagons, which two servants, Mordecai and Joseph drove. Kalespel the old Indian squaw, was the cook.

The Commanding Colonel at Fort Leavenworth, with prudent care for their creature comforts, had added a cow, remarking that coffee was always improved by the addition of milk, a remark in which they all concurred.

Father Gregg was an old campaigner, and was familiar with prairie life, and with the untrodden plains over which they were to make their journey. He was known far and wide among the trappers and hunters and was always addressed as Black Robe, the name the Indians had given him.

On the day before their departure the soldiers commenced loading two ox wagons, with kegs of gunpowder, barrels of flour, sacks of bacon, besides boxes and bales containing presents for the Indians. Towards evening a cessation of noise and clamor in the neighborhood of the storehouse gave token that the task was accomplished.

Ian had been lingering at Fort Des Moines until he was weary of inaction, and was anxious to commence his new adventure.

In the course of an hour, the two oxen were yoked before each wagon, and the teamsters, Mordecai and Joseph departed. They were to encamp on a small stream a few miles distant and await Father Gregg, Catlin, Ian, and the soldiers.

There was no more beautiful prairie country in the world than that which is to be seen in the vicinity. In looking back from one bluff towards the West there was to an almost boundless extent one of the most beautiful scenes imaginable. The surface of the country is gracefully and slightly rolling, like the swells of the retiring ocean after a heavy storm and everywhere covered with a beautiful green turf and with occasional patches and clusters of trees. The soil in this region is also rich and capable of making one of the most beautiful and productive countries in the world.

They had heard little of the Hasanun but the red cry of a savior was felt in the air, and around the campfire in the evening, Father Gregg would talk of this.

"Since the Indian, during centuries of conflict with the white race, has been largely lacking the ability to express themselves in clear and effective speech, it is all the more difficult for us to comprehend the psychological effects of the discouragements and disappointments he has experienced. We can measure, here and there, the material effects of war, epidemics, and such, in lives and dollars; but it is not so easy to comprehend or to measure the spiritual bitterness of continuous moral and physical defeat."

"The illuminative nature of a study of the Indian 'prophets or messiahs,' with a characterization of the mission or aim of these preachers of apocalypses, is well indicated in two excellent views of one who knew the Indian well from time to time in every great tribe. At every important crisis of Indian history we find certain men rising above the position of ordinary doctor, soothsayer, or ritual priest, to take upon themselves an apostleship of reform and return to the uncorrupted ancestral beliefs and customs as the necessary means to save their people from impending destruction by decay or conquest."

"Prophets thrive on despair; of despair the Indians have their fill."

"The prophets of the American Indians carried messages similar to the prophets of other peoples. In addition, rising out of their native religious environment, their tenets have some interesting peculiarities which appear as more or less general among the native prophets' teachings."

"Prophets have been more numerous in aboriginal North America than among any other race of people or culture save the Jews. There were apparently none in Mexico and Central America, and but few in South America."

"I think it can be explained only by the fact that the Indians of Latin America were in general accepted into the circle of Spanish cultural, political, social and economic life, and were Christianized. They may have been oppressed, massacred, enslaved, overworked and made to suffer much, in many regions, but the facts remain in contrast to those for North America beyond the sphere of Spanish domination, for in North America only were the Indians rejected and cast off, exiled, yet permitted to remain in the status of independent political communities, with their own religions and cults, forced to stand on the frontier, or beyond it, and meet alone the ever-increasingly difficult problem of subsistence amidst the devastation of war with firearms and the firebrand, of epidemics brought by traders and of decreasing game."

"The life of the serf, slave, or peon, to which the Latin American Indian was subjected in the sort of life of hard labor and security which produces contentment among the individuals of the masses. It is when a subjected people retain the fact or the consciousness of a political independence that the dream of past greatness remains with the hope of a renewal of that greatness, which in the mind of the religious prophet, is to be obtained only by traveling backward to the manner of life of that Golden Age. Inasmuch as his hearers utterly despair of being able to attain anything by mere human action, they find acceptable his message of a promise of supernatural help if they return to the ways of the Age of Innocence, the habits and the worship and the purity of their ancestors."

"Various evangelical Protestant groups in the United States today periodically revive the idea of an imminent Second Coming of Christ and the ushering in of a millennium for believers, only because they have had diffused to them ideas which originated in Palestine in the first century of our era."

"With the ancient Jews, the situation is in contrast to that among the more modern Irish. There was the same longing of a people for the restoration of their former political "glory" and independence. But their religion was a distinctly national religion in sharp contrast to the mystery religions such as that of the cult of Isis or of Mitra then beginning to spread around the Mediterranean Sea. And among the Jews there were present variant dogmas— Pharisee, Sadducee, Essene, and so on—making more practical the emergence of a new heresy. Moreover, Rome did not war on the religion of the Jews as England did war upon the religion of the Irish. Among the Jews, where several cults already existed, there was room for another—another, moreover, which would be more intensely national and unifying than those already existing which tended to develop a tolerant policy with regard to the tolerant Roman conquerors. For Christianity before Paul was a cult for Jews and for Jews alone."

*   *   *

Except in the time of war there is but little variety in prairie life. The experience of one day is but a repetition of that of another.

It was near mid-day when they set out, following the broad trail left by the baggage wagons as they had passed through the high grass.

As long as they were in the garrison, where the busy face of man was seen, where active forms were moving around them, and the everyday concerns of life were going forward, they felt that, though distant from home, they were still connected with society; but when they bade farewell to those at the garrison and as they watched their forms until they were hid by the distant hills, they felt that the last link was broken which had hitherto united them to the world and its occupants.

It was late in the afternoon of the next day when they crossed the Indian border, and issued from the forest upon a beautiful prairie, spreading out as far as the eye could reach, an undulating carpet of green enameled with flowers and lighted up by the rays of the setting sun.

They were now on the look-out for Indians, but not for hostile ones, for they were on the "Reservation Lands" to which the United States Government had a few years before removed some of the tribes from the eastern States.

These were friendly, and far different from the wild tribes whom they were afterwards to encounter, and, who claiming these lands as their own, looked upon the Indians who occupied them and the white men, who had placed them there, as bitter enemies.

Several days later after they had camped for the night, Ian had spread out his bear-skins and buffalo robes and devoted his attention to Catlin who had an unusual fund of information about the Indians and enlivened the whole evening with tales of Indians and mountain trappers.

He and Father Gregg thought alike about Indians. Catlin commented to Ian how much more kind it would have been for the historian, who never saw him, to have enumerated with this—other characteristic actions of his life (for the verdict of the world), or to have allowed, in charity, their bones and their names to have slept in silence, instead of calling them up from the grave, to thrust a dagger through them, and throw them back again.

"Book-making now-a-days," George continued, "is done for moneymaking; and he who takes the Indian for his theme and cannot go and see him, finds a poverty in his matter that naturally begets error, by grasping at every little tale that is fabricated by their enemies. Such books are standards, because they are made for white man's reading only; and herald the character of a people who never can disprove them. They answer the purpose for which they are written; and the poor Indian who has no redress, stands stigmatized and branded, as a murderous wretch and beast."

"If the system of book-making and newspaper printing were in operation in the Indian country awhile, to herald the iniquities and horrible barbarities of white men in these western regions, which now are sure to be overlooked; chapters would soon be printed which would sicken the reader to his heart, and set up the Indian, a fair and tolerable people."

*   *   *

On the following day their horses were saddled, the oxen harnessed to the wagons, Joe cracked his whip, and in full expectation of they knew not what, they set out for the region of adventure.

Traveling was slow, for at times they came to streams whose banks had to be dug away to render them passable for wagons. Bushes had to be cut down and thrown in the river to form a footing for the teams, and to prevent their miring, and the four oxen were often yoked to one of the wagons to drag it up the roadway that had been dug.

Their efforts were accompanied by shouts and yells on the part of the teamsters, Joseph, upon being told that his noise and language was too loud and vulgar replied, "I have drove oxen since Adam was ten, and when an ox has a hard pull to make, the louder I yell, the harder he pulls."

They struck the Saline River about forty miles from the Pawnee village; then taking an easterly direction, they followed the course of this tributary of the Missouri.

On the first night, their camp was upon a high bank of the Saline, a river which flowed through the prairie until it emptied into the Platte.

During the spring of every year moisture exudes from the soil near its source, covering the prairie for the distance of many miles.

This is dried up by the heat of summer, and leaves in its place a thick incrustation of salt. This in turn is dissolved by successive rains and carried into the Saline River, giving to its water the brackish taste, from which it had derived its name. There is a barrenness around the stream contrasting strongly with the other rivers that grace the prairie. Around them is always a rich forest of the deepest green, and everything marks the luxuriance of the soil, and the nourishment yielded by the streams to the lofty trees, which hang over their waters.

But the Saline has no groves to fringe its banks. Here and there a huge dead tree may be seen leaning over its surface, or lying prostrate in the water which gurgles around its branches.

Altogether it was the most cheerless camping ground that they met with, and to add to their discomforts the mosquitoes swarmed about them in clouds.

Ian strolled some distance down the stream and pattered rifle bullets on the water to the great annoyance of several ducks who were quietly dozing upon its surface, and some sprawling turtles who were floating down the stream.

A loud hail from the camp, and the voice of Mordecai announcing that supper was ready, recalled Ian to the spot. His fellow travelers had already commenced, with knives of all sizes and descriptions, and the venison disappeared like magic before their repeated attacks.

Though at all times very well qualified to play a conspicuous part, in work of that description, they were now more than usually fitted for the task, owing to their eating only two meals a day—one at sunrise and one at sunset—the rest of the time being occupied in their journey. When they had finished, the sun had set, and the stars were glimmering in the sky.

The powerful tributary of the Platte river was reached in two days. The Indian name for La Platte is Nebraska, signifying the shallow river. A village of Delawares was a few miles off, and to this they directed their course.

When they reached it a loud barking of dogs announced their arrival to the Indians, who flocked from their cabins to ascertain the cause of the canine uproar. From them they learned the route, which they were to take, and, following their instructions, they kept on through the woods until they came to a prairie on which was strongly marked the broad trail which led to Leavenworth.

The rain cloud of the morning had left nothing but beauty behind it. A cool freshness exhaled from the tall grass glittering with its water beads; the parched foliage seemed to have become fresh and green, and the drooping flowers again raised their heads.

In the spring of the year, these prairies were covered with a profusion of pale pink flowers, rearing their delicate stalks among the rough blades of the wild grass. Too fragile to withstand the scorching heat of summer, they had disappeared, and others had succeeded them.

There was a gorgeous richness in the summer apparel of the prairie. Flowers of red, yellow, purple, and crimson were scattered in profusion among the grass, sometimes singly and at times spreading out in beds of several acres in extent.

There is a strange sensation of pleasure in traversing these vast and boundless lands. Sometimes they came upon the crest of a wave-like hill, which commanded a wide view of the green prairies beyond it. Here and there small clumps of trees were resting, like islands upon the bottom of a sea. Far off a long line of trees, winding across the country, marked the course of some hidden stream. But a few steps of their horses carried them from the point of lookout. Passing down the hill, they splashed through the water at the bottom, tore a path through the grass and weeds, which frequently rose, in these hollows, to the height of six or seven feet, and in a few minutes stood upon the crest of a hill similar to the first. This was again cut off as they descended into another trough, which divided the long surge-like swells of land.

Such is the prairie—hill follows hill—and hollow succeeds hollow with the same regularity as the sweeping billows of the ocean. Occasionally a broken bluff rears its solitary head up, overlooking the country. Upon the top of these they frequently saw an Indian, standing in bold relief against the sky, or seated upon some pleasant spot on its summit, and basking in the sunshine, with that air of lazy enjoyment which characterizes the race.

They had been traveling several hours through scenery when a loud cry from Joseph announced that they had come in sight of the cantonment. There was a speck resting upon the distant green; behind it rose a forest of lofty trees that shadowed the Missouri. This was Leavenworth. But still, many miles intervened; for the prairie is like the ocean—the view is wide and boundless; and it requires an eye trained by long residence in these regions, to measure accurately the distance of objects.

It was mid-day when they first caught sight of Leavenworth, but it was near sunset before they arrived.

The garrison at Fort Leavenworth consisted of about 120 men—sufficient to keep in check the wild tribes who claimed the ownership of the whole country from the Platte to the Arkansas River, and now and then made an onslaught on the whites who lived near the frontier line.

The small party was greeted very cordially by the commander and his officers.

On the following day Ian strolled through the forest which skirted the fort and overhung the Missouri. At times flocks of gaudy little parakeets flew swiftly through the trees, screaming as they went. There were plenty of bright-colored woodpeckers flitting from tree to tree; and here and there a sedated old bird of the same species busily engaged in examining the interior of a decayed trunk.

In another direction he spied a raven sitting upon the limb of a dead tree, apparently brooding over the mistakes of his past life, and wondering where he should get his next meal.

*   *   *

Fort Leavenworth was a place of rendezvous for parties of Indians from the neighboring tribes. They would make their appearance quite unexpectedly and then disappear as suddenly as they came.

They hung round the garrison for several days, and passed their time in lounging about the quarters of the soldiers, or strolling through the woods; peering into the windows of the houses, or now and then stealing through an open door into the interior.

Their step is so hushed and noiseless that there is nothing to warn one of their approach and Ian had frequently been surprised to find several of these fellows quietly seated around him in his room, and all apparently very much at their ease. With all this, there was an unobtrusiveness in their manners, which soon reconciled the troopers to their presence, and were it not for their eyes, which were ever fastened on one's face, creating a feeling of restless uneasiness, there was little else in their company to annoy.

It was near the close of a warm afternoon, and Ian had thrown himself upon a bearskin on the floor, with that feeling of listless languor which is apt to pervade a stranger when visiting the Western country for the first time. The drum was pouring out a dull, melancholy roll, at the far end of the green, occasionally enlivened by the shrill tones of a fierce little fife. Under the window a lounging soldier, half asleep, was drawling out a tedious ditty, with a strong nasal accompaniment, which did not add much to the liveliness of the tune.

Ian's eyes were yielding to slumber; present things were fast vanishing, or only appeared blended with the fitful forms of a drowsy imagination.

"Ho! Ho! Ho!" shouted a dozen voices at his sides. A group from the Kansas tribe was seated in a ring around his bear-skin. For a moment he was bewildered, but they soon convinced him of the reality of their presence. They were a detachment who had been sent out to forage. Although their language was unknown to him, their object was perfectly intelligible. They looked around the room for any kind of food but seeing none they left. Ian lay back down half asleep, but he could see what took place in the outer room as they were leaving. They caught sight of a bottle containing the cholera antidote. An Indian can never resist the temptation of liquor.

The colonel, with anxious forethought for the party under Father Gregg's charge, which had just returned, consulted several physicians as the best remedy to use in case of an attack of the epidemic.

One old gentleman urgently recommended a mixture of brandy and cayenne pepper, sold in the drug store under the name of "Preparation No. 6."

He said that when Preparation No. 6 was swallowed, the cholera was "bound to quit."

It was made by putting about half a pint of the pepper into a quart bottle, and filling up the bottle with brandy, and was to be administered a teaspoonful at a time in half a tumbler of water. However they had returned to Fort Leavenworth without having any occasion to use it, but kept the bottle on the mantelpiece in their quarters ready for an emergency, as the cholera was slowly creeping up the Missouri River.

These Kansas were the first to test its virtues.

A great swarthy fellow skulked stealthily to the mantelpiece, took up the bottle, drew out the cork, smelt at the mouth of the bottle, he then took a long draught, containing about twenty doses.

Few Indians have ever replaced a bottle more quickly than he did. A sound between a hiccup and a yell burst from him as he rushed out of the room.

He was followed by all the others except one, who lingered behind and eyed the bottled with a longing, yet distrustful eye.

Preparation No. 6 carried the day. He strode up to the flask like one determined to dare the worst, seized it, and took a huge swallow.

The next moment, a smothered howl, he darted out of the room as if shot from a cannon.

These two Indians made better time down to the Missouri River than had ever been made before, and if it was not drunk dry it was not their fault, nor the fault of Preparation No. 6. None of the band again visited his quarters, but they lingered around the fort for several days.

When the night grew dark there was a bright fire gleaming under the old oak tree, and the whole group was huddled together around it. From the piazza in front of the barracks the troopers could see their forms flitting round the blaze and could hear their song as it rose up in the night air with a wildness not unmixed with melody. In the morning Ian visited their camp, but it was deserted. The embers had fallen to ashes, the fire was extinguished, and the whole wild troop had again set out upon its wanderings.

*   *   *

About the year 1800 an epidemic of religious frenzy, known as the Kentucky Revival, broke out in Kentucky and Tennessee, chiefly among the Methodists and Baptists, with accompaniments that far surpassed the wildest excesses of the Indian. Fanatic preachers taught their deluded followers that the spiritual advent of the kingdom was near at hand, when Christ would reign on earth and there would be an end of all sin. The date generally fixed for the consummation was the summer of 1805, and the excitement continued and grew in violence for several years until the time came and passed without extraordinary event, when the frenzy gradually subsided, leaving the ignorant believers in a state of utter collapse. The performance at the meetings of these enthusiasts were of the most exaggerated camp-meeting order, such as may still be witnessed in many parts of the South, especially among the colored people. Evans, the Shaker historian, who was strong in the gift of faith, tells us that "the subjects of this work were greatly exercised in dreams, revelations, and the spirits of prophecy. In these gifts of the spirit they saw and testified that the great day of God was at hand, that Christ was about to set up his kingdom on earth and that this very work would terminate in the full manifestation of the latter day of glory."

People remained on the grounds day and night, listening to the exciting sermons, and engaging in a mode or worship which consisted in alternate crying, laughing, singing, and shouting, accompanied by gesticulations of a most extraordinary character. Often there would be an unusual outcry; some bursting forth into loud exultation of thanksgiving; others exhorting their careless friends to 'turn to the Lord;' some struck with terror, and hastening to escape; others trembling, weeping, and swooning away, till every appearance of life was gone, and the extremities of the body assumed the coldness of a corpse. At one meeting not less than a thousand persons fell to the ground apparently without sense or notion. It was common to see them shed tears plentifully about an hour before they fell. They were then struck with a general tremor, and sometimes they uttered one or two piercing shrieks in the moment of falling. This latter phenomenon was common to both sexes, to all ages, and to all sorts of characters.

After a time these crazy performances in the sacred name of religion became so much a matter of course that they were regularly classified to categories as the rolls, the jerks, the barks, etc. The rolling exercise was affected by doubling themselves up, then rolling from one side to the other like a hoop, or in extending the body horizontally and rolling over and over in the filth like so many swine. The jerk consisted of violent spasms and twistings of every part of the body. Sometimes the head was twisted round so that the head was turned to the back and the countenance so much distorted that no one of its features could be recognized. When attacked by the jerks they sometimes hopped like frogs, and the face and limbs underwent the most hideous contortions. The bark consisted in throwing themselves on all fours, growling, showing their teeth, and barking like dogs. Sometimes a number of people crouching down in front of the minister continued to bark as long as he preached. These last were supposed to be most respected and endowed with the gifts of prophecy, dreams, rhapsodies, and visions of angels.

Twenty years later the jerking epidemic again broke out in Tennessee. The jerking commenced with trembling among the wicked. One and a second fell from their seats. For eleven hours there was no cessation of the long cries of the people, some who were standing and sitting fell like men shot on the field of battle, and then a tremor would run through their soul and veins so that it took away their limb power, so that they fell to the floor and by faith saw a greater blessing than had been hitherto experienced.

At another place a preacher said that "after taking a cup of tea, I began to speak to a vast audience, and I observed about thirty to have the jerks, though they strove to keep as still as they could. These emotions were involuntary and irresistible, as any unprejudiced mind might see." At Marysville, many appeared to feel the word, but about fifty felt the jerks. On Sunday, at Knoxville, the governor being present, about one hundred and fifty had the jerking exercise, among them a circuit preacher, Johnson, who had opposed them a little while before. A camp meeting commenced at Liberty, Missouri. Many had the jerks, and some danced. The people are taken with jerking irresistible, and if they strive to resist it, it worries them more than hard work. Their eyes, when dancing, seem to be fixed upward as if upon an invisible object, and they are lost to all below. At one meeting house the undergrowth had been cut down for a camp meeting, and from fifty to a hundred saplings left breast high, which appeared to be stripped of leaves and were topped so high and left for the people to jerk by. People laid hold of them and jerked so powerfully that they kicked up the earth as a horse stamping flies. Persecutors are more subject to the jerks than others, and they cursed and swore and damned it while jerking. One preacher said: "I have seen Presbyterians, Methodists, Quakers, Baptists, Church of England, and Independents exercised with the jerks—gentlemen and ladies, black and white, rich and poor—without exception. Those naturalists who wish to get it to philosophize upon it and the most godly are excepted from the jerks. The wicked are more afraid of it than of the smallpox or yellow fever."

Several ministers of the region had joined forces in a revival at Fort Leavenworth. Ministers cooperated regardless of denominations: predestination, regeneration, universal salvation, were jumbled in one theological scramble in which "the sweetness of redeeming love," "the overflowing fountain of grace," seemed uppermost. When the excitement of the Great Revival began to subside, churches were deserted to the open field, families drove to the camp meeting in wagons, bringing provisions and bedding with them, from thirty, fifty, a hundred miles away. The meeting began on Thursday or Friday, and lasted through the following Tuesday, while soul saving went on night and day.

Four hundred people were present at the rousing revival. The evangelists rose to the occasion; they had learned how to handle such huge crowds. A tract of ground two hundred or three hundred yards square was lined with tents; behind the tents was cleared space for the wagons and horses. A speaker's stage was built, one at either end of the enclosures, and benches were huddled in. A day's religion-feast began at dawn when a trumpeter blared as he strode in front of the tents; then minutes later a single long flare called the people to pray at their tent doors. Breakfast was a punctuation between sermons, one at sunrise and one at ten. Dinner was at one and supper at sunset; preaching was at three in the afternoon, and an orgy of preaching at night. The cook-fires in front of the tents were rekindled, candles fixed to the stages and to the trees were lighted, making blotches and dots of yellow and amber light against the night arousing sexual desire. The rut of whiskey drinking had been frontiersmen's only emotional indulgence in sensual pleasure, and that had not an answer to the uneasiness, the unspoken awareness of the hopeless conflict between the pioneer's search for power and his search for personal freedom. And whiskey drinking, of course, was a way open to few women; prejudices of the coastal plains society died harder with them, and the interminable grind of working and childbearing left their constitutions precious little strength for any bodily debauchery. The Revival brought forth the surging up of emotions so strong that they burst the body's control, with its invitation, "Whosoever will, let him come and take of the water of life freely," was an opportunity for them all, adolescents, women, huskies. To see a bold pioneer, undaunted by the horrors or war, turn pale and tremble at the disapproval of a woman, a little boy, or a mean African; to see him sink down in deep remorse, roll and toss, and gnash his teeth, till black in the face, earnestly implore the prayers of those he came to devour (presumably his womenfolk, first to follow the "New Light"); and, through their passionate prayers and kind instructions, obtain deliverance; and return in the possession of the meek and gentle spirit he set to oppose; who would say the change was not supernatural and miraculous.

Confession and exhortation became a delirious orgy. How striking to see hundreds who never saw each other in the face before, moving uniformly into action, without a preconcerted plan, and each, without intruding upon another, taking that part assigned him by a conscious feeling, and in this manner, dividing into bands, over a large extent of ground, interspersed with tents and wagons; some uniting their voices in the most melodious songs; others in solemn and affecting accents of prayer: some lamenting, with streaming eyes, their lost situation, or that of a wicked world; others lying, apparently, in the cold embrace of death, some instructing the ignorant and directing the doubtful, and urging them, in the day of God's visitation, to make sure work for eternity; others, from some eminence, sounding the general trump of a free salvation, and warning sinners from the wrath to come; the surrounding forest, at the same time vocal with the cries of the distressed-sometimes to the distance of half a mile. How persons, so different in their education, manners and natural dispositions, without any visible commander, could enter upon such a scene, and continue in it for days and nights, in perfect harmony, has been one of the greatest wonders that ever the world beheld.

Frenzies were contagious. Confronted with something that fascinated them, evangelical religion—"Make me, Savior, what thou art; live thyself within my heart; then the world shall always see Christ the holy child in me"—camp meeting crowds were receptive, nerves in a sympathetic tremor. Then some overwrought soul began it; falling in a stupor, rolling on the ground, jerking and twisting, or barking like a dog. These exercises were faintly humiliating before and after camp meetings, to victims and friends; but scoffers at a camp meeting, once their self-satisfaction wavered-were caught up in the emotional violent activity as easily as twelve year old girls. In spite of all the efforts of nature, both men and women would be forced to personate that animal whose name, appropriated to a human creature, is counted the most vulgar stigma-forced. For no argument but force, could induce anyone of polite breeding in a public company to take the position of a canine beast, move about on all fours, growl, snap the teeth, and bark in so personating a manner. It was commonly acknowledged by the subjects of these exercises, that were laid upon them, as a chastisement for disobedience, or a stimulus to incite them to some duty or exercise, to which they felt opposed.

Jesse Cane, an older minister, remained aloof and counted the devastation; three hundred had fallen to the ground. Some had early symptoms, they afterwards described as a throbbing of the arteries, a rush of blood to the heart; others collapsed suddenly, and recollected nothing. The persons who were struck were generally first observed to pay close attention to the preaching; then to weep and shed tears plentifully for a while; after this a twitching or jerking seized them, and they fell to the ground helpless, and convulsed through their whole frame as if in the agonies of death. In the beginning of this awakening, it was common for those who fell after they had been lying for awhile to speak in an astonishing manner as to the length of time, matter, and loudness of voice. Some of the most powerful sermons heard from mortals came from the mouths of persons of the above description, unable to help themselves. Some spoke almost without cessation for the space of five hours, and some parts of the time so loud that they might be heard at a distance of a mile.

The camp meeting continued for five days. Backsliders were restored. Geniuses at revival preaching were ferreted out in theological schools and at ministers' annual conferences, and their abilities nurtured. Confession of sin, "coming forward" to be saved, the milling of a congregation's elect ones about the doubtful and repentant in their midst, the synchronous overlapping of exhortative phrases and hymn music.

The sobbing of sin-burdened hearers was constant, mournful accompaniment to the preaching; and on the last day of the "religion-feast" a woman lost self-control, and shouted in victorious competition with the ministers. The congregation lingered after the sermons, tearful and distraught. The Reverend sank unconscious upon the floor of the pulpit. John Hodge attempted to preach, but a violent spasm of trembling shivered his words. The shouting woman was at it again, and Preacher John Hodge, too, was in a moment of shouting and exhorting. Nerves snapped, people writhed between the benches and moaned for mercy "religion-feast," shook and exalted alike by repentance and exhortation.

Ian studied the phenomenon around him but did not come under the influence, but he could never forget the fire and brimstone sermons of the colored circuit evangelists back in Georgia warning of the "long, hard road of struggle and anguish before you . . ."

Perhaps this was what was bothering Ian! His whole life didn't make any sense. He was just existing. There seemed no direction for him to follow.

Ian's life was already changing although he did not realize it. Samuel Colt's revolving pistols that his father had sent him made shooting more satisfying and accurate.

Revolvers were really not new, as several were made in flintlock times, probably the most notable being the old Collier. As early as the Revolutionary War, over-under rifles were made in the flint percussion and the barrels were revolved for firing. But Sam Colt's revolving pistol was so superior to the flintlock Collier revolver with the No. 9 percussion cap, in its ignition system that it would soon overshadow that excellent arm. Prior to that time the single shot or double-barreled muzzle-loading pistol supplemented by the sword or knife were the commonly accepted side arms. Sam Colt's new pistol would revolutionize weapons of self-defense.

The muzzle loading pistols were notoriously inaccurate. A passenger trying out his aim from a stage coach aimed at a hole in a live oak tree, but "fetched the nigh mule of the hitch."

Back in the seventeenth century, hand guns, usually the long flintlock variety, were carried shoved under the sash or waist belt. Small pocket pistols were hidden in the pockets of great coats and sometimes in pockets of capes. Military pistols, owned by officers of various armies, were usually found in holsters fastened over the pommel in pairs, with a big flintlock pistol on each side of the fork of the saddle. Heavy cavalry pistols of flint lock and percussion lock were often holstered in the same manner, as were the first Colt Walker revolvers.

Ian was the first of the evolution of the gunman as the Colt revolver displaced the sword as the common personal weapon. The fact that Ian had an extra cylinder and carried it loaded, greatly facilitated quick recharging of the arm. All that was necessary to make the change from an empty gun to a loaded one was to drive out the key, pull the barrel off the base pin, then slip on the loaded cylinder and replace the barrel and key, and a man had another five rounds at his disposal. Extra cylinders could be cleaned and reloaded at camp or at home, and when in a fight this interchangeability of cylinders made the early Colt a priceless weapon to men who sorely needed the best. Colt's design was even better than he realized. His five-shot pistols made one man the equal of five armed with swords or Bowie knives. As the revolver replaced the sword, the belt holster replaced the saddle holster. The Colt revolvers were neat weapons compared with the huge military flint and percussion pistols. Cavalrymen and gun fighters of a later era were not slow in developing holsters for these weapons that could be carried on the belt so that the gun would be instantly accessible. Fighting Indians, they often had horses shot out from under them and once in the clear could go on fighting on foot with their revolvers.

Early cavalry fighting soon indicated the need of carrying revolvers with the butt to the front so the gun could be grasped with either hand when the other held a saber or was engaged in managing the horse.

Percussion pistols needed to be protected from the rain or snow to ensure certain ignition and for that reason holsters of the period were more often of the flap than open-top style. The open-top holster was developed in the southwest in a dry, arid climate, where rain was mostly non-existent and where speed of gun handling was paramount.

Ian had first carried the guns, butts to the front, in covered flap holsters but he soon learned that open-top holsters were much faster. He in turn developed the belt holster. In close range conflicts, the man who could draw and deliver accurate fire first, lived. He soon found that the best possible way to carry his early gun was on a comfortable gun belt on his right side, as he was right handed and carried the other in an open-flap holster on his saddle.

Ian carried his belt gun butt to the rear, just the opposite of the dragoons' method. Ian's gun belt was two and one-half inches in width and made of double oil grain chap leather. His holster was open-top and cut out a bit for the trigger.

The westward course of the United States produced a breed of men unique in history. Living was cheap and killings commonplace. Outlaws preyed on the honest miners, citizens and early ranchers. About the only law was the town marshal and the early sheriffs. These men were hired or elected more for their ability with a gun than for their knowledge of the law. They had to try to control the toughest elements of society ever thrown together in one widely dissimilar mass of humanity.

The menace of wild Indians and organized bands of outlaws preying on immigrants moving westward to California and the rich farm lands of Oregon was ever present. The law was confined to small communities backed by a gun fighting marshal, or was nonexistent. Over a goodly portion of this continent the law was a gun that was packed by each individual. The age old law of nature, the survival of the fittest, ruled. Many outlaws and peace officers became very fast and deadly with a gun; they had to in order to survive. There are only two classes of gun fighters-the quick and the dead. Those on the side of the law, backed by honest citizenry, gradually shot some semblance of decency and order into each community. Many a Western town had a dead man to bury every morning. Many outlaws became professional killers and for a fee would dry gulch anyone, or if necessary, provoke a gunfight and murder their man as surely as if they had shot him in the back. The killing of many an honest citizen was thus arranged and carried out for a price. While many of these professional killers ran up long lists of victims, either dry-gulched or killed in so-called fair fights, they sooner or later met a peace officer, equally good with a gun and wound up in the cemetery. Usually nothing was done about such fights. If the killer had witnesses to swear the victim had an even break, he got away with it. A horse thief was considered beyond the pale and, if caught, was left dancing on air at the end of a rope.

So Ian became one of the first gun fighters and he practiced his fast draw as much as he could. One night, Ian had rode down to the city of Leavenworth when he noticed something wrong in a saloon across the street which was located near a big fur and hide house. The building was peculiarly shaped, a sort of wedge on the corner, or intersection of a side street. A door entered the tip of the wedge and a line of windows ran along one side. On the side street was another door. While nothing was visible from the street, everything inside was plainly visible to a man on a horse looking over the curtained windows. He trotted by the place to see what was going on. Two gunmen had everyone lined up in front of the long bar that extended almost the full length of the east side of the building. At the end of this bar there was a break and a short bar against the back or north end of the building. One man held two guns on the small crowd while the other frisked them.

As Ian went in the front door at the extreme tip of the wedged shaped building, one holdup whirled around and fired, then both bandits jumped over the bar. The others in the saloon dropped flat on the floor. The holdup's slug went through the transom over Ian's head. Ian had his Colt cocked and waited. Soon one man's head popped up over the bar; as he fired, Ian's slug hit him square between the eyes. The other holdup ran down the length of the back bar, keeping low out of Ian's vision, but when he attempted to cross the opening between the ends of the two bars at the corner he was exposed and Ian's second slug caught him squarely through both shoulders and he landed on his face kicking. He had intended firing on Ian from the other bar, thinking Ian would still be watching the place where his partner had been killed.

Ian's accurate firing Colt had saved his life. Another time, Ian entered a hotel as a robbery was in progress. The man raised a double barreled sawed-off shotgun, but Ian proved faster with his open-flap belt holster and killed him with his .44 caliber Colt. With this experience, Ian usually carried his Colt on a belt holster whenever he left the fort.

*   *   *

From the time of his arrival back at the garrison small parties of Indians had been constantly coming and going. They were Kickapoos, belonging to one of the tribes which had been removed from the States. Scarcely a day elapsed that he did not catch a glimpse of some gaudily dressed band, their tin trinkets glistening in the sunbeams, and their garments fluttering in the wind, as they galloped towards the fort. They carried on a species of traffic with the sutler, exchanging furs and skins for ribbons and such other showy articles as are likely to catch the eye of an Indian. From long intercourse with the whites they had become accustomed to driving bargains, and were looked upon by the generality of traders as pretty shrewd customers; yet even from them the profits derived by the whites were great.

From seeing these different bands constantly coming and going to and from their village, Ian and Catlin conceived a desire to visit them, and accordingly upon a fine clear morning they started.

The path was for the most part through the woods. They rode about an hour, crossed several brooks, traversed several small patches of prairie, and at last found themselves upon the summit of a bluff, which overlooked the little Indian town. At their feet lay a prairie dotted with wildflowers. Three of its sides were enclosed by a ridge of hills, at the foot of which meandered a brook with a range of trees along its borders. The fourth side of the green was hemmed in by a thick forest, which extended back to the banks of the Missouri.

In the edge of this stood the Kickapoo village. It was a retired, rural spot, shut out from the world, and looked as if it might have been free from its cares also.

When they arrived, they were told that there was to be a horse race between two rival braves, and that nearly all the village had turned out on the occasion.

They made their way to the starting-place, which was under an oak tree not far off. One or two of the chief men of the tribe who had seen them at Fort Leavenworth came forward to meet them and placed them where they could see what was going on.

After that, they devoted themselves to the business on hand, which was soon completed.

A little hard-headed Indian was appointed umpire, and the two riders were at their posts. Both were young men, dressed in hunting shirts and cloth leggins. Their horses were not of the class that might strictly be denominated racers. One was black, the other cream-colored. The black one had fierce little eyes, glittering like fire, beneath a long, shaggy forelock, which reached nearly to his nose. The eyes of the other were water-colored, and had a sneaking slyness about them-an air, which seemed to insinuate that their owner "knew a thing or two."

Both horses were round-bodied, bull-necked, with thick legs garnished with fetlocks of matted hair, extending from the knee joint down to the hoof, and trailing on the ground.

They appeared but little ambitious of distinguishing themselves in the coming contest, and, had their own inclinations been consulted, it is probable they would have declined it altogether. Not so their riders; they sat as eager as hounds on the leash. Their eyes were intently fixed upon the umpire, who seemed to take the matter with wonderful coolness. At last he gave the signal; there was a hard, quick thumping of heels against the ribs of the horses, and a great clattering of hooves. Their bounds were short but rapid. The riders whooped and yelled, and the lookers-on shouted as loud as either.

The little cream-colored pony was working wonderfully hard, but the black was gaining upon him. They were to pass round a tree which stood about half a mile off, and return to the starting-place. The black had the lead by a length; his legs were invisible as he turned the tree, but the cream-colored pony pushed him hard.

"Two to one on the black!" shouted Ian to George.

"Lay it on, old boy!" hollered George.

Both riders exerted themselves to the utmost, the black still keeping the lead.

As they rushed in, the crowd shouted and opened a passage for them; they dashed through, running nearly a hundred yards beyond the mark.

When the race was finished, Ian and George rode to the Indian town. About thirty huts constructed of bark composed the village. A strong gale of wind would have prostrated even the best of them, had it not been for the shelter of the forest in which they were built.

Their arrival seemed to have created quite an excitement, especially among the children, who followed at their heels in troops until they came to the house of the Indian Agent. This officer was appointed by the United States to live with the tribe, and see that the annuities due them from the Government were not frittered away by going through several hands before they reach the Indians.

His house was a small log cabin, and they found him at the door expecting them. They were cordially welcomed and introduced to the head chief, and also to a tall, bony Indian with a keen black eye. The latter, who was the prophet of the tribe, had been converted to Christianity, and on Sundays delivered addresses on the subject to such as would listen.

His face was full of intelligence, but his outward appearance was rather unclerical; for when Ian entered he was leaning on a long rifle and appeared to be dressed for a hunt.

He laid aside the gun as Ian came in, and with the aid of an interpreter commenced a conversation with him.

At the end of the conversation, the tribe prophet calmly informed Ian, "Soon . . . you shall meet the Great Hasanun."

This statement startled Ian; how did he know he was searching for the leading Indian prophet? It was incredible.

With this statement the conversation ended as the Indian walked away. Ian was told afterwards by the Indian Agent that this was something unusual, as he habitually kept aloof from intercourse with the whites, and that he had more influence with the tribe than any man in the village. Ian did not mention what the prophet had said.

From the little they saw it was evident that the chief yielded to him, and listened to his remarks with the deference of one who acknowledged his superiority. There was, however, no appearance of jealousy or heart-burning between them.

It was late when they left. The sun was sinking in the west, and its last beams were resting on the tree-tops as they rode out of the woods. An hour's ride brought them to their quarters at the cantonment.

Ian was finding out through Father Gregg, George Catlin, Indian prophets and chiefs that not all Indians were savages. Many were more civilized, whatever that meant, than he.

The civilized, self-righteous white men, who indulged so much in his intolerant criticisms upon the Indian character for his barbarous practices and ill-founded superstitions, assuming so much perfection for his own race in this regard, should take the trouble to read a brief chapter on the witch mania in the early colonies and Europe. He will find a history here of superstitious beliefs and barbarous conduct of the Christian white man which far eclipses the most extreme Indian barbarity.

*   *   *

The hostile feelings was hardened between the tribes who had been removed to the land surrounding Fort Leavenworth by the Treaty of 1829 and it was being manifested towards the white man. The Pawnees and Kickapoos could see their treaty rights were sooner or later to be violated by the emigrant tribes. This led to the calling of a conference. A commission was appointed by the Government to come to Fort Leavenworth to purchase the contested lands of the Pawnees, intending to move them north of the Platte river, and to effect a treaty peace between them and their new neighbors.

As soon as the Commissioner arrived at the fort, Major Dougherty sent messengers to the neighboring tribes, summoning them to meet their old enemies in council.

For several days now the delegates and their followers had been coming in, and their camps were scattered through the woods around the fort.

The Pawnees and Otoes were encamped in the forest overlooking the Missouri River; but care was taken to keep the different bands apart until a permanent peace had been established between them.

Additional officers and troops had been brought in to handle any potential Indian problems during the council. While this larger garrison was gathered at the post it offered an opportunity for social civilities and recreation, as well as the amusements incident to refined society.

Among the outdoor events, horse and mule races were sports in which the entire garrison indulged.

There was a track on the reservation located in the bottoms on the northeast portion of the post, where horses were timed, and many happy hours were spent glorying in the speed, and beauty, the endurance of the animals owned by the dragoons, officers and citizens of Leavenworth City. The track was on the side farthest from the town and apart from the active portion of the post. There was a little stand for the group of ladies who accompanied their husbands or their lovers for there was much sweethearting at the post, and the joyous cavalcade over the pretty road to the track made music with their voices and happy laughter.

While the preparations of the council was going along, a mule-race was arranged to be run on the track, and the preparations were most elaborate; hearing the arrangements so much talked of and studied over, the ladies could scarcely wait for the day. It was to be a grand social event.

A purse of fifty dollars was made up for the prizes. In the first place, the women were all tranquil in their minds. There would be no lofty leaps over dangerous hurdles, for reasons that the mule could offer; and as one of the conditions was to win, even the most timid woman need not dread reckless speed. The Government sent out from Fort Leavenworth great trains of supplies for the far-distant posts; consequently there were many mules always in the quarter-master's corral. And they were not only many in number, but various in character, from the skittish little leaders to the ponderous wheelers. The latter were no one knows how old; they were stiff and lumbering, and their tough old sides seared and hairless, in long welts, where the harness had worn into the flesh in many a pull through sand or muddy river-bottom, or up the steep banks of streams.

Everyone seemed to be down at the racetrack and having a good time. There was free beer for all, and it was going fast as it was quite warm. The magnificent band from the Fort was on hand to discourse sweet music.

A few Indians that were gathering for the council meeting were at the track also. They were restrained and aloof in manner and did not socialize with the whites. They stood in small, speechless groups. Even these civilized Indians were considered outsiders. The white men were uncomfortable with them around and avoided them like the plague. The Indians didn't seem to enjoy the white man's company either.

Ian rode down to the flats with Sergeant Beidler and Corporal Lyon. There was quite a crowd. People were everywhere. The only area where the white people avoided was near the Indians so Ian rode quite close to a small group of Indians as Beidler and Lyon tied their mounts and made their way over to the beer.

Ian slipped his leg over the pommel of his saddle, and watched the crowd and mules prepare for the race as he slumped comfortable in the saddle. He was not over ten or twelve feet from the Indian group but he hardly noticed them. Like most people, he ignored them completely, at times looking right through the group as if they did not exist.

But a pretty girl in a fine dress with a yellow flowered hat and a matching parasol walked by, and as always, Ian's eyes followed her. His eyes shifted back to the Indian group for a moment. He had not bothered to look them over closely when it occurred to him that maybe he should try to figure out from what tribe they were from. There appeared to be three young girls and two men nearly the same age. It was then that one of the maidens turned slightly and looked intently at him. He took a quick short gasp and his heart pounded for a moment. She was absolutely gorgeous.

But more noticeable than anything else was her eyes—dark, beautiful, quiet. Her hair fell closely to the side of them. But they seemed different, he couldn't explain it. Something of a mystery shown through those long dark lashes. She had an air of royalty about her. Ian smiled but she continued to look at him with no expression on her face at all. Maybe this is what disturbed him, usually girls smiled back at him. As their eyes met, she looked deep and long at his face as though she must remember him but made no other show of emotion. Ian felt strange, very strange; like all the rest of the world was gone, as if there was only her and him. He felt a yearning to know this lovely creature. Not his usual sexual passion, but something different—very different.

In a moment she was gone, walking away with the rest of the group. He had a strong urge to follow her, to meet, to get to know her, but be behaved undemocratically, as an intellectual snob. His aristocratic upbringing held him back until it was too late. She was gone! His thoughts grappled with each other as he tried on one hand to tell himself she was only an Indian squaw, an uncivilized Indian. But deeper thoughts told him he had missed the most wonderful thing that could happen to him.

"Have a beer, Lieutenant," Sergeant Beidler hollered drunkenly, thrusting a large tin mug at him. This jolted him back to reality as the race started.

Every now and then Ian would catch himself looking for the beautiful Indian vision, but he never saw her again that afternoon. Later in the day he met two of the girls he had danced with at the hotel downtown and forgot the dark-skinned dream maiden.

*   *   *

The evening gun had thundered, the last notes of "retreat" had died away, and the sun, that had been obscured all morning, went down in a golden radiance, leaving a sheen of beautiful color lingering along the crest of the opposite bluffs and reflected in myriad millions of rain-drops still clinging to the clumps of buffalo-grass. Tempted by the loveliness of the evening, Ian saddled his horse and rode down to Rialto to visit with Sergeant Tom. Soon after the death of Annie and three of their children, Tom had taken a six-month furlough from the army and Fort Leavenworth.

On an earlier expedition he had saved an Arapaho brave from a grizzly. The Indian had came down with the white man's cholera and wandered off into the forests. A grizzly had attacked him, and Tom just happened by and killed the bear. The bear had torn off the Indian's ear and scalp, and his claws dug deep into his face but he somehow survived, and they became blood brothers. So Tom had went back out to Arapaho country to forget the painful past.

Tom had left the remaining children with a woman at Rialto and he sometimes stayed there whenever he could to be with the children. She lived in a low log house of two rooms, connected by an enclosed passageway, which served the purpose of an eating room.

The woman was the wife of a steamboat captain, but owing to some irreconcilable difference of sentiment, she refused to live with him, and she was miserably poor. In pity to her sad case, Ian took some articles of clothing, which he hoped might be of use to her, and this errand served as his introduction. She was a tall, fine looking woman, and received and welcomed Ian with the air of a princess dwelling in a palace. She was a niece of James Fennimore Cooper (author of *The Last of the Mohicans,* and other books), and her grand and stately manner in the midst of such squalid poverty, would have been amusing, but for the pity of it.

Her father, a very old man, lay dying of consumption in one of the rooms, and one of the little boys and his sister were assigned for the night to a bed directly opposite the death couch. The one tallow candle on the stand beside him, guttering down in its socket, the fitful light from the vast fireplace, which made fantastic shapes and shadows on the rough dark walls, and the clear cut profile of the dying man, with the erect dignified figure beside him, rising occasionally to arrange his pillow, or give him water, impressed Ian most painfully, effectually driving sleep from the children's eyes, which, under a kind of fascination, gazed intently on what they would rather not see. From time to time the dogs outside howled dismally, and this forced night-watch was made most hideous by the occasional hooting of an owl, or the prolonged baying of hungry wolves in the distance. The children were very weary, and at last fell into a troubled slumber, but were haunted even in sleep by the ghastly face across the room and the weird shadows on the wall.

Ian and Tom sat out on the porch and discussed the past months experiences. Tom who knew of Ian's search for the Hasanun, related a curious tale of such a Messiah . . . Medicine man . . . or whatever you called them.

For several years an abandoned medicine lodge stood beside the trail a few miles short of the foothills of the Rocky Mountains.

The white man had brought the Asiatic cholera to the plains, and it swept away half the Indian population between Mexico and the British possessions. Strange tales were told of the desperation of the Indians, and their frantic flight from the dreaded disease. Sometimes they left the dying in their tents, sometimes where they fell on the prairie, prey to the wolves. Friendly Indians implored the help of every passing white man, though most of the emigrants had no better remedy than a solution of cornmeal in raw whiskey.

The plague seems to have struck the Arapahos when they were all assembled for their annual Sun Dance on the Arkansas River, below Chouteau Island. Before the dance was over so many died that the survivors moved camp a little distance above the island, and immediately performed a second Sun Dance. Two such dances in one summer went without precedent. While the second was in progress, the medicine man directing the ceremony dropped dead within the dance lodge.

Despairing of help from their own dreamers, the Arapahos sent an embassy north to the Sioux, begging for help. On the way north, all the party were stricken except one old man named Waksenna, the least important of them all.

Waksenna appears to have been a typical "Dreamer," living in his subconscious mind most of the time, and utterly lacking in shrewdness of practical affairs.

When he arrived in the Sioux camp, driving a string of pack animals loaded with gifts, the Sioux medicine man entertained him gladly, accepted all those rich gifts, and in return gave Waksenna an old broken-down white nag.

Waksenna was so impressed by the Sioux shaman and his hocus-pocus that he failed to look the gift horse in the mouth, and set out for home with his flea-bitten scarecrow, humbly trusting that his mission was successful.

On reaching the old camp of his people, he paused on the bluffs above it, amazed by what he saw. The gnarled cottonwood trees were brown with clusters of buzzards all gorged with human flesh, drunk on putrid ptomaines. At the foot of the bluff lay the bones of men who had leaped upon the rocks in their despair, and a woman's body dangled from a limb where she had hanged herself. As he crossed the river, his horse shied at a withered old woman whose talons still clutched the bail of a brass bucket where she had fallen on her way to the river for water.

As he rode on through the old encampment, he disturbed a cloud of ravens, which rose and fluttered down again behind him. Dogs and wolves sullenly gave way before him. The odor of the camp was horrible—a stench like that on a battlefield.

The dead were everywhere—lashed to trees, on scaffolds, in their tents—wherever death had reached them. It had been days since anyone had had the courage to touch the sick—let alone the dying. Here and there he saw mourners sitting, crying, bleeding from self-inflicted wounds, or staring at him as he passed with stony, apathetic eyes. He rode on down the stream into the new encampment where the people stood watching him come, hardly daring to hope, discouraged by the sight of the miserable nag he rode.

Waksenna rode into the middle of the camp circle and dismounted before his small sacred tent. His tent was painted all over with the symbols of Arapaho religion; the turtle, the buffalo, the four-pointed star, eagles, suns, and moons, all representing the hopes and fears of the Arapaho dreamer. These paintings were on the inside of the tent, not to be seen by common men. There, Waksenna was at home.

Waksenna was a berdache—a man who dressed and acted like a woman. The vision which had led him to adopt woman's customs had arisen from his shrinking nature. As a man he would have been lost in a throng of his betters; as a berdache, he was freed of the obligations of a warrior, free to dream and prophesy. Throughout his long life, he had served the tribes so, divining their dangers, foreseeing their successes. Now, he thought his hour of triumph had come. Soon they would be striking his face, blessing him, loading him with gifts, for he had come back to kill the cholera—with a dream!

The remaining chiefs brought him a pipe to smoke, eagerly awaiting his message. When the old man had finished smoking, they asked him what he had brought them in return for all their gifts.

"That horse there," said Waksenna, in his senile whine.

They all stared at the glass-eyed white animal, apparently some old woman's pack horse, half asleep in the sunshine. The chiefs looked sidelong at each other. The pipe passed from hand to hand in silence.

"There will be no more dying among the Arapahos," Waksenna declared.

Even while he spoke, one of the chiefs stood up, looked around wildly, and said: "My friends, something terrible is about to happen. I feel it." The chief doubled up and fell to the ground in convulsions. Before their eyes, he died.

The Arapahos were furious. "Look," they said, "the Sioux has deceived us. He had made a fool of this man-woman. Kill him!"

Frantic with fear they closed around Waksenna and struck him down with their war clubs while the old white nag ran to the end of its tether, snorting. They ripped the tent to pieces. Then they went away. Waksenna lay unconscious under the wreck of his tent of dreams. After a while the white pony began to graze around the tent. There was no one to drive it to water.

That night there was a thunderstorm. Great masses of blue clouds swept over, showing the color of cut lead, and poured down a deluge, while the thunder roared and the light-

ning flashed and spiked the ground, stabbing savagely at the bluffs, the trees, the tents—
flooding the river bottoms, scouring every slope and gully.

The water roused Waksenna at last. He crawled into the tent and sat up. His head
rocked. He could hardly tell reality from a dream even then. Only the white horse, garish
in the light of the retreating storm, seemed real.

Inevitably the berdache prayed there in the darkness and the storm: "My Father, Man
Above, Giver-of-Food, take pity on me, Morning Star, my Mother. I belong to you. be merciful to me. Save my people. Grandmother, Old Woman Night, hear my words. Let the people live. Take pity on your servant."

He fell down while his head swam from that great effort. The night passed while
Waksenna cried and prayed, and the white horse paced restlessly outside the ragged tent. It
had eaten every blade of grass within reach down to the roots, and now it began to graze
within the tent itself; sticking its ghastly long muzzle through the rents, snapping off
bunches of grass within. Its lips made a clapping sound, and in the flicker of the lightning,
the white eyes were very weird.

The man stirred from time to time, and whenever this happened the old nag snorted,
blowing in soft surprise upon the upturned face. And so the vision came.

It seemed to Waksenna that the horse was speaking: "My grandson, do as I tell you. My
medicine is strong. Take your paints and paint as I shall tell you. Then, when it is daylight,
lead me into the camp and call the people. Whoever touches my flesh shall live."

Waksenna got up and staggered around with his paints, smearing a zigzag, a moon
there-whatever his crazy imagination suggested. Afterward, he led the horse into the middle of the camp circle and spoke to it.

"Grandfather, you are strong. You can make us live. That is what you say. Now, do it. I
promise you that no man shall ever throw his leg across your back. You shall never carry a
pack. You shall have four boys to keep the wolves from your heels in winter, and plenty of cottonwood twigs to eat while the snow is deep. Grandfather, be good to us. Do as you have said."

The old horse, eager to get fresh grass, tugged at his lariat. Waksenna took that for an
omen and began to call the people together: "Ooooooooooh! Come, my children. Lay
your hands on this horse. Touch it, and you shall live. There will be no more dying. Hurry,
my children. Then we can move from here and go where this wonderful horse can get
some grass."

Nobody paid any attention to Waksenna for a long time, but he kept on yelling in his
high thin voice. At last he began to lead the horse around the camp circle close to the tents,
pleading with the Arapahos to touch the horse.

The people mocked him. None of them would have anything to do with Waksenna or
his wonderful horse.

340

But at last Thiyeh, an old woman, haggard and decrepit and worn to a shadow by fasting and waiting, hobbled down on her stick and laid a gnarled hand upon the horse's flank.

She felt the better for it, she thought. The sun was out and warmed her old bones.

She told her old man to go and try his luck. He too felt better, it seemed, and soon began to rout out his relatives, greatly relishing his new importance as advisor to the family, which had long ago forgotten him.

And so they came by ones, and twos, and dozens, and then in crowds, crying, laughing, praying, stroking the white horse, stroking Waksenna, bringing presents, hopeful for the first time in months.

Waksenna gave commands: "Take down your tents, my friends. We are going to leave this place. You shall all live a long time. This horse is holy."

Whether the epidemic had spent its force, or the storm had washed away the contagion, who can tell? At any rate, no more Arapahos died of cholera that season.

Waksenna was as good as his word. He and the chiefs appointed four young men to look after the wonderful horse, and so long as it lived, it enjoyed complete freedom. Nobody rode it; nobody beat it. It never carried a pack. The Arapahos took it with them wherever they went and guarded it most carefully.

At last the horse died of old age somewhere in western Kansas. Within living memory, old Arapahos made periodical pilgrimages to visit the bones of the animal and leave offerings of tobacco, red paint and feathers.

*   *   *

A drizzling rain had set in, so Ian decided to stay the night. Tom and him wrapped up in their blankets and lay on the porch under the sheltering roof.

The children were aroused by the woman's morning kiss and cheery call to breakfast, which banished all their disturbing dreams, and they awoke to the realities of a bright sunshine morning, and the morning meal, which the grand hostess had prepared for them. The meal consisted of potatoes boiled "au natural," and some kind of drink which she announced as coffee, and which she served with the grace of a queen, dispensing the delicacies of her table.

Ian never ceased to admire the admirable tact and grace with which Tom added to this choice menu. There was always some very nice boiled beef and other choice food with which his bountiful friends the Taylor's had packed in his mess chest; also, some choice tea, which Tom, accustomed to camping, knew how to prepare to perfection.

All this he did in such a way as to make the lady feel that it was an honor to us to share these things with her, and it was really gratifying to see her calm enjoyment of delicacies to which she had long been a stranger. Ian thought, too, that the fragrant cup of tea and the

delicate bit of toast, taken to the sick man, may have brought to his mind tender recollections of a time when he lived like a gentleman, and dispelled for a little while the memory
of the family troubles, and complications of misfortunes which had reduced him to poverty
and a dying bed in this comfortless log cabin in the wilderness.

*   *   *

It was a lovely morning, and a warm south wind was blowing through the open windows of the bachelor officer quarters and billowing the dainty curtains of the breakfast
room. Down in the bottoms of the river valley, close under the bluffs, a white mist was creeping upward from the shallows of the stream, and here and there among the furrows of the
company gardens, little wisps of fog hovered over the soaking earth.

It had rained in torrents during the night, but Nature emerged from her bath glowing
in the rays of a sunrise that the officer of the day pronounced simply gorgeous, as he turned
out for reveille.

Ian took charge of the guard in the late afternoon. The trumpet loudly pealed orderly
call as the men came marching up from the stables, their sabers clanking and their spurred
heels ringing along the road.

The instant the ranks were broken in front of the barracks a rush was made by dozens
of their number for the cool refreshment of the trader's beer, and the bar was speedily
crowded with their stalwart forms and ringing with their jovial voices.

After Ian had mounted the guard he joined them at the bar. One or two non-commissioned
cavalry officers drew away to one side by themselves and signaled to the barkeeper that they
wished to be served privately and not included in the infantrymen's joyous good-fellowship.

The roll of the drum and the peal of the trumpet sounding mess-call speedily emptied
the bar of the blue-bloused throng; only those on guard duty who had messed earlier stayed
on for a few more drinks before they had to stand guard.

Ian finished his beer and left the bar to check on the guard.

The long June day was drawing to its close. Hot and strong the slanting sunbeams beat
upon the roofs and threw distorted shadows through the woods and plains that stretched to
the far horizon.

Out in the center of the parade, a little party of the guard had just lowered the great garrison standard, whose folds of scarlet and white lapped out lazily in response to the soft
breeze now rising from the river bluffs.

Ian pulled the required duty of inspection of the soldiers and glancingly approved the
glistening surface of their top-boots and the brilliant polish of their spurs. The sergeant of
the guard stood before his men, every item of his dress and equipment was model of soldierly trimness.

Black sheep, they say, exist in every flock, and while fifty or more of his men swore by their lieutenant, and were proud to serve under him, there were perhaps two soldiers in the troop who seemed to lose no opportunity of defaming him. One of these was a man named Doss, who had long been on extra or daily duty as clerk for the quartermaster, and whose errors at inspection were of such an exasperating character that the quartermaster got authority to make him pull extra guard duty until he was reported proficient. This, of course, made Doss, who prided himself on his scholarship and superiority to the general run of men, anything but happy; and in his wrath and discontent, he vented his anger whenever possible to do so at the expense of his lieutenant.

The other man was a tall, dark-eyed, gypsy-looking fellow, whose name was Welsh, and who for several months off and on had preferred to be the captain's "striker," or soldier servant. He would take care of his horses, black his boots, polish his spurs and saber, hew wood, draw water, make the fires, sweep the kitchen, run errands, and do all manner of small chores about the house--than to do soldier duty with his comrades. When the captain closed up his quarters and left the post, taking his family eastward with him, Ian moved in to look after the quarters until a new captain arrived. This was by the captain's own request; and, having no use for the services of Welsh, he notified that worthy to return to duty with the troop forthwith. This Welsh bitterly resented. He insisted that the captain had told him before going that he was to stay in charge of his quarters and be excused from all military duty. He replied that there was probably some mistake, but Ian wrote to the captain and obtained immediate reply to the effect that he had never given the soldier any such promise, and that he desired that he be now returned to duty with the troop and taught something of the practical duties of a soldier, which he had too long neglected.

Ian smiled to himself as he had read the message, thinking whose fault it was that Welsh had been allowed to live in ignorance of much of the drill, and wondering not a little at the change of heart that seemed to have come over the captain, now that he was fairly away. A smart young corporal was detailed to give the two men thorough instruction in the saber exercise and the manual of the carbine and pistol, in addition to which Welsh was now required to attend all roll-calls, stable-duty, and drills with the troop, and take his guard tour every fifth day, and a disgusted man he was in consequence.

As the captain's "striker" he had led a life of comparative ease, for that veteran officer had long since outlived any ambition to shine in the service, and looked upon it only as a means of livelihood. At the outbreak of the war, old Blauvelt was keeping a country store in Ohio, but dropped his yard-stick and sugar-scoop at the first call for volunteers, fought like a man all through the four years contest, was wounded, and, having risen to be a major of volunteer infantry, he decided to stick to soldiering, for at that time it was easy to obtain a commission in the regular service if a man had any congressional influence or connections at all. When the army was remodeled, as a first lieutenant; he was dropped to the supernumerary list from the regiment of infantry with which he had been serving. Blauvelt decided that he was now too old to begin storekeeping over again, and so he made vigorous effort to be retained in the army. Together with a few other men who did not know a horse from a hand-saw, he was transferred to a vacancy in the cavalry, and there the placid old fellow had been ever since.

Ian and the sergeant strode over to the barracks for an inspection.

"Attention!" Came the order from a sergeant who happened to be nearest the door as Ian entered. Every man on the instant whipped off his cap, and facing the middle of the long room, stood erect at the foot of his bunk—every man except one. With his cap on the back of his head, his matted hair hanging down over his eyes, Welsh sat there at the table, coolly polishing the spur.

"Get up there, Welsh!" the first sergeant growled in low, stern tones.

"Off with that cap, sir."

For an answer, Welsh cocked his head on one side, and apparently unmindful of the presence of an officer, became critically and approvingly absorbed in studying the polish which he was imparting to the smooth surface of the spur.

"Did you hear that order? Come to attention, sir!" repeated the sergeant. And the men, astonished at the breach of discipline, looked curiously at the recruit, now slowly and scowlingly finding his feet. He had not removed his cap when the lieutenant stood before him.

"Why didn't you rise with the other men, Welsh?" asked Ian, in a quiet and deliberate tone oddly at variance with his usually quick and snappy manner, and the young officer looked straight into the soldier's eyes as he spoke.

For an instant every nerve and muscle in the soldier's athletic frame seemed to quiver. His blue eyes blazed with wrath and his lips set firmly under his blonde moustache.

There was a moment of death-like silence—a gasp or two among the men.

Ian knew how Welsh felt, he hated most of the silly things in the service, some things can be tolerated but some cannot. If Welsh got away with this insubordination, he would give others courage and they would do the same and then what kind of an army would this be?

"Take this man under guard," were at last the words that fell from Ian's lips.

This affair would lead to Welsh's third court martial in less than a month.

The lights were already beginning to twinkle in the quarters across the parade, and darkness, "wafting downward like a feather," was shutting out the long line of shadowy bluffs beyond the river.

In the soft, June-like weather of Fort Leavenworth the ladies spent but little of their waking moments indoors, and even the broad verandas of the colonel's quarters on the north side were no more popular or populous than those of Captain Lane at the southwest corner. Mrs. Lane attributed this to the fact that the sun on its westward way passed behind their cozy home and left the front piazza cool and shaded, whereas even the canvas hangings in front of the other cottages could not quite shut out the glare. There were other young ladies in garrison, just then Miss Warton, visiting her brother, and Miss McCrea, staying at the Burnhams. There were several pretty girls in the neighboring town, who frequently came out and spent a few days with the families at the post; and all these, of course, as well as the young married ladies, were the recipients of much attention on the part of the officers, young and old. It is a fact well understood in army circles that few officers are too old to tender such attentions, and no woman too old to receive them.

At ten o'clock Ian went over to the hop-room to check on the dance. It was well-filled. A number of pleasant people had driven out from town. All the garrison girls were there, most of the elders among the mammas, all the juniors among the matrons, and dance went merrily on.

Winifred Lane
Daughter of Captain and Mrs. Lane

Mrs. Lane asked Ian to dance with her daughter and, though he was on duty, he could not refuse his commanding officer's wife's request.

The orchestra of the Twelfth was ever ready to play, and this night their leader seemed inspired. The affair was entirely informal. No written invitations had been sent out. Officers were all in undress uniform, but, with few exceptions, all were there, and the broad stripes of scarlet or yellow or white were to be seen everywhere throughout the room. Mrs. Lane, a smile of motherly pride in her handsome dark eyes, was chatting pleasantly with the wife of a local magnate, who could not say enough about Winifred's grace and beauty. The gaze of both women seemed to follow the child as she appeared literally to float over the smoothly-polished floor, just lightly borne on Ian's stalwart arm.

It was one of the oldest and sweetest of the Strauss waltzes that was being played at the moment. "Geschichten aus dem Wienerwald," and, slowing reversing and turning, with the eyes of more than half the spectators and wall-flowers upon them, Ian and Winifred glided across the upper end of the hall within a few feet of the smiling row of lookers-on, almost within touch of the mother's hand. For the first time Ian began to realize it was a woman, not a child, who danced with him.

Ian excused himself to attend to his duties. It must have been nearly midnight. The lights in the barracks and the old hospital beyond had long since been extinguished, and only here and there along the row of officer's quarters and at the guard-house were there signs of wakeful life. One or two upper windows gave forth a feeble gleam, and there was a quite a jovial glow pouring from the open door-way of the colonel's big house across the dark rectangle. It fell upon the tall white flag-staff and displayed it from base to cross trees. It was a solitary, ghost-like shaft, and then, with gradually diminishing power, illumed the graveled pathway that bisected the parade and led from the broad flight of steps in front of the commanding officer's to the major's quarters on the southern side. Overhead the stars were glittering in an absolutely cloudless sky. Not a breath of air was stirring the forest down in the black depths of the valley to the south. Softened by distance, the rush of the river over its muddy bed fell upon the ear like a soothing lullaby. Ten minutes earlier the sound of silvery laughter and cheery voices had come floating across the garrison, and half a dozen little groups had strolled away from the colonel's gate, some turning to right and left, others crossing in the broad stream of light from his open portals. One by one the doors of the various quarters had opened to admit their occupants. A few lingering good-nights had been exchanged between gallant young bachelors and some dainty form enwrapped in fleecy burnous (long cloak with a hood), and then even those night-owls, "the youngsters," had betaken themselves to their domiciles. One after another doors were closed, lights popped up in the second-floor windows, curtains were drawn, the lights enshrouded, and finally a silent solitude spread its mantle over the parade.

Half a dozen of the guards were seated about the rough stone porch of the gloomy old guardhouse as the carriage came rolling by, and at sight of the occupants they quickly laid aside their pipes and respectfully arose and raised their hands in salute. The sentry on No. 1, facing sharply to the front, brought his rifle to the carry with a snap that made the bayonet ring.

*   *   *

Somewhere about twenty minutes after midnight, Ian was crossing the main parade inspecting the guard posts. The call of No. 7 had just sounded. It was now the turn of the farthest sentry, No. 8, whose post was down the winding road at the haystacks and wood-yard. A rich, musical Irish voice, softened by distance, began its soldier troll:

"N-umber Eight. Tw-el-ve o'clock—and a-a-all's—Who goes there? Halt! Halt! Officer of the gu-a-ard—Number Eight!" Bang!

The shot startled Ian into a full run. There was trouble at the guest house.

Outside the guest house, Corporal Kenyon waited for help.

"What's the matter," asked Ian as he saw Kenyon.

"Sir, its Doss," answered the corporal, "he's drunk."

"Light the lantern, Kenyon."

The corporal struck a lucifer on a strip of sandpaper, but was shaking so much he missed the wick, so Ian took the match and lit the oil lantern.

"Come on," Ian ordered.

The door of the guesthouse was wide open and Ian ran to the room where the sounds of scuffling were coming from.

As he held up the lantern in one hand, Ian saw Doss bending over the form of a woman on the floor. Ian noticed the woman's dress was torn open at the bosom. Ian was conscious of the sickening odor of sour whiskey.

Handing the light to Corporal Kenyon, Ian grabbed Doss by the blue collar at the throat, his long, slender fingers gripping tight, and threw him across the room.

"Damn your soul!" sputtered Doss. The soldier's eyes were blazing with pent up anger as he staggered up.

The sergeant had arrived by now and grabbed Doss.

"Shut up, you drunken fool," the sergeant ordered. "Don't mind him, lieutenant."

The sergeant again ordered, "Stand still, or I'll smash you!"—this to Doss, who half suffocated, was writhing in his effort to escape.

"A--ch!" the sergeant cried, with sudden wrenching away of his brawny hand, "the bastard bit me," and the broad palm, dripping with blood, was held up to the light. Deeply indented, there were the jagged marks of Doss' teeth.

Doss, with flushed and sodden face and angry eyes, lunged at Ian with a volley of mad threats.

Ian, tired of all this and worrying more about the woman than Doss struggling with the fumes of the liquor he had been drinking, had picked up the carbine that Doss had knocked out of the first guard's hands as the bullet had crashed through the plaster overhead. Doss' long knife flashed in the lamplight as he charged head on straight at Ian's throat. Ian, in less time than it takes to tell, sent the steel butt of the rifle crashing into Doss' forehead just in time to stop the gleaming steel. The buttplate of the rifle cut through the flesh and the bloody skin dropped down over Doss' eyes. In the next instant he staggered backward, seeing a multitude of twinkling, whirling stars, and fell over a chair. It was all over in a moment.

A number of guards had arrived by now and they rushed upon Doss and dragged him to the guardhouse.

Doss kept muttering as he grappled with the soldiers, "She's only a squaw bitch. A damn Indian. That's all she is . . .," as if it wasn't a crime to rape an Indian.

The sergeant, staunching the blood as best he could, bandaging his hand with his own kerchief, went with the soldiers looking a trifle faint and sick. It was a brutal bite.

For a moment Ian could distinguish no living object. Asking Kenyon to raise the lantern higher he saw a woman lying on the floor in the corner of the room where she had crawled. Kenyon, bending down for a closer look, exclaimed, "She's an Indian, lieutenant?"

Walking over to the girl and bending over the prostrate form, Ian had her up in his arms and over to the door while the soldiers stood by, not knowing what to do.

Ian decided to take her to Kalespel at Father Gregg's house. She was trembling violently. She looked into Ian's face with eager, questioning, imploring eyes. She did not faint, though the world swam around and the only thing she was conscious of was that she was held in strong arms and held closely, and the beat of a heart that was not her own throbbed against her body.

Kalespel was aroused by Ian's kicking on the door and she motioned Ian to lay the girl on a bed in the guestroom. Her eyes were half closed in the content of being found, and the safety of his presence. Opening her eyes wider, she looked up into Ian's face that had a strange expression in the yellow light from the lantern—his eyes searching her own so curiously. She had not spoken a word, but she half smiled in answer to what she thought an unspoken query.

"Hyas till nika," she murmured.

Waiting for Kalespel to come back, Ian looked at the woman for a long moment. This was the same girl he had seen at the racetrack two days before. She was Indian. She was dark, yet with so rich a glow mantling the soft creamy skin, with such glorious deep brown-black eyes, so lovely and slender and graceful a form.

Ian had never seen so beautiful an Indian before. She was a young woman with well-nigh perfect features.

Ian gazed at her in fascination. Then, all of a sudden, her face became suddenly clouded by distress and pain. Ian noticed there were bruises on her bare breasts and blood on her face when Kalespel returned and pushed him out into the night.

"Why would an Indian girl be staying at the guest house?" he asked himself as he walked back to the guardroom. She probably had some connection with the council meeting tomorrow, maybe a chiefs daughter or something. He didn't think about it much more but he kept seeing her face all night as he tried to get some fitful sleep.

In the morning, Ian was up early to check on the girl but she was gone and Kalespel would tell him nothing.

On this particular morning he strove to hurry matters through the court martials. There were only four cases where the accused were only too ready to plead guilty.

The rest of the day was occupied with making arrangements for the peace council.

*   *   *

Fort Leavenworth was for many years a location of the utmost importance to the Indian department. It was surrounded by many tribes and became a constant resort for both the Indians generally and those who migrated west of the Mississippi. They met each other here every day, talked and counseled in conjunction with the whites and formed acquaintances, all of which tended towards a promotion of the most friendly relations. Colonel Leavenworth recognized this situation and urged the War Department to direct the transfer of the Indian agent from the agency near Council Bluff to the cantonment to thus be nearer to the department and to supervise Indian affairs more readily than he could at the up-river point. To this the department, which also had charge of Indian affairs, consented, and it had a good effect upon the Indians in this section.

By the treaty of 1829, it was "solemnly" decreed that the new lands assigned the Indians should never become a part of any state or territory. The first important Indian conference to be held at the Cantonment was called by Major Dougherty, the Indian agent, for the purpose of maintaining friendly relations between the different tribes. The agent impressed upon the Indians the importance of peace and good-will towards each other. Of the tribes who were represented in this conference by delegates were Otoes, Omahas, Ioways, Sacs, Delawares, Shawnees, and Kickapoos.

Notwithstanding, all the efforts to keep the peace between the tribes, the transfer of the eastern Indians under the treaty of 1829, to the lands lying between the Platte River in Nebraska and the Arkansas river, brought on a state of war with the prairie Indians who resented the action of the government in thus intruding these "newcomers" upon their hunting preserves, which they claimed as their own. It brought on a serious conflict between the many tribes who came from the more civilized sections of the country. They had sold their land and now, having been located in new homes, were not permitted by the "old-timers" to enjoy the privileges they supposed would go with the trade.

To end this warfare, the government hastened to take steps to purchase the contested lands from the prairie Indians and to effect a "treaty of peace" between these warring tribes. In some instances, however, the aborigines remained unappeased. This was especially the case with the fierce and numerous tribe of Pawnees inhabiting the banks of the Platte river, and who were backed in their hostility by their allies, the Otoes, who, though less numerous, were even more daring than the Pawnees. These two tribes laid claim to all the land lying between the Platte and Kansas rivers, a region comprising several hundred square miles. It had long been their favorite hunting ground, in which it was death for a strange hunter to intrude.

This forbidden tract, however, had been granted by the United States to the Delawares, and the latter had made it the scene of their hunting excursions. The Delawares had been attacked by the Pawnees while hunting and many of their tribe had fallen. The Delawares in revenge had burned some of the Pawnee towns, while the warriors were absent on a buffalo hunt.

The hostile feelings thus awakened among these tribes had been manifested towards the white men. A commission was appointed by the government to come to Fort Leavenworth to purchase the contested lands of the Pawnees, induce them to remove north of the Platte river, and to effect a treaty of peace between them and their new neighbors.

The commission came here in the summer to carry out the designs of the government.

As soon as the commissioners had arrived at the Fort, Major Dougherty sent messengers to the neighboring tribes, summoning them to meet their old enemies in council.

For several days now the delegation and their followers had been coming in and their camps were scattered through the woods around the fort. The Pawnees and Otoes were encamped in the forest overlooking the Missouri River; but care was taken to keep the different bands apart until a permanent peace had been established between them.

Early the next morning a report of a piece of artillery announced the hour for the council; and before long the different delegates with their friends were seen making their way to the place of meeting, which was under a grove of trees southwest of the Main Parade.

First came the Delawares, gay with silver ornaments and ribands.

They were not very warlike in their appearance, but the Pawnees had discovered that their looks belied them, and regarded them, few as they were in number, as their most formidable foes.

At their head was their chief, Sou-wah-nock. It was he who had led the attack upon the Pawnee village when it was sacked and burnt.

He alone of his tribe wore no ornaments except a silver medal, which hung down upon his breast.

There was an expression of grim defiance on his face as he looked around upon his former foes.

After the Delawares came the Shawnees, headed by the same portly old Indian whom Ian had met when he first entered as a stranger into the Indian country. The same enormous pair of spectacles was astride of his nose, and for aught Ian knew may have remained there undisturbed since Ian last saw him.

Following him came the fighting men of his tribe, reeking with paint and gaudy ribands.

These seated themselves beside the Delawares.

Then came the rest of the migratory tribes, the Peorias, Piankashawas, Pottawattomies, and Kickapoos, who all, as they arrived, took their places among their civilized brethern.

After they were seated the Otoes made their appearance, coming across the green in single file, headed by their old chief the Iotan.

They seated themselves at a short distance apart from the civilized Indians.

Last of all came the wild band of Pawnees. In front of them strode Wild Horse, his savage features not rendered any the less hideous by a drunken frolic in which he had been engaged on the previous day.

His hair hung in tangled masses about his head and shoulders, and his body as usual was smeared with red ochre; and although the weather was cool, his neck and chest were bare. He walked to his allotted place without appearing to notice the congregated bands of civilized Indians. Next came Long Hair and several other chiefs, and after them followed the whole Indian horde from the four Pawnee towns.

They stationed themselves opposite the civilized tribes and waited for the Commissioner to open the council.

After they had all assembled and were ready for business, the Commissioner rose up and stated the object of the meeting—that war had been carried on long enough between them, and that they had now met for the purpose of becoming friends. He then entered explicitly into the conditions of the intended peace.

When he had ended, the speakers of each tribe addressed the council. All professed the greatest friendship for their enemies, and closed their speeches by throwing the whole blame of every offence upon the shoulders of some other tribe.

The delegates of several little villages, which had barely inhabitants enough to hang a name upon, also eased their importance by speaking. The Delaware chief Sou-wah-nock then rose. He spoke of the destruction of the Grand Pawnee village. He did not deny his part in the deed. "The Pawnees," said he, "met my young men upon the hunt and slew them. I have had my revenge. Let them look at their town. I found it filled with lodges, I left it a heap of ashes." The whole of his speech was of the same bold, unflinching character, and was closed in true Indian style.

"I am satisfied," said he; "I am Sou-wah-nock, a Delaware warrior; but I am willing to bury the tomahawk, and smoke the pipe of peace with my enemies. They are brave men, and fight well."

When he had finished, he presented a string of wampum to Wild Horse, as being the most distinguished warrior of the Pawnee nation. When the slight bustle of giving and receiving the present had been finished, the chief of the Republican village rose to answer his warrior enemy.

His speech abounded with one of those wild bursts of eloquence which peculiarly mark the Indians of North America, and concluded in a manner which spoke highly of his opinion of what a warrior should be.

"I have promised to the Delawares," said he, "the friendship of my tribe. I respect my promise, and I cannot lie, for I am a Pawnee chief."

When the Delawares had spoken, Ian's little fat friend from the Shawnee village rose. After frequent coughing and spitting, he at length succeeded in clearing a passage for the escape of his voice.

He contrived, with great difficulty, to wheeze through a speech of about ten minutes in length, after which he seated himself, perfectly convinced that he had thrown a great deal of light upon the subject.

There was a strong contrast between the deportment of the civilized and wild Indians. The first, from long intercourse with the whites, had acquired many of their habits. Their iron gravity had yielded to a more changeable temperament.

Even in the midst of the council they gave free vent to the merriment, and uttered their gibes and jests. They were constantly on the move, coming and going to and from the place of assembly, and paying but little heed to the deliberations.

The Pawnees sat motionless, listening in silence and with profound attention to those who spoke.

They rarely uttered a word, and the only smile, which curled their lips, was one of scorn at the frivolous deportment of their enemies.

From early in the morning till near sunset, the council continued. They then adjourned until the following day, in order that the delegates from some of the small villages might have an opportunity to display their eloquence.

On the following morning the report of a cannon announced the hour of council. Once more the tribes met, but just as they had assembled, word was brought to the commissioner that the delegates from the Kansas tribe had just arrived, and word was sent to them to attend the meeting.

They soon made their appearance, all clothed in blankets, and each carrying a rifle.

In front of them was their chief, "White Plume."

He wore a large drab overcoat with enormous pockets that gaped open.

This article of dress deprived him altogether of dignified appearance.

He, however, seemed perfectly satisfied with his attire, and, in truth, believed that there was scarcely a Pawnee who did not envy him the possession of an article of apparel with pockets of such size that, in case of emergency, they could hold nearly a bushel of scalps.

The arrival of this chief and his delegation had been anxiously expected; for the hostility between them and the Pawnees had been bitter; and it was all-important that peace should be established between two such warlike and powerful tribes.

The Pawnees eyed them in grave silence as they came up and took the places set aside for them, but they evinced no hostile feeling.

The business of the council then proceeded, and the chiefs of various small tribes in the vicinity addressed the Pawnees—all agreeing to bury the tomahawk and regard them for the future as friends.

These offers were graciously received by the Pawnees, though one of them afterwards remarked to the interpreter "that they had now made peace with several nations with whom they had never been at war, and of whom they had never heard until they rose to address them in council."

This was little to be wondered at, as the speakers were one or two short-winded fellows, dressed in dirty calico and bedraggled ribands, and their delegation probably comprised their whole tribe.

The deliberations lasted during the whole day, for as these Indians had no particular injuries to dwell upon, they rambled on things in general, and each speaker continued his address until he had exhausted his wind. The Pawnees listened with commendable patience, though Ian doubted if there was one who was not glad when the council ended.

The next morning the Pawnees and Kansas met to settle their grievances. A large room in the garrison had been selected for the purpose. The two bands occupied opposite sides of the room. There was a strong contrast between them. The Kansas had a stately appearance, and their white blankets as they hung in loose and graceful folds around them, had the effect of classic drapery.

The Pawnees had no pride of dress. They were wrapped in shaggy robes, and sat in silence—stem, wild, and uncouth.

At length the speaking commenced. The first of them was White Plume. He had boasted that his speech would make the Pawnees wince. At first, in order to conciliate the whites present, he expressed a high opinion of them. After this he gradually edged off into a bitter denunciation against the Pawnee tribe.

There was a dead silence among his own people as he spoke, and every eye was fastened upon the grim group opposite.

The chief of the Tappage village was sitting directly in front of the speaker; his eye glowed like a coal of fire, but he remained silent until the speech was finished.

When White Plume sat down, half a dozen Pawnees sprang to their feet, but the Tappage chief waved them down. Then stepping out, and fixing his eye on the Kansas chief, in a calm, quiet voice, he commenced his answer, and told the story of the wrongs inflicted upon his tribe by the Kansas, which had first kindled the war between the two nations.

"My young men," said he. "visited them as friends; the Kansas treated them as enemies. They were strangers, and the Kansas fell upon them, and slew them, and concealed their death." He then entered into the particulars of the quarrel, which, unfortunately for the Kansas, were strongly against them. The chief of the latter tribe received the answer with great philosophy, nor did he attempt to reply. Perhaps, too, he did not wish to invite a second attack from so rough a quarter. When the Pawnee had finished, the commissioner interposed, and dropped a few words of oil upon the troubled waters, and after a short time harmony was restored.

Several other speeches were made. They were of a more calm and conciliating nature, and gradually tended to soothe the feeling of both. The council lasted until sunset, when the terms of the treaty were finally adjusted.

On this occasion Ian was made sensible of the justice of the complaint made to those who have had public negotiations with the Indian tribes, of the inefficiency of the interpreters through whom they are obliged to receive the sentiments and language of the Indians. They are, with few exceptions, ignorant and illiterate. Those employed by the army spoke a wretched rural French, and a still more miserable English. On such, the high imaginative vein, the poetical thought, which runs through Indian eloquence, is entirely lost.

There was not an Indian who addressed the council who did not at times clothe his ideas in beautiful language, and make use of wild and striking similes drawn from the scores of his only teacher—nature.

This was ascertained from educated persons present who were well versed in some of the Indian tongues. As to the interpreters, they reduced every thing to a bald, disjointed jargon. To give an instance of this-one of the chiefs, in speaking of their treaty, said he was much pleased at meeting his old foes as friends, "That it made his bosom glow with warmth."

The interpreter's version: "He say, 'he so glad, he sweat a heap.'"

On the day following the council the articles of peace were signed, and most of the tribes departed for their respective homes. A few of the Pawnees and Otoes remained to accompany the Commissioner to the village of the Osages, for the purpose of negotiating a peace with that tribe, with whom they had long been at deadly hostility.

Ian's friend, George Catlin, the English artist and writer recorded the council tales and drew sketches of the participants. With curiosity satisfied, Catlin determined to return home to London on the following day. A feeling of sadness came over him as he prepared to leave those with whom he had for months associated. However different in dispositions and feelings, the soldiers and Catlin had until then been united by a link of sympathy. They had led the same life, viewed the same scenes, and undergone the same privations. For months together one tent had sheltered them and they had eaten from the same board.

A rough, untrammeled friendship had sprung up between them increasing with the distance between themselves and their homes, and strengthening as they retired farther from the abode of civilized man.

But now they had returned from their wanderings, and were once more in the circle of their fellow soldiers. Still old recollections bound them together by a golden tie that was painful to sever; although his home in England with all its attractions rose in his fancy, he felt sad when one of the orderlies informed him that all was ready. He shook hands with his friends and comrades of the wilderness, and mounting his mule, with a heavy heart, turned his back upon Leavenworth City and the fort.

The Hasanun

*A*nd *it came to pass, a prophet was sent from the Lord, whose name was Shenga Wassa, that man and woman through her might believe.*

Early the next morning, as Ian left his quarters, he was met outside of the barracks by Sergeant Beidler, Father Gregg, and three young Indian warriors mounted on their prairie ponies.

Sergeant Beidler informed Ian they were to accompany the Indians to a private council off the fort, so Ian mounted his steed and rode out with his escort. They showed him unusual esteem and respect during the journey. They evidently were warriors of the Grand Osage villages with spirited ponies and acted as if they had a sense of importance of escorting Ian, Father Gregg, and Beidler to the council.

The party passed the stone wall and blockhouse and in a short time they passed the Indian watchtowers on the ridge west of the main parade ground.

As they crossed Salt Creek, Ian noticed a number of chiefs from all the different tribes assembled in a large circle.

Ian and the sergeant were the only soldiers present. As they dismounted, Ian noticed an Indian girl in the middle of the circle of chiefs. Her whole appearance was that of a delicate flower-like beauty. Her chief attraction was a pair of big brown-black eyes, which had dash and spirit peculiar to the western country. Her bright, fresh beauty attracted attention. She had a trim figure and a graceful stimulating, provocative manner. She was tall, admirably proportioned and filled out, without being too much so. She had small and perfectly shaped hands and charming little feet. She walked better than any Indian in the West, holding her head upright with dignity and grandeur. Her expression was clear and very soft, her nose thin and pretty, her mouth was not large with full lips.

A stalwart Indian close to the young woman's side threw back his buffalo robe from his shoulders, and letting all the covering he had on down to his waist fall gracefully about his loins to his feet. He looked an ideal chief, standing over six feet in height, and being slender, sinewy and muscular. The scars of the sundances were very prominent; his cheekbones were high, and his upper arms and breast, and dignity and grace marked his every movement and gesture.

As Ian, the sergeant, Father Gregg, and their escort had been seated, the Indian close to the woman's side motioned for attention and silence of the assembled chiefs.

As they quieted down, she spoke in Indian metaphor and sign language, which all assembled could understand and which Sergeant Beidler, sitting close by Ian's side, interpreted for him.

She retold the story, according to Tenkswatarwa, the Shawnee prophet, so they would remember well what he had told them years ago.

"A wind blew west over the ocean of the East, driving before it a frothy foam. It blew this scum, which was evil and unclean, upon the shore of this land and the scum took form. The form that it took was that of a white man—of many white people, both men and women. Wherever the scum lodged on the shore of the land it took this form."

Of the present warring, she said, "The tomahawk is raised. The blood of our women and children smokes from the ground. The bones of our warriors and old men lie uncovered, whitening the earth."

Talking about peace being preserved with other tribes, she said, "The path between us must be kept clean."

The manner in which she incorporated into her discourse striking and instructive metaphor was typical of the Indian love of oratory, which, with them, is a native accomplishment. With a language strong, comprehensive, smooth and grammatical, it is not strange that her utterances were unequaled in powerful argument, stirring eloquence improved in its effect by apt Indian metaphor and gems of native similes.

The grace of which the woman's metaphor was used stirred the gathered chiefs.

Shenandoah, a celebrated chief of the Oneida tribe of the Six Nations, who was at a great age, stood up and uttered sublime sentiment to the woman and the fellow chiefs, "Brothers, I am an aged hemlock. The winds of a hundred winters have whistled through my branches, and I am dead at the top."

Everyone who had seen a tall hemlock with a dry and leafless crown surmounting its dark green foliage felt the force of this simile. His memory, his vigor, and his powers of youth had departed forever.

Another venerable chief of a western tribe stood, and alluding to his extreme age and the probability that he might not survive a war, said, "my children will walk through the forests, and the Great Spirit will whistle in the tree tops, and the flowers will spring up in the trail, but Pushmataha will hear not. He will see the flowers no more. He will be gone. His people will know that he is dead. The news will come to their ears as the fall of a mighty oak in the stillness of the woods."

He looked at the gathered chiefs mostly old beyond the age of youth and vitality, then turned to the woman orator and asked, "Who will lead us in battle?"

The woman stood tall and spoke with all the prophecy she was capable of. "O, Hear ye this! All my people. We shall overthrow our enemies and tread them under that rise up against us."

"Now, singing birds keep you in the dark." (meaning tale-bearers, story tellers, and liars that wish to deceive you. They have concealed their intentions from you, they keep you in ignorance.)

"The council-fire has been extinguished." (Blood has been shed by an enemy at the seat of white government, which has put the fire out.)

"Look this way!" (Join us; join our endeavors.)

"We have no room enough for a camp." (We are too much confined to a small place. We have not sufficient range for the buffalo to feed on, or sufficient hunting ground.)

"Throw the hatchet to the sky!" (We must wage open and terrible war.) "Suffer no grass to grow on the war path!" (Carry on a war with vigor. Be at perpetual war with the white enemy.)

She continued slowly and deliberately, "A great warrior, one of your enemy, has been sent to you."

This statement stirred the emotions and unbeliefs of the chiefs. One by one they rose up shouting, arguing, and muttering their disbeliefs with their fellow warriors. They could not believe what this woman was saying, and a germ of thought of the validity of this woman's words coursed through the gathering.

The woman stood aloof of all this, gathering all the poise she could muster. Sure of vision, she spoke loudly and firmly in Indian metaphor, "It is written!" (meaning the Great Spirit had already willed this situation and nothing or no living mortal could change it.)

Many rebelled at the very thought of her words, yet overborne by the eloquence and authority with which she spoke, they were constrained against their will and judgment, to assent to her words.

Several chiefs still voiced their disbeliefs and demanded, "Who is this warrior? Show us this chief. Show us!"

The woman walked through the crowding chiefs. As she made her way from the circle, she stopped in front of Ian Douglass and pointed directly at him, and said, "This is he! This is the one the Great Spirit has sent."

She stood before Ian for a long moment still pointing him out.

Ian rose to his feet in disbelief. What was this, he wondered. What was happening? I am no warrior. I cannot lead these people against my own kind. She is wrong, wrong! Whoever she is, prophet . . . mystic, or whatever, she is wrong!

In utter disbelief he stood there, saying nothing, knowing nothing that could be said.

She met his eyes for a moment and then was gone.

As chiefs filed from the meeting place, they slowly passed Ian, looking and staring and measuring him up to the task the woman had laid on him. Few accepted the prophecy, but later, maybe later they would. Her powers of prophecy had proceeded her and they all believed or wanted to believe that in her was a strain of the Great Spirit.

Ian noticed that after mounting her pony the woman had turned to Father Gregg and said to him, "O' Black Robe, follow me! I shall lift you up from this place. I invite you to rise from this life, and come and live where I live."

Then, without looking at Ian she turned to Sergeant Beidler and commanded in Sioux dialect, "Come to my campfire at the Mission House this evening." And then wheeled her steed and disappeared into the forest accompanied by her followers.

The sergeant told Ian of her request and, still numb with her remarks, he reluctantly agreed to meet with her.

*   *   *

Later in the afternoon the trio rode out to the Kickapoo Mission House. The old mission was one of the region's earliest landmarks. When in 1827, the military stockade was established by General Henry Leavenworth, protection against Indian attacks was afforded missionaries who came to educate and convert the Indians. A year after the founding of Fort Leavenworth, the Reverend Van Quckanebo of the Jesuit order came from Maryland to establish a mission for the Kickapoo Indians six miles north of the fort on the Indian Territory (Kansa) side of the Missouri River. With the assistance of his Indian converts, the missionary erected the mission from native walnut and oak, of which the region abounded. The logs were hewn, notched and put together with large wooden pins. Nails were not to be had at that time. A chapel addition was built later in honor of St. Francis Xavier.

In this crude chapel was performed the first marriage ceremony in Kansas between a Frenchman named Poncemaux and a Catholic Indian woman. It was also the scene of the baptism of their first child.

When the trio arrived at the mission the Jesuit priest met them and exchanged greetings, and the head priest pointed out the Indians a little way from the house. As Ian approached the fire, with Father Gregg and Sergeant Beidler, he saw a vision as never before. It was one of those moments when the fate of a man is decided through all eternity. Ian felt it; it was a supreme moment.

Tall, slender, with long legs and black hair falling past her shoulders, she was dressed in soft deerskin to her ankles and slit up the sides to her thighs. Numerous bracelets with gold and silver and colors of the rainbow were on her arms. She wore a headband with ornaments, which drooped down and almost covered her dark expressive eyes and with an ornament around her neck. Her dress was cut low to reveal full, firm breasts and the pendant laid between her bosoms. Ian was visually impressed. She was the same girl he had rescued from the drunken soldier but she was much more provocative in the flickering fire light. The quarter inch wide line of red makeup extended from her high forehead, down her nose, and stopped directly above her full red lips, and then continued down her chin. The three black decorative lines radiating from both eyes and terminating with a delicate black makeup around her flashing eyes made her the most exciting woman he had ever seen. Her wind blown dark hair about her eyes and cheeks presented a most mysterious and stimulating picture as she removed her headband. She spoke to him in hesitant broken English. "I am . . . the one . . . you have been seeking!"

Ian was startled that she could speak so well. He questioned her, not really knowing what to say but somehow the words came out. "Are you the Hasanun?"

She looked straight into his eyes and replied, "Some call me that."

She waited until her answer soaked deeply into his soul. Ian's mind was whirling like a top, trying to absorb all this mystery. She continued, "I am Shenga Wassa." She turned to the handsome Indian man standing close by saying, "This is my brother Saba . . . of the Levi tribe." This simple introduction made Ian momentarily lose his breath as he pondered the fact that many scholars thought the American Indian and the lost tribes of Israel had a connection and here was supposedly a descendant of one of the tribes. He did not question her statement as she seemed to be so confident and positive and spoke with a great intelligence. He was temporarily overcome by her positiveness and regal bearing.

She motioned for Ian and the Sergeant to sit with them by the fire as she settled gracefully cross legged across the fire from Ian, exposing only enough leg to really bother Ian but not enough to be vulgar. For several minutes she conversed with Sergeant Beidler in a Sioux dialect which Ian recognized but could not understand.

She let Ian study her for several moments, then turned again to him.

He had regained some of his senses by this time and he asked her, "How did you know I was searching for you?"

She slowly replied as if everything she said was very important, "I know things that pass man's understanding."

Ian questioned, "Are you of the Kansa nation?"

She replied, "I am not of this world. I have not seen the darkness of the womb!"

"I was thought into being, not born, not of blood, nor of the will of the flesh, nor of the will of man, but of the Great Spirit."

Ian's mind was whirling from her statements, of the Great Hasanun, of the Lost tribe of Levi, "What? What is this?" This was not ordinary talk, Ian reasoned. "Not army, not Indian. This was something else!" She was speaking a knowledge he could not understand.

Ian could not handle any more of these thoughts so he changed the subject to what he thought was her most absurd statement she had made to him at the council earlier in the day. Ian, matter of factly told her, "I am not the person to lead your people."

She slowly replied, "It is written!" In the Hasanun's mind that meant that history had already been written and there was no changing the fact that she had only to read the happening in the Book of Destiny. But this was not in old history that had happened. She also seemed to read the future just as easy. Ian was beginning to understand why she was called the Great Hasanun.

Shenga explained, "Hear what the Great Spirit has ordered me to tell you. My people are destined to die! The Great Spirit will give them a war leader that the remnants of the race can tell their children and their children's children. This war chief will give them hope, and pride, and dreams. You are the chosen one, Ian Douglass."

Ian could not answer, his mind was still in a state of confusion. Nothing like this had ever happened to him before. First Louisa, his true love, then the search request out of nowhere, then the Great Hasanun.

She continued, "In the course of history when a race such as mine confronts a more "so-called" civilization, the aboriginal people will die."

There were tears in her voice as she continued, "Help my people! Within your time they will suffer disease, cruelty, and death!"

"The lodges will disappear. Whole nations will be lost. Fifteen thousand Blackfeet will die. Others will be so deformed, they will kill themselves. They will be degraded and lied about. They will revert to their old ways. The Great Spirit will let this happen. To withstand this grief and hardship, they must have some great deeds to remember. Some great calling . . ."

She hesitated, and choosing her words very carefully, she continued, "You have been chosen to suffer with them and lead them."

She continued slowly, "This will happen to your people also, but not in your time. They will become corrupt, even to killing each other. Their corruption shall make them suffer the wrath of the Great Spirit!"

Ian asked seriously, "Why me? I am not strong enough. Why not you?"

She replied, "I am Love . . . I cannot kill. The Great Spirit will give you strength enough. He will never desert you!"

She abruptly stood up, turned and walked away, terminating any further conversation.

Later that evening after everyone else had retired, Ian stretched down at the edge of the river and thought of all that had happened this day.

Certain resemblances between the myths of the American Indian and those of the Israelites increased the belief that the American race is of the Lost Tribes.

The peculiar interest, however, which attaches to a comparison of American and Israelite myths lies in the fact that they resemble each other, not only generically but specifically. They are alike in their details. Authors have given much attention to this subject and that "an Ojibway tradition tells the adventures of eight, ten, and sometimes twelve brothers, the youngest of whom is the wisest and the most beloved of their father, and especially favored by the high powers."

He delivers his brothers from many difficulties that were brought about by their folly and disobedience. Particularly he supplies them with corn. The Chahta have an elaborate story of their migration, in which they were guided by a pole leaning in the direction which they should take, and remaining vertical at each place where they should encamp. A still closer resemblance of the guidance of the Israelites in the desert by a pillar of fire is found in the Tusayan (Mokis), when indication was made by the movement and the halting of a star. The Pai Utes were sustained in a great march through the desert by water that continually filled the magic cup given to the Sakus Waiunats in a dream until all were satisfied; and a similarly miraculous supply of food to the starving multitude is reported by the same people. In the genesis myth of the Tusayan the culture hero was enabled to pass dry-shod through lakes and rivers by throwing a staff upon the waters, which were at once divided as by walls.

W.W. Warren, in his History of the Ojibway Nations, tells that he sometimes translated parts of Bible history to the old Ojibway men, and their expression invariably was, "The book must be true, for our ancestors have told us similar stories generation after generation since the earth was new."

As for Shenga Wassa herself, there is a theory in Indian religion that the Great Spirit, the creator and ruler of the universe, the upholder not only of the cosmic, but also of the moral order of the world; when the enemies to his rule endanger the order of the world, the god sends someone for the purpose of defending it. Whenever there is a decline of the law and an increase of sin, then the Great Spirit puts forth himself (in a new birth) for the rescue of the pious and for the destruction of the evil-doers and for the establishment of the Law. This does not happen often. The Great Spirit may not take action for a thousand eons, then becomes manifest for the purpose of action, at the end of a thousand years. Strictly speaking, incarnation means the putting on of flesh by the divine; it need not necessarily be, although as a matter of fact, it usually is- the flesh of man. A particular member of a human family might have in him or her a strain of the divine.

Shenga was clothed in human form, lived as a woman amongst men and women, and yet could supposedly associate with God on a higher footing than other humans.

Christian theology pre-supposes a reasoned conception of the universe, in which the natural and the supernatural, or the divine and human, are set over against one another. The native Americans conceived that gods, men, and animals form a single society, and even

Shenga Wassa

plants were sometimes thought to have a connection with this society. They pictured the manifestation of the divine as exhibited in springs of water, trees, and crags of natural rock.

An early stratum of thought discernible in a few passages of the Old Testament conceived of God as taking the form of a man and then discarding it at will. Such was the man who came to Abraham's tent in Genesis 18, the one who appeared to Gideon in Judges 6, to Manoah's wife in Judges 13, and to Joshua in Joshua 5:13-15. There were special manifestations of Jahweh in Genesis 2:7. God is said to have breathed into man's nostrils the breath of life, and man became a living soul. This implies that man has a kind of kinship to God. In Genesis 6:2-4, it is said that beings of the divine order (bene ha-elahim) married human wives, and that the issue of such marriages consisted of the heroes and men of renown of older time.

The view that unusual persons were god-begotten was undoubtedly universal in the early Semitic world. It lingered in a weakened form down to the beginning of the Christian era. Zipporah was found by Moses "pregnant by no mortal;" Isaac was "not the result of generation, but the shaping of the unbegotten." Samuel was "born of the human mother" who "became pregnant after receiving divine seed."

Shenga Wassa seemed to perceive more sounds and works than human beings could perceive. Maybe Shenga Wassa was born as an apparitional being as the Suvarna hold that the Buddha was born as such a being. Her body could, therefore, be defined as spiritual which means "produced by the spirit" without the aid of the elements of generation.

The running water symbolizes the passing on of generations, one following another. The little child looks on the water and sees its own likeness, as it will see that likeness in its children and its children's children. The running water gives promise that the life of the child shall go on, as the waters flow over the land.

"Heru! Hotoru! He!" is the Pawnee appeal to the winds. Hotoru is not the ordinary word of winds, but refers to them as supernatural powers.

Even the universe and the wind in some early philosophies is conceived as having a soul.

A Navaho legend tells of the creation of man and woman. It was the wind that gave them life. The soul is fundamentally the life of the body. As the child grows up, the soul which he or she was born gradually develops in strength, experience and wisdom, so that after the age of ten or twelve years, it is fairly competent to look after the child and begins to do so. Breath is the wind that comes out of our mouths, now that gives us life. When breath ceases, we die.

The Sioux tell of a beautiful woman who possessed supernatural powers who was sent to them by the Great Spirit. She was one of those uncommon geniuses which spring up occasionally to produce revolutions and overturn the established order of things.

According to the Sioux tradition, two young men were sent out from the Sioux camp in search of buffalo. In their wanderings they spied a beautiful young woman, who was more fair to look upon than any of the Sioux maidens. One of these young men by the name of Saba, was wise and good, his heart was brave and strong; the other was foolish. The latter said, "Here is a beautiful young girl on prairie alone; let us overpower and enjoy her." The young man of sense said, "No, that would be wrong; this is a holy woman."

They were as yet some little distance from her, and she had attracted their attention by singing. After making signs to her she approached. In spite of the protests of his companion the foolish young man, crazed by his passion, forced her to the ground, when a great mist suddenly arose, enveloped them, and spread over the prairie, and the air was filled with terrible and hissing sounds. As suddenly as it came the fog lifted, and it seemed to take with it numberless rattlesnakes.

Then the wise young man saw the woman standing near him, and between her and himself the ghastly bones of his comrade, from which the flesh had been entirely consumed by the rattlesnakes. The woman said to the surviving young man, "You are wise, brave and good; I have taken pity on you and your people. This young man was wicked, and he has suffered the fruit of his own misdeeds."

"Go and tell your people that I will take pity on them."

The young man, returned to camp and told what he had seen and heard.

A large lodge was pitched in the center of the camp for the woman's arrival.

The beautiful woman had followed the young man, and as she approached the village she was met by the medicine man. A large fire was built in the teepee. Circle after circle of men, women, and children formed outside, and a great circle of fires was also made around the lodge. All eyes were on the beautiful woman.

She said, "I have taken pity on you. I have brought you this sacred pipe, which tell you by its increased weight when buffalo are near and plenty."

(*This holy pipe was handed down from father to son for many generations and was in the early 1800s in the charge of Elk Head, a Sans Arcs chief living near Standing Rock on the Missouri River. It was carefully wrapped up and few people were allowed to see it.*) Many believed the God-begotten woman had returned.

*   *   *

When Ian awoke in the early morning, the Hasanun and her party had already departed with Father Greg going with them on his mule.

Breakfast at the mission was cornbread and wild meat and rare rich milk.

Ian decided to accompany Sergeant Beidler to his cabin at Rialto for several days.

Sergeant Tom had two faithful, intelligent dogs, and to divert his mind from his great sorrow he spent much of the pleasant weather hunting. Deer, antelope, coons, squirrels, turkeys and prairie chickens were all within easy reach on the land, and on the waters wild geese and ducks of every variety known to the hunter.

It was a beautiful warm day so Ian and Beidler took their guns and fishing rods and strolled down to the river. They then headed up its shaded shore a mile or two to a point opposite some immense and picturesque cliffs, which rose from the water's edge, nearly perpendicular, about 200 feet; it was an inspiring scene. The river at this point was very narrow and deep, apparently having cut its way into the very roots of the gigantic stone barricade on its short and fretful sweep around this unexpected obstacle.

Nothing but the chirping of birds and the solemn hush of the forest disturbed his meditations as he sat for some time on an old pecan log, waiting for some member of the Finny tribe to excite his attention by a "nibble."

As he viewed the country across the river he thought about its history and original inhabitants.

Known as the Illinois country under Spanish rule, Missouri is the mother of all the great west.

Missouri was admitted as a territory in June 4, 1812. Missouri Territory then embraced what later became Missouri State, Arkansas, Iowa, Minnesota west of the Mississippi, Oklahoma, North and South Dakota, Nebraska, Montana, and most of Kansas, Colorado, and Wyoming. It was admitted as a state on March 2, 1820. Missouri was occupied by the Osage (or Ouachage) Indian tribes and the Grand.

The Great Osage were the largest and finest specimens of manhood and womanhood among all the wild tribes of the hills or prairies. The men were tall, straight, athletic; the woman well-formed, with regular Greek-line faces, and of a uniform lighter color than other Indians.

This tribe may be fairly considered the most admirable of the Indian race. They had a weird and uncanny notion of a Great Spirit—a notion born of their experiences with the forces of nature manifest about them in the storms and lightnings and other, to them incomprehensible phenomena. In these powers of nature they say dimly something above and beyond themselves and for the want of a better name they called it the Great Spirit, and

**Osage
First Chief—
Artist,
George Catlin**

ARMY DIGEST
December 1967

ascribed to it all those events and forces which they could not understand. At least they seemed to have had no conception of the God of the Christian world and their morals were limited indeed.

The Osage were a restless, vagrant, nomadic people. They lived in temporary villages easily moved or easily rebuilt. They roamed the country in so-called villages in considerable numbers only in the winter season. They were not a fierce and war-like tribe; yet they were brave and strong in war when so engaged with other tribes. So far as white men were concerned, they were not hostile and were always disposed peaceably towards the whites. Mentally and morally, they never had risen much above the average Indian.

But George Catlin, who had traveled for eight years amongst the wildest tribes of Indians in North America, observed that the Osage studiously rejected every luxury and every custom of civilized people—amongst these, the use of whiskey, which was on all sides tendered to them, but almost uniformly rejected! This was an unusual and unaccountable thing.

The sergeant told of the death of a beautiful daughter of a warrior who he was a friend of. She was devotedly attached to a pretty pony and when she died the pony was killed and buried with her so that she might have it to ride in the land of spirits. All of her playthings were buried with her. So whatever we may think of the heathen Osage we cannot deny to ourselves a certain respect for their religious conceptions and customs. They are beautiful, tender and sincere. Who among us is competent to say certainly how or in what respect their customs, beliefs, and philosophy were wrong?

Thus we see that their religion was full of the human; that is; was just what might be expected to prevail among the children of the forest and prairie. They got comfort and hope from their beliefs, even as we are comforted and made hopeful by our beliefs. At least their view of the life of the soul beyond was so strong that the devoted Missionaries could not shake them or get them to accept the Christian view.

One settlement within the bounds of the state was Saint Genevieve founded in 1735, the oldest in the state. Saint Charles was formed in 1762 and Saint Louis in 1764.

Missouri's sons and daughters have followed the sun to the Pacific Ocean, and every state west of the mouth of the Kaw is indebted to Missouri for many of the brave pioneers who blazed the way to statehood and greatness in the land of their adoption and settlement. The "Mother State" has waxed great and strong and fat.

Farming the lands of the Fort Leavenworth reservation was an occupation early indulged in by Uncle Sam with the troops forming the garrison, and through lease with private parties, or "shares."

At the time of the post's establishment, the Clay County Court House at Liberty, Missouri, was the market point for its residents. It supplied such vegetables and produce not secured by the labor of troops. The river was crossed on a flatboat ferry, opposite the post. Zadock Martin, a frontiersman, who came to the vicinity in 1826, was licensed by the military authorities to operate a ferry across the Missouri River and Little Platte River.

Martin hailed from the county of Clay, and on his settlement near the post had with him his sons and slaves. He located near the falls of the Platte where he kept a tavern. His force consisted besides his six stalwart sons, of a half dozen Negro slaves. His wife and three daughters were also with him. He had no neighbors within fifteen miles of his cabin.

Martin was peculiarly fitted for his calling. Tall and brawny, he weighed about 175 pounds. He wore a broad-rimmed hat and carried a hickory cane. His eyes flashed lightning and his mouth reverberated thunder. He demanded instantaneous obedience of friend or foe. Yet, he was just and charitable, and loved by his family and servants. His sons and Negroes formed a military troop that even the commander of the fort hesitated to exasperate. He cultivated corn opposite his house, in the bottoms and in a thirty-acre field (where Tracy now stands). He also had a field of corn in Sand Prairie, opposite the fort, and another in Fancy Bottom, opposite Weston. He had a sugar camp on the bluff, above the present mouth of Bee Creek. His hay was cut on the prairie three miles southeast of his home. His cattle wintered on the rushes that abounded in all the Missouri bottoms. His hogs ran wild and fed upon the mast that consisted of acorns, hickory nuts, and pecans. His hog killing was done with dogs and guns. When pork was wanted, he shouldered his rifle, called his dogs, and went game hunting. His Negroes had cabins scattered around his lands and were ready at all hours to do him feudal service.

In the fall of 1829, the quartermaster at the fort paid 1¼ cents per pound for bacon. It was brought by team from Clay County. They crossed the Missouri in a flatboat, constructed at Liberty, and brought up the river by steamboat. Two yoke of oxen were first taken over, and then the wagon. Net pork sold for 75 cents per hundred; horses brought $15 to $20, oxen per yoke $30, and large steers for $10. A purchaser of horses took a lot to Ohio. After selling the horses, they returned on foot.

The settlers visited the Platte territory, hunting deer and bees. Both were abundant. Ben Cornelis was the champion bee hunter. He often camped on Bee Creek and gave it its name. He would go out into the woods and cut a bee tree from which they got a pail of honey.

One fall, Zadoc Martin and family killed 120 deer. There were no buffalo on the Missouri side of the river. Zadock never saw but one elk, and that was after it was killed.

*   *   *

Ian, soldier that he was, had done his utmost to improve the drill and efficiency of his men.

The captain had completed his rigid inspection of the equipment and the glossy blacks and Major Montgomery had supplemented the words by a nod and a glance that spoke volumes.

Captain Lyon had ordered Ian and six of his men to accompany him to the Dixon farm situated southwest of the reservation. Ian had heard of the trouble in which some influential people had told Major Montgomery that those Irish should be got off the claims because they wanted to build a town there. The company suggested the plan of raising $1200 or $1500 to offer them for their claims, and if they would not take that, they wanted Montgomery to have the reserve surveyed, so as to have the Irish out. Then they were to send agents to Washington to get the reserve curtailed; the matter being kept secret until they could put men on the claims to hold them. Captain Lyon was kept in ignorance of the reasons for driving the Irish off their claims, as it was thought he would have conscientious scruples against doing so.

Two settlers named Dixon, and their families (there were four brothers James, John, Thomas and Patrick); had settled upon land outside of the military reservation, as they had a clear right to do. When offered money for their claims they declined to sell or surrender their right to their 160 acres.

Determined to compel them to go, the reservation was extended so as to include their settlement, and then Lyon, with his company, was ordered to go and pull down the Dixon's houses, and put them and their families off the reservation. Lyon was, doubtless, selected for this work because he had stated his belief that the action of the commanding officer was wrong and that the men had a right to the land upon which they had settled. And further, some were filled with the expectation that he would disobey this order as he had a previous one. As Ian was considered to be Lyon's aide and abettor, he was ordered to accompany him on this expedition of a company of cavalry against two men and some women and children. If they refused to carry out the orders both Ian and Lyon could be court-martialed and they would be rid of the two trouble-makers. Ian had sided with Captain Lyon on several court-martials they had sat on, this upset the higher officers who ran the court martials and they would not tolerate being rebuffed by some junior officers.

At the Dixon's farm Ian refused to pull down the houses in violation of a direct order and he was immediately placed under guard.

Ian had to go with his conscience. He knew this was wrong and direct order or no direct order he would not obey the command. He sympathized with the Dixon's as he had been born and raised on a plantation farm. No calling in life brings out and develops stronger, nobler qualities of manhood or insures a better success and more ample competence than does the ancient and honorable vocation of farming. To the early pioneer, the hardships and privations incident to spending the best years of life in transforming dense forests and trackless prairies and dismal swamps into rich, cultivated fields, orchards, and gardens, thriving villages, towns, and cities, were but stronger stimulus to build both his own toil-worn, weary hands a comfortable home which should be a place of rest and happiness in his declining years. The older men had many satisfying thoughts of the difficulties encountered and overcome, of the long, hard, upward struggle of the days gone recompensed by the sure reward, of the old scenes, and of the old, tried, and true friends. Thus is the heart of him made glad, who labors long and diligently with an honorable purpose.

But Captain Lyon knew the difference between an outrage and a violation of the military code. He had been informed by his military superiors that the land upon which the

Dixon's had settled was a part of the military reservation. Whether it was or not was not any of his business. That was a matter that specially concerned the Dixon's, and that might safely be left for them to bring to the notice of the highest authority.

So he and his command proceeded to obey the order while Ian, under guard, watched the demolition of all the Dixon's buildings. The Dixon's were at first a little disposed to resist, but Lyon told them if they fired on his men he would return the fire, and as to the ultimate result there would be no doubt. So they submitted. They went off and Lyon with a yolk of oxen tore down the houses and barns and effectively demolished them. Then after his bloodless victory he marched back to the fort, and placed Ian in chains at the stockade to await the court-martial hearing.

Captain Lyon then set himself to work preparing charges of corruption and other crimes against the commanding officer. The court-martial of Ian was short and to the point. There was no defense. Ian had refused a direct order. Lyon was effectively stopped from telling about the beforehand intrigue against the Dixon's. That had no direct bearing on Ian's case. So a week later Ian was found guilty and stripped of his rank.

A military officer is bound to promptly obey, and without hesitation, every order he may receive, which does not affect his honor.

With the extended absence of Colonel Williams, the Post Commandant, Colonel Dodge, was temporarily in command and had his opportunity to vent his dislike of Ian. He had selected officers who he could easily intimidate and coerce. In fact the entire makeup of the court was of newly arrived officers, who for one reason or another were compelled to act and think in a manner dictated by the colonel.

It was the first occasion in many a long year on which Colonel Dodge had appeared in the roll of judge-advocate, that complex and contradictory position where in the so-called legal adviser of the court having prosecuted in the name of the government to the extent of his ability. He has always held that when an officer was under trial the moral obligation of the government was to find him guilty. No one on the court could quite understand why Dodge had this authority. It was a most unusual thing to call upon the officers of the Department of Military Justice itself to furnish the prosecutor; rather was it their province to remain at the office of the division or department commander, and, in reviewing the records to sit in judgment of the judges. Colonel Dodge saw opportunity for distinction hitherto unequalled, he asked of his general in the department of the Mississippi, a Brigadier General James Wilkerson, the detail as judge-advocate of the court, and the general, though surprised, saw no way to refuse.

So carefully had the court been chosen that of its entire array of five members, every man was personally a stranger to the young officer whose fate lay in their hands. Of all his regiment not another officer was at the post when the court found Ian guilty of disobedience of orders in the 1st charge.

2nd charge was conduct to the prejudice of good order and military discipline. Finding to the 2nd charge—Guilty.

The sentence was severe. He was to be stripped of his rank and sword in front of the entire regiment, to have his head shaved, and to be branded on the left hip with the letter D. He also was to be confined at the post guardhouse for a period of one month—the first fourteen days in solitary confinement on bread and water.

After the fourteen days, he would stand on the head of a barrel on the Main Parade on every alternate day from Reveille to Retreat, allowing one-half hour for each meal, wearing a ball weighing forty pounds attached to his left leg by a chain four feet long. At the expiration of his confinement, he was to be dishonorable discharged and drummed out of the service of the United States Army.

Certain officers had reasoned that Ian would have conscientious scruples against the orders to drive the Dixon's off their claims. By a legal court-martial Ian Douglass could be permanently removed from causing any more difficulties for the Secret Committee of Correspondence of the West.

But the conspiracy did not work as well against the Dixon's. After their houses were thrown down and destroyed, the Irish then dug holes in the ground and lived in them. Again other troopers came back and the roofs fixed over the holes were torn off, but they were never driven off their claims.

The court-martial was enforced and the men were to witness the punishment and disgrace of one of their number. Ian, under guard of a soldier with drawn bayonet, stood firmly and proud while the adjutant in monotonous, formal tones, read aloud the record of his offense, his trial and his sentence. Hardly had the sound of the last words of the officer died away, when the sergeant-major, with a few rapid cuts of his knife, severed the gold bars from the shoulders of Ian's tunic. As the badges of his former rank dropped to the ground, Ian, bringing his hand to his forehead in salute to his officers, rapidly marched down the front of the line and returned to the guardhouse. It was a painful scene and made an impression on the men as they were dismissed and moved silently off the grounds.

*   *   *

Someone decided that Ian should be kept in solitary confinement and guarded more closely than was thought possible in the garrison guardhouse. Orders were to transfer him to a notorious stockade far out on the plains.

A man by the name of Perkins was in charge of the five men of the escort on the journey to the Prairie Prison. Perkins was from the Secret Committee's Grenadier Company; the shortest man was six feet two inches; real Samson's.

Ian wore the dress of the backwoodsmen, of coarse, homespun pantaloons the color of copperas, a jacket of common drab cloth, and an old hat, with a broad, flapping brim. He rode a superb horse, his hat hanging over his face, but not concealing his brilliant eyes, that his appearance and bearing were distinguished.

The prisoners' guards struck into the woods by the Indian trail, and marched, from necessity, in the Indian manner—the gigantic Perkins at the head of the line; the prisoner in the middle.

At night, the only tent carried by the party was pitched and assigned to Ian, who slept guarded by armed men and lulled by the howling of innumerable wolves. The men were very attentive to his wants and treated him with the respect due rather from an escort than a guard. He, on his part, was courteous to them, and a kind of silent, friendship grew up between them.

It was a perilous and fatiguing march. For several days in succession, the chilling spring rains fell in torrents upon the unprotected horsemen, swelling the rivulets to rivers, and the creeks to rushing floods. Sometimes, the whole party was swimming their horses over a rapid stream. Often, they toiled wearily through mire, more dangerous than the flood itself. But, amid angry elements, wild beasts, vast swamps, boundless forests, and treacherous Indians, the dauntless Perkins held his course, marching swiftly at the head of his company, and urging them along at the rate of forty miles a day. The party always slept in the woods where possible, near swamps of reeds, upon which the horses, "belled and hobbled", fed during the night. After breakfast, it was their custom again to mount their horses and march on, with a silence that was sometimes broken by a remark about the weather, the creeks, or the Indians. Ian sat firmly in the saddle and was always on the alert, and was a most excellent rider. Although drenched for hours with cold and clammy rain, and at night extended upon a thin pallet, on the bare ground, after having rode forty miles he never complained that he was sick, or even fatigued.

It was five days before they reached again the abodes of the white man.

Stopping at a solitary ranch house for a meal, Perkins snatched his pistols from his holster, sprang to the ground, and in an instant was at the side of his prisoner. With a pistol in each hand, he sternly ordered him to dismount.

The prairie prison that they took Ian to was on the Arkansas. There was a palisade and shelter. The fort was simply four log houses, connected by angles of timber framework, in which loopholes were cut for small arms. The fort was about sixty feet across inside, with walls twenty feet high. There was no corral for the animals.

With a negligence characteristic of the War Department throughout the Indian wars on the Plains, no adequate facilities were built, and no adequate garrison ordered out. In fact, the fort was manned by "irregular rangers." The Rangers were made up principally of volunteers who had offered their services at the time of the Black Hawk War. They were hardy, weather-beaten fellows, accustomed to western life, ready with rifle, and first-rate Indian fighters.

But they were basically outlaws. They were allowed to keep all the spoils of war and when the Indian killing did not provide enough loot, they had no qualms about murdering the immigrant and his wife and children, looting everything of value, and then burn the wagon, of course leaving a few arrows stuck in a cow or plow horse to prove that the Indians had done the dastardly deed.

The fighting force consisted of a man named Smith with his squaw and two children, Samuel and his half breed Rosalie, and twelve other rangers. Smith had seven mules and horses, Samuel had one, Garrard had two, with three old government scarecrows, and five broken-down United States steers, and an Indian cur.

Even a visit to the river for water, a hundred yards distant, required the bucket in one hand and the rifle in the other, for the Pawnee and Comanche ranged this land—both tribes noted for their dexterity and willingness to take the white man's "hair," or his caballada (horses). One structure served as a guard house with a sentry on duty at all times.

The next day Ian was brought into the office of a man by the name of Strickler who seemed to be in charge, being the toughest and meanest of the bunch. As he stood in front of his desk, Ian's bound hands were tied to a rope fastened loosely to a timber rafter above.

"Where is the Hasanun, lieutenant?" Strickler asked. Ian did not answer the question.

Strickler asked again to no avail.

"You'll tell us, lieutenant."

In a second the floor that Ian stood on, opened up as the trap door sprang open. Ian dropped all at once with a hideous wrenching and tearing of his joints till his feet were but a foot from the basement floor.

Then he felt the blacksnake whip across his back. After ten lashes he was pulled back upstairs and asked the same question.

Ian did not reply.

This happened the next day and the next, with the sudden change of agony renewed each day and each time more unendurable.

When he was awake he imagined impossible schemes for getting possession of a knife.

Everyone who has dealt with humanity under the influence of pain or fear knows that the effect of either is cumulative, and that in each individual there seems to be a limit beyond which the nerves will resist no more, and the will power altogether ceases. A man may bear a certain grievous pain the first day without a sign; on the second day he will grind his teeth; on the third he will wince; later he will groan, writhe, and at last break down, like a mere child, under one tenth of the suffering he bore manfully and silently at first. And it is the same with any given fear. In a smaller degree one's temper under constantly renewed irritation of the same kind.

Ian had almost reached the limit of endurance after the third day of lashings, and the mere idea of being beaten was almost intolerable to him. But here was a man of iron will, full of courage, and brave blood.

He was faced with gloomy forebodings. Scarce fifteen yards distant, brutal wolves fought over the grave of a man who succumbed to the whip. A large black one, whose faint outline Ian could see, gave a most unearthly howl, which, going out in the stillness, sent back its lonely echo from the distant hills, and met a response from others afar, who with fiendlike screams, congregated over the grave growling and bristling in fearful wrath, or continuously loped around the fort in hungry expectation.

In the afternoon succeeding the third beating, a small military squad of six dragoons from Fort Leavenworth arrived. Lieutenant Tharpe had brought the rangers thirty days rations of flour and coffee. The rangers did not provision themselves well, and these clever fellows welcomed the supplies. Smith's squaw and Rosalie made the monotonous rations quite palatable.

Lieutenant Tharpe handed Strickler, the ranger in charge of the prison at the time, an order from the Commander of Fort Leavenworth to turn over Ian to them to return to the cantonment.

Strickler, with fiery beard and mustache of no small retentions, intently read the orders as a ranger guard leaned against the entry, a long government blunderbuss at rest in the bend of his arm, and nearer the gateway, in attitudes of indecision, stood Cowhorn, Cain, and Andrew, with perturbed countenances that they were being robbed of two thousand dollars to have Ian share the cemetery with the other fellow the wolves had torn to pieces.

But Strickler was no dummy, he had been a schoolmaster and he would not jeopardize the dreams of the "Grand Conspiracy," so he complied with the orders. To his surprise, Ian was set at liberty—a different fate from that he expected at the hands of the Rangers.

Lieutenant Tharpe had explicit orders, precise and specific—Lieutenant Douglass was to be brought back alive, if he was alive, and if he had expired, his body was to be returned to Fort Leavenworth. Sensing the traitorous mood of the Rangers, they left the prairie prison in the early afternoon, leaving six mules at the fort.

Supper was at sundown, after which the dragoons congregated together surrounding their prisoner, to take any assassin's bullet that came Ian's way, and to smoke and talk, with guns in repose on their arms. They made shots at the skulking wolves, who not infrequently took ugly balls with them in their ignominious flight.

The sun, in setting, cast flickering beams far up on the meandering, broad-sheeted Arkansas, and shone on the numerous flourishing vegetation teeming islands. The slow winging of the forsaken-looking crane, or the more merry flight of smaller birds of the stream, darting into the glittering spot, to disappear as if by magic, often excited Ian's attentive admiration. His back hurt terrible but he was thankful to be alive.

*   *   *

Ian Douglass, standing on the head of a barrel in the hot sun with the ball and chain chafing his ankle, knew nothing of the immense intrigue that he was victim of. The branding and whip lashing bothered him and the blood still oozed down his leg and glued his trousers to the open wound.

But he had been in the way of the "Secret Committee of Correspondence of the West" and he had been effectively removed. He had made a blunder and the Secret Committee had taken full advantage of it. Their "Brigadier General" in Louisiana and $18,000 had taken care of the problem. Disgraced before his peers, drummed out of the service, it was thought by the committee that he would give no other trouble to the Grand Conspiracy.

The Grand Conspiracy had started with Aaron Burr, a lieutenant colonel in the Army of the Revolution, United States Senator, and Vice-President of the United States.

*   *   *

One morning at eight o'clock in the town of Richmond Hill, Connecticut, Colonel Burr killed General Hamilton in a duel. He was wholly unprepared for the excitement that arose. It never, before the duel, seemed once to have occurred to him that the public, which had seen with comparative indifference so many bloody conflicts of the kind, would discover anything extraordinary in this one, whatever might be its result. He supposed, and had good reason to suppose, that, on the day before the duel, he was a more popular and more important man than Hamilton. Was he not Vice-President? Had he not just been voted for by a majority of the freeholders of the city, in spite of Hamilton's most strenuous exertions? Yet, the day after the duel, the dying Hamilton had the heartfelt sympathy of every creature in the town.

"No one," said the embittered John Adams, "wished to get rid of Hamilton in that way."

A week later the duel had driven Burr into a sort of exile. The political Federalists or Tories, and the Clintonians united in exciting public sympathy in Hamilton's favor. Thousands of absurd falsehoods were circulated against Burr. The most unprincipled Jacobins were the loudest in their lamentations of the death of General Hamilton, who, for many years, was uniformly represented as the most detestable and unprincipled of men— their motives were obvious. The object of this unexampled measure was to obtain an inquest of murder.

In several months an indictment of murder was handed down and the States of New York and New Jersey disputed which should have the honor of hanging the Vice-President.

It was soon understood by the politicians that, though nothing favorable to Burr could be openly done, he should not be molested. Among the officials, and in the society of Washington, during his last winter there, he was received with, at least, as much consideration as before. The President seemed to have been more complaisant than usual. He gave one or two appointments to Burr's particular friends, and General Wilkinson was made governor of the newly acquired territory of Louisiana.

Mr. Burr, the "well-graced actor," exited from the drama of public life by impeachment.

*   *   *

On Monday the 29th of December, 1803, at noon, the tri-colored flag of France, which floated from the staff in the public square of New Orleans, and upon which the eyes of expectant thousands were fixed, began to descend. At the same moment, the stars and stripes of the American Union appeared above the crowd and slowly mounted the staff.

Louisiana was now the United States. The mouths of the Mississippi were free! The tide of emigration, for sixteen years held in check by the intolerance of the Spaniards, was now free to pour itself into the most productive region of the earth! The insolence of His Catholic Majesty was signally rebuked.

Colonel Burr, now without a country, was one of the thousands who looked westward, as the scene of a new career. He had many friends in the West—old army acquaintances, members of Congress with whom he had acted, and senators over whom he had presided.

In 1796, when the Federalists had delayed the admission of Tennessee into the Union, Burr had been zealous in her cause, and thereby won great popularity in the new state. General Jackson had appeared on the scene as her representative in Congress; "a tall, lank, uncouth-looking personage," with long locks of hair hanging over his face, and a queue down his back tied in an eel-skin, his dress singular, his manners and deportment those of a rough backwoodsman. With him, it was natural that Burr should become intimate.

All over the valley of the Mississippi, there were men who resented the late proceedings of New York and New Jersey, and were ready to go all lengths in showing respect to a man whom they regarded in the light of a martyr to federal crafty schemes and puritanic bigotry.

Burr's oldest friend in the west was General Wilkinson, commander-in-chief of the army, and recently appointed Governor of Louisiana. Wilkinson and Burr had climbed together the heights of Quebec in the war in Canada, and formed, amid those scenes the friendship which fellow soldiers know. They had seldom met since, but had corresponded, confidentially and in cipher, at intervals, for many years. In 1787, Wilkinson had emigrated to New Orleans, then a Spanish post, where, till 1791, he had traded in tobacco, a subject, by residence, of the King of Spain. Not prospering in trade, he resumed his military career in 1791, and obtained command of the western posts.

The character of this man was not unblemished. Wilkinson was fond of the table and of show, boastful, and otherwise weak. There was strong, but not convincing evidence, that while holding a commission in the American army, he was pensioner of the King of Spain.

There was a party in the west, in 1796, who favored a separation of the Western States from the Union. Wilkinson was of that party and had dreams of leading the revolt, and becoming, to use his own words, "the Washington of the West."

The Spanish viceroy favored a project calculated to weaken a neighbor that was growing powerful, and of whom the home government was beginning to stand in dread.

Wilkinson was paid by the Spanish to promote the scheme, and drew up, for the viceroy, a list of leading citizens of Kentucky known to be disaffected to the Union, who, he thought, would also accept money for the same purpose.

During the administration of John Adams, the Union had not the sacred charm to backwoodsmen. The noise of party discontention filled the land. The Union, as Wilkinson himself said, seemed to hang together by a thread, which any moment might break.

Wilkinson had thoughts of hastening the catastrophe, of founding a western republic, and of becoming its Washington, without being, in any sense of the word, a traitor.

General Wilkinson was a portly, red-faced individual when he wore the blue and yellow uniform of the Revolution. He was a bon vivant, merry, extravagant—the last man for a conspirator though of easy virtue enough.

In 1805 the great west was not content. The acquisition of Louisiana had reduced the malcontents to a very inconsiderable minority. But, there were still those who were dissatisfied with the monopolizing of the great federal offices by the politicians of the East, and who thought it absurd and undesirable to be connected with a government whose capital was a two month's journey's distance.

And now Aaron Burr traversed this magnificent domain. A variety of projects lay half-formed in his mind—projects of land speculation, of canal-making, of settling in some rising city of the West in the practice of law, of becoming anew his political life as the representative of a new State of Congress. Burr could see himself that the tie, which bound the province of Louisiana to the Union, was not strong. The French population, who had for a few months enjoyed a reunion with their mother country, and had hoped that the reunion would be perpetual, merely acquiesced in the recent cession. The Spaniards would not give up the hope of regaining the province.

Sixty years before, the map of North America that was now the United States, reflected glory chiefly upon the Spanish name. Except that along the Atlantic coast there appeared a narrow red stripe denoting the English colonies, that map was one expanse of green, the northern part of which was called Canada, the southern, Louisiana; and the whole was claimed by the French. A few years later, the latter province embracing the most productive part of the valley of the Mississippi, and the mouth of the river, upon which the value of all the rest depended, was ceded to Spain. After a half a century of possession, the Spaniards had lost all of their domain east of the river, but still hoped that the next European peace would give it back to them. Some of the Spanish officials remained in New Orleans for eighteen months after the cessation, in expectation of that event.

About the middle of September, Burr reached St. Louis, where General Wilkinson was. What passed between them no one knows for certain.

But it seemed Burr was revolving some great project. After Burr went back east, Wilkinson received six letters in cipher from Colonel Burr.

In November, Colonel Burr dined with the President in Washington and gave an account of his western travels to the company. From members of the cabinet, he learned that there would be no war with Spain. Napoleon, now stalking toward the summit of his power, had intimated that a declaration of war against Spain would be considered a declaration of war against him. For the moment, Napoleon's word was law everywhere in the world, out of range of British cannon.

Precisely when, precisely where, it was that Burr conceived the enterprise upon which his heart was now fixed, he could not perhaps himself have told.

From an early day, schemes for revolutionizing the ill-governed Spanish provinces of America had been familiar to the people of the United States. His design was to conquer the Spanish provinces, to establish in that fine country a strong, liberal, enlightened government, and to place himself at the head of that government. That done, it would be for the states west of the Alleghenies, in the exercise of their right as independent powers, to decide whether they would remain in the Union, or join the new empire. If they choose the later, Burr might select New Orleans for his capital, and rule from thence the whole of the vast valley of the Mississippi.

Whether the execution of the project should be attempted soon or late or never, depended upon the turn which affairs might take on the southwestern frontier.

To provide for carrying out these schemes a large purchase of land was contemplated, far to the southwest beyond the Mississippi, on the banks of the river Washita, (Ouachita) a branch of the Red River. There the choice spirits of the expedition would have, at least, a rendezvous and a refuge. There, the chief could, if necessary, fortify and maintain a position. There, if the grand scheme should fail or be abandoned, he would found a colony composed of persons of wealth, education, refinement and talent, who would embark capital in the most productive region of the southwest, and form the most brilliant, accomplished, and enlightened society of the continent.

In July of 1806, this purchase was made. It comprised of four hundred thousand acres for which Burr was to pay forty thousand dollars, the first installment of which, five thousand dollars, he did actually pay. Who were his confederates? Burr's connections in New York were not backward in aiding him.

Probably, five hundred persons in all knew something of Burr's plans, and had entered into some kind of engagement to follow his fortunes. There were also four or five thousand whose names were on Burr's lists, who would hasten to his standard as soon as he obtained a foothold on Spanish soil.

Colonel Burr received encouragement that a British naval squadron would be furnished to aid the expedition.

The Catholic Bishop of New Orleans was also consulted, and prepared to promote the enterprise. He designated three priests of the order of Jesuits as suitable agents, and they were accordingly employed.

The superior of the convent of Ursuline nuns, at New Orleans, was in on the secret. Some of the sisterhood were also employed in Mexico.

General Wilkinson had never before been so important a personage as now. Besides being the governor of a Territory, he was the commander-in-chief of the army; and the critical relations subsisting between Spain and the United States fixed upon him, for the time, the eyes of two nations.

Prodigious was his zeal, enormous were his labors, terrible was the excitement he created. The belief was that the "conspiracy" extended from one end of the Union to the other, embracing immense numbers of the most wealthy and influential citizens.

Colonel Burr was rather under the medium height, but well proportioned, of light but sinewy frame, and of great powers of endurance both of body and mind. His gait was measured, and rather that of the soldier than a civilian. But, he moved along so quietly that his pace to some might seem almost stealthy.

The character of Colonel Burr's mind was not large, comprehensive, and philosophical, but rather quick, penetrating, and discerning. He was a shrewd planner, and indefatigable and persevering in carrying out his plans, although he did not always succeed in accomplishing them. He was a good scholar, acquainted with polite literature, and spoke the French and Spanish language—the former fluently. His heart was not in the profession of the law, but that he followed it principally for its gain. He was, however, a good lawyer, and he was versed in the common, civil, and international law, acquainted generally with the reports of adjudicated cases, and in preparing important cases usually traced up the law to its ancient sources. But political and military life seemed to interest him more than anything else, although he never neglected his business. He prided himself more upon his military qualities than upon any other. If he could gratify his ambition by becoming King or Emperor of Mexico, he would be in his glory.

*   *   *

While standing in the sun with leg irons on, just west of the main parade ground, Ian noticed a movement through his sweat-dimmed eyes. It was hot in the Kansas summer sun, 103 degrees in the shade, and the perspiration ran into the whip lash welts on his bare back and pained him considerably. The blurred figure became more recognizable; it was the Indian girl Ian had talked with at the mission several weeks ago.

Saying nothing, she came close up to Ian, looking at him intently,; the guard not bothered by an Indian girl's closeness to his prisoner, even when she gently ran. her cool, petite fingers down the wounds. Immediately the burning pain ceased somewhat. Still without saying anything she circled to the front of Ian.

Looking into his eyes for a long moment, she said with great confidence in her voice, "The prophecy is being fulfilled."

She turned and walked a ways, then turned back to Ian and said, "I wait for you on the Washita.""

Ian blinked several times to wash the blinding sweat from his eyes and shook his head to remove the moisture from his forehead, which was dripping into his eyes.

As quickly as she had appeared, she was gone.

Ian looked all about him, but there was no Shenga Wassa. Maybe it was all a dream. Maybe not . . . but, at first opportunity he would travel to Oklahoma Indian Territory to look for the mysterious Indian woman.

*   *   *

The guardhouse was a poor old structure, dilapidated and very unsanitary. The dungeon was unmerciful, with a stone basement and heavy log superstructure.

The provost marshal had been to the depot quartermaster office and told him all about the worthlessness of the guardhouse, and asked the depot quartermaster's advice as to the method to be taken to have it replaced by a new one. The depot quartermaster told the provost marshal, Colonel Jennison, he would have to make plans and requisition for one and send these through the usual military channels to the War Department. The quartermaster said that so long as the old guard house was in existence he doubted if he would get a favorable response to his application; but should anything happen to the old building by being blown down or by burning, he probably would get a new one at once. The provost marshal left his office and the depot quartermaster thought no more of their conversation.

Eventless days dragged wearily for the prisoners, a pound and a half of bread each day, ten pounds of pork a month for each prisoner, sometimes the pork was taken away, and rice and bear's oil were given them instead.

Ian spent profitless hours in revolving means of escape. He had been confined over two weeks when the opportunity came. A prisoner by the name of Baredran, who Ian had met previously at Sergeant Tom's cabin, had escaped and been recaptured and kept fast in irons. He was a miserable French trapper who Ian became intimate and familiar with, he was an active man, and knew the country. He promised, if Ian could help him off with his irons, and they all got clear of the prison, he would conduct them until they were out of danger.

Baredran got a small file from a soldier to cut the irons and put their design into practice. While the Frenchman was busy in the dungeon cutting the irons, Ian and two others were as industrious in breaking the door of the dungeon. Each finished their jobs at one instant of time, which had held them for about six hours, by 3 o'clock in the morning. With the help of rope, which Ian had gotten from Jamie Bill beforehand, they let themselves down over the guardhouse walls, and made their escape two miles from the reservation, where they lay close at the Dixon's for two days.

About four hundred hours that night the depot quartermaster was startled by hearing the long drum roll, and rushing to his front porch saw the guardhouse on fire from top to bottom. It being impossible to save it, the fire ended it.

The next morning the provost marshal came to the depot quartermaster's office and said: "Well, the damned old thing caught fire last night and burned down. What is to be done now to get a new one?"

The quartermaster said, "You must write for authority to have a new one built."

Colonel Jennison at once wrote a letter to the Secretary of War. He cared very little about "military channels" and asked for authority to build a new guardhouse.

Colonel Hodges, the depot quartermaster, often wondered how the honorable Secretary of War received and acted upon the dispatches sent him direct without question, but he did. He always got on with Jennison in the nicest manner. Jennison frequently told Colonel Hodges about matters connected with his command, and kept him posted on the many plots and plans to get him relieved from the charge of the depot. Jennison had a way of finding out things that were remarkable, and he always found out correctly.

Oh, several prisoners had escaped; they would send out a party in the morning to search for the missing men, but that was not too important to Colonel Jennison. The important thing was that he would now get a new guardhouse, in fact, laborers were already cutting the blue limestone, quarried on the reservation.

But the Secret Committee was enraged that Ian had escaped and sent out trusted and loyal men to find him and kill him on sight, so they would be done with Ian, once and for all.

A good friar at Kickapoo Mission sheltered Ian and his companion fugitives for two days, while they regained their strength, and from him they got a gun and ammunition.

380

Jamie Bill had decided to travel with Ian and had brought her belongings to the mission, including the two colt revolvers and all the ammunition-making paraphernalia. Ian had obtained a revolver for Jamie and she was very good at the fast draw and accuracy. In fact, she was as good as Ian. She made a holster designed for an especially fast draw. She carried her heavy revolver handle to the front on her left hip and pulled with either left or right hand. She and Ian were the first fast-gun woman and man, which later became very popular with the western marshals.

At the edge of the county, they shot two deer. They passed through thirteen men lying in wait for them. Through mercy they escaped from them undiscovered. The Frenchman, a brave and enterprising man was much beloved by the Indians. The Choctaws were friendly, and kept the adventurers concealed for three days, while the soldiers with orders to shoot at sight scoured the woods about. On the fifth day out of Fort Leavenworth, south of Flint Hills of Kansas, Ian and Baredran noticed an approaching body of men, and finding them Indians made their guns ready for firing.

Two rode up to them; Baredran saluted them in the Cheyenne tongue. They were Kansas, and wished to join them. Baredran asked for Warratoria (the most peaceful and renowned of their chiefs) and was told he soon would arrive. Ian and Baredran were escorted to the Indian encampment, which was three hundred yards above the banks of the Washita River. When Warratoria came, Baredran knew his friendly disposition towards the whites. Shaking hands as old friends Warratoria's face wore a benign expression, and the slight furrows of age were so tempered as to give his countenance a cast of deep thought. His expansive brow, slightly receding, was worthy of a statesman. Baredran was filled with reverence for the old man. He spoke in short sentences only (so different from the fluent speech of most Indians, though many persons give them the character of being uncommunicative) as if conscious of the lasting impression he was making on his listeners.

The pyramidal lodges dotted the ground at irregular distances; before the large ones, the stainless shield and medicine bag with blue-enrolled pipe-stems were supported on the three whitened wands. Where, a short while before, lay a bare spot of turf, was now the site of eighty lodges, nearly three hundred human beings, and eleven hundred horses capering, rolling, and cropping the sweet bottom grass. The girls, from twelve years up to womanhood, waded in the river for fuel; some crossing, a few returning laden with sticks, others carrying water, and all laughing, talking, and splashing. Boys played their favorite game of arrows, or astride of ponies ran races over the smooth prairie. This commingled scene of comfort, youth and hilarity brought back to Ian the yearnings for a repetition of his experience of the Crow camps. Ian's whip welts and pain all but disappeared by now, but he didn't give the miracle much thought.

Early the next morning as Ian was washing at the river, Shenga Wassa rode out of the morning mists that hung over the river. She was as beautiful as Ian remembered her—straight, slender, lithe as a yearling doe.

As she dismounted her pony, she turned to Ian and said something in Indian and sign language. Ian could not understand but sensed what she was saying. Wide bracelets of copper encircled her arms, her skirt was laced and beaded with delicate dyed shells, the braids of her jet-black hair were bright with scarlet feathers of the tanager.

$$*\qquad*\qquad*$$

The village was a tribal gathering assembled on the Washita, at the mouth of Rainy Mountain Creek.

An Indian sacred ceremony of something called the Ghost Dance was to be held here. The dance ground was consecrated before the performance, one of the leaders going all about the place, sprinkling some kind of sacred powder over the ground and praying the while "A-HU HU HA' GEN' STI' TI BA' HU."

The dance began after sundown. The announcement was made by the criers, old men who assume the office apparently by tacit understanding, who go about the camp shouting in a loud voice to the people to prepare for the dance. The preliminary painting and dressing had commenced in the middle of the afternoon.

The painting of the dancers was done with the same ceremonial exactness of detail, each design being an inspiration from a trance vision. Usually the dancer adopts the particular style of painting which, while in the trance, he or she has seen worn by some departed relative. If they had not yet been in a trance, the design is suggested by a vision of one who does the painting. The painting consists of elaborate designs in red, yellow, green, and blue upon the face, with a red or yellow line along the parting of the hair. Suns, crescents, stars, crosses, and birds (crows) are the designs in most common use.

The crow (ho) is the sacred bird of the Ghost Dance, being revered as the messenger from the spirit world because its color is symbolic of death and the shadow land. The raven, which is practically a larger crow, and which lives in the mountains, but occasionally comes down onto the plains, is also held sacred and regarded as a bringer of omens by the prairie tribes. The crow is depicted on the shirts, leggings, and moccasins of the Ghost Dancers, and its feathers are worn on their heads.

The dancers in one camp had a crow, which it was claimed had the power of speech and prophetic utterance, and its hoarse inarticulate cries were interpreted as inspired messages from the spirit world. The eagle, the magpie, and the sage-hen are also sacred in the Ghost Dance, the eagle being held in veneration by Indians, while the magpie and the sage-hen were revered for their connection with the country of the messiah and the mythology of the tribe.

When all was ready, the leaders walked out to the dance place, and facing inward, joined hands so as to form a small circle. Then, without moving from their places they sang an opening song, according to a previous agreement, in a soft undertone. Having sung it through once they raised their voices to their full strength and repeat it, this time slowly circling around in the dance. The step is different from that of most other Indian dances, but very simple. The dancers move from right to left, following the course of the sun, advancing the left foot and following it with the right, hardly lifting the feet from the ground. All the songs are adapted to the simple measure of the dance step. As the song rises and swells, the people came singly and in groups from the teepees; one after another joined the circle until one hundred fifty or two hundred men, women, and children were in the dance. When the circle was small, each song was repeated through a number of circuits. When large, it was repeated only through one circuit, measured by the return of the leaders to the starting point. Each song was started in the same manner, first in an undertone while the singers stood still in their places, and then with full voice as they began to circle around. At intervals between the songs, more especially after the trances had begun, the dancers unclasped hands and sat down for a few minutes. At such times the leaders delivered short addresses or sermons, or related the recent trance experience of the dancer. In holding each other's hands the dancers usually intertwine their fingers instead of grasping the hand. Only an Indian could keep a blanket in place as they do under such circumstances. Old people hobbling along with sticks and little children hardly past the toddling period sometimes formed a part of the circle, the more vigorous dancers accommodating the movement to their weaknesses. Frequently a woman would be seen to join the circle with an infant upon her back and dance with the others, but should she show the least sign of approaching excitement watchful friends led her away that no harm would come to the child. Dogs were driven off from the neighborhood of the circle lest they should run against any of those who had fallen into a trance, and thus awaken them. The dancers themselves were careful not to disturb the trance subjects while their souls were in the spirit world. Full Indian dress was worn, with buckskin, paint, and feathers, but among the Sioux the women discarded the belts ornamented with disks of German silver, because the metal had come from the white man. Among the southern tribes, on the contrary, hats were sometimes worn in the dance, although this was not considered in strict accordance with the doctrine.

With most tribes the dance was performed around a pole planted in the center and variously decorated. On breaking the circle at the end of the dance the performers shook their blankets or shawls in the air, with the idea of driving away all evil influences.

As trance visions became frequent the subjects strove to imitate what they had seen in the spirit world.

In some instances, an immense drum, rattles, and other musical instruments were an important feature. Men and women took part, and the songs referred to the general subject of the crow and the messiah, and were set to a variety of dance steps and evolutions performed by the dances. As the leaders, who were chiefly young men and women and constantly studying new features, the crow dance was one of the most attractive ceremonies among the prairie tribes. Hypnotism and trances formed an essential feature of the Ghost Dance.

The most important feature of the Ghost Dance, and the secret of the trances, was hypnotism. It has been hastily assumed that hypnotic knowledge and ability belong only to an overripe civilization, such as that of India and ancient Egypt, or to the most modern period of scientific investigation. The fact is, however, that practical knowledge, if not understanding, of such things belongs to people who live near to nature, and many of the stories told by reliable travelers of the strange performances of Indian shamans can be explained only on this theory. Numerous references in the works of the early Jesuit missionaries, of the Puritan writers of New England and of English explorers farther to the south, indicted hypnotic ability no less than slight-of-hand dexterity formed part of the medicine man's equipment from the Saint Lawrence to the Gulf. It cannot be said that the Indian priests understood the phenomenon, for they ascribe it to a supernatural cause, but they know how to produce the effect.

There were numerous stories of wonderful things that occurred in the Ghost Dance—how people died, went to heaven and came back again, and how they talked with dead friends and brought back messages from the other world. Quite a number who had thus "died" were mentioned and their adventures in the spirit land were related with great particularity of detail. A number of women started to tremble violently and staggered away from the dancers, who opened the circle to let them pass. They fell to the ground unconscious and with great rigidity.

Sometimes before falling the hypnotized subject ran wildly around the circle or out over the prairie. In many instances the hypnotized person spun around for minutes at a time like a dervish, or whirled the arms with apparently impossible speed until the final fall.

The hypnotic subjects were unusually as strong and healthy as the average of their tribe. It seemed to be a question more of temperament than that of bodily condition or physique. Not every leader in the Ghost Dance was able to bring about the hypnotic sleep, but anyone could try who felt so inspired. Excepting the seven chosen ones who started the songs, there was no priesthood in the dance. Any man or woman who had been in a trance, and had thus derived inspiration from the other world was at liberty to go within the circle and endeavor to bring others to the trance.

The first woman may lie unconscious for ten or twenty minutes but no one went near to disturb her, as her soul was communing with the spirit world. At last consciousness gradually returned.

The doctrine and ceremony of the Ghost Dance found more adherents among the tribes than any similar Indian religious movement. The Ghost Dance became part of the tribal life.

384

It is still performed at infrequent intervals, although the feverish expectation of a few years ago has now settled down into something closely approaching the Christian hope of a reunion with departed friends in a happier world at some time in the unknown future.

After the business of the day was disposed of, and when the dusk of the evening came on, preparations for the dance began. The people gathered in large numbers to witness the performance, while in an adjacent area the band of performers assembled to array themselves in their costumes, and to paint and decorate their persons for the occasion. A keeper of the faith, in the meantime, occupied the attention of the people assembled, with a brief speech. A war-whoop announced the approach of the band, who, preceded by their leader, marched in single file to the beat of a drum into the dance area surrounded by campfires for light.

They grouped themselves within a circular area, standing thick together, when the singers commenced the war song, the drums beat time and the dancers proceeded. After a few moments the song ceased, so also the dance, the band walked around a common center to the beat of the drum at half time. Another song soon commenced, when the drums quickened their time, and the dance was resumed. In the middle of the song there was a change in the music, accompanied with a slight cessation of the dance, after it became more animated, until the song ended, and the band again walked to the beat of the drum.

Each tune or war song lasted about two minutes, the intervals between them being about the same. The drum beat time about twice a second, the voices of the singers keeping pace, thus making a rapid and strongly accented species of music.

Unlike the mode of dancing as an amusement among the whites on the toe of the foot, with rapid changes of position, the Indian method was chiefly upon the heel, with slow changes of position and rapid changes of gestures. The heel is raised and brought down with quickness and force of muscular strength, to keep time with the beat of the drum, making a resounding noise by the concussion, at the same time shaking the knee rattle, contributing materially to the pomp and show of the dance.

The striking, wild costumes of the performers, their activity and wild music, the rattle of the dance, made up a scene of uncommon interest.

Chapter 9

Kansas Ghost Woman

Plains Indian Life

The Indians use the word medicine to indicate the mysterious and unknown. God is the Great Mystery rather than the Great Spirit, as it is usually translated. The whites have no one word which can convey the meaning of "medicine" as used by the Indians. Sometimes it shadows forth holiness, mystery, spirits, luck, visions, dreams, prophecies, at other times the concealed and obscure forces of nature, which work for them as good or evil.

They attempt the cure of disease in many cases mainly by an appeal to the "unknown," and try to propitiate this power, as in the Sun Dance. They have "medicine men" who claim to have visions, to prophesy, to cure the sick by remedies known only to themselves, and which, they insist, were learned from the whisperings of some animal to them while they were asleep. If success crowns their efforts, their medicine was good. Defeat, suffering, and death are all the legitimate fruits of bad medicine. They live close to nature, and are impressed and awed by her wonders and mysteries. Anything that is beyond their comprehension, they call "medicine." Their faith in their medicine to secure their personal protection from physical harm, as well as to promote their general happiness, is simply marvelous.

Ian noticed during the following days that Indians were very fond of their children and treated them with the greatest respect and consideration as soon as they are able to understand anything. They very rarely whip them, and no children are happier than these little half-clad specimens of humanity.

Indian mothers nurse their children about as long as the child wants or desires this method of nourishment, sometimes the child is four or five years of age, and in the meantime another child may have sprung into existence. This practice accounts, in a measure, for the small number of children usually born to Indian women. Their babies do not cry as much as white babies, as they do not get what they want by simply crying for it. As a rule, they are healthier.

Reared as these people are, surrounded by so much that to them is incomprehensible, it is strange that the seeds of blind faith should find in their untutored minds a fertile soil to germinate, burst, bud, blossom, and yield a fruitful harvest of superstitious fancies.

The squaws cooking at most of the camp-fires, around which, lounging in indolence or seated cross-legged on the ground, the older braves smoking their pipes and discussing in low guttural tones the events of the day, while the young men woo their sweethearts in the shadows of the lodges, or stroll and stalk through the village in quest of such entertainment as the occasion afforded. Everywhere Ian was struck with the servitude to which the female was subjected. In her social world she was a veritable hewer of wood and drawer of water, and in her subdued looks, shrinking mien, and poor apparel, is read the story of toil, drudgery, and degradation. Neither in feature nor person can she compare favorable with her lord and master, for she is a striking example of that law of nature by which, of every created species, whether the human race or the fish of the sea, the male is made the model of beauty for its kind. Female beauty is undoubtedly the product of civilization, and the estimation in which woman is held is and will always be the best proof of its quality and the excellence of its institutions. Man has taken from her hands the rougher implements of labor, has clothed her in fine raiment, and bedecked her with jewels, has lavished upon her kindness and affection. She, all the while, like some wild flower that, transplanted to a more generous soil and softer atmosphere, grows each succeeding year in fragrance, delicacy of texture, and richness of tint, has gone on increasing in loveliness of feature and graces of person till, long ceasing to be but the mother of his children, she has become the ornament of his home and the object of his respectful adoration.

What a contrast is presented by the old, withered woman before the fire! As she kneels, supporting the upper part of her body on her left hand, and clutching with the long, bony, talon-like fingers of the right a stick, at the end of which is cooking a piece of meat for the husband behind her, there is much in her attitude, the hanging breasts, the expression of the eye, and the beak-like shape of the nose to fix one's faith in Darwinism. Can it be possible that the common ancestors of us all moved upon all fours, and that from such a root was evolved the beautiful flower of womanhood?

Indians are not only fond of, but think there is some charm in many of the sweet-smelling roots, herbs, and grasses, and frequently have tiny sacks filled with something of the kind tied to the hair or fastened to a string round the neck. It is wonderful how many sweet-smelling grasses they will find in a country where white men fail to find any.

Many of the Indians have separate lodges for the women at child-birth, and such attention as they may get is extended by the old women, though the medicine-men sometimes assist. The woman is usually put in a kneeling posture, the umbilical cord is wrapped around the finger of the attendant, left about six inches long, cut and a little coil is slipped off the finger and placed against the abdomen of the child, and fastened with a bandage, which goes around the body.

With the Shoshone and Bannack, medicine-men are not allowed to assist, and the woman sometimes goes away to the solitude of the brush or timber, and there alone passes through pains of childbirth, though it is customary for some of her women kinsfolk to go with her. Sometimes the absence is prolonged from four to six weeks. Frequently a little lodge is pitched adjacent to the large one, and used for this purpose. It is about as cheerless and uncomfortable as the one used during the menstrual periods.

With the Cheyenne, when a woman feels the pains of approaching childbirth, an old medicine man is sent for, and also an old woman. The man prepares the medicine, usually a liquid decoction made from herbs and roots, and the woman takes immediate charge of administering it, and assists in cutting the umbilical cord.

Sometimes when an unmarried woman has a child she kills it. If the child is raised, there is no prejudice against it, and it receives the same consideration as other children. The mother has a perfect right to kill the child; it is hers, she can throw it away if she wants to, and it is not considered a crime or even an offense to do so.

Delivery in childbirth was generally very easy. No special preparation seemed to be made, the woman continuing about her ordinary duties till the moment actually arrived. In traveling she simply fell out of the line, near water, if possible, and in the course of two or three hours resumed her place, carrying the infant on her back. If in the village, she retired to some secluded spot near a stream alone, as before. Sometimes, at the birth of the first child, the mother was attended by a woman acting as midwife; but the principal part of her service consisted in busily shaking a rattle—a gourd containing a handful of shot. After birth the infant was immediately washed, bandaged, and fastened to the baby board, where it remained most of the time for the first twelve or fifteen months of life. As soon thereafter as they could begin to walk they were loosened from the board and allowed more freedom.

The young men of the Plains Indians do most of their courting in a standing position. An Indian lover will stand and wait near the lodge where abides the object of his admiration until she appears, when he walks up alongside of her and throws his blanket round her. If she reciprocates the tender sentiment, they will then stand for hours, his blanket covering both their heads and closely wrapped round their bodies. Ian had seen as many as half a dozen young men waiting by the path which led down to the water near the camp, and one after another throw his blanket around a girl as she was going down to fill the water-vessel. If the girl liked to be held, she made some reply to the first tender greeting; if she expressed dislike to his advances, the man, by the law of courtship, must at once desist.

As a rule, the dress of an Indian discloses his tribe. Pawnee boys are allowed to go without any dress, other than such bits of clothing as they might pick up, till about six years old. Girls, after three years, were covered with a skirt. The dress of both sexes was quite simple. That of the men consisted of a girdle about the loins, to which was attached the breechcloth, and from which suspends the buckskin leggings covering the thighs and legs. On the feet were moccasins. In winter the body was wrapped in a buffalo robe or blanket; in summer a light blanket or a thinly dressed skin was worn. But in warm weather they were often without either of these. Moccasins and breechcloth alone were considered indispensable; the former, because without them traveling on the prairie was impossible, the latter from considerations of modesty.

The dress of the woman consisted of moccasins, leggings, tightly laced above the knee and reaching to the ankles, a skirt covering from the waist to below the knee, and a loose waist or jacket suspended from the shoulders by straps. The arms were bare, except when covered by the robe or blanket. The garments of the women, other than the moccasins, were made, if the wearer could afford it, of cloth, otherwise of some kind of skin dressed thin and soft. The making and keeping in repair of moccasins was a ceaseless task. The last thing each day for the women was to look over the moccasins and see that each member of the family was supplied for the next day.

The full-dress toilet of a young brave was a matter of serious and protracted study. His garments might be few, but the decoration of his person was a slow and apparently not unpleasing process. With his paints mixed in a dish before him, and the fragment of a mirror in his left hand, he would sit for hours trying the effect of various shadings and combinations on his face and person, wiping off and reapplying the pigment with seemingly inexhaustible patience when the effect was not satisfactory. No devotee of fashion ever labored more diligently to produce striking results in dress than some of the braves.

The Indians have, without much doubt, been called red men on account of the universal custom of painting their faces and bodies, and for this purpose they used fine clays containing different oxides of iron. Since the establishment of their trading stores they purchase these ochres to a great extent, but usually have some of the similar character, which they have themselves found. Some advantages are claimed in the use of these paints as a protection against the rigors of climate, both the icy winters of the North and the torrid summers of the South, but is also used because of their superstitions in regard to it; that it is conducive to good luck, and that its original use was in obedience to the direct command of God. In applying it, an Indian puts a little ochre and grease in the palm of the hand, and then the palms are rubbed together to thoroughly mix and obtain the proper consistency; this is used for the "flat tints," and the strippings and fancy touches are put on afterwards. Some Indians take more kindly to a particular color, imagining that it gives better luck than another. When the paint is rubbed on the face the eyes are closed, so that the lids may have their full share, and it may be for this reason that some tribes pull out the eyelashes, as these, by holding an extra allowance, might cause irritation of the eyes. The skin of many Indians' faces, especially that of the nose, often becomes full of little holes, caused, no doubt, by the paints used. The squaws ordinarily use red for the cheeks, and a bright vermilion does add to their beauty, or rather, in a way hides their ugliness. A perpetual atmosphere of smoke, grease, and dirt, with such accessories as long and fatiguing rides, severe work, and rough food, is not conducive to female beauty. War paint, so called is only an excessive use of any color. After returning from an expedition most tribes paint the faces black of those who have been out, that being the color for rejoicing. Frequently these ochres are rubbed over the uppers of moccasins and on clothing, and at their dances horseshoe-marks are painted on the body or on the clothing, and the pony is also decorated in this way.

When painting for war they use many stripes and rings of different colors, but on return-ing only black-colored paint is used. For courting, they claim that they paint themselves as handsomely as possible.

Michelle, chief of the Pend d' Oreilles, said to Ian, "I do not know exactly why we use paint. When I was young, many kinds were used—black, yellow, red, etc. The priests tried to stop its use; I asked them if it was any worse to paint the face than it was to paint the church, and if the church would last longer by being painted, why would not an Indian? I think God made all things to be used—the paints for the Indians; and this is why we use all kinds of color on our face and hair when we go to war."

The different colors are produced in different ways by different tribes. The Sioux use bull-berries, a shrub something like sumac; moss on pine-trees for yellow paint. Generally speak-ing, black means joy; white, mourning; red, beauty; and an excessive use of any of these or other colors, excitement.

Paint was an important part of the toilet, particularly with men. Young women some-times used vermilion quite freely on the face, but with men in full costume paint was indis-pensable. There was no special guide other than individual fancy in its use for personal ornamentation. Sometimes the entire person was bedaubed, but more usually only certain parts, especially the face and breast. When painting the whole body, frequently the nails, or the notched edge of a sort of scraper, were drawn over the body, producing a peculiar barred appearance. Sometimes the figure of certain animals, as the totem of the family to which the person belonged, was conspicuously painted upon the body. In the religious and ceremonial dances various kinds of fantastic and grotesque designs were exhibited. After killing an enemy the lower part of the face might be painted black. The paints used were vermilion, or, if this was not procurable, a kind of clay was burned till it assumed a bright red hue, and then pulverized. Red ochre was also obtained in certain localities on their hunting grounds. Sometimes a white clay was also used. A yellow paint was gathered from the flowers of a species of solidago. All paints, when used on the person, were prepared with buffalo-tallow; when for ornamenting robes, they were mixed with water.

To the Indian, eating was an act that claimed something of deferential respect. The question of what he should eat was perhaps as potent as any other that influenced him dur-ing life. It demanded his serious thought, provoked his ingenuity, taxed his energy, and

The Squaws' Work

largely controlled his movements during the entire year. When traveling they had but one meal a day, at the close of the day's march, but when at home they cooked and ate as often as hunger prompted. The ability and readiness to eat whenever occasion offered was in their estimation an exponent of health, and if an invalid failed to take food at all, hope of recovery was immediately relinquished.

Their food was in the main, course but wholesome. The staple articles of daily fare were buffalo-meat and corn. The flesh of smaller game, and when on the hunting-grounds that of the buffalo also, was eaten fresh, but for the greater part of the year they had only the dried flesh of the buffalo. Dried meat was frequently eaten raw, a mouthful of lean and of fat alternately, to facilitate chewing and swallowing, and in case of extingency fresh meat was so taken, but usually both were cooked. The more common way of preparing was by boiling; hence one of the most important articles of household furniture was a large vessel for this purpose. Prior to coming in contact with the whites they used rude pottery of their own manufacture. Their favorite method was to boil the meat alone, or with corn and beans, till the whole was reduced to a pulpy mass and eat it as a thick soup with spoons. If time or appetite did not permit this, it was simply boiled. Fresh meat and sometimes dried meat if sufficient fat adhered, was also broiled by being held in suitable pieces over coals. Another usual way of preparing the meat was to cover large pieces in a bed of coals till sufficiently cooked. This method was in high repute, as it preserved most of the native juices in the meat and rendered it especially palatable.

Dressing
The Skins

There were a number of wild plants, the root or fruits of which afforded a partial subsistence at certain seasons. The poorer people were sometimes obliged to live almost entirely
upon food of this kind. Among the edible roots were the wild potato, wild turnip, pomme
blanche, ground-beans, cucumber-root, a sort of artichoke, and some others. A species of
mushroom growing freely in some localities on the prairies was sometimes gathered in con-

siderable quantities. The umbels of the large milkweed were cut when in bloom, with the tender extremities of the stalks, and boiled as a relish. When traveling in the summer they often picked and ate, as a preventive against thirst, the fruit of the ground plum. Various wild fruits, as strawberries, plums, cherries (especially sand-cherry), and grapes were gathered in their season and eaten fresh, or dried for preservation. In the preserved state they were much used in flavoring other dishes.

Breakfast was the only regular meal with Indians, or rather the only meal taken at a regular hour each day. Meals were prepared at other times whenever they were hungry, and whoever may be present when it was ready was asked to partake.

The Shoshone found a shrub on the mountains which, when boiled in water, made a drink possessing the characteristics of tea, the same in taste and effect. The entire shrub was used. This was found at an altitude of about eight thousand feet, and near by it the Indians also found a bulbous root, which made excellent soup.

The Indians, like Hebrews, are very rigid in refusing to touch pork in any form, but a fatted dog constituted a most delicious repast. The Blackfoot, Crow, Flathead, Nez Perce, Shoshone, Bannack and Ute do not eat dog, but the Sioux, Cheyenne, Arapaho, Kiowa, Apache, and others prize them highly, and for a special feast dog is considered better than anything else. The meat combines the flavor of bear and pork, and is wonderfully nutritious. One can undergo a great deal of hard work especially hard riding, after a hearty meal of dog, without inconvenience, and could go longer without special desire or need for food than after a meal of almost any other substance.

In former times the moccasins of the different tribes were made so differently that for an Indian to see the moccasin was to know the tribe; and even now, its shape, construction, or garnishment, it is the strongest characteristic mark of each tribe, so far as any clothing or covering is concerned.

The moccasin is the last thing an Indian gives up as he travels towards civilization, and the first thing adopted by the whites who, as hunters, trappers, traders, or "squaw-men," mix, mingle, and live with the Indians. In hunting, it possesses many advantages over a boot or shoe, and in dry weather is comfortable and serviceable. But is utterly demoralized by moisture, so that an Indian in crossing a stream, going through the dewy grass, or in the mud and melting snow of spring, takes off his moccasins, and goes with bare feet.

The Comanche moccasin is composed of sole cut (from rawhide) as near the shape of the bottom of the foot as practicable, tapering rapidly from its greatest width at the little toe to a point at the big toe.

The upper part is made from buckskin, cut generally in one piece, having but one seam at the heel. Although sometimes each side is cut separately, with a seam in the middle on top of the foot. On each side of the seam is a row of beadwork, and on the outside of the foot, near the beadwork, there is attached a row of short fringe, composed of buckskin strings, ornamented with pieces of German silver.

They are generally cut low at the sides, with turndown flaps about two inches wide and finished with beadwork around the edges. Some of them are made with a narrow piece set in the front part, forked at the upper end, and finished with beadwork to match the flaps or pieces turned down at the sides. The upper part when finished is sewn fast to the rawhide sole with sinews, and finished with a row of beadwork around and near the seam.

In the winter season the moccasins are made of buffalo-hide or the skins of fur bearing animals, the hair being turned inwards. The Indians never wear stockings, but the leggings are an excellent substitute when one has fur shoes to cover the feet.

Each Indian tribe had their moccasins of different shape, so that an expert frontiersman could readily tell to what tribe Indians belonged by seeing their tracks. This is true in a limited sense only. The Chippewa track could be told from the Sioux, but the Sioux could not be distinguished from the Cheyenne or Arapaho.

Among many tribes the old people are treated at times with indifference and neglect. The old women particularly lead a hard and cruel life, and are little, if any, better than beasts of burden, and seem to take it as matter of course that they should labor constantly. The hard work, constant exposure, and reckless disregard of any precaution to protect them from the inclemencies of the weather cause them all to grow prematurely old and withered, seamed, wrinkled, wretched. They usually look forward to death with feelings more of pleasure than of pain. Ian heard many of the men express regret that they had not been killed in battle while still young.

As age approaches they abandon the warpath, give up horse stealing, and seek what little comfort they can get in eating and smoking. In some rare cases Indians reach a very great age, but as a rule the average is not equal to that of the white race.

Ian saw an Arapaho woman who was one hundred and fourteen, and a Red River half-breed woman who was one hundred and thirteen. The latter, when Ian saw her, was building a fire with which to cook her supper, and though wrinkled and bent was yet quite active and strong. The comforts and respect which cluster about the gray hairs of an honorable old age in civilization are rarely found paralleled in primitive culture. Never having accumulated sufficient property to maintain them, or having given away what they had, they become a burden upon the charity of their kinsfolk, and, as a rule, death is a most welcome visitation, relieving them from the most wretched condition of hunter life.

Whiskey has been and is called "black water," "white-man's water," "crazy-water," and "fire-water," the latter by the Sac and Fox, Shawnee, Shoshone, Nez Perce, and the Eastern tribes, generally.

Indians seem to have a natural fondness for whiskey, and the Hudson's Bay and American Fur Companies traded it to them in former years in unlimited quantities, working incalculable damage to the different tribes. To those Indians who have come in close contact with civilization it has been a greater curse than either war or disease, and perhaps one might say both. They never mix water with it—the stronger it is the better; and they drink it as though it were some pure and mild cordial, softened by care and age. Some Indians had perfect control of their appetites, but the vast majority did not. Many wars, much unnecessary bloodshed, and great wretchedness to them have grown out of their fondness for liquor, and the rascality of white traders in selling the article to them never thinking, or at least not caring for the consequences. We have certainly in some cases made them barbaric, and then cursed and killed them for being such.

Scattered all along the frontier the same sad spectacle is presented. First robes, skins, and beadwork are sold, then the ponies; then the women are debauched and diseased, and thefts and murders are committed, either to secure whiskey, or as the result of drinking it. None of the northern tribes had ever manufactured anything at all like it, but they claim that the gall of the buffalo produces intoxication.

Indians drink as they smoke, seated in a circle on the ground; the bottle or vessel is passed round and round until empty.

Among the established customs of the aborigines of America, that of dancing appears to be the most prominent and firmly fixed in their social usages. These people are not alone in a custom of this kind. It is an institution of great antiquity among some of the more enlightened nations of the Old World, especially among the Jews, and there is a singular coincidence in the purposes of dancing among this latter people and the aborigines of America.

When Jephthah returned from his conquest over the Ammonites, "his daughter came out to meet him with timbrels and with dances." Judges 11:34. When the men of Benjamin surprised the daughters of Shiloh, the latter were dancing at "a feast of the Lord." Judges 21:19-21. When David returned after the slaughter of Goliath, the Israelite women met him with singing and dancing. 1 Samuel 18:6.

Lucretius ascribes the invention of instrumental music, or mode of producing "sweet sounds" by artificial means, to the whistling of the winds in the hollow reeds. Another writer supposes the invention to have arisen from the sounds produced by the hammers of Tubal Cain.

The American Indian and the native African are naturally musicians. Vocal music, or the practice of singing, after the manner of every race, is supposed to be as equally old as man's existence, or at least with his power of speech. In regard to vocal music, in the art of singing, the same coincidence occurs, between the Indian and the races of the Old World, that is found in various other respects. The singing of psalms, as a devotional manifestation, was a very ancient custom among the Jew, and so the like custom of singing on devotional occasions and for the purposes of praises and fidelity to the Great Spirit, prevailed among the American Indian tribes. In all their religious feasts and ceremonies they addressed their prayers and praises to superior beings in songs.

The Indian had, also, various instruments of music. One was something like a flute, which was made of two pieces of cedar, half round, then hollowed out quite thin with four holes in it, and then glued together, so as to form a perfect tube. The music was produced by blowing at the end. Whether the plan of this instrument was borrowed from the whites is not known; but, among many tribes, it was known to be improved from the example of other like instruments amongst the whites.

The Indians had, also, a kind of drum, much like the tambourine. It was constructed from a skin drawn over a keg or hollow vessel. This they used on various occasions, as an instrument for keeping time with vocal music, or for marking time without other music.

They had also an instrument of music constructed of a gourd-shell, called by the Algonquins she-she-quoy, wherein beans were placed to produce a rattling sound when shaken. Sometimes this instrument was made of birch bark. They also had an instrument used for the like purpose, but differently constructed, called a rattle, composed of the hoofs of the deer or some other animal. They were constructed by taking a large number of these hoofs, through which they bored a small hole in the narrow end of each, and tied then to a short stick. The rattling was produced by jerking them suddenly up and down.

Mr. Catlin thus described the Indian drum, "Their drums were made in a very rude manner, often times with a mere piece of rawhide stretched over a hoop, very much in the shape of a tambourine; and at other times are made in the form of a keg, with a head of rawhide at each end; on these they beat with a drum-stick, which oftentimes itself is a rattle, the bulb or head of it being made of rawhide filled with pebbles. In other instances the stick has, at its end, a little hoop covered with buckskin, to soften the sound, with which they beat on the drum with great violence, as their chief and heel inspiring sound for all dances, and also as an accompaniment for their numerous and never-ending songs of amusement, of thanksgiving and medicine."

Catlin also speaks of another instrument of music among the Indians, which he refers to as the mystery whistle, concerning which he says, "The mystery whistle is another instrument of their invention, and very ingeniously made, the sound being produced on a principle entirely different from that of any wind instrument known in civilized invention, and the notes produced on it, by the sleight of trick of an Indian boy, is so simple and successful a manner as to baffle entirely all civilized ingenuity, even when it is seen being played." An Indian boy would stand and blow his notes on this repeatedly, for hundreds of white men who might be lookers on, not one of whom could make the least noise on it, even by practicing with it for hours. When Ian first saw this curious exhibition, he was charmed with the peculiar sweetness of its harmonic sounds, and completely perplexed as to the mode in which the sound was produced, even though it was repeatedly played immediately before his eyes and handed to him for vain amusing endeavors. The sounds of this little simple toy are liquid and sweet beyond description.

Indians make whistles out of the wing-bones of eagles, hawks, geese, and some other birds, the eagle's wing being the most highly prized. These large bones from the wings are cut off at the end, and a small orifice made near the end like a boy's whistle, producing, when skillfully played upon, a sound exactly like that made by the bird itself, usually, as in the case of the turkey, like the plaintive note of the turkey.

They wear them attached to a string, around the neck, and use them for various purposes. In dances, in courting a girl, making a signal for a meeting, in battle, particularly in making a charge; and when small parties are scouting, to give the alarm whether their game be of human family or the brute creation; but whenever used these sounds convey a meaning, easily and quickly understood, from a love-note to the shrill cry of war. With small scouting-parties they are particularly useful in giving a warning.

It is extremely difficult, almost impossible, to describe an Indian dance so that a person who has never seen one can form any correct idea of it. To better understand the matter, however it is necessary to clear one's mind of the thoughts of the sensuous pleasures of our modern dance, and try to contemplate the subject as it is handed down to us through the history of the ancient Spartans, who, it seems, like our Indians, made the act of dancing an expression of their emotions, relating mostly to religion and war.

The violent physical exertion and mental excitement, with such accessories, in the scalp—and other dances, as blackened faces, painted bodies, full war costumes, weird singing, "tum-tums" of the drums, gory scalp-locks held high in the air on slender poles, the wind playing with the straight black locks, perhaps at night, their wild faces and bodily contortions thrown into a bold relief by the flickering light of the tongues of flame from a huge fire, all combine to throw the dancers into a state of excitement bordering on frenzy.

There is a great similarity among all the tribes in their dancing, and their motives and objects are also the same. The Ghost Dance is the most strongly of a religious character, not unlike Holy Communion rituals of the Americans religions.

Generally they form a circle. The music consists of drums and rattles, and from two to four singing-girls, who are located just outside the group, and keep time to the drums in a shrill, nasal, metallic chant. The heels of the dancers are raised from the ground, the weight of the body resting on the balls of the feet. The body is raised, lowered, contorted, sometimes resting on one foot only, and every motion keeping time to the "tum" and singing. Gaudily decked out, half-naked, and gorgeously painted, they make a fantastic picture. In most of their dances they first sit down in a circle, and get up at short intervals to participate in the dancing.

Some of the different dances are distinguished by the songs for each, some by the dress, and a few of them by the steps, as in the *Scalp Dance*, they move around and around in a circle by short sideways hops. As a rule, the different dances take their names from the names of the different soldier bands.

The Birthold Indians have a special dance for the women, called the White-Buffalo Dance. They use masks of buffalo-heads for the dance and wolf--skins for the Wolf Dance. The Cheyennes have a special war dance when all the soldiers are wanted for war-purposes. A large fire is made in the center of the camp, where the warriors assemble, mounted and dismounted, but wearing all their war-toggery, weapons, etc. Men, women, and children join in the dance, and when the excitement has become intense, has reached its greatest height, the headmen go among the dancers and pick out twelve of the best and bravest soldiers, and place two lines of each on opposite sides of the fire. Then the headman tell them they must be vigilant and brave, and their people will, after their return, sing of their brave deeds, but should they be killed on the battle-field, which there is no more glorious death, they will be great chiefs in the hereafter.

The conical-shaped wigwams used when camps are moved every day or so, and which can be hastily put up by making use of three poles, placed together very much on the principle of stacking of arms for infantry; other poles are then placed equidistant on the ground, their tops resting on the tops of the three poles first placed in position. The number of poles and their length depends on the size of the wigwam required to accommodate the family. The poles are placed on the ground from twenty to twenty-four inches apart. This style of wigwam is altogether used in the winter time—its conical shape and birch-bark covering reflecting heat of a moderate fire built in the center. The outside of the wigwam is banked with snow to the height of one and one-half feet, preventing a draft or the cold from coming in at the bottom. The doorway is generally well closed with a blanket or two. A crosspiece is tied on to two poles opposite each other, upon which a piece of green wood, notched at both ends, was forked to hang kettles and pots when cooking; one end of this piece of green wood was forked on to the crosspiece, the other holding the bail of the kettle.

The material next to the ground in these wigwams, and upon which matting is placed, is boughs of balsam, fir, or cedar. Hay is also used. The covering of these wigwams is always of birch bark. Being in a country where timber is abundant, the poles are not removed on moving camp. Cooking is generally done outside, except in rainy weather. When mosquitoes are unusually numerous, smudges are built in the wigwams; but they are generally remarkably free of these pests.

In placing birch-bark on wigwams of any description, it is laid on as siding would be on a house, sufficient lap being allowed to prevent drifting in of snow or leaking in rainy weather. The birch-bark covering for wigwams is cut from ten to twelve feet long and about four wide. The bark is gathered in June. A tree a foot in diameter will produce bark a yard wide. In removing bark from trees, it is done according to the use for which it is needed; consequently for wigwams it is removed in lengths of four feet. All the rough parts on the outside are removed, and it is then sewed with a certain root of a tree found in damp places, or the inner bark of basswood. After the strips are sewed together, slender cedar or pine sticks are fastened at each end, to which strings are attached to tie the bark in place, or tie up the bark when the bark is rolled up. Red-elm and ash-bark are also used for teepees.

The material used in making bows depend on the locality. On the almost treeless prairies nearly every species of wood found is used. Ian was with a party of Indians, and it was desirable that they should have bows. There seemed to be no suitable material, but one of them found an old, broken ash wagon-bow lying along their path. It was taken into camp, greased, warmed by the campfire, trimmed with their hunting-knives, slowly, carefully, and skillfully bent into shape, and quite a shapely and serviceable article was the result. Among the Plains Indians, bows are made from oak, hickory, ash, elm, cedar, Osage-orange, one or two varieties of willows, plum, cherry, bull-cherry, and other bushes, and from the horns of the mountain-sheep and elk.

The bow—the weapon so long in use among the different Indian tribes of this continent—so typical of Indian life, and the mere mention of which always associates our ideas with the red man—its manufacture is the work of no little labor. Although an Indian may have a gun, he is seldom without his long-bow and quiver well-filled with arrows. The gun may get out of order, and he cannot mend it; the ammunition may become wet, and there is an end of hunting; but the faithful bow is always in order, and its swift arrows ready to fly in wet as well as dry weather. Thus reasons the Indian, and so keeps his bow to fall back upon in case of accident. The Indian boy's first lesson in life is to shoot with a bow. He is furnished with a small bow and "beewaks" or blunt arrows, so he will hurt nobody, and with these he shoots at marks. By and by, when he has acquired some skill in handling his weapon, he is given arrow-points and with these he shoots birds, squirrels and small animals. As he grows older he receives the long bow, and at last the strong-bow. These strong-bows are powerful weapons, and some are so stiff that a white man could not bend them scarce four inches, while an Indian would, with apparent ease, draw them to the arrow's head. A shaft fired from one of these bows will go through the body of a buffalo, and the arrow-head have been found so firmly imbedded in the thighbones of a man that no force could extract them. The parents take great pride in teaching young Indians to shoot, and the development of the muscles and strength of their arms is watched with much interest. A stout arm, ornamented with knots of muscles, is a great honor to an Indian and no one but those who can handle the strong-bows are deemed fit for war.

In traveling, the bow is carried in a sheath attached to the arrow-quiver, and the whole is slung to the back by a belt of elk or buckskin, which passes diagonally across the breast,

Plains Indian Life

and is fastened to the ends of the quiver. The quiver and bow-sheath are generally made of the skin of an ox or some wild animal, and is tanned with the hair on. The quiver is ornamented with tassels, fringe of buckskin, and the belt across the breast is painted or worked with beads.

To shoot with the bow properly, it must be held firmly in three fingers of the left hand (this description intended for a right-handed man). The arrow is fixed on the bow-string with the thumb and forefinger of the right hand, and the other three fingers are used to pull the string. The shaft of the arrow lays between the thumb and forefinger of the left hand, which rests over the grasp of the bow. To shoot, the bow is turned slightly, so one end is higher than the other, and the arrow is then launched.

One day while hunting, Ian's Indian companion rode alongside a large buffalo cow going at such speed that it required the best exertions of his very fleet pony to overtake and keep up with her. Leaning forward on his pony, and drawing an arrow to its head, he sent it entirely through the buffalo.

The Sioux claim that the Cheyenne first had arrows given them by the Great Spirit—two for hunting, which were black, and two for war, which were red. The Shoshone admitted that before they met the whites they used poisoned arrowheads, and for this purpose they were dipped in a compound made of ants pounded to a powder and mixed with the spleen of an animal. The mixture was then placed in the sun and allowed to partially decay. The result was such a deadly poison that if the arrow broke the skin in touching a person it was sure to produce death. They also said the Plains Indians had never used them. The Blackfoot use goose—and eagle-feathers as arrow-guides, while most tribes prefer the feathers of smaller birds.

There is some difference in the feathering, some nations employing three feathers tied round the shaft at equal distances with fine tendons. The Tonto-Apaches have their arrows winged with four feathers, while some of the Comanche use only two. All have some distinguishing mark in their manner of winging, painting, or carving on their arrows.

Much labor was also expended in the construction of arrows. These shafts were made from sprouts of dogwood of a year's growth. After cutting, the bark was removed and the rods were rubbed between two grooved stones, held firmly together in one hand, till reduced to a proper size and smoothness. The head, made of hoop iron, was then inserted in one end of the shaft and bound in position with sinew. The back end of the shaft was then furnished with a triple row of feathers, attached by means of glue and sinew, and the end notched to fit the bow string. With a small chisel-like instrument three slight grooves or channels were cut along the shaft between the head and the feathers, and the arrow was complete. Various reasons were assigned for this channeling. Some claim that it caused the arrow to adhere more firmly in the wound; others were simply designed to facilitate the flow

401

of blood. The manufacture of arrows, as of bows, was a slow and irksome process. Three or four were the limit of a day's work, even after the rough material was already at hand. So exact were they in making them that not only were the arrows of different tribes readily distinguishable, but even individuals could recognize their own arrows when thrown together with those of others of the same band. Disputes sometimes arose, after the slaughter of a herd of buffalo, as to whose some particular carcass rightfully was. If the arrow still remained in the body, the question was easily decided by drawing it out and examining the make of it. Some Indians made two kinds of arrows, one for hunting and another for war. In the war arrow the head was so fastened that when an attempt was made to draw the shaft from the wound the head was detached and remained in the body of the victim. The Pawnee never used such. When once he had possessed himself of a good bow and a supply of arrows, the Pawnee was as solicitous in the care of them as a hunter would be of a choice rifle. Great pains were taken that the bow and arrows should not become by any chance wet, and much time was spent in handling them that the bow should not lose its spring and the arrows should not warp. The average length of the bow was four feet, and the arrows twenty-six inches.

Ponies are hobbled by means of a short thong or rope tied to the front fetlock and the hoof, fettering the legs, the length of the rope between the legs being usually about one foot. This prevents the animals from straying too far, places an obstacle in the way of a stampede, and causes a delay in that pleasant amusement known as "running off the stock," which tribes at war practice on each other so constantly.

The young men of a war party or horse-stealing expedition travel so as to leave no trail. They wind through the dry beds of streams, ravines, and low places, thus keeping concealed day and night. They frequently, and especially in the winter, go on foot and, with wonderful craft and cunning, creep up to within a short distance of the camp or herd of ponies they are after. Then watching their opportunity, some of their number, with knives in hand, crawl around among the animals, cut the hobbles and lariats, and then with a shout make a dash at the herd, accomplishing the stampede.

It is rarely the case that after attaining such success the marauders are overtaken, as from the stolen herd they can select plenty of relays.

It has been often asserted and quite generally believed, that Indian warfare is but simple assassination and murder. Viewed from the white man's standpoint, it does partake strongly of the characteristics that we associate with these crimes and certainly success with Indians is due mainly to the constant practice of stealth and crafty vigilance. Regarding it, however, from the standpoint of the Indian, which is that the object to be attained in war is to inflict the greatest possible amount of damage upon the enemy with the least possible risk to themselves.

The original conquest of their tribal domain and the maintenance of their prestige and position as tribes depended entirely on their prowess; and where existence depended upon the possession of warlike qualities, it is no wonder that they were fostered. War was the burden of all oratory and song, and the highest ambition of an Indian is to gain distinction as a warrior, especially as this ambition was stimulated by the knowledge that success in war would be rewarded by the highest honors and greatest powers in peace. Nearly every tradition of the tribe was richly colored with deeds of valor and daring; and the murder of a helpless woman and the stealing of a few ponies took rank not from the act, but from the "blow" inflicted on the enemy. Not only was the hope of reward held out to those who survived the dangers of the "warpath," but those killed in battle were (according to their beliefs) received with great demonstrations of joy, and made chief in the life beyond death. Indians possess as much courage as any people and when young, sometimes not only scorn the fear of, but readily court death. Age brings wisdom and recognition of the fact that more is accomplished by craft and cunning than by reckless daring. The cheap bravado which has led so many to imagine them cowardly was the result of their training to constantly remember their maxim of war, "Greatest amount of damage to the enemy with the least amount to one's self."

Again, people in the hunter-state have no pension lists, and the death of the head of the family left that family to the mercy and charity of their people. In barbarism as in civilization, mercy and charity are at times both blind and deaf to the sufferings of humanity. This, taken in connection with the fact that their wars were, as a rule, waged for glory and spoils alone, bred in them a courage capable of great things for a sudden dash, but left them without the fiber of true bravery in tenacity of purpose and capacity of prolonged endurance under a severe strain.

Their war tactics are the stealthy approach and sudden onslaught when, if the surprise and numbers sweep everything before them, a heroic display of courage is sometimes made; but a determined or unexpected resistance, and they scatter and retire.

The practice of the custom of trusting everything to a single effort undoubtedly has had its effect in their not harassing an enemy after their effort was made; but at any rate, it is a fact that they are woefully lacking in enterprise in this way. It is a common custom among all the northern tribes for war-parties to start out and go hundreds of miles through an enemy's country on foot, these are usually horse-stealing expeditions. Their equipment consists of the ordinary dress of an Indian, a lariat wound diagonally over the right shoulder and around the breast, a waist-belt full of cartridges and a breech-loading rifle of modern pattern, and an extra pair of moccasins at the waist-belt. These small parties on foot leave no trail, are less liable to detection through being seen, can cross any kind of country, have no care of animals at night, and for many other reasons find it to their advantage to go in this way.

The return of a successful war party was an occasion of most extravagant demonstration. Men, women, and children united in welcoming the victorious braves. The following night a Scalp Dance was celebrated, in which each one had opportunity to magnify his exploits. Prisoners, unless women and children, were rarely taken, and hence scenes of delight in inflicting torture were unusual. If, on the contrary, the party had been unfortunate and suffered loss, its return was quiet, and gave rise to dejection and unrestrained lamentation on the part of the friends of the lost.

Many of the most daring adventures were made by braves who, unaccompanied, penetrated the enemy's country and watched opportunity to inflict some signal stroke of surprise. This was a favorite mode of warfare, and sometimes scalps were brought back as the trophies of one exploit, and secured for the adventurers a life-long notoriety. Trips of this character might be extended hundreds of miles and require weeks of absence in their accomplishment.

In all of the Indian wars it has seemed necessary to use Indian allies, and these have usually been permitted to perpetrate all kinds of atrocities, so that we have not taught the Indians by example any more civilized warfare. These isolated cases, filled with more horrors than pen can picture, are to Indian warfare generally what the actions of an infuriated mob are to civilized war.

In relating an engagement, a chief in the most friendly and pleasing way explained to Ian that they "killed the women and children so that made them (the enemy) afraid." He spoke of the killings as he would have spoken of the destruction of any other property of the enemy; he looked at it merely in the light of a blow to be inflicted.

In covering long distances, such as with war parties, a fast, "scuffling" walk or slow trot are the usual gaits, making about five miles an hour, and a halt made at noon, the animals unsaddled, and turned out to graze, or picketed close by the little fire for cooking. There are several species of sage, and in some sections the bush grows sufficiently large to make very good fuel. The trident and a smaller white species are used for making a tea, which is administered in fevers, and used in fumigating. There is also one species which, by rubbing between the palms of the hands, emits a pungent smell and is said to be excellent for producing wakefulness. It is used by Indian scouts in passing through an enemy's country where sleeplessness is the price of success.

Indians are bred up to trailing, scouting, and horse-stealing, until their natural and instinctive powers are wonderfully increased. The object of scouting is to see and not be seen.

The Americans who settled in the Southwestern Territories never saw any great evil in slavery. The trapper or trader who desired a squaw, purchased one, and the settler who wanted servants very commonly purchased them.

In the north, slavery prevailed everywhere, and was abetted and encouraged by the Hudson's Bay Company, owned by John Jacob Astor. The price of a slave varied from five to fifteen blankets. Women were valued higher than men in the north, also. If a slave died within six months of the purchase, the seller returned one-half the purchase money. Many instances occurred where a man sold his own child. The Indian slaves were generally employed to cut wood, hunt and fish for the families of the men employed by the Hudson's Bay Company. Each man of the trapping parties had from two to three slaves, who assisted to hunt and take care of the horses and camp. They thereby saved the Company the expense of employing at least double the number of men that would otherwise be required on these excursions. Slavery was, in fact, more extensive in Oregon than anywhere else in the West, and more similar to the African and Oriental systems.

All through the Rocky Mountains, this system of human slavery extended, and it had obtained such a root that it was very hard to extirpate. In Colorado it was brought to a summary end, so far as white slaveholders were concerned through the efforts of the government.

The Indian Agent visited all owners of Indian slaves and informed them that they must be released. There were captives who knew not their own parents, nor could speak their mother tongue.

The female captives were nearly always subjected to indignities both among the Indians and the whites, and among the whites they were frequently made public prostitutes for the gain of their owners. The Apache women were noted for their chastity. The fate to which their captive wives and daughters was doomed often caused poignant sorrow among them.

Indians place great confidence in their dreams and visions. Not only are the dreams of a natural and healthy sleep prized, but artificial means are constantly resorted to secure these visions, the sweat-bath, solitude and prolonged fasting and mutilation. Some Indians had only their dreams for their "medicine" or charm to protect them from evil.

The Indians are essentially a religious people, or more correctly, a superstitious people. They believe that everything in the world has its "spiritual essence" made manifest in the forces and laws of nature, something akin to the superstitious feeling which many of the white race still have in regard to the influence exercised on our fortunes by a horse-shoe nailed over the door. One who knew nothing of Christian religious view might be led into error by seeing a Catholic or Moslem solemnly counting his beads, and reverently bending the knees and bowing in worship before a cross. And so the sight of an Indian piously whispering his prayer to a painted stone, or devoutly pointing his pipe and humbly making his petition to the white skull of a buffalo instead of the Holy Communion ritual might lead one to form erroneous opinions.

It is as difficult to obtain a definite and clear understanding of the Indian's view of the "spiritual essence" propitiated by their worship as it is to define our own ideas of God.

What a calamity to the religious nature of man were we all compelled to find one import to words, and to live and die with one interpretation. The creator of man, having made him to be of broad and varying taste, did not forget to make equally the realm where he must pass his life. An unlimited mind demands an unlimited material form and an unlimited world taking place within an individual's mind. The wings of an eagle bespeak for it the open air.

It, therefore, comes to pass that all cannot and need not think of the foundation of religion, the God, with the same thoughts. He may appear before one in the likeness of man, His raiment glistening in excessive light, His hair white as snow, with the wisdom and dignity of eternal years. To another He may seem as broad as all space, as omnipresent as the sweet air, as invisible as music. To another He may seem within all life, the soul of all that lives, while others may say in humility, and who by searching can find out God! To another He may be embodied in the loving, caring, tender Goddess that has been your lifelong wife mate which has mothered and cared for your dear children and cared for you ignoring her own need. In its simplest terms, religions, including Indian religion, is basically thoughts and beliefs that make life worth living and meaningful. Therefore, it is natural that they should believe in the direct action of superior powers, and, consequently, their system is the natural result of their belief. Their vision-seeking, through steam-baths, fasting, and self-mutilation, is the only means of ascertaining the will and wishes of these mysterious powers, as well as to gain their assistance. Morality has no place in their worship, and hence we find that the morals of the Indians are not sensible controlled or regulated by any religious views they may have. Crime is not a violation of the laws of any of their mysteries or Gods, but an infraction of the material laws that they find necessary to their physical existence as a people or tribe. The sweet promises of future rewards, or the dire threats of future punishments, are totally and entirely eliminated, except so far as virtue in bravery is concerned. Those killed in battle go to the hereafter by the starry trail in the heavens (Milky Way) and are met in that "far-off land" with songs and feasts and made chiefs.

In addition to the general mysteries which all Indians hold in common superstitious awe, individuals frequently have a personal mystery, which exercises a direct influence upon all the more important events of their everyday life, and from whom information is received by means of visions or inspirations, in the shape of warnings of danger or advice, which will secure success. This personal God may always appear in the same form, and indirectly foreshadow coming events, or may cause the thunder-bird to flash forth an omen; an owl in the stilly darkness of the night to solemnly hoot an admonition, the toes of moccasins thrown in the air to fall pointing in a certain direction, so that the flight of a bird or the direction of the wind has determined the course and result of many war expeditions. ~

And so it is, the Indian is locked into his religion by his timeframe of simple and singular life style, so is the American in their beliefs, both cannot assimilate a more comprehensive religion.

Far down beneath the surface of the sea a kind of life goes on which is totally different from that with which we are familiar on the upper surface of the globe. It is inhabited by creatures who have never seen the light of the sun nor felt the touch of the air. Their conditions of life are at such complete variance with those in which we live that they could not, in their wildest imagination, conceive of air, and light, and dry land, and all the rest of it. Occasionally some inhabitant from the upper world may momentarily touch their realm of existence on a deep-sea diving expedition. Such a visitor might startle the denizens of the deep but would leave them in all their former blank ignorance as to what life on the higher level could mean.

There is nothing illogical in supposing that there is still another level of existence above that in which we live and equally unknown to us. It might be a spiritual world peopled with life forms of a very different nature, living in conditions which are beyond our comprehension, and which we could not understand if it were described to us because we have so little basis of comparison.

There are other orders of creation, quite distinct from us in the human sphere. There are spiritual beings, possessed of different properties from ours, and serving different purposes in God's universe. Is there any reason for thinking that creation ceased with man, that there are not other life forms of created beings of which we are capable of knowing little or nothing?

It seems a startling assertion, but it was, Ian thought, true, that there are no people who pray more than Indians. The Great Spirit, or force to which they appeal is in their thinking as omnipotent as all the forces of nature; as indefinite and intangible as all space and both superstition and custom keep always in their minds.

*   *   *

One early morning Two Bears rode into the village very excited. He stopped in front of Ian's and Shenga's teepees, shouting and calling the tribe together. As Ian came up to him, Two Bears knowing Ian could not understand their language yet, gave him the sign language. He brought his hands, palms towards and close to the sides of his head, index fingers partially curved, others and thumbs closed; raised his hands slightly and carried them a little to front. Ian understood the sign used for buffalo.

The large geographical area over which these animals ranged, their countless numbers, their importance and necessity to wild Indians, all led Ian to make close investigation into the uses made of every part of the animal.

It is no exaggeration to say that thousands of buffalo had been slaughtered by white hunters and emigrants merely for the pleasure of killing these animals to gratify that innate craving for destruction of life which all human beings seem to possess, and at times for the tongues, which are a special delicacy. This wasteful and wicked course had in many

An Indian Buffalo Hunt

instances so irritated the Indians that they wrought revenge by outbreaks and by killing innocent emigrants.

The Indians universally believe that the buffalo were made by the Creator especially for their use, and certainly when they are plentiful they can get along quite comfortably with very little else. When one considers the uses made by them of the buffalo, both at the present day and prior to the advent of the whites, one is not surprised at the claim and belief.

Of the skin, they make robes, lodges, lariats, ropes, trunks or par-fleche sacks, saddles, saddle-covers, shields, frames for war bonnets, gloves, moccasins, leggings, shirts, hats, gun-covers, whips, quivers, knife-scabbards, cradles, saddle-bags, saddle-blankets, decorations for saddles, beds, bridles, boats, a kind of sled for hauling the meat over the snow, and from the thick part of the skin of the neck a glue is made by boiling and skimming.

Ropes and lariats are made from the scalp lock, or long tuft on the forehead (some of this hair is a foot in length and straight), and pillows from the hair.

From the horns, spoons, cups, dishes, powder horns, arrowheads, bows, by splitting the longer horns, and the tips are fastened to slender poles, which are used in certain games.

From the fascia (thin tendinous covering which supports the muscles, and by the interpreters called sinew), found under the shoulder-blades, the abdominal fascia, the two strips on each side over the hump, and the strip on each side of back they make thread, bow-strings, rope for softening robes by rubbing, fasten feather-guides to arrows, and stiffen and make bows more elastic.

From the thick ligament of the upper portion of the nape of the neck is made a pipe. An instrument used to straighten arrows is fashioned from the center bone of the hump by cutting a hole in it, and from some of the smaller bones arrow-heads are made, and an instrument for "flushing," or scraping the meat from hides. From shoulder blades, axes, knives, arrow-points, instruments for dressing robes and smoothing down porcupine-work. The trachea is used as a sack for paints, etc. The rough papillae of the tongue for hair brushes.

The brain, liver, and fat for tanning skins. Instruments for shaping bows and small dog sleds from ribs.

From the paunch, water pipes or sacks, in which meat and blood are sometimes cooked by boiling with heated stones, the latter being dropped into the sacks.

From the thigh bones, traps similar to our deadfalls. From the tail, knife-scabbards, handles to war-clubs, and medicine-rattles. The utter, dried, becomes stiff and hard, and is used for dishes, tobacco-bags, medicine-rattles, etc.. The pericardium (the membranous sac enclosing the heart) for sacks.

The amniotic fluid, in which the fetus floats is used by them to quench thirst when water cannot be obtained, and is also generally used to cook or boil the fetus in, the latter being specially prized as a dainty and delicate morsel of food. The marrow is eaten both raw and cooked, being roasted in the larger bones by laying them on the coals.

The teeth are used for necklaces, and are also put in medicine rattles.

They consider the contents of the paunch an excellent remedy for skin diseases, and in case of frost-bit if the afflicted member is thrust into the paunch of a freshly-killed buffalo, relief obtains without evil after effects. Very little buffalo fat is sometimes mixed with the tobacco and red-willow bark for smoking. The liver is often eaten raw, and while still warm with the animal heat, the gall-juice being sprinkled over it as a sauce. The kidneys are eaten both raw and cooked. The meat, fat, and most of the intestines are staple articles of food, and are kept for months by being simply dried in the sun; the hump is considered particularly fine for drying. The contents of the paunch furnish food for ponies, and the liquid in same, cleared by the gall, is prized for drinking, is cool and tasteless; devoid of any unpleasant taste.

The "buffalo chips" are used as fuel, and before the days of flint and steel and matches, were particularly good when dry for making a fire by the friction of wood. These "chips" pounded fine and kept dry, are used to keep the small children warm, they being partially buried in the powdered material. The value of these chips can scarcely be appreciated by those who have not suffered for the want of fuel on the treeless prairies.

The tanned buffalo skin without the hair furnishes the best material for teepees.

Before the introduction of guns many devices for killing buffalo were resorted to. They were lured over precipices by a decoy, such as an Indian disguised as a buffalo, who, when the herd was stampeded, would run toward a precipice, the herd following. Natural enclosures were strengthened by fallen timbers, and animals driven into them.

An Indian camp during the cutting up of the meat after a buffalo hunt was a scene of the most joyous activity. When a grand hunt was contemplated, preparations were made for days and weeks ahead. Couriers were sent out to collect the neighboring bands at a common rendezvous, medicine men began their prayers and ceremonies to attract the herd, the buffalo songs were sung, and finally when all was ready the confederated bands or sometimes the whole tribe—men, women, children, horses, dogs, and travois—moved out into the buffalo grounds. Here the immense camp of hundreds of teepees was set up, more ceremonies were performed and the mounted warriors rode out in a body to surround and slaughter the herd. The women followed close after them to strip the hides from the fresh carcasses and cut out the choice portion of the meat and tallow and bring it into camp. Here the meat was cut into thin strips and hung upon frames of horizontal poles to dry, while the tallow was stripped off in flakes. In the dry prairie atmosphere one day was usually sufficient to cure the meat, without the aid of salt or smoke. When thus dried it was known as "jerked beef." While the meat is fresh, for the first day or two the camp was a scene of constant feasting, the juicy steaks or the sweet ribs being kept broiling over the coals in one teepee or another until far into the night. It was the harvest home of the prairie tribes. As soon as the meat was dry the teepees were taken down and packed into the wagons along with the meat and one family after another started for home until in a short time the great camp was a thing of the past.

The jerked beef or venison was commonly prepared for eating by being boiled until reasonably tender. In eating, the Indian takes a strip thus cooked, dips one end into a soup made of dissolving some salt in warm water, takes the portion thus salted between his teeth, and saws off enough for a mouthful with a knife held in his other hand. Between mouthfuls he takes bits from a strip of dried tallow placed in the dish with the meat.

For pemmican the jerked beef or other meat was toasted over a fire until crisp and was then pounded into a hash with a stone hammer. In the old times a hole was dug in the ground and a buffalo hide was staked over so as to form a skin dish, into which the meat was thrown to be pounded. The hide was that from the neck of the buffalo, the toughest part of the skin, the same used for shields, and the only part which would stand the wear and tear of the hammers. In the meantime the marrow bones were split up and boiled in water until all the grease and oil came to the top, when it was skimmed off and poured over the pounded beef. As soon as the mixture cooled, it was served up into skin bags (not the ordinary painted parfleche cases) and laid away until needed. It was sometimes buried or otherwise cached. Pemmican thus prepared would keep indefinitely. When prepared for immediate use, it was usually sweetened with sugar, mesquite pods or some wild fruit mixed and beaten up with it in the pounding. It was extremely nourishing, and has a very agree-able taste to one accustomed to it. On the march it was to the prairie Indian what parched corn was to the hunter of the timber tribes, and has been found so valuable as a condensed nutriment that it was extensively used by arctic travelers and explorers. The name comes from the Cree language, and indicates something mixed with grease or fat.

In the process of dressing and tanning buffalo robes, the fresh skins are first stretched very taut on the ground by means of pins driven through the edges, or the hides are lashed to the lodge-poles until thoroughly dry. The fatty matter and a portion of the hide are removed in their shavings by means of some sharp instrument, usually a piece of steel fas-tened into a piece of horn. A thin coating of the tanning material, which was a mixture of about one part of brains to two parts of well-cooked liver, with a little fat added, was then spread over the inner surface of the hide, which is then rolled up and allowed to remain two or three days, when the tanning material was washed off. Sometimes the hide was dipped three separate times in brains and liver water. A small rope made of sinew was tied to a tree or stake at an angle with the ground at about forty-five degrees, and the robe rubbed over it until it is dry and soft. In tanning deer, antelope skins, beaver, etc., the skin was soaked in water, and the hair scraped off; after which they were treated the same as the buffalo-hides and then smoked. The process of tanning and dressing skins and robes is very labori-ous and slow.

For teepees, buffalo and elk-skins were considered the best, the hair, of course being removed before tanning. Buffalo hides used for this purpose, and the soles of moccasins and parfleches, are usually from animals which were killed when the fur was worthless.

The Ghost Dance Religion

*D*ancing is an instinctive mode of muscular expression of feeling, in man, woman, and many animals, especially birds.

In the social life of the human race it has played a part which touches every activity of the individual and society. Dancing may be described as "play" in its absolute form.

Rhythm is inseparable from its movements, as it is from any bodily function, and therefore belongs to it without saying.

It is in the middle stages of culture that dancing is seen at its highest development. Here it is much more, and also less, than a "poetry of motion." It is rather life and religion expressed in muscular movement. The human instinct of play is closely connected with the human love of excitement. The dance satisfies both, and its rhythmical character also makes it suitable for the expression of the most solemn and controlled emotions.

In its simplest terms, dancing is the voluntary application of the rhythmical principle, when excitement is induced an abnormally rapid oxidation of brain tissue, to the physical exertion by which the overcharged brain is relieved.

Muscular movement, of which the dance is the most complex expression, is a method of auto-intoxication of the very greatest potency. A girl who has danced for a quarter of an hour is in the same condition as if she had drank champagne.

Primitive dancing of the Indians embraced all movements of the limbs and body expressive of joy or grief, all pantomimic representations of incidents in the lives of the dancers, all performances in which movements of the body were employed to excite the passions of hatred or love, pity or revenge, or to arouse the warlike instincts, and all ceremonies in which such movements express homage or worship, or are used as religions exercises. The sensation of motion is a pleasure-giving sensation.

On the physiological side, dancing develops energy and releases it.

Ian had seen a young fellow's muscles quiver from head to foot and his jaws tremble, without any apparent ability of his part to control them, until foaming at the mouth, and with his eyes rolling, he fell in a spasm upon the ground.

The dance is a translative engine of emotional energy, the mysticism found in it is a replica of the movements of the stars in their courses, when the morning stars danced together. The dance is a natural method of celebrating anything, and of expression individual or social emotions or ideas. In the imitative dances of the simpler cultures, there are combined worship, drama, exercise, excitement, pastime, play, and art.

The range of movements in dancing is very considerable connecting on the one side with marching steps, "parades," and on the other with the gestures of the hands used in conversation. In modern dancing of the white man as pastime, movement is practically confined to the legs, but in earlier stages the rest of the body and especially the hands were employed. Movements of the trunk are conspicuous in ancient and primitive dancing.

The powerful neuro-muscular and emotional influence, leading to auto-intoxication, is the key to both to the popularity of dancing in itself and to its employment for special purposes such as the production of cerebral excitement, vertigo, and various epileptic results, in the case of medicine men, shamans, prophets, oracle-givers, and visionaries, even in modern culture. The medicine men, by dancing and singing for several hours, and by incessant smoking, works himself up into a state of ecstasy. The Hebrew prophets often availed themselves of this method of inducing inspiration and also of the Shakers in more recent times. The primary aim of the Ghost Dance seemed to be the development of physical excitement, and consequential courage, in the dancers, and secondarily, as magical ideas attach themselves, the aim of overcoming the enemy is added.

The Ghost Dancers thought themselves as invincible spirits, thus the name was derived. Many of the Ghost Dancers wore "ghost shirts." They were made of coarse white cloth sewn with sinew. The "ghost shirt" was worn by all adherents of the doctrine—men, women, and children alike. During the dance it was worn as an outside garment, but was said to be worn at other times under the ordinary dress. The shape, fringing, and feather adornment were practically the same in every case.

The beginnings of the Ghost Dance religion is lost in antiquity. In the story of ghost dancing, the Ogalala Sioux heard that the Son of God was truly on earth in the west from their country. The first people who knew about the Messiah to be on earth were the Shoshoni and Arapaho. So four or five of them visited the place where the Son of God was said to be. They said the Messiah was there at the place, but he was there to help the Indians and not the whites.

The people said that the Messiah would come at a place in the woods where the place was prepared for him. When they went to the place a smoke descended from heaven to the place where he was to come. When the smoke disappeared, there was a man of about forty, which was the Son of God.

The man said, "My grandchildren! I am glad you have come far away to see your relatives. These are your people who have come back from your country."

"My father commanded me to visit the Indians on a purpose. I have come to the white people first, but they not good. They killed me, and you can see the marks of my wounds on my feet, my hands, and on my back (showing his scars)."

The Messiah said, "I will shorten your journey when you feel tired of the long ways, if you call upon me." This we did when we were tired. The night came upon us, we stopped at a place, and we called upon the Messiah to help us, because we were tired of the long journey. We went to sleep and in the morning we found ourselves at a great distance from where we stopped.

The Son of God said, "When you get home, you make dance. When you dance four days and in night one day. That is all to tell, I am in to you. Be a good behave always. It will find a satisfaction in your life. You will receive good words again from me some time."

Chasing Hawk, who had died not long ago, was there with Juses. A son of Good Thunder, who was one of the party, had died in war long ago. He was there and his father saw him.

The Christ talked to them in their respective tongues. They related later that you could see this Juses in your sleep anytime you wanted after you had seen him and shaken hands with him once. Through him you could go to heaven and meet your friends. Since Good Thunder's return, he saw him often in his sleep.

Good Thunder told his people, "Do not tell the white people about this, Juses is now upon the earth, he just like cloud. Everybody is alive again."

The Ghost Dance was at once inaugurated among the Shoshoni and northern Arapaho. Reports of wonderful things beyond the mountains were constantly coming to the northern prairie tribes, and the excitement grew.

The Messiah doctrine gained many converts among the Comanche, and others living on the Little Washita.

The Ghost Dance was brought to the Pawnee, Ponca, Oto, Missouri, Kansa, Iowa, Osage, and other tribes in the Oklahoma Indian Territory by delegates from the Arapaho and Cheyenne in the west.

Many started dancing in confident expectation of the speedy coming of the Messiah. The Osage gave but little heed to the story perhaps from the fact that, as they were the wealthiest tribe in the country, they felt no such urgent need of a redeemer as their less fortunate brethren. The Sac, Fox, Kickapoo, and Potawatomi engaged in the dance only to a limited extent, for the reason that a number of the natives of these tribes, particularly the Potawatomi, were under Catholic influences.

The Ghost Dance doctrine spread to the Caddo, Wichita, Kichai, Delaware, and Kiowa.

At the tribal gathering, the Ghost Dance was held with Ian and Shenga Wassa in attendance. Shenga consecrated seven men and women as leaders of the dance and teachers of the doctrine by giving to each one a sacred feather was to be worn in the dance as the badge of priesthood. Until the Ghost Dance came to the prairie tribes, their women had never before been raised to such dignity as to be allowed to wear feathers in their hair.

After "giving the feather" to the leaders thus chosen, they were taught the songs and ritual of the dance. At first the songs were all in the Arapaho language, but after the trances began to be frequent, the other tribes composed songs of their own.

Among the leaders was Mo'ki, "Little Woman." On account of her frequent trances and consequent leadership in the Cheyenne Ghost Dance, she had assumed the title of the Crow Woman (the woman messenger from the spirit world).

Mo'ki was a young Cheyenne woman married to a young Arapaho, Grant Left-Hand, about 30 years of age, the son of Nawat, the principle chief of the southern Arapaho.

Although Grant had several years of English education, he was a firm believer in the doctrine and the dance. He was the principle organizer and leader of the Crow Dance in his own tribe, while his wife was as prominent in the Ghost Dance among the Cheyenne and had composed a series of a dozen or more songs descriptive of her various visits to the other world.

Her first child had died soon after birth, and the young mother was sadly affected by the death. Afterwards a boy was born to them, and became the idol of his parents, especially the father. He grew up into a bright and active little fellow, but when about four years of age was suddenly seized with a spasm in the night and died in a few minutes, almost before his father could reach his bed. This second loss brought deep sorrow to them both, and the mother brooded over it so that there was serious fear for her own life. Then came the Ghost Dance and the new doctrine of a reunion with departed friends. The mother went to the dance, fell into a trance, met her children as in life, and played with her little boy. On awaking and returning home, she told her husband. He could hardly believe it at first, but it required but little persuasion to induce him to attend the next Ghost Dance with her because, as he said, "I want to see my little boy."

He himself fell into a trance, saw his children, and rode with his little boy on the horse behind him over the green prairies of the spirit land. From that time both became devoted adherents and leaders of the Ghost Dance. Their trances became frequent, and every dance was welcomed as another opportunity of reunion with departed friends.

The young man was deeply affected as he spoke of his love for his children, the sudden death of the little boy, and their second meeting in the other world. As his wife sat by his side looking up into Ian's face and listening intently to every word, although she understood but little English, it could not be doubted that their faith in the reality of the vision was real and earnest. Every Indian parent who has lost a child, every child who has lost a parent, and every young man and woman who has lost a brother, sister, or friend affirms a similar reason for belief in the Ghost Dance.

The dancing of the Amerinds (Indians) is everywhere much alike, and is generally performed in a circle. It has been described as a heel dance, and with some tribes is apparently that because they seem to strike the ground only with the heel, but it is usually a toe-and-heel step, the toe first touching and then the heel being brought down with more or less force. When rapidly done, the separate touching of the toe is hardly noticeable. The movement of the circle is commonly from left and right, and during this progress various contortions are gone through with, more or less violently according to the intensity of the occasion.

Nearly 600 to 800 Indians were in the dance circle at one time. Nothing unusual occurred for several hours until the dancers had gradually worked themselves up to a high state of excitement, when Shenga Wassa stepped into the circle, and going up close in front of a young Arapaho woman, she began to make hypnotic passes before her face with the eagle feather. In a few seconds she became rigid and fell to the ground unconscious. Shenga then turned her attention to another and another, and the same thing happened to each in turn until nearly a hundred were stretched out on the ground at once. In the trances some lay thus for a long time, and others recovered sooner, but none were disturbed, as Shenga told the dancers that these were now beholding happy visions of the spirit world.

When next they would come together those who had been in the trance related their experiences in the other world, how they had met and talked with their departed friends and joined in their old-time amusements. Many of them embodied their visions in songs, which were sung that night and afterward in the dance, and from that time the Ghost Dance was naturalized in the south and developed rapidly along new lines. Each succeeding dance resulted in other visions and new songs, and from time to time other hypnotists arose, until almost every camp had its own.

Another Ghost Dance was held on the South Canadian River, about two miles below the agency at Darlington, Oklahoma Territory. Around 3,000 Indians were present, including nearly all of the Arapaho and Cheyenne, with a number of Caddo, Wichita, Kiowa, and others.

Before going into the dance the men, or at least the leaders, fasted for twenty-four hours, and then at sunrise entered the sweat house for the religious rite of purification preliminary to painting themselves for the dance. The sweat-house is a small circular framework of willow branches driven into the ground, bent over, and brought together at the top. This is done in such a way that when covered with blankets or buffalo robes, the structure forms a diminutive round-top teepee just high enough to enable several persons to sit or to stand in a stooping posture inside. The doorway faces the east, as is the rule in Indian structures, and at the distance of a few feet in front of the doorway is a small mound of earth, on which was placed a buffalo skull, with the head turned as if looking into the lodge. The earth of which the mound is formed was taken from a hole dug in the center of the lodge. On the outside near the sweat-house, there was frequently a tall sacrifice pole, from the top of which are hung strips of bright-colored cloth, packages of tobacco, or other offerings to the deity invoked by the devotee on any particular occasion.

The sweat bath was in frequent use, both as a religious rite of purification and as a hygienic treatment. Like everything else in Indian life, even the sanitary application was attended with much detail of religious ceremony. Fresh bundles of the fragrant wild sage were strewn upon the ground inside of the sweat-house, and a fire was kindled outside a short distance away. In this fire, stones were heated by the medicine men, and when all was ready the patient or devotee, stripped to the breech cloth, entered the sweat house. The stones were then handed in to him by the priests by means of two forked sticks, cut especially for the purpose, and with two other forked sticks he would put the stones into the hole dug in the center of the lodge. Water was then passed in to him, which he poured over the hot stones until the whole interior was filled with steam; the blankets were pulled tight to close every opening, and he sat in this aboriginal Turkish bath until his naked body was dripping with perspiration. During this time the doctors outside were doing their part in the way of praying to the gods and keeping up the supply of hot stones and water until in their estimation he had been sufficiently purified, physically or morally, when he emerged and resumed his clothing, sometimes first checking the perspiration and inducing a reaction by a plunge into the neighboring stream. The sweat bath in one form or another was common to almost every tribe in the United States, but as an accompaniment to the Ghost Dance it seemed to have been used only by the Sioux. It may have been used in this connection among the Shoshoni or northern Cheyenne, but was not among any of the tribes of the southern plains. The Ghost Dance sweat-house of the Sioux was frequently made sufficiently large to accommodate a considerable number of persons standing inside at the same time.

After the sweating ceremony the dancer was painted by the medicine men who acted as leaders. The design and color varied with the individual, being frequently determined by a previous trance vision of the subject, but circles, crescents, and crosses, representing respectively the sun, the moon, and the morning star, were always favorite figures upon forehead, face, and cheeks. As this was not a naked dance, the rest of the body was not usually painted. After the painting the dancer was robed in the sacred ghost shirt. This also was painted with symbolic figures, among which were usually represented sun, moon, or stars, the eagle, magpie, crow, or sage-hen, all sacred to the Ghost Dance. In connection with the painting the face and body were rubbed with the sweet-smelling vernal grass (Hierochloe), used for this purpose by many of the prairie tribes, and sometimes also burned as incense in their sacred ceremonies or carried as a perfume in small pouches attached to the clothing.

The painting occupied most of the morning, so that it was about noon before the participants formed the circle for the dance. Among the Sioux, unlike the southern and western tribes generally, a small tree was planted in the center of the circle, with an American flag (in later years) or colored streamers floating from the top. Around the base of this tree sat the priests.

At the beginning the performers, men and women, sat on the ground in a large circle around the tree. A plaintive chant was then sung, after which a vessel of some sacred food was passed around the circle until everyone had partaken. When, at a signal by the priests, the dancers rose to their feet, joined hands and began to chant the opening song and move slowly around the circle from right to left. The rest of the performance, with its frenzies, trances and recitals of visions, was the same as with the southern tribes.

As previously mentioned, about the year 1800 an epidemic of religious frenzy known as the Kentucky Revival, broke out in Kentucky and Tennessee, chiefly among the Methodists and Baptists, with accompaniments that far surpassed the wildest excesses of the Ghost Dance.

In a few days preparations were made for a great dance near Walker Lake with all the delegates from thirty-four different tribes and hundreds of Indians in attendance, they danced two nights in anticipation that the Messiah herself would lead the ceremony.

The dance place was a circular piece of ground a hundred feet in diameter, enclosed by a fence of poles and bushes, and surrounded by high mountain walls of granite, which reflected the light from half a dozen fires blazing within the circle. The dancers, to the number of two hundred, clad in white robes with fancy trimmings, their faces and hair painted white in various decorative designs, moved slowly around in a circle, keeping time with a wild chant, while two hundred more stood or crouched around the fires, awaiting their turn to participate. The dancers faced toward the center, each holding the hands of the ones next to them and joining in the chant in unison. The dust issued in clouds from beneath their feet, and with the dust and exertion together the performers were soon exhausted and dropped out, when others took their places. After each circuit they rested a few minutes and then started around again. At each circuit a different chant was sung, and thus the dance continued until midnight, when, with a loud clapping of hands, it ended, and the people separated and went to their homes. Throughout the performance two or three chiefs of medicine-men were constantly going about on the outside of the circle to preserve order and reprimand any merriment, one of them explaining to the visitors that, as this was a religious ceremony, due solemnity must be observed.

At the end of the two days, on the third morning, hundreds of people gathered at the place.

Just before sundown, Shenga Wassa, the Messiah, spoke to the great many Indians gathered, saying, "Hear what the Great Spirit has told me to tell you. Put off entirely the customs which you have adopted since the white people came among us." After a few more words, the dancing commenced. Two hours later, Shenga was hot from the dancing so that her cheeks glowed red and her breath came fast as she moved along the moonlit path to the river, glancing over her shoulder now and then at Ian, as if inviting him to join her. Near the riverbank, she waited for Ian to catch up to her.

She was a very exciting woman—hot and with cheeks flushed from the dance. Ian opened his handsome blue eyes wide and looked at her. She was slight and delicate. She could never conquer the world by brute force, being barely five feet six inches in height, and weighing scarcely one hundred pounds.

She was no flirt. She appeared as if she could not waste her life to the lengthy stages of acceptable lovemaking by the so-called civilized society. Her passions were more like a wild animal—bold, definite and forceful.

As Ian approached, Shenga grasped his shoulders firmly and pulled him onto her as she sank to the ground in a passion of vehement emotion. Although decorous and self-poised, she let her animal instincts, impassioned language, and gestures of willingness hold full sway for the moment.

And it came to pass that Shenga Wassa and Ian Douglass fell in love and became husband and wife.

Journey to Sacred Mountain

A number of weeks later, Shenga Wassa said she would like to winter at a sacred place, the Holy Mountain according to the Blackfoot. The next day Shenga and Ian departed the village alone, accompanied only by two packhorses.

The day was beautiful, the sky clear and cloudless, the air fresh and balmy. On one side of them was the river, on the other a vast extended prairie, not a tree in sight, or a moving being save themselves. It was the stillness and solitude of nature. They traveled twenty miles, the next day sixteen, and on the third day, eighteen.

On the fourth day the country, at this period of their march, began to assume a different character. They had been traveling through a level and fertile valley, terminated by hills alternating from high to low, with a sufficient quantity of wood for fuel.

The elements of the scene now were an unbounded prairie, a broad river with innumerable herds of buffalo grazing upon its banks, and occasionally a solitary tree standing in bold relief against a clear blue sky. These elements, combined with the skill of nature's artist formed one of the finest landscapes Ian had ever seen. The horses were in fine order; the weather also fine.

The buffalo surrounded them in large herds, making the prairie almost black by their immense numbers. They also saw great numbers of antelopes and some deer. The soil was of coarse, dry sand or gravel, the grass thick and dry. No timber; they were obliged to make use of buffalo dung in cooking. This section of country was what was called neutral ground, and extended from the forks of the Platte almost to the foot of the mountains. It will not admit of the permanent residence of any Indians, and is only frequented by the war parties of different nations.

The Arapaho and Cheyenne sometimes moved into this country for a short time during the summer to hunt buffalo.

The next morning they saw a large drove of wild horses. The weather was remarkably fine, as many are in the Kansa Country, the air clear and pure, with a fresh breeze from the mountains.

The next few days they traveled twenty miles, then twenty-two, then twenty, then twenty in the direction of south, 60 degrees west. The general face of the country was more broken and irregular in its appearance than heretofore. They passed a long high range of hills on the opposite side of the river, containing a considerable quantity of rock. The valley became more narrow and terminated by sand hills, which gave to the country a barren appearance. Prickly pear and wild sage, plants that indicate bare soil, began to abound. They crossed dry creeks, some of them of considerable size. Most of these creeks contained water near the mouth; but before it reached the Platte, it was all absorbed by the soil, which at this place was very sandy.

The next day they crossed a serpentine creek of considerable size, entered upon a high prairie, and came upon an old deserted Indian camp, which Shenga said had been lately occupied by the Arapaho. The poles of the medicine lodge were still standing, and some of the emblems of their worship, such as buffalo heads, painted arrow, etc. Towards night, after they had encamped, the clouds that had been lowering around the western horizon cleared away, and discovered to them a beautiful bird's eye view of the Rocky Mountains. The sight was hailed with joy. The two lovers saw the end of their journey very near.

The mountains resembled white conical clouds lying along the edge of the horizon. The rays of a setting sun upon their snow-clad summits gave a beautiful and splendid appearance.

After a long ride over the prairie, there was nothing more appetizing, than to rest under the cottonwoods at sunset and hear the sizzle of broiled buffalo meat on the red coals, and have the aroma of coffee borne to you on the breeze that would lull you to sleep if you were not so hungry.

Shenga looked as if both the appetite and the wild living agreed with her.

In their looks, they were gaining a tinge of wildness. The meal in the evening was the event of the day. Sometimes eaten on a large flat stone if any were handy and again on the grass, where the knives and salt would lose themselves in the tall spears.

At midday there was often but a hasty lunch; breakfast was simply a preparation for travel; but in the evening they were prepared for rest and the enjoyment of a hearty meal. And until darkness fell, both would bathe in the river naked, washing away the dust of the trail.

Shenga looked very feminine as she bathed; slender, and brown from the tan of the winds; the unruly, fluffy hair clustering around her face and caressing her neck was womanly in every curve.

Around her bronze throat was usually a necklace of bear claws. And in the dusk of the evening, in the low, glowing light of the fire, Shenga would sing an Indian ballad or a love-song in a sweet, fresh voice.

Shenga was the dearest creature Ian had ever met or ever expected to meet this side of heaven, only Louisa was on an equal to her.

Shenga loved with all her heart, laughed like a gentle spring wind, her voice was like soft church bells, tingling in the breeze.

Lying close they talked quietly. In a short time, Ian could not resist her. He pressed her lovely head backwards, and his lips met hers.

*   *   *

The following day the country was uneven, with sand-hills in the background. They passed the mouth of the Cache de la Poudre, a large stream emptying into the Platte on the opposite side, with timber on its banks. The buffalo were still numerous.

At times when Shenga was out of sight of Ian on the trail, she was located by that boyish habit she had of echoing the songs of many of the birds, learning their notes, and imitating them so well as to bring many a delayed answer from the woods.

The river at this point was clearer, narrower, and more rapid, and the water much colder. There were immense herds of buffalo in every direction.

As they approached the mountains the country began to assume a more rough and broken appearance; timber more abundant, with several sorts of wild fruit, such as plums, cherries, and gooseberries. They passed several creeks that were dry; some of them skirted with timber. One of them the traders usually ascended in going from the Platte to the Arkansas. The distance from the Platte to the Arkansas was about ninety to one hundred miles, and this was considered the nearest and most accessible point between them.

After about five miles the next day, they came to a small valley near the mountains, then made a detour to the left, and took a direction parallel to the mountains. Leaving the Platte at this point, and commencing across to the Arkansas, which was near the point where the Platte issued out of the mountains, it took its rise in a valley some distance back and before it reached the foot of the last range it was a considerable stream, running with the rapidity of a mountain torrent; the water very cold and clear as crystal.

The valley, which they ascended was terminated on both sides by a high range of mountains. On the west, at a distance of four or five miles, the first range of the Rocky Mountains commenced. On the west were mountains of the dividing ridge between the Arkansas and the Platte. The mountains of the first range were covered with pine of a low growth.

The creek they ascended they called Crystal Creek, from the circumstance of them finding some specimens of rock crystal of considerable size.

They crossed the dividing ridge between the waters of the Platte and Arkansas. Upon the summit level there was a lake about half a mile long and four or five hundred yards wide.

The small streams on one side of the lake ran into the Platte and on the other into the Arkansas. After crossing the dividing ridge, the view became more extended. The hills on their left not so high, and the country began to assume the appearance of a high, rolling prairie. They struck the headwaters of one of the branches of the Fontaine que Bouille, down which they continued their course of the main valley.

Pike's Peak was in full view, its snow-clad summit towering up to an immense height. From this valley it was a two day's ride to the waters of the Rio del Norte, and but three to Taos, one of the Mexican provinces.

They remained encamped and visited the Fontaine que Bouille, or spring that boils, a mineral spring near the foot of Pike's Peak. The water boiled up out of a limestone rock forming a basin two or three feet in diameter, and about the same depth. It had a pleasant acid taste, and was thought to possess healthful properties. It was directly in the pass leading from the Fontaine que Bouille to Rio Salard, a large valley in the mountains, where the Arapaho frequently pitched their lodges and remained encamped for a considerable length of time during the summer.

Shenga and Ian ascended the mountains along the ravine that formed the bed of the Fontaine que Bouille, and saw the mountain torrent washing down through the pass, forming numerous cascades and waterfalls as it came tumbling down over the high rocks.

From here they ascended one of the peaks to the distance of about a mile above the level of the plain. From the top they had a beautiful and extensive view of the country for many miles. They saw timber upon the Arkansas and the Platte, and a large extent of waving prairie country lying between the two rivers.

To the right, at an immense distance, they could see the feathery and indistinct outline of the Spanish Peaks just rising above the visible horizon. Behind them, there lay a long succession of high ranges of mountains until the snowy summits of the last and highest appeared to meet and mingle with the clouds.

Nature appeared here to have thrown aside her wild and sportive mood, and to have given the whole scene the deepest impress of grandeur.

The valley of the Fontaine que Bouille was very much frequented by the Indians, especially by the Arapaho, who came up here in the fall to gather the wild fruit that grew in abundance near the base of the mountains.

The whole route from the Platte to the Arkansas was frequented by large parties of the Blackfeet, Crows, Snakes, and sometimes the Eutaus, who live upon the waters of the Rio del Norte, but frequently come over through the mountain passes to steal horses from the Arapaho and Cheyenne.

Two days later as they encamped on the Arkansas they were visited by three Arapaho. They informed Ian and Shenga that there were fifty lodges on the opposite side of the river; that the remainder of the nation, with a large number of Cheyenne, were hunting buffalo about two day's ride from there, between the Platte and the Arkansas.

When they found that Shenga was the Great Hasanun, which they had heard many stories, the fifty lodges came over from the opposite side of the river and encamped about two or three hundred yards from Ian and Shenga. These Indians had long been friendly to the whites. They had a large number of horses, having lately stolen about one hundred and seventy from the Eutau, with whom they were at war. They subsisted upon buffalo meat, and when out of the range, live upon dogs, of which they had great number and of a large size.

The Arkansas at this point was five or six hundred yards wide, deep, rapid, and the water clear. It was fordable at the shallowest places.

A council was held several days later to hear Shenga give them counsel. The chiefs were seated around in a circle, with their pipes in their hands and listened with the most profound attention to every word that was uttered. They appeared like prodigal children returning once more to their father's house. The whole scene was one of the most grand and impressive Ian had ever witnessed.

As Ian admired Shenga from a distance he had vague thoughts that maybe she was a Great Hasanun or Messiah as the Indians truly believed.

The next day while walking together alone from the others, these thoughts still troubled Ian. Shenga's favorite occupations here with her people seemed to be strolling about, looking at the grass, the trees, the flowers, the varying aspects of the sky, and listening to the birds, the tree-frogs, the wind in the trees, and all the hundreds of natural sounds. It was evident these things gave her a feeling of pleasure far beyond what they gave ordinary people.

Until Ian knew Shenga it had not occurred to him that anyone could derive so much absolute happiness and fulfillment from these things as she evidently did.

She never spoke of all this pleasure. She had a way of singing, generally in an undertone, wherever she was or whatever she was doing, when alone.

All natural objects seemed to have a charm for her, all sights, and sounds, seemed to please her.

Her clear, musical and earnest voice made a good part, though not all, of the charm of the simplest things she said.

If she said, as she sometimes would involuntarily as she awoke in the morning, "Oh, the beautiful sky!" or "Oh, the beautiful grass," the words produced the effect of sweet music.

Ian had never heard her speak in anger, and apparently she never was angry. She never exhibited fear, and Ian did not believe she ever felt it. Her conversation, mainly toned low, was always agreeable and usually instructive.

Ian wanted to believe the same as the simple Indians; that she was a prophet, a Hasanun. But raised in the modern society, his mind could not accept their complete acceptance of this fact. Four out of five people believe in miracles but Ian was not one of them.

Alone with her on the prairie, he turned to her, held her shoulders with firm hands and pleaded with her, "Show me a miracle, . . . just one miracle, so I can believe."

She looked at him long, saying nothing. Ian saw a tear detach itself from her long eyelashes and roll down her cheek. She began crying softly and started to utter something, then stopped, then tried again; bowing her head, then looking up into Ian's eyes, she sobbed softly, "I am . . . the miracle!"

Then throwing her hands over her face, she turned and ran away from the stunned Ian.

Ian's arms dropped to his side. It took a full minute for her words to sink into his mind and soul.

"What is the matter with me?" he asked himself. "Am I blind?"

Maybe he was in the presence of an angel and didn't know it. Was he too stupid to recognize it, he wondered.

The people who were with Jesus didn't believe that He was the Messiah and they had let Him die—in fact, demanded it. He would not make that mistake. Maybe she was not a miracle but then again maybe she was. He was not going to disbelieve her.

Ian recollected from the Bible that when Jesus made the same type of claim, many of his hearers were upset. They had their own ideas, as he did now, as to how things were supposed to be and to happen in this world.

When Jesus came back to his own country, his disciples followed him. And on the Sabbath he began to teach in the synagogue as his Father told him to do. Many who heard him were astonished, saying, "Where did this man get all this? What is the wisdom given to him? What mighty works are wrought by his hands? Is not this the carpenter, the son of Mary and brother of James and Joses and Judas and Simon, and are not his sisters here with us?" And they took offense at him.

Jesus said to them, "A prophet is not without honor, except in his own country, and among his own kin, and in his own house." And he could do no mighty works there, except that he laid his hands upon a few sick people and healed them.

Rejection is part of a prophet's lot. Like the prophets, Jesus spoke the words of truth. And to hear the truth about oneself is often painful. The easy way to deal with hurtful truth is to ignore, or even try to get rid of the one who speaks it. The ultimate rejection was played out before Pilate, the governor: "Which of the two do you want me to release to you?" And they said, "Barabbas."

Ian naturally was skeptical; on the defensive. True, Shenga Wassa was doing the thing that a holy person, an angel was expected to do, in his idea, that is. But in spite of what he saw with his own eyes, his mind kept insisting Shenga was not a Holy One, not a prophet. Had he not heard her, made love to her, lived with her? If there was a God, why would He bless him with such a gift? She must be a fake, an impostor. After all, the scriptures said there would be false prophets.

"No prophet could ever rise out of these plains of the Kanza—this wilderness;" Ian's logic told him as he viewed the landscape.

But, then again . . . he thought . . . what rules out the possibility that she was truly a miracle?

How much longer are we to wait for things to be exactly the way they are supposed to be for a Messiah to appear?

"Yes," he admitted to himself, "there was an immediate need for hope and faith . . . and love . . . in this wilderness."

"But God just doesn't respond immediately to every need at the very moment He is needed," Ian reasoned, "and why give such a gift miracle to me?"

"I don't claim to be a believer of God, or Jesus, or any other thing like that."

"But, . . . if there was an Almighty, wouldn't some of His actions be beyond human comprehension?"

"Could it be that there were many prophets in the world today and we are just as short-sighted in our thinking as the same people that rejected Jesus, because the time and place were not right, and His or Her credentials are not proper?"

He thought to himself, "What if she is a true miracle, and he rejected her."

The thought made his whole body sick and weak.

All of this sickness convinced him that his society-formed thinking was wrong—oh, so wrong!

"Accept her!" something in him cried out, "Accept her as she is. Believe her!"

"Escape from these narrow-minded views. Better to be wrong and ridiculed for his belief than to be blessed with a miracle and reject it!"

So he ran to her and held her gently as she lay sobbing on the grass.

"I will never doubt you again," Ian promised, "Never . . . but . . . but give me time. I must learn to live with a miracle."

Shenga smiled as her tears of sorrow changed to tears of joy. As they embraced, the world was momentarily forgotten and the life-giving miracle of love flowed from her to Ian, there on the plains of the Kanza Indian Territory.

Ian sensed that she was not of this world. He knew not whom he had married.

*   *   *

Ian and Shenga left the Arapaho encampment to continue on into the mountains. She pointed out where they were headed. There was a trail the Indians used, some called it Trail Ridge. It was across the backbone of North America, separating the Pacific drainage from that of the Atlantic. Lieutenant Zebulon Pike who had visited this area in 1806 called it the Continental Divide because the snow melt flowed from there to both oceans.

Ian, with his scientific turn of mind recalled the geology of the Rocky Mountains he had studied in school.

Not long ago as geologists measure time, perhaps a hundred million years, a great sea covered much of the area now occupied by the Rocky Mountains and extended from the Gulf of Mexico to the Arctic Ocean. Subtropical forests lined the shores. Animal life included giant reptiles in the sea and on the land, and gliding or flying reptiles in the air. As animals died, their remains became fossilized and were trapped in sedimentary layers of sand and silt brought down from the low hills. The sand, silt, and mud hardened into sandstone and shale. These rock layers were now exposed in the foothills to the east.

The geology of the region was fascinating evidence of the power of the forces of nature. What carved the magnificent mountains of the Front Range? What caused the smooth and gentle slopes on Trail Ridge, the U-shaped valleys, the up-tilted rock strata?

The Front Range, some two hundred miles long and averaging forty miles wide, is the rough, spectacularly beautiful section of the Rocky Mountains that rises from the central Great Plains.

The range, ancestral to the present range, was formed when great forces within the earth caused a gigantic lifting of the land under the sea. This land buckled, and the old sea floor was uplifted and bowed into a long ridge, like a wrinkle in a carpet. Rock layers were fractured, and the fractures became faults as the rock layers slipped or were thrust along the fracture zones. Through some of the fractures, molten lava oozed up from the earth's interior to form lavas on the surface and granite beneath the surface.

The highland thus formed was slowly worn down by water, wind, and freezing action until most of the sea-laid rock layers and lavas were eroded away from the high center of the range, exposing the more ancient crystalline rocks that formed the core. Through continued erosion, the surface of these mountains was slowly reduced to a rolling upland. The gentle slopes atop Trail Ridge are remnants of this erosional stage. Volcanic eruptions occurred in the western section of the area along the Never Summer Range. Specimen Mountain is the remnant of a volcano. More erosion followed this period of activity.

At the end of the Mesozoic era and continuing into the Cenozoic, some forty to sixty million years ago, another series of uplifts raised the eroding mountain range successively higher, giving the streams renewed vigor and allowing them to carve deeper and sharper valleys.

Then, about a million years ago the climate grew colder and the ice age began. Giant snowdrifts compacted into ice, forming glaciers of tremendous size. The slow, ponderous down valley movement of the glaciers—glaciers holding tons of rock debris in their masses of ice—sculptured the sharp valley bottoms into u-shapes. As the glaciers moved down the valleys, loose rock material carried in and on the ice was deposited along the sides, forming lateral moraines. At the ends of the glaciers, ice-carried rocks were dumped to form terminal moraines (glacier-formed ridges).

Other evidences of glaciation, such as ice-polished rocks, erratic boulders, and marks called striations, could be plainly seen in many places.

The early history of Rocky Mountains is one of gigantic earth movements, eons of building and wearing away.

The first Indians probably reached the vicinity of the Rocky Mountains between 10,000 and 20,000 years ago. Just who these first-comers were is unknown. They were followed by many other Indians who the modern Ute and Arapaho were the latest. The way of life of the earlier inhabitants is known only through the few artifacts revealed by the spade of the archeologist. Objects of stone, bone, and burned clay alone told of the first inhabitants of the area. A few objects found have been estimated by archeologists to be about 8,000 years old.

After the United States acquired the region through the Louisiana Purchase, explorers, trappers (the famous mountain men), and adventurers passed near the area.

Ian and Shenga and a small party of Arapaho with their squaws, continued the slow journey into the higher mountains past towering peaks, flowered meadows, alpine lakes, sculptured mountain valleys, rugged gorges, plunging streams, and the wild creatures that live amidst this splendor. They saw elk, bighorn sheep, beaver, golden eagle, and a myriad of other creatures of the wild in their natural habitat.

The mountainous terrain ranged in elevations from 7,600 to over 14,000 feet. Perpetual snows mantled the highest summits and valley walls. Small glaciers still existed at the heads of sheltered gorges. At one extreme are the summits of the high mountains, with their widespread areas of alpine tundra (dense carpets of tiny dwarf plants strikingly adapted to severe climatic conditions). Tundra is uncommon outside the Arctic Circle. At the other extreme are the sheltered valleys, with their stands of ponderosa and lodge pole pines, blue spruce, and narrow-leaf cottonwood.

They followed the trail up to Trail Ridge that had been used for centuries by the Ute and Arapaho.

From this trail, they could see many of the eighty-four peaks that were over 11,000 feet in height. Longs Peak was the highest at 14,256 feet. There were seventeen 13,000 and 14,000 feet and forty-four more were between 12,000 and 13,000 feet above sea level.

Summer was almost over. Autumn had turned the aspen leaves a beautiful red and gold. Whole hillsides seemed on fire. The air was clear and crisp, and the warming sun and blue skies were perfect.

Elk bugled in the hills and chipmunks scurried to get the last seeds stored away. Soon the majestic mountains would be covered by a mantle of white.

Just off Trail Ridge path was Hidden Valley where the small party would encamp for the winter. There was a fine stand of spire-like spruce and fir, typical of the sub-alpine zone forest. Downstream beavers had dammed the stream to form many ponds in the willow bottom. The valley was "hidden" by a glacier formed ridge.

Above Hidden Valley, the tree line ended with dwarfed, stunted trees. The elevation of the tree line here was 11,500 feet (more than two miles above sea level). Above that altitude was the alpine tundra – a flower-rich meadowland not unlike the vast treeless wastes of northern Alaska and Siberia. Trail Ridge path passed for eleven miles across this tundra.

These mountains seemed to be a holy place as Shenga said it was.

Nothing could exceed the romantic delight of this land. The beauty of its landscapes — hills, cliffs, valley, lakes and rivers—of its trees, of its inhabitants, of its birds.

The mountains' heights, their vastness, the mystery of their recesses, the veil of mist and clouds now shrouding them, dispersed from them, the strange noises the wind makes in the gorges, the crash of a fall of rock, the effect of the echo, their suggestion of power, their appearance of watching the intruder upon their solitude—all gave to them an air of personality, and easily inspire an attitude of reverence and eventually of worship.

They are thought to have a spirit akin to, yet greater than, man's.

The natural dangers encountered by the traveler or mountain-dweller, as well as the mystery of gorge, precipice, or cavern, suggested the presence of spirits, dangerous or at times beneficent.

Their summits, being near the sky and often surrounded by clouds, suggest their connection with gods of sky or rain; of the remoteness and mystery of their peaks cause them to be regarded as dwellings of gods or of spirits.

They were now in the sky-land, which is so often associated with God. These mountains were lofty and mysterious . . . some believed sacred mountains.

Legend clustered thickly around them and they were places of pilgrimage. Because of their supposed nearness to heaven—to be the seat of God . . . or the Great Spirit . . . or whatever name you call the supernatural.

Ian could feel something different here. The wind blew the cobwebs of society-thinking from his mind. He was receptive to Shenga's pure thoughts that she spoke of almost every evening.

Ian found there was no greater adventure than exploring the mystical power of the mind and the secrets of the universe in which we live. In private talks with Ian, Shenga explained there was no supernaturalism. There are no mysteries, except our ignorance and misunderstanding make them appear so.

One evening with snow falling lightly outside, Shenga sat in the warmth of the cave by the fire and she talked softly and quietly to the chiefs that yearned for her counsel and advice.

Ian, sitting outside the circle watched Shenga as she spoke in different dialects together with sign language to the gathering.

The cave became crowded. One dusky form after another glided with noiseless step to the darker corners of the cave, wrapping their shaggy robes around them, so as to completely screen the lower part of their faces.

At the entrance to the massive cave, a large iron kettle had been filled with buffalo meat and hard corn, and placed over the fire. The women poured its contents into bowls with a large dipper made of buffalo horn.

Shenga Wassa was the presiding genius of the fireside, where she created an atmosphere of serenity and contentment suitable for the nurture and growth of character in its best forms. She was by her very constitution compassionate, gentle, patient, and self-denying. Loving, hopeful, trustful, her eyes shed brightness everywhere. They shined upon coldness and warmed it, upon suffering and relieved it, upon sorrow and cheered it. She seemed quiet tonight, disturbed by something. Ian particularly noticed this, because she was always cheerful, but tonight something was bothering her. She would glance quietly at Ian, then continue to answer the chiefs' questions.

After several hours, she became visually tired, and Ian suggested everyone get some sleep as he was worried about Shenga. In an isolated section of the cave, where she and Ian slept under a pile of robes she quietly undressed and gently lay next to him. Ian embraced her tenderly trying to comfort her. After a short time, she got up, put on a wolf's robe that a Blackfoot chief had given her, wrapped it around her and made her way between the sleeping guests and out into the cold night. She had done this several times before so Ian did not follow as he thought she wanted some quiet time to herself.

After ten minutes or more he became concerned for her and slipping on his trousers and fur boots he made his way to the cave's entrance.

He did not see her at first glance so he walked a ways down the path. He found her standing in the cold with the wolf-skin head covering her dark tresses, looking off into the distant stars. Ian quietly approached her, not wanting to disturb her thoughts. As he got closer, he could hear her talking in unfamiliar language to someone or something in the heavens. She seemed to be pleading for something but Ian could not understand. Then in the midst of her pleadings, she cried out, "Tsit owo' taki'. Eli . . . Eli. . . ." Then she was quiet as if listening to an answer to her plea.

Ian had never ever heard Shenga talk in such a depressed voice. She must be experiencing terrible, terrible agony. Ian was paralyzed; not knowing what to do with her grief.

For a long moment she stood there, in the falling snow, looking up into those silent depths with unspeakable longing for some answer to the wordless questions within her. But if the stars heard her pleas they gave no sign.

Her robe fell off her body and she stood naked to her God. In a moment of eternity Ian heard her say quietly, "Tai a ney" and nods that she understands.

She began to cry softly, not noticing the cold. Her nakedness was accepted and respected by Ian. In communion with her God, nothing else mattered, naked or clothed, and he had only the most tender thoughts for her well-being. As she cried, Ian came to her, picked up the robe and put it around her shoulders. Her body was ice cold. As she turned to him, tears streamed down her face as she lifted her arms about his shoulders. He gently asked her what was the matter. She only gazed into his eyes and sobbed some more.

After a long moment, she began trembling from the cold and he picked her up in his arms and carried her back to her bed. As she cried softly, Ian went to the fire and thought a lot about what had happened. Then he went out to where she had stood and tried to think her thoughts but no answer came to him. Something was terribly wrong, but his mind could not grasp it. After a long while gazing at the stars, moon, distance mountains with wolves howling their laments, he returned to the cave's fire and sat there until he fell into a fitful sleep.

In the early morning, Shenga gave no inkling of last night. She smiled her sweet smile, gave a fond farewell to her guests as they donned snowshoes, and departed down from the mountain top. Ian mused about the incident for several days but Shenga seemed to have forgotten it, so after a while Ian did not think about it as other things occupied his thoughts.

*   *   *

The morning was chilly, raw and gusty, but the sweet-scented, light-filled air, full of vivid, tender green of spring, and vibrant with life, seemed to share sensation of joy and uplift.

He turned to Shenga pleading, "Please let me see some of what you see, so I may believe more strongly of your messages and visions."

Shenga slowly and thoughtfully replied, "I shall give you a moment in history," as she walked close to him and placed two fingers on his forehead.

He seemed to lose consciousness as the earth spun around him. Falling down on the grass, he was wholly prostrated. He lost himself in the wrestle, and was carried away in a whirlwind of the universe.

He soared with the eagle and then rose farther still to the sun and stars. Still farther beyond the stars into the hollow of space.

The consciousness of the soul, the permanent identity, the thought, the something, before which the magnitude even of democracy, art, literature, and life dwindles, becomes partial, measurable—something that fully satisfies which those do not. That something is the All and the idea of All with the accompanying idea of eternity, and of itself, the soul, buoyant, indestructible, sailing space forever, visiting every region, as a ship of the sea. And again lo! the pulsations in all matter, all spirit, throbbing forever and the eternal beats, eternal rhythmical dilations of life in things.

He returned as quickly to earth as he had journeyed through space and then he saw it; the crucifixion. The whole impressive tragedy of the passion moved vividly and rapidly before his eyes. The scourging, the pillory, the cuffs and blows, the jibes and jeers, the mockery and derision of that crowning with thorns; the powerful progress of Golgotha, hooted by the blind and cruel mob, the torture and ignominy of the nailing to the cross, the cry of agony, telling that the last dregs of the cup had been drained; the shout of victory that proclaimed, "It is finished!"

Ian beheld Christ face to face. He saw then the spear thrust; the sublime temple of the Divine thus laid low. Crowned with thorns—buffeted and spat upon, mocked, insulted, scourged and on the pillory, a man of sorrow and acquainted with grief; nailed to the cross, pierced in the side, utterly despised and rejected of men, killed as a malefactor, buried, and then the great thought—the truth which maketh free; the absolute demonstration of man's mastery of fate and command of all conditions—the victory of man and woman—all men and women—in this radical man.

In the vacuum of time and the stars, Ian thought vaguely that the divine reincarnation of Christ on our insignificant atom of a world seemed out of keeping with the august spectacle of the infinite universe and its immeasurable duration.

Ian's mind wondered to himself. "What is my fate? What is to happen to me?"

As he thought, he found himself lying again on the ground.

He rose and looked around him and as the cannon smoke cleared he found himself on a field of dead.

Artillery fired salvo after salvo of grapeshot into the ranks of men standing on either side of him.

Ian walked a little way to each flank to get a glimpse of what was going on, but nothing met his eyes, except the mangled remains of men and horses.

Then out of the smoke the cavalry charged.

He had been disabled in both his arms as he feebly tried to raise his sword. The first line of cavalry dealt him a blow to his head with a saber. He fell senseless on the ground.

Recovering, he raised himself a little to look around, being at that time in no condition to get up and fight, when a lancer riding by struck his lance through his back. Blood gushed into his mouth as he fell.

Then the charging horsemen galloped over him again and again, trampling him into the earth. Ian struggled with all his strength to call for Shenga to save him.

"Shenga. . . . Shenga" he feebly cried out.

He felt Shenga's warm hand touch his outstretched bloody and mangled fingers as he fell into deep unconsciousness.

As he awoke, he was lying on the grass where he had fell at the beginning of his dream vision.

Now he understood that Shenga and other gifted souls could see not only into the future, but also into the past; it was thus, that the Mohave shamans explained their knowledge of creation—they were present at the beginning of the world, as in a dream.

As a result of his flight into the past and future, Ian was to become known as White Eagle—"the one who lives with the Messiah."

*   *   *

On rare occasions, when only a few travelers were around the campfire, Shenga would sometimes make music on her mystery flute.

While Ian fueled the fire, Shenga would play for him.

On several occasions Shenga Wassa would ask Ian to guard her physical body as she experienced out of body travel in the four-dimensional space to the Shoshone or Great Dakota Nation or elsewhere. She would explain there were dimensions beyond our material plane. There was a higher reality. No one can point to the fourth dimension, yet it is all around us. She seemed to be able to exist on several levels.

*   *   *

Springtime in the Rockies! With the last frost over, the wildflowers on the sunny slopes, and grassy meadows burst into a rash of colors. Sometimes during the night a moist fall of snow blankets the trees; it sparkles in the morning sun until the warmth of day melts it away. Nature awakens, and streams run bank-full. Much of the snow along the Continental Divide melts during this season, but many large snow banks linger, shrinking gradually in summer.

Spring comes to the lower altitudes in late April, and flows up the mountainsides as the weeks go by. By early June, it has reached the high country; the short summer season of the tundra does not begin until July.

Down the Mississippi

*T*he boat was making a landing at Fort Leavenworth to pick up travelers and supplies and refill their fuel woodbins. After all the bustle was over, Ian and Shenga made their way across the gang-plank and climbed the hill up to post headquarters.

The commander on his return had reviewed Ian's court-martial and saw the unfairness of it, had recommended it be dismissed completely, and forwarded it to higher headquarters. Although General Wilkinson, Commander of the Army of the West, had actively railroaded Ian's court-martial, he was intelligent enough not to draw attention to his hidden treasonable acts of conspiracy and prudently agreed with the post commander. He also knew that his disapproval would cause it to be forwarded to Washington for final review by the War Department, so it was stopped at his office and Ian's dismissal from service reversed.

Ian still had his orders to find the Hasanun and report to Colonel Williams. Following military etiquette, he had decided to carry out the orders and report to Colonel Williams.

As they entered the outer office, the colonel happened to be conversing with a captain and a lieutenant. Upon noticing Ian, he immediately came over and heartily shook his hand in warm welcome and ushered Ian into his office. He closed the door for privacy, nodding acknowledgment of Shenga Wassa as she followed closely and quietly behind.

After a few moments of small conversation, Colonel Williams sincerely apologized for the unfair treatment by the court-martial.

Ian then in a military manner reported to his commander, "I would like to introduce you to Shenga Wassa," moving closer to her and touching her back tenderly. Ian had a reverence for Shenga; indeed, his ideas of womanhood were very exalted. He guarded Shenga most sacredly from anything, which might offend her sense of delicacy, and was ready to do battle with anyone who spoke slightingly of her.

The colonel, being equally graceful to a lady, smiled and nodded his recognition of her.

There was a moment of awkwardness as the two met for the first time, each studying the other.

Shenga Wassa began trembling violently; her breath came in short gasps as she turned to Ian and pleaded, "I am in the presence of my Judas!"

Shenga uttered to the colonel; "May God forgive you—what you are about to do!"

Colonel Williams was surprised by this comment, but said nothing.

Laboring for breath, with open mouth, she continued, "I must leave this place!"

Her voice faltered, as she became faint. Ian turned to her, through quick sympathy at the touch of her hand, and caught her arm, as she was about to fall forward. In an instant she was lifted into Ian's arms, and his face was as white as hers was as he looked at her.

Down to the waterfront he carried her, never looking back. As the crowd respectfully made way for his passage, he crossed the gangplank and laid her gently onto the bed in their cabin.

Shenga lay there long after the boat pulled out into the river and continued the voyage to St. Louis.

At St. Louis, Ian and Shenga stayed at the Plantation House Hotel—civilized Indians being common in the city and tolerated by society. The ever-increasing emigrants and traders used many Indians as guides and scouts.

They both rose early in the morning, dressed for the trip down river, and had breakfast in the dining room.

Ian had told Shenga he would like to visit his friend, Jeff Davis, who now lived at Hurricane Plantation in Mississippi. She was anxious to get back to her people but agreed to the journey.

Ian mentioned to Shenga that they should leave for the docks to board the Moselle. At the mention of the boat's name, Shenga hesitated with her preparations and asked Ian, again, the name of the steamboat.

"The Moselle," he repeated.

She straightened up erect and stared out the window at the boat moored to the dock, as if reading something.

"We must not take the Moselle down river."

Ian explained that if they missed the Moselle they would have to wait until tomorrow afternoon for another boat.

Shenga was firm, "It is written, we must not travel on the Moselle."

Ian knew any further decision was out of the question. When she said, "It is written," he knew she had read what she explained was the "Book of History" or something to that effect. He could not understand it, but respected her seemingly supernatural ability. Supernatural vision is only natural to a supernatural person.

The Moselle was built at Cincinnati, and she reflected great credit on the mechanical genius of that city, as she was truly a superior boat. She was new, having been begun the previous December, and finished in March, only a month before.

The Moselle was regarded as the finest example of western steamboats; she was perfect in form and construction, elegant and superb in all her equipments, and enjoyed a reputation for speed that admitted of no rival ship. As an evidence that the latter was not undeserved, it need only be mentioned that her last trip from St. Louis to Cincinnati, seven hundred and fifty miles, was performed in two days and sixteen hours, the quickest trip, by several hours, that had ever been made between the two places.

The Moselle left the landing with an unusually large number of passengers, not less than two hundred and eighty or according to some accounts, three hundred. It was a pleasant morning and all on board anticipated a delightful voyage. The Moselle proceeded about a mile up the river to take on some German emigrants. At this time, it was observed by an experienced engineer on board, that the steam had been raised to an unusual height, and when the boat stopped one man, who was apprehensive of danger, went ashore, after protesting against the injudicious management of the steam apparatus. The passengers had no thought that any danger might exist, crowding the boat for the sake of her beauty and speed, and making safety a secondary consideration.

When the emigrants were nearly loaded on the Moselle and the bow of the boat just turned in preparation to move from the shore, at that instant the explosion took place. The whole of the vessel forward of the wheels was blown to splinters; every timber, appeared to be twisted, as trees sometimes are, when struck by lightning. As soon as the accident occurred, the boat floated down the stream for about two hundred yards, where she sunk, leaving the upper part of the cabin out of the water, and the baggage, together with many struggling human beings, floating on the surface of the river.

The force of the explosion was unprecedented in the history of steam; its effect was like that of a mine of gunpowder. All the boilers, four in number, burst simultaneously; the deck was blown into the air, and the human beings that crowded it were doomed to instant destruction. It was asserted that a man, believed to be a pilot, was carried, together with the pilothouse, to the shore, a distance of a quarter of a mile.

A fragment of a boiler was carried by the explosion high into the air, and descending perpendicularly about fifty yards from the boat, it crushed through a strong roof, and through the second floor of a building, lodging finally on the ground floor.

The master of the Moselle, at the time of the accident, was standing on the deck, above the boiler, in conversation with another person. He was thrown to a considerable height on the steep embankment of the river and killed, while his companion was merely prostrated on the deck, and escaped without injury. Another person was blown a great distance into the air, and on descending he fell on a roof with such force, that he partially broke through it, and his body was lodged there. Some of the passengers who were in the after part of the boat, and who were uninjured by the explosion, jumped overboard. There were sixty or seventy in the water at one time, of whom comparatively few reached the shore.

It happened, unfortunately, that the larger number of the passengers were collected on the upper deck to which the balmy weather seemed to invite them, in order to expose them to more certain destruction. The captain of the ill-fated steamer had expressed his determination to outstrip an opposition boat which had just started; the people on shore were cheering the Moselle, in anticipation of her success in the race, and the passengers and crew on the upper deck responded to these acclamations, which were soon changed to sounds of mourning and distress.

Intelligence of the awful calamity spread rapidly through the city; thousands rushed to the spot, and the most benevolent aid was promptly extended to the sufferers, or rather to those who were within the reach of human assistance, for the majority had perished. The scene here was so sad and distressing, that no language can depict it with fidelity. Here lay twenty or thirty mangled and still bleeding corpses, while many persons were engaged in dragging others of the dead or wounded, from the wreck or the water. The survivors presented the most touching objects of distress, as their mental anguish seemed more insupportable than the most intense bodily suffering.

Death had torn asunder the tenderest ties; but the rupture had been so sudden and violent, that none knew certainly who had been taken, or who had been spared. Fathers were distractedly inquiring for children, children for parents, husbands and wives for each other. One man had saved a son, but lost a wife and five children. A father, partially demented by grief, lay with a wounded child on one side, his dead daughter on the other, and his expiring wife at his feet. One gentleman sought his wife and children, who were as eagerly seeking him in the same crowd. They met, and were reunited.

A female deck passenger, who had been saved, seemed inconsolable for the loss of her relatives. Her constant exclamations were, "Oh! My father! My mother! My sisters!"

A little boy about five years old, whose head was much bruised cried continually for a lost father; while another lad, a little older, was weeping for a whole family. Another man was deprived of his whole family, consisting of nine persons.

A touching display of maternal affection was evinced by a woman, who on being brought to shore, clasped her hands, and exclaimed, "Thank God, I am safe!" But instantly collecting herself, she suddenly exclaimed in a voice of piercing agony, "Where is my child?"The infant, who had been saved, was brought to her, and she fainted at the sight of her child.

Many of the passengers who entered the boat had not registered their names, but the lowest estimated number of persons on board was two hundred and eighty; of these, eighty-one were known to be killed, fifty-five were missing, and thirteen badly wounded.

*   *   *

The trip on the other steamboat that Ian and Shenga booked passage was uneventful. Ian reminisced the good times Jeff and he had at Fort Leavenworth; he wondered what had happened since the two served together.

At the Hurricane, Ian found Jefferson bedfast with agonizing seizures of facial neuralgia, which rendered him literally blind with pain.

Sarah's illness was also serious, her frail body suffering from an alarmingly worse condition.

As Jefferson's fever worsened, he slipped into a delirium state of clouded consciousness of his past life.

West Point and his life as a soldier on the frontier, strengthened by the military tradition of his family, inculcated patriotism and loyalty to the national government. But his was a conditional loyalty, dependent on the national government observing the compact of the Constitution strictly and honorably. When that government threatened to trample on the rights of sovereign states by coercing South Carolina in the nullification crisis, Jefferson Davis opposed it.

In his young manhood, he presented a handsome cavalier appearance—tall and slender just less than six feet in height with strongly marked features, deep-set blue-gray eyes, blond hair, and a notably erect carriage. Although he retained a certain aristocratic reserve, beneath the reserve there was an affectionate, affable personality that was most attractively displayed in his great love affair with Sarah Knox Taylor.

After his graduation from military academy, Brevet Lieutenant Davis was granted a three-month's furlough before reporting for duty at Jefferson Barracks in Missouri. While at Rosemont, he became better acquainted with James Pemberton, the servant his father had given to him shortly before he died. It had been Samuel Davis' custom to give each of his children a favorite slave when he or she left home, but since Jeff could not take James to West Point, he had remained as a house boy at his mother's place. When they were both youngsters, James had chosen the youngest Davis for his master as surely as Jefferson had chosen him. The Negro was of "a dark griffe color," for he had a strain of Indian blood. Already he had acquired gentlemanly manners and soon he was imitating his young master in diction.

Jeff spent some weeks with his brother Joseph at the plantation, which he had bought in 1818. Isaac and his family had moved to a farm of their own after a cyclone had destroyed his house, wrecked the improvements he had made, killed one of his little boys, and made him a cripple. He and Susannah could not endure the unhappy associations.

Though still connected with law firms in Natchez and Greenville, Joseph himself had not hesitated to abandon a lucrative career as a lawyer when he saw what wealth cotton planting and stockbreeding could bring.

After four years of West Point dormitory living, the seductive plantation routine, with so much family love, made it hard for the young soldier to say goodbye. When he took the northbound riverboat for St. Louis, it was comforting to have with him James Pemberton, who, as his body servant in the ensuing years in the wild North Country, was to prove a blessing beyond all reckoning.

Davis' military life ended when he was twenty-six years old, but his days as a West Point cadet and as a frontier soldier continuously influenced his career. The erect military carriage acquired as a soldier he retained, and the splendid horsemanship developed during service in the dragoons was valuable consequence of his military training. In the army Davis had learned to manage men and exercise authority.

But he was never as robust after his severe bout with pneumonia in Wisconsin as before, and his eyes were permanently injured by over-exposure to the blinding snows of the Northwest.

When Knox begged her father's blessing the last time, she pointed out that she had been engaged for almost two years and that he had found no fault in Lieutenant Davis' character or conduct. "Some day," she insisted, "you will see his rare qualities as I do." Then she declared with Taylor-like determination that she would marry Jefferson Davis, with or without parental consent. Her decision was a rash one for the times. Even young men in the 1830's hesitated to marry in the face of a father's strong disapproval.

Lieutenant Davis sent in his resignation from the army. Arriving in Louisville some time before the fifteenth, he persuaded Knox to have the wedding almost immediately and in the early afternoon so that the couple could catch the New Orleans riverboat that left at four o'clock. Invitations were sent by hand to relatives and a few close friends. So there was no romantic elopement, despite many erroneous and fantastic stories that have been told, including one depicting the wedding as performed at night by a priest in the middle of the Mississippi River.

Neither the members of the Davis family nor Zachary Taylor and his wife were present at the marriage. Knox, as Sarah called herself, wrote an affectionate letter to her mother on her wedding day in a plea for "affection for a child who has been so unfortunate as to form a connection without the sanction of her parents." Sarah was enthusiastic about a beautiful colt that Joseph had given her to ride. She ended her letter with "Mr. Davis (her husband) sends best respects to you."

With the lack of parental blessing, there was little joy in the parlor where the couple at last stood before the Reverend Mr. Ashe, rector of Louisville's Christ Episcopal Church. During the ceremony the bride's eyes were filled with tears, and some of the other ladies openly wept.

Nevertheless, Zachary Taylor sent her a liberal supply of money and may have finally given a grudging assent to the marriage. After the wedding the bride and groom took passage on a steamboat for Hurricane.

As their steamboat made its way slowly down to Vicksburg, the young couple had every reason to expect an enriching life of exceptional happiness. The state of an established Southern planter before 1860 was an enviable one. He had the leisure in which to be a gentleman, much like the lord of an English manor. His lady could indulge herself in the art of gracious living. With all the responsibilities and "noblesse oblige" that such a situation entailed for master and mistress, there was yet time for reading, hunting, entertaining, and for travel. It was an unflurried existence, in which life might be savored.

Of course, both Jefferson and Knox were aware they were not headed for any inherited plantation home furnished with heirlooms. They were going to be the guests of Joseph Davis until Jeff had cleared some acres, planted his first crop, and built a house for his bride. But there was no hurry, no urgency. For Hurricane was commodious and maintained an abundance of trained servants. Relatives and friends were always welcome and the presence of Jeff and his bride greatly desired. Joseph, who was only sixteen days younger than Knox's father, was eager to have his favorite brother close, to discuss all he had been reading these late years, while accumulating a fortune. Knox would be company for Eliza, Joe's frail young wife. The bride would have time aplenty to become accustomed to Delta plantation life before assuming responsibilities herself. Although in a sense she and Jeff would be pioneering, carving out a home for themselves in a wilderness, they were to do it gradually, from a base marked by luxurious comfort.

Except for the obstinate disapproval of the bride's father, which they both trusted would soon dissolve, there was everything to point to a rarely blessed union, for they were deeply in love. A long boat trip was not at all undesirable for a honeymoon. It had its own characteristic diversions. The steamers carried freight, as well as passengers, and sometimes they would spend a day or two tied up at Cairo, Memphis, and smaller river towns, unloading and loading. The passengers would go ashore to see what was to be seen, present letters of introduction, or visit old friends. There was a mild kind of kaleidoscopic variety to river travel, which both Knox and Jeff enjoyed.

Less than a fortnight after his marriage, and about the time they reached their destination; Lieutenant Davis' resignation from the army became effective. He had served seven years, more than the term considered requisite to repay the Government for education at West Point. But if Jefferson had not fallen in love with Knox Taylor, it may be doubted that he would have given up a profession, which in so many aspects he found congenial to his temperament. Though scholarly in his tastes, he had the bearing and the qualifications of a man born to command. He had proved himself peculiarly adept in dangerous crises. He had not balked at undertaking direction of such unfamiliar jobs as timber cutting and sawmill building. He had earned a reputation both for diplomacy and fearlessness.

Now Jefferson was entering an entirely different career—those of Southern planter. The land he was to transform into productive fields was virgin, overgrown with gigantic trees and rank with cane and briers. The initial task had elements of the Herculean, but Jeff had the needed will and the persistence.

Sarah Knox was peculiarly fitted to be both helpmate and mistress. By nature, sympathetic, amiable, and charming, she was also lively and energetic. She had been taught the wifely virtues by her blue-blooded mother, who was a born homemaker, delighting in such domestic activities as handling cream, making cheese, preserving fruits, rearing children and pleasing the menfolk. And having been brought up with devoted slaves as household servants, Knox could understand the needs and appreciate the loyalties of Negroes.

The Davis plantation in Warren County lay on what was then a peninsula about thirty miles by water south of Vicksburg. Altogether the peninsula contained some 11,000 acres, of which Joseph then owned about 6,900. The peninsula became known to river boat captains as "Davis Bend," though Joseph's estate was called the "Hurricane" after that disastrous cyclone of 1827, in which one of Isaac Davis' sons was killed and Isaac himself suffered a broken leg.

When Joseph bought the property that was incorporated into Hurricane, it was composed mostly of wild land, but partially of several small farms, which original settlers had cleared. With the help of Isaac, Joseph had consolidated various forty-acre farms, cleared much new land, and brought a tract of some 5,000 acres under profitable production. Joseph told Jefferson that if he wanted to become a planter he would give him some 1,800 acres of uncleared land and lend him the money to buy the needed slaves. Though Jeff had never farmed, he felt he could learn with Joseph as mentor. And he was greatly tempted by the richness of his brother's library, which was reputed to be the finest private library in the state; for Joseph, who had never had the advantage of a college education, was a voracious reader.

It cost Jefferson some pain, however, to throw over an army officer's career. But above all else he desired Sarah Knox. To provide a respectable living for her, he was determined to become a planter. He wrote her his intentions; she spoke with her father. But even with the prospect of Jefferson's becoming a private citizen, for some unexplained reason the colonel still would not approve the match.

It is possible that Zachary Taylor dreaded the Delta climate with its miasmas and mists that were believed to breed malaria. He had pertinent reason to be fearful, for in 1820 when his wife and four daughters were living at Bayou Sara, Louisiana; all of them went down with the "bilious fever," as he called the disease. The two youngest girls died. His wife came very close to death. The probability of losing her nearly unmanned him. Taylor was a truly devoted husband.

In an apprehensive letter, he declared positively, "I am confident the feminine virtues never did concentrate in a higher degree in the bosom of any woman than in hers." Mrs. Taylor eventually recovered, and so did Ann and Sarah Knox, who was six years old at the time. But the haunting fear of the fever remained with him.

The house that was to be Knox's temporary home was more elegant than any in which she had lived. It was huge, with two main stories and a third story that alone could house a dozen guests with their body servants. While Hurricane House had dignity and solidity, the surrounding galleries did not give it the grace of some of the mansions in Natchez. But it had bathrooms with running water, for Joseph had brought from Cincinnati mechanics who understood rudimentary plumbing. They had constructed an enormous tank in the attic, into which the Negroes pumped water early each morning. Adjoining the main house and connected by a pergola was an annex containing the dining room and a large sitting room on the lower floor and a study and music room on the second floor. Joseph's books were shelved in the annex sitting room, in his office, and in the cottage library in the garden, a replica of a Greek temple with square Doric columns on all four sides.

To one side stood an array of stout stables and barns, the cotton gin and blacksmith shop, and conglomerations of cribs and outbuildings. Farther away still spread the hamlet of clustering Negro cabins, gleaming with whitewash and each provided with vegetable garden and chicken run.

Governor John Anthony Quitman, who had come down from New York in the 1820's, told how a guest was treated when visiting a gentleman's plantation: "Your coffee in the morning before sunrise, little stews and soporifics at night, and warm foot baths if you have a cold. A horse and saddle at your disposal. Everything free and easy and cheerful and cordial." Quitman, often a guest at Hurricane, was captivated by the gracious quality of southern life, and bought a plantation on Davis Bend, as well as building a splendid mansion of Natchez.

To Knox, who had spent so many of her years in frontier army posts, Hurricane had aspects of an Eden. Her only apprehension was of the miasma that sometimes rose in the evening and hung about until morning, for it was supposed to carry the contagion of malaria. Jefferson, too, mistrusted the fog from the swamps, and he urged his bride to remain indoors until the sun had dissolved the mists.

Almost immediately the bridegroom plunged into the work of clearing some of the acreage on the south of the peninsula which Joseph had assigned to him. It was harder and more expensive business than he had expected. Clearing Mississippi bottomland cost many times the price of the acres themselves. The impenetrable walls of cane and briers had to be burned, trees felled, ditches made, and the wet heavy land broken.

At daybreak, Jeff would rise from his wife's side, and as soon as he had coffee and a light breakfast, he and James Pemberton would mount their horses and start out to direct the slaves Joseph had sold him on credit. At noon the brothers would meet at Hurricane to talk over the work of the morning. Then they would have a one o'clock dinner with Knox and Eliza and whatever relatives were in residence. After a "resting spell" or siesta they would start out again. Though he had competent overseers, Joseph kept an eye on everything himself, so he and Jeff would ride to this field and that, then around the barns and the gins until late afternoon.

Knox seemed to delight in Hurricane's daily routine and had no yearning for town life. Eliza, who was the personification of amiability and sweet nature, made her feel more than accepted. Davis' kin came in quantities to welcome her.

Jeff's first love, Sarah Knox, possessed that special appealing quality women native to the sign of Pisces are reputed to have, a quality, which supposedly frames them to be adored by their husbands.

Everything was going harmoniously on August 11, when Knox wrote her last extant letter to her mother at Fort Crawford.

> Dearest Mother:
>
> I have just received your affectionate letter forwarded to me from Louisville; you may readily imagine the pleasure it afforded me to hear from you. . . . How often, my dear Mother, I wish I could look in upon you. I imagine so often I can see you moving about attending to your domestic concerns—down in the cellar skimming milk or going to feed the chickens. . . . Tell Dick I have a beautiful colt, prettier than his I expect. Mr. Davis sends his best respects to you. . . . My love to Pa and Dick. . . . Remember me most affectionately to Sister and the Doc [Dr. Wood]. Kiss the children. . . . Do not make yourself uneasy about me; the country is quite healthy.

Before her mother received the letter with the reassuring last line, Knox was stricken with malaria—one day after Jeff had developed the disease. When the bride and groom did not respond to such treatment as the nearest physician prescribed, it was decided the change of a river trip might prove beneficial.

Ian and Shenga arrived at Hurricane three days before and both Jeff and Ian reminisced about earlier times. Shenga would walk around the grounds alone, visit with the slaves, watch the animals, but seemed impatient to continue their journey back to Indian Territory so Ian resolved to finish his visit quickly.

Four of the weeping old men slaves carried Sarah Knox on a litter to the boat, and they went to Bayou Sara to stay with Jeff's eldest sister, Anna, Mrs. Luther Smith, who lived nearby at Locust Grove in West Feliciana Parish. Jefferson hoped their recovery would be speeded by the higher ground of Locust Grove. As they disembarked at Bayou Sara, Knox must have had foreboding, for it was here in 1820 that two of her little sisters had died of the fever, while her mother and her sister Ann and she herself had been quite ill. Ian and Shenga accompanied them, helping comfort Jeff and Knox.

Both Jefferson and Knox became alarmingly worse after their arrival at the plantation and were put to bed in different rooms. Anna devoted herself tirelessly to nursing, and a sister-in-law, widow of Dr. Benjamin Davis, came to assist. At first Jefferson was thought to be the more dangerously ill of the two. Then Knox's fever rose so high she became delirious.

Ian asked Shenga if she could help make Jeff and Knox well. Shenga shook her head sorrowfully with tears in her eyes. All she said was, "It is written," meaning the conclusion of their sickness had been determined by a higher power.

The bride's critical condition was kept from the husband, who was forbidden by the doctor to leave his bed. But hearing Knox burst into eerie singing—the song was "Fairy Bells," something connected with their courtship—he got up and staggered fever-ridden into her room. She did not recognize him. He saw she was dying. There was nothing he could do for her except hold her in his arms, until, like the Lady of Shalott "singing, in her song, she died."

Brokenhearted, the young husband was led back to his own bed by Ian and James. To his critical condition was added the complication of a searing grief and a troubled conscience. If he had not persisted in marrying her against her father's objection, if he had not brought her to the Delta, Knox would be alive. Now, she who had been his wife for less than three months was dead at twenty-one. The physician and the family feared Jeff would die too. Weak as he was, however, he insisted that the funeral service be held in his sickroom. Knox was buried in the Smith's family cemetery in the southwest corner not far from Jefferson's brother Benjamin and Luther Smith, Anna's husband.

Ian, melancholy with great depression of spirits with the gloomy foreboding, left Jeff's death bed to sit under a tree where Shenga sat exposed to the drizzling rain. A poor Negro woman, returning from the labors of the field, took compassion upon them, conducting them into her hut, and there gave them food, compassion, and shelter. As Ian lay down to a fitful sleep on the mat spread for him on the floor of the hut, his benefactress called to the female part of the family to resume their task of spinning cotton, in which they continued far into the night. They lightened their labor with songs, one of which was composed extempore, for Ian was himself the subject of it. It was sung by one of the younger women, the rest joining in a chorus. The air was sweet and plaintive, and the words, literally translated, were these; "The winds roared, and the rains fell. The poor white man, friend of our master, faint and weary, came and sat under our tree. He has no mother to bring him milk." Chorus—"Let us pity the white man, no mother has he in his sadness!" Trifling as the recital may appear to a person in Ian's situation; the circumstance was affective to the highest degree. He was so impressed by such unexpected kindness, that sleep fled before his eyes. Shenga remained at his side displaying her sympathies and affections in his suffering.

For a day or two Jeff's life hung in the balance. But under Anna's tender ministrations he began to recover. The convalescence was slow. It was more than a month before he was able to return to Hurricane. It was eight years before he overcame his grief.

While Ian and Shenga sojourned at the guesthouse of Joseph Davis waiting for Jefferson to recover, frequently travelers stopped to enjoy the hospitality of the Davis'.

One of the visitors was Samuel Houston. He was at that time called an elegant gentleman, was fine looking and very vain of his personal appearance; but domestic troubles completely changed his whole life, and leaving his wife and family he under oath, solemnly renounced the world and went into exile, as he termed it. He stopped at the Hurricane on his way to the wilderness and excited the children's admiration by his fanciful hunter's garb and the romance that surrounded him. He begged a fine greyhound and a pointer from Joseph, who gave them up, but not without a great struggle with himself, for he loved them—little thinking that this man, fantastically clad in buckskin, would one day, as President of Texas, repay him amply.

Ian and Shenga left for the Western Territory immediately after the services and traveled with Samuel Houston for two days after which he turned south to the Republic of Texas.

Texian Dream of Empire

*T*he Texians strongly captured the imagination of a large part of the people of the southwestern frontier. The survivors of expeditions spread their tales around, of American heroism, Hispanic cruelty, fortresses taken and lost, dramatic councils of war, and chests of silver coins. The miserable, struggling Spanish towns became cities rich in gold and lovely, dark-eyed women. The soil of the coastal prairies was said to be far superior to that in the United States, and the climate the best in the world. Through these tales shone the shimmering image of a fabulous empire, of broad vistas and plateaus where a man could see for miles, of Indians and millions of buffalo and cattle hardly less wild. This was country where a man could be a man, and a good man could make himself a king. In these years a lasting legend was born.

But in the year 1820 an era seemed to be closing, rather than great opportunities opening. Anglo-America, after three-quarters of a century of incredible growth, and almost everywhere reached what seemed its natural limits. The Southwest beyond the Sabine was Spanish, and was so recognized by formal treaty. The United States, with the purchase of the Louisiana Territory, extended to the Rocky Mountains, and, in addition to Texas, Jefferson had claimed the Northwest Pacific, too. But up against the barriers of the mountains and Great Plains, the United States appeared to be entering a period of consolidation. Since 1800, its territory had more than doubled.

While there were still appetites for raw land in the West, there were evidences of actual opposition to any new expansion in the northern and eastern States. The question of the extension of slavery in the Union was becoming difficult.

When it was apparent that the United States had won its independence, most of the Americans west of the Mississippi River took the oath of allegiance to the King of Spain. In 1783, Galvez was able to secure a royal edict that all refugees in His Most Catholic Majesty's dominions should enjoy the right to stay. Many did. In 1787, the Spanish Minister at Philadelphia was empowered to recruit Anglo-Americans for the Missouri country, while General James Wilkinson of Kentucky, one of the oldest and most successful scoundrels ever to wear an American uniform was paid to separate the western settle-

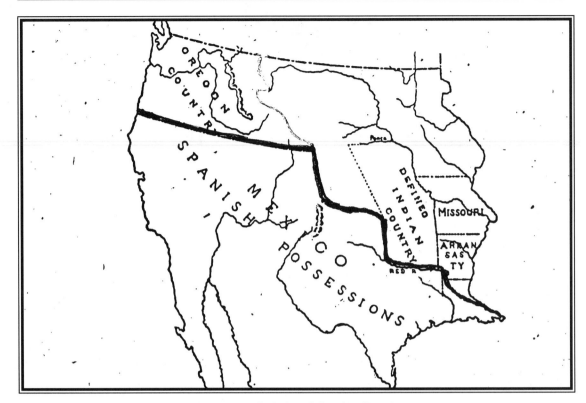

Map of Kansas included in defined Indian Country

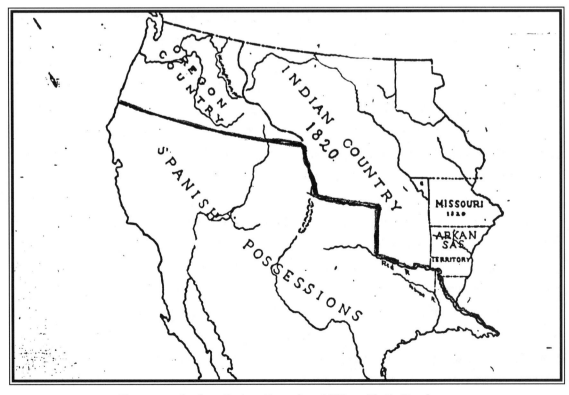

Kansas received an Eastern Boundary 1820—a Platte Purchase.

Nla Heiska
(Means White
Cloud)
**This man was
my great great
grandfather.**

Lucille Gerhardt

Chief White Cloud went to top of King Hill in South Saint Joseph, Missouri to pray for guidance before signing the Platte Purchase Treaty in 1836. The following year, the Pottawatomie tribe, the Sac (Sauk) and Fox band and the Ioway tribe were relocated west and the land was opened for settlement.

White Cloud was Chief of the Ioway Tribe.

St. Joseph (Mo.) News Press, September 14, 2002

ments from the United States. As part of the conspiracy, Wilkinson secretly took an oath of allegiance to Spain.

The Spanish policy of recruitment was successful. One revolutionary veteran, Colonel William Morgan of New Jersey, contracted to settle a number of American families at the mouth of the Ohio, at a town called New Madrid. The Spanish offered lucrative deals to responsible men who could recruit and found a colony at their own expense. They were granted the title Impresario and given enormous acres of free land. The families they brought with them were also well rewarded. Spain granted rich land—leagues of it—under terms immensely better than those administered under the public land policies of the new United States. Missouri had other advantages; the French, long before, had already wiped out the powerful Indian tribes through a combination of warfare, smallpox and venereal disease.

Several thousand American citizens emigrated to Missouri. Among these were a number of men who later became prominent in the state. Although these colonists agreed to become Roman Catholics, they were officially assured they would be left in peace. They did, however, all become citizens of Spain.

The Spanish officials considered their policies eminently successful; Missouri was filling up, with Spanish subjects whose only fault was that they still spoke English.

Two things bothered the Spanish dream of a great new Mississippi empire. First, the United States was able to hold the western settlements in Kentucky, and through the device of statehood, begin its rapid, organic growth. One of the Americans who took up lands in Missouri, and became a loyal citizen of Spain, was a Connecticut Yankee named Don Moses Austin. He and his son, as Impresarios, were to bring the first Anglo-Saxon colony to the country north of the Rio Grande.

At the close of the 18th century, an exhilarating sense of opportunity pervaded the entire Anglo-American frontier; the Indians had been pushed back into northwest Ohio; settlers were in Illinois. Kentucky was a prosperous state. Georgia had acquired title, under federal law, to all its former Indian territories. Everywhere, thousands of settlers were pouring west and the Territory of Mississippi was being organized. The Indians of the old Southwest were in their tragic century of full retreat toward the desiccated lands of Oklahoma.

Jefferson's purchase of Louisiana was in the nature of support of the steady movement west.

President Jackson thought that the better part of valor was to secure land by diplomacy or purchase to avoid the risk of war.

The Americans of the Southwest had a taste for territorial expansion, and a sense both of far horizons and ethnic superiority—a feeling that then pervaded the whole English-speaking world. They were also belligerent, a lasting American folkway that seems to have formed its base in the old Southwest.

The west was determined on three goals: more land, dominion over the continent, and expansion of its folk. The national government was frequently painfully caught between eastern pacifism and southwestern expansionism and belligerency, swinging one way or the other, depending on where the immediate power lay.

Besides the farmers and plantation makers of the border West, another class of expansionists was rising in the land. These were the men called freebooters, who cut a brief but bloody illegal swath across the old Southwest. These English freebooters (some called them pirates) in most Anglo-Saxon eyes served a national and ethnic as well as a personally profitable purpose.

The freebooters were supposed not to attack their own kind.

Sir Henry Morgan and Jean La Fitte, the supreme freebooters, were considered to have done necessary things their own cowardly government would not, or could not, approve.

The French called them boucaniers (buccaneers).

There was something about the open spaces of the Southwest that strongly affected the Anglo-Saxon mind and they saw the various governments' weaknesses.

General Wilkinson was busy with many things. He wore his nation's uniform, but his service was always strictly for himself. He was not typical, but not entirely unusual for the times.

Neither the American Army nor diplomatic service was yet professional; men went in and out of offices as their influence allowed, but few thought in terms of a federal career. Wilkinson became one of the greatest double agents, but not quite traitor, of all times.

While in command of the Kentucky militia, he made a secret concordat with Spain. He became a Spanish citizen, promised to separate the Western counties from the United States, and went back north with Spanish gold. When he took command of Louisiana, after Jefferson's purchase, he was still a citizen of Spain, and drawing Spanish gold in return for regular reports.

The United States government insisted that it had bought not only Louisiana, but also everything north and east of the Rio Grande as well. The French, to sweeten the Louisiana pot, had revived their old claims to Texas, and sold them as part of the purchase. President Jefferson indicated to Spain that he expected their people to evacuate Texas, with great popular support.

Now, there was extreme tension on the Texas-U.S. border. Spain responded by throwing more troops into east Texas, and by standing fast. They argued that even Napoleon could not sell a province he had never owned.

Wilkinson mentioned the possibility of detaching Texas and New Mexico from Spain. The original idea was Wilkinson's, but Aaron Burr, who whatever his faults was a man of action, "matured it." Making, as he thought, a secret compact with Wilkinson that the general would resign and join his project at the proper time. Burr made a trip west in 1805, seeking and obtaining considerable support, raising men and arms and shipping to carry them down the Mississippi. By this time, Burr had left the office of vice-president.

If Spain revealed Wilkinson's secret dealings—or even the fact he was a Spanish subject—Wilkinson would be a candidate for a firing squad.

Realizing his schemes could no longer be sustained, Wilkinson extracted himself with brilliance, if utter immorality.

He wrote President Jefferson that he was on the trail of a great conspiracy. Having caught Jefferson's interest, he next revealed the traitor's name—Aaron Burr. For Jefferson, and for a great part of the country, he could not have named a more fortunate choice. Burr was unpopular; now he became an arch-ogre. To defray his great expenses in tracking his conspiracy down, Wilkinson asked the president for a large sum of money and collected.

He personally ordered Burr's arrest. Wilkinson was the sole source of this charge, and he was to be the principle witness at Burr's ensuing treason trial.

Burr was acquitted on a technicality, but it effectively silenced Burr, who otherwise might have talked and brought Wilkinson down in his own destruction.

The Grand Conspiracy has always been an unhappy subject for historians. One capable scoundrel can cause enormous riptides in the currents of history.

The United States government was shaken to its roots by accusing Burr, a former vice-president of the United States.

The last thing the administration of President Jefferson wanted was a Spanish war.

Texas had a desperado army of American, Louisiana French, Mexican rebels and Indians.

This army was soon reduced to freebooters (pirates). Washington protested that it had little control of the Texas freebooters.

Self-government in Texas really meant the absence of government.

Some Texans found the U.S. attitude hard to comprehend, but it was this: the U.S. government was prepared to assist a band of civil rebels fighting for a constitution unofficially, but these bands were not to be allowed to predicate their lawless acts in U.S. territory.

President Jackson himself held this view: he branded a Texas declaration of independence a "rash and premature act."

Mexico had a hard, blooded, professional army, an adequate treasury filled by its silver mines, and Santa Anna's energetic leadership. The Texans could not possible raise as many soldiers, and they had no money or industry or supply system at all.

The United States had a tremendous strategic stake in Texas. Texas blocked American expansion to the Pacific, and a weak, unstable nation on American borders invited penetration by still-ambitious European powers.

The Texans swallowed their frustration and tried to keep in President Jackson's favor.

It is very seldom that a man arises from an obscure and humble position to an exalted pre-eminence, without peculiar fitness for the work on which his fame rests, and which probably no one else could have done so well. He may not be learned or cultured; he may even be unlettered and rough. He may be stained by vulgar defects and vices which are fatal to all dignity of character, but there must be something about him which calls out the respect and admiration of those with whom he is surrounded, so as to give him a start and open a way for success in the business or enterprise where his genius lies.

Such a man was Andrew Jackson. Whether as a youth, or as a man pursuing his career of village lawyer in the backwoods of a frontier settlement, he was about the last person of whom one would predict that would arise to a great position and unbounded national popularity. His birth was commonplace and obscure. His father of Scotch-Irish descent, lived in a miserable hamlet in North Carolina, near the South Carolina line, without owning a single acre of land—one of the poorest of the poor whites. The boy Andrew, born shortly after his father's death in 1767, was reared in poverty and almost without education, learning at school only to "read, write, and cipher;" nor did he have any marked desire for knowledge, and never could spell correctly. At the age of thirteen he was driven from his native village by its devastation at the hands of the English soldiers, during the Revolutionary War. His mother, a worthy and most self-reliant woman, was an ardent patriot, and all her boys— Hugh, Robert, and Andrew—enlisted in the local home guard. The elder two died, Hugh of exposure and Robert of prison small-pox, while Andrew, who had also been captured and sick of the disease, survived this early training in the scenes of war for further usefulness. The mother made her way on foot to Charleston, South Carolina, to nurse the sick patriots in the prison-ship, and there died of the prison fever, in 1781. The physical endurance and force of character of his mother constituted evidently the chief legacy that Andrew inherited, and it served him well through a long and arduous life.

At fifteen the boy was "a homeless, sick, and sorrowful orphan," working for a saddler in Charleston a few hours of the day, as his health would permit. With returning strength he got possession of a horse; but his army associates had led him into evil ways, and he became indebted to his landlord for board. This he managed to pay only by staking his horse in a game of dice against $200, which he fortunately won; and this squared him with the world and enabled him to start afresh, on a better way.

Poor and obscure as he was, and imperfectly educated, he aspired to be a lawyer; and at eighteen years of age, he became a law student in the office of Mr. Spruce McCay in Salisbury, North Carolina. Two years later, in 1787, he was admitted to the bar. Not making much headway in Salisbury, he wandered to that part of the state which is now Tennessee, which was then an almost unbroken wilderness, exposed to Indian massacres and depredations. Finally he located himself at Nashville, where there was a small settlement filled chiefly with adventurers who led lives of license and idleness.

It seems that Jackson, who was appointed district attorney, had a considerable practice in his profession of a rough sort, in that frontier region where the slightest legal knowledge was sufficient for success. He was in no sense a student, like Jefferson and Madison in the early part of their careers in Virginia as village lawyers, although he was engaged in as many cases and had perhaps as large an income as they. But what was he doing all this while, when he was not in his log office and in the log courtroom, sixteen feet square? Was he pondering the principles of precedents of law, and storing his mind with the knowledge gained from books? Not at all. He was attending horse races and cockfights and all the sports, which marked the Southern people of that time. His associates were not the most cultivated and wealthy of them either, but ignorant, rough, drinking, swearing, gambling, fighting rowdies, whose society was repulsive to people of taste, intelligence, and virtue.

The young lawyer became a favorite with these men and with their wives and sisters and daughters. He could ride a horse better than any of his neighbors; he entered into their quarrels with zeal and devotion; he was bold, rash, and adventurous, ever ready to hunt a hostile Indian, or fight a duel, or defend an innocent man who had suffered injury and injustice. He showed himself capable of the warmest and most devoted friendship as well as the bitterest and most unrelenting hatred. He was quick to join a dangerous enterprise, and ever showing ability to lead it—the first on the spot to put out a fire, the first to expose himself in a common danger commanding respect for his honesty, sincerity and integrity; exciting fear from his fierce wrath when insulted. He was a man terribly in earnest, always as courteous and chivalric to women as he was hard and savage to treacherous men. Above all, he was now a man of commanding stature, graceful manners, dignified deportment, and a naturally distinguished air, so that he was looked up to by men and admired by women. What did those violent, quarrelsome, adventurous settlers on the western confines of American civilization care whether their favorite was learned or ignorant, so long as he was manifestly superior to them in their chosen pursuits and pleasures and was capable of leading them in any enterprise. And so long as he sympathized with them in all their ideas and prejudices—a born democrat, as well as a born leader. His claim upon them, however, was not without its worthy elements. He was perfectly fearless in enforcing the law, laughing at intimidation. He often had to ride hundreds of miles to professional duties on circuit, through forests infested by Indians, and towns cowed by ruffians; and he and his rifle were held in great respect. He was renowned as the foremost Indian fighter in that country, and as a prosecuting attorney whom no danger and no temptation could swerve him from his duty. He was feared, trusted, and boundlessly popular.

The people, therefore, rallied about this man. When in 1796 a convention was called for framing a state constitution, Jackson was one of their influential delegates, and in

December of that year he was sent to Congress as their most popular representative. Of course, he was totally unfit for legislative business in which he never could have made any mark. On his return in 1797, a vacancy occurring in the United States Senate, he was elected senator, on the strength of his popularity as representative. But he remained only a year at Philadelphia, finding his calling dull, and probably conscious that he had no fitness for legislation, while the opportunity for professional and pecuniary success in Tennessee was very apparent to him.

He was made chief justice of the Superior Court of Tennessee, with no more fitness for administering the law than he had for making it, or interest in it. Mr. Parton tells an anecdote of Jackson at this time which, whether true or not, illustrates his character as well as the rude conditions amid which he made himself felt. He was holding court in a little village in Tennessee, when a great, hulking fellow, armed with a pistol and bowie-knife, paraded before the little court house, and cursed judge, jury, and all assembled. Jackson ordered the sheriff to arrest him, but that functionary failed to do it, either alone or with a posse. Whereupon Jackson caused the sheriff to summon him as posse, adjourned court for ten minutes, walked out, and told the fellow to yield or be shot.

In telling why he surrendered to one man, when he had defied a crowd, the ruffian afterwards said: "When he came up I looked him in the eye, and I saw shoot. There wasn't shoot in nary another eye in the crowd. I said to myself, it is about time to sing small; and so I did."

It was by such bold and fearless conduct that Jackson won admiration—not by law, of which he knew but little, and never could have learned much. The law, moreover, was uncongenial to this man of action, and he resigned his judgeship and went for a short time into business, trading land, selling horses, groceries, and dry goods, then he was appointed major general of militia. This was just what he wanted. He had now found his place and was equal to it. His habits, enterprises, dangers, and bloody encounters all fitted him for it. Henceforth his duty and his pleasure ran together in the same line. His personal peculiarities had made him popular; this popularity had made him prominent and secured to him offices for which he had no talent, seeing which he dropped them; but when a situation was offered for which he was fitted, he soon gained distinction, and his true career began.

It was as an Indian fighter that he laid the foundation of his fame. His popularity with rough people was succeeded by a series of heroic actions, which brought him before the eyes of the nation. There was no sham in these victories. He fairly earned his laurels, and they so wrought on the imagination of the people that he quickly became famous.

But before his military exploits brought him a national reputation, he had become notorious in his neighborhood as a duelist. He was always ready to fight when he deemed himself insulted. His numerous duels were very severely commented on when he became a candidate for the presidency, especially in New England. But dueling was a peculiar Southern institution; most Southern people settled their difficulties with pistols. Some of Jackson's duels were desperate and ferocious. He was the best shot in Tennessee, and, it is said, he could lodge two successive balls in the same hole. As early as 1795, he fought with a fellow lawyer by the name of Avery. In 1806, in a duel, he killed Charles Dickinson, who had spoken disparagingly of his wife, whom he had lately married, a divorced woman to whom he was tenderly attached as long as she lived. Still later he fought with Thomas H. Benton, and received a wound from which he never fully recovered.

Such was the life of Jackson until he was forty-five years of age—that of a violent, passionate, arbitrary man, beloved as a friend, and feared as an enemy.

It was the Creek war and the war with England that developed his extraordinary energies. When the war of 1812 broke out he was major general of Tennessee militia, and at once offered his services to the government, which were eagerly accepted, and he was authorized to raise a body of volunteers in Tennessee and to report with them at New Orleans. He found no difficulty in collecting about sixteen hundred men. In January, 1813, he took them down the Cumberland, the Ohio, and the Mississippi to Natchez, in such flat-bottomed boats as he could collect; another body of mounted men crossed the country five hundred miles to the rendezvous and went into camp at Natchez on February 15, 1813.

The Southern Department was under the command of General James Wilkinson, with headquarters at New Orleans. He was a disagreeable and contentious man, who did not like Jackson.

Through his influence, the Tennessee detachment, after two months' delay in Natchez, was ordered by the authorities at Washington to be dismissed without pay, five hundred miles from home. Jackson promptly decided not to obey the command, but to keep his forces together, provide at his own expense for their food and transportation, and take them back to Tennessee in good order. He accomplished this, putting sick men on his own three horses, and himself marching on foot with the men, who, enthusiastic over his elastic toughness, dubbed him "Old Hickory"—a title of affection that is familiar to this day. The government afterwards reimbursed him for his outlay in this matter, but his generosity, self-denial, energy, and masterly force added immensely to his popularity. Jackson's disobedience of orders attracted but little attention at Washington, in that time of greater events, while his own patriotism and fighting zeal were not abated by his failure to get at the enemy. And very soon his desires were to be granted. In 1811, before the war with England was declared, a general confederation of Indian's had been made under the influence of the celebrated Tecumseh, a chief of the Shawanoc tribe. He was a man of magnificent figure, stately and noble as a Greek warrior, and withal eloquent. With his twin brother, the Prophet, Tecumseh traveled from the Great Lakes in the North to the Gulf of Mexico, inducing tribe after tribe to unite against the rapacious and advancing whites. But he did not accomplish much until the war with England broke out in 1812, when he saw a possibility of realizing his grand idea. From the British and the Spaniards, the Indians received arms and ammunition.

The first attack of these Indians was on August 13, 1813, at Fort Mims in Alabama, where there were nearly two hundred people who were collected for safety. Red Eagle, who utterly annihilated the defenders of the fort under Major Beasley, and scalped the women and children, led the Indians, chiefly Creeks. When reports of this unexpected and atrocious massacre reached Tennessee the whole population was aroused to vengeance, and General Jackson, his arm still in a sling from his duel with Benton, set out to punish the Indian foes. But he was impeded by lack of provisions, and quarrels among his subordinates, and general insubordination. In surmounting his difficulties he showed extraordinary tact and energy. His measures were most vigorous. He did not hesitate to shoot, whether legally or illegally, those who were insubordinate, thus restoring military discipline, the first and last necessity in war. Soldiers soon learn to appreciate the worth of such decision, and follow such a leader with determination almost equal to his own. Jackson's troops did splendid marching and fighting.

So rapid and relentless were his movements against the enemy that the campaign lasted but seven months, and the Indians were nearly all killed or dispersed.

His early dangers and adventures, and his acquaintance with Indian warfare ever since he could handle a rifle, now stood him in good stead. On the 21st of April, 1814, the militia under his command returned home victorious, and Jackson for his heroism and ability was made a major general in the regular army, he then being forty-seven years of age. It was in this war that we first hear of the famous frontiersman Davy Crockett, and of Sam Houston, afterwards so unique a figure in the war for Texan independence.

It is probable that had the Secretary of War sent Jackson to the North, he would have driven the British troops out of Canada. There is no question about his military ability, although his reputation was sullied by high-handed and arbitrary measures.

What he saw fit to do, he did, without scruples or regard to consequences. In war everything is tested by success; and in view of that, if sufficiently brilliant, everything else is forgotten.

His private life was by no means a model for others to imitate, yet showing great energy, a wonderful power of will, and undoubted honesty of purpose. His faults were those which may be traced to an imperfect education, excessive prejudices, and a violet temper. In his conversation he used expletives not considered in good taste, and which might be called swearing, without meaning any irreverence to the deity. But whatever he deemed his duty, he made every sacrifice to perform. Although fond of power, he was easily accessible, and he was frank and genial among his intimate friends. With great ideas of dignity, he was unconventional in all his habits, and detested useless ceremonies and the etiquette of courts. He put a great value on a personal friendship and never broke them except under necessity. For his enemies he cherished a vindictive wrath, as unforgiving as nemesis. Sam Houston knew Jackson years before he was elected president in 1829. Houston also knew that Jackson was the most popular man that this country ever saw, excepting perhaps Washington.

After the defense of New Orleans the legislatures of different states, and congress itself, passed grateful resolutions for his military services, and the nation heaped the entire honor on the hero that was in its power to give with medals, swords, and rewards.

Meanwhile, the struggle for Texan independence was drawing national attention, and although his sympathies lay with his old crony, Sam Houston, President Andrew Jackson was allowing no man to embroil the United States with Mexico.

Jackson was a frontiersman, the same as the Texians. But all their quarreling kind of faded into the dust—the land was wide and went on forever, and Jackson's America was still pointed toward the Pacific Ocean.

There was talk of Texas building its own empire in the west, if need be, in hostility and opposition of the United States. There were discussions among ambitious burning-eyed men.

The Indians became increasingly restless and difficult to control, on the edges of Anglo-Texas. The attitude of the majority of Texans expressed Indians had no inherent title to American soil and white men might dispossess them without formal legal action.

Militia, regular-Texas army forces and local bands called "ranging companies" were employed to control the Indians. In these operations, a large number of whites, and many Indians were killed; the warfare was bitter, bloody and brutal.

However, these wars expelled virtually all the immigrant Indians from Texas and opened up all east Texas to white settlement.

The Texas government claimed everything east of the Rio Grande, but the territory was effectively beyond reach and held mostly by bluff and talk.

There were important men in Texas who saw a Texas Empire stretching to the Pacific.

Plains' Indians in the north and Mexican vaqueros in the south were outside the experience of Americans, who did not understand the ways or minds of either. Yet they had to encounter both in a long, bloody, running war on their own ground for mastery of it. This was a war that never engaged more than a handful of the Americans, but it was to engage the American consciousness and create images and legends that would never die.

Small, deadly, burn-kill-rob-and-run raiding parties descended regularly off the high plateaus during the light of the summer moons. The Comanche raid became a certainty. These horse Indians were incredibly mobile by white men's standards. They rode enormous distances by night, then hid in brushy streambeds by day. The great distances and the thinness of white settlements made any kind of passive white defense ineffective.

Americans suffered from three great deficiencies: they were not horsemen; they lacked an effective war organization; and they were ill armed to face Indians on the open plain.

The old militia system was too cumbersome. It reacted with fatal slowness on a widely scattered frontier; by the time American horsemen assembled, the Indians were gone. The militia foot soldier could not give effective pursuit. Militia could not sustain the far-ranging punitive expeditions.

Also, while some Americans rode horseback, they were hardly cavalrymen or mounted warriors equal to the Kiowa and Comanche braves. The average Indian could ride rings around the average mounted white. Worse yet, the American weapons were not designed for horse combat. The Kentucky rifle and the tomahawk were woodland weapons. The long flintlocks (percussion caps began to come into use about 1820) were awkward arms in the saddle; they lost their accuracy, and could not be recharged easily. In the time it took a frontiersman to reload, a Comanche could charge three hundred yards and shoot twenty arrows. In a land without trees to hide behind; as in the Revolutionary war against the British; the whites were at a great disadvantage.

When whites engaged Comanches, they had to dismount and make a stand, firing some of their pieces to hold the Indians off, but always keeping some loaded rifles in reserve against a charge by what was the best light cavalry in the 19th-century world. Many Americans were saved, not by the stubbornness of their defense but by the fact that it was against Indian sensibilities and tactics to push an attack home. The best the Americans could achieve with their single-shot rifles was a standoff. If they ran, however, they were doomed, unless they quickly found timber or rock. Frontier manuals and books were emphatic, in detail, against trying to outrun Comanches; when the enemy fled, it brought out the hunting and killing instinct, and the Comanche was splendidly armed, with the bow, to kill fleeing horsemen during pursuit.

The American regular soldier was superior to the Plains Indian in only two respects: discipline and the courage to make a sustained fight.

In Comanche-American combat, pursuit of Indians out in the open was dangerous. If the whites fired their rifles, the Comanches charged behind a cloud of arrows, shooting as they rode. At ten feet, the long rifle made a poor club; the long Plains lance was ready and deadly.

The worst defeats the early Texas forces suffered from the Mexicans came when they engaged Mexican cavalry out on open ground. Some Mexican cavalry forces wiped out every unit of Americans they caught. The embattled farmers were not equipped to stand their ground on the wide prairie.

Comanche Warrior—Artist, George Catlin

ARMY DIGEST, December 1967

Many Americans who came out to the Indian frontier arrived with the basic necessities for survival. They were aggressive, competitive, ambitious, and given to prejudice and hate. They possessed the mental and moral nature to wage a sustained campaign, if the need arose.

But above all, they showed the two most important traits of a genuine dominant race: intelligence and the ability to cope and adapt to the situation.

The Indians cultures were peculiarly static, and stagnant; they would repeat their strengths and weaknesses to the end. The frontiersmen had one final, priceless asset; they were the far extension of a race with industrial skills. The adaptation of these skills to the frontier marked the turning point in the long European failure to conquer the Plains.

The frontiersmen who collided with the formidable Comanche, Pawnee, Osage, Sioux and other horsemen, found they had to change the traditional American system of war. The first great change involved the horse.

They had to learn to use the horse as a military implement, in other words, to ride like Mexicans, and the Cossacks of Russia and Mongols of China. The distances of the Western Territory were so vast that this came quickly and instinctively to the frontiersman, but it took many years of hard failures of infantrymen until the army recognized the necessity of cavalrymen and mounted tactics.

A number of men made the judgment that a man who could not ride well, or who detested the saddle and the horse, had no business in the Indian Territory. He could not prosper, or even survive. The men who loved the saddle were irresistibly drawn to the western frontier.

Another factor that came about was the deliberate improvement of the American horse breed. Farm plugs and mules could take a wagon to town, but Americans had to have breeds that could race the Spanish Arabians and the Indian's mustangs. They captured or developed them out of Kentucky racehorses, mustangs, and steeds with Arabian blood.

Texas did not have the means to garrison or police their bloody frontiers. Both Sam Houston and President Jackson knew this. Bluff did not work too well on the frontier. Farmer militia could not fight or even find Indian raiders, and Texas could not afford a large regular army, as the republic was always on the verge of bankruptcy. The same situation prevailed with the United States government. Both governments provided protection to their citizens as best they could under the circumstances and with the means at their disposal, graciously permitting the citizens to protect themselves by organizing ranging companies or "rangers." Ranging companies had been formed in Texas in 1823. The term ranger was already old in the United States; it referred to Indian fighters, the kind of men who carried the war to the enemy.

The rangers were unique. They were first a type of mounted militia, long before the army recognized and formed the military cavalrymen, though from the first it was realized that they needed a semi-permanent form. Ranger companies guarding the frontier had more or less permanent duty, because the danger never ceased. There were never sufficient funds to pay or equip them, at any period of the long expansion of the frontier from Ohio, Kentucky, and Illinois. They could never become an established, regularized force standing from year to year.

Both Texas and the United States authorized rangers as a paramilitary force and supported them when it could. Their recruitment was left to the frontier communities, as, to a great extent, was their support.

Some ranger commanders complained that, when they had fought and drove off the Indians, the local farmers complained about the rangers killing his hogs.

The ranging companies, without uniform, badges, or even government-supplied horses or arms, evolved slowly but in strikingly adaptive ways. At first the leaders were not appointed by the government, or honored with recognized commissions. The state, accidentally but fortunately let an indigenous brand of frontier leadership arise.

They were apart from the regular army, the militia or National Guard. They were instead one of the most colorful, efficient and deadly band of irregular partisans. They were not typical farmers. The man with a farm and family could not spend his time riding the wild frontier. They were for the most part extremely young. They were adventurous and uniformly courageous and all volunteers. The officers showed an utter absence of fear. This breed of captain was needed due to the rough nature of the men he led, and the incredibly perilous situation of the tiny bands on the war frontier.

To fight Indians and Mexicans, ranger leaders had to learn to think like both, or at least, to understand what Mexicans and Indians feared. The collision between the Americans and the Mexican on the southern frontier was inevitable. Contact did not improve either race; it seemed to strengthen and enhance the vices of both. The Ranger arrived with instinctive Teutonic directness, preferring the honest smash of the bullet to the subtlety of the knife. But, against the Indian, bluntness turned into brutality, because it was almost impossible for the Protestant Anglo-American to understand the Indian mind. Impatient with Indian deviousness, the rangers reacted with straight force. Some of the ranging companies clopped from deviousness to outright treachery. Still others became barbaric, devoid of all gentlemanly manners. They soon learned they could not surrender with war honors to the Indian. So the Rangers not only adopted the horse, but also adapted their warfare to reply in kind.

The morality of this open border warfare was meaningless because morality could only be defined within a culture—never across two cultures. The moral, upstanding Comanche lived by the laws of gods of his tribe.

The moral American who lived in peace with his fellows would bash an Indian infant's head against a tree, or gut-shoot a "Mexican" if he blinked. The ranging companies soon learned, those that survived the early fighting, that the Indians were different.

But depredations against their own kind increased to an intolerable level. When there weren't any Indians to kill or steal from, he would sneak up to an unsuspecting farmhouse, exactly like a Comanche. They would kill the farmer, rape his wife, shoot the children, burn the barn and house, take his horses, cattle, and hogs and any clothing, rifle, food, furniture, or anything else that took his fancy.

In all Army frontier history and wars, despite all the individual single cases of barbaric conduct, for the most part, in fact overwhelming part, the officers of this western frontier army conducted themselves within the gentlemen's rules of war. Intelligent, fair, courteous, but tough, persistent men, who gave honor to the United States of America.

Leavenworth, Sheridan, Sherman, Riley, Taylor, and dozens of others fought as a respectable force as much as they could under the circumstances. Only a few stretched the gentleman's code beyond recognized rules of ethics.

The frontier army served its country well and carried out the mandates of the infant United States in expanding its frontiers from ocean to ocean.

The most decisive factors in the winning of the West, was the invention of the revolving pistol by Samuel Colt, the repeating rifle by Winchester, and the inbreeding of the mustang with the Kentucky thoroughbreds.

Colt and Winchester could not market their arms in the East. There was no civilian need, nor could they interest the military in their use. Colt's only outlet was in the West. Colt's enterprise sank slowly into bankruptcy.

The United States Army ordinance experts saw no need for them, but they had never seen a Comanche war party.

A superb horseman in open country, armed with one or more long-barreled Colts, represented the most effective weapons system known in the world, but only Ian Douglass and Jamie Bill Childers recognized this at present time.

The Indian took up better tactics, avoiding open combat, resorting more and more to the hit-and-run killing and stock-stealing raids.

Expedition Against the Hasanun

*T*he American troops were going to meet the wandering tribes of Marauders, exasperated to the highest pitch against the whites. They were five to six thousand warriors in number, mounted for the most part on swift horses. War to them was not only a business or a pastime, but also the occupation of their lives. The tactics followed by these Indians rendered the regular system of warfare impotent or almost useless. They were here today and somewhere else tomorrow. All at once they were scattering panic among the horses and mules of the emigrants, who were crossing the territory in long caravans, and then they reappeared once more on the Missouri River, waiting for the passage of boats to pillage them and massacre the feeble crews. The Indian had the gift of being everywhere without being anywhere. These Indians assembled at the moment of battle, and scattered whenever the fortune of war was contrary to them.

The Otoe, Pottawatomie, and Omaha were forced by the civil and military authorities to leave their peaceful abodes, their fair fields and gardens, and immediately their "reservations," which had been guaranteed them in perpetuity was invaded by the whites. The allotment made by the government for the transportation of these poor unhappy, banished folk was quite considerable, and there was abundance of provisions. Nothing was omitted from the large promises that were made them, to manage everything for them, to make them happy and comfortable in their new home, where they would lack nothing. About 2,000 submitted, forcibly, to this agreement. They were put on board steamboats, which were chartered for the conveyance of these strange figures, and set ashore on their new reservation. What preparations had been made to receive so many wretched beings who saw themselves forced to leave their tents, cabins, fields, gardens, mills, fishing grounds? They were given in exchange a portion of land, comparatively uncultivated and miserable, almost destitute of animals and game, and besides this, they were set down in the vicinity of Pawnees, their mortal enemies from ancient times.

When they reached the place, the planting season was already too far along for favorable results with winter coming on; these civilized Indians were put on short rations. They found themselves in addition without grain or seed. A great number of their children had already died.

One would imagine himself among Christians, rather than among unhappy pagans. They kept saying to Father Gregg, "Black-robe, give us strong words, because our hearts are so hard; we are ignorant as the animals on our plains; we need to hear thee. Speak; we are listening!"

They had been relocated in Nebraska Territory on the west side of the Missouri River on both sides of the Platte River just 120 miles from Fort Leavenworth.

Ian's little band of 200 dog soldiers was to visit the relocated tribes and impress upon the Pawnee that the Hasanun expected them to live in peace with those newly arrived.

*   *   *

At the Planters House in the city of Leavenworth, a swarthy captain, ordered his aide, "Pull down the shades, orderly; and one lamp will be enough."

"That'll do. Close the door, and remain outside."

The captain threw off his cape, then silently waited until the aide had carried out his orders and vanished. Two other men came silently in; noting the silence of the captain simply removed their caps and waited the colonel's pleasure.

For a long moment the colonel stood tapping the lid of the desk with the butt of his pen and studying the long dispatch which he held in his hand. Then he looked up, "The Hasanun is within three hundred fifty miles of Fort Leavenworth and we have an excellent opportunity to stop her exhortations of war in the frontier territories."

"Gentlemen, we are ordered to the field immediately, the regiment to march in four days. Berrien, you will lead off."

When the Grand Conspiracy took over the Western frontier, they wanted the Indian problem reduced and the extermination of the Messiah would help considerably.

Captain Cooke had been ordered into Fort Leavenworth from the field and given four days in which to prepare his command for a march of more than seven hundred miles, over an uninhabited wilderness.

In that time six companies of the regiment which were to compose the expedition were reorganized; 110 transfers necessarily made from and to other companies; horses to be condemned, and many to be obtained; the companies paid, and the commanders of four of them changed. About fifty desertions occurred. To these principal duties and obstacles—implying a great mass of writing—were to be added every exertion of experience and foresight to provide for a line of operation of almost unexampled length and mostly beyond communication. On the morning of the 16th of September, at the commencement of a rainstorm, an inspector general made a hurried inspection by companies, which was not very satisfactory to him and others. Amid the confusion of Fort Leavenworth, the company commanders presented their new men—raw recruits—who they had scarcely seen under the effects usually following the pay-table.

It was discovered that three or four more days were to be lost in waiting for the quartermaster department to supply the absolutely necessary transportation. On the 18th, 107 mules were furnished, which the same day had arrived from a march of 1,000 miles from the mountains to the north. Another one hundred were nearly worthless from want of age, and requiring several hours to harness a team. Twenty-seven teamsters were needed and men were furnished, utterly ignorant of the business and without outfits. But they marched that day, fourteen miles, and the last of the train reached the camp at twelve midnight. On the next day, eleven wagon tongues had been broken. On the next day, after a hard rain, they marched six miles, which, on slippery ground, was as much as such a train could accomplish.

For eleven days, the rainy weather continued, clearing up with thick ice. The grass was very scarce and poor. It was not a season for prospects for delays.

Every care was taken to sustain the horses; they were led about two hours a day, and grazed on spots of grass found in the march. The long rain made the want of fuel more severe, it rendered useless the now scarce bois de vache "buffalo chips," used by travelers on the plains as fuel from time immemorial.

The dragoons crossed the South Platte with a very cold northwest wind and marched a mile or two on the North Platte in the vain search for any grass. After this the horses began to die and necessarily be left on the trail.

Next day there was a snowstorm falling three or four inches which the teams were forced to face; and twenty-three mules, all three year olds, were relieved from their harness, exhausted. The thermometer was thirty-three degrees; but a fierce wind made the cold excessive. Ice began floating in the river.

Mounted expeditions of the Army west of the Missouri depended entirely on the seasonal buffalo grass as forage for their animals. Rations of grain were usually carried in the baggage trains, but never hay.

A critical examination and report was made upon all the mules, and the oldest experienced company officer reviewed the inspection. Fifty-three horses were found ineffective for active service, and two hundred and seventy-eight fit to continue the march. The Regimental Quartermaster reported his ability to proceed with a loss of ten wagons, but eleven others of the train were only capable of going five or six days, when their loads of corn would be consumed if the others were not lightened. The corn trains were expected in a day or two. It was absolutely necessary to await their arrival.

Ian and Shenga's band of Indians always stayed ahead of the dragoons as they would dismount their ponies and trot along their mounts, resting them tremendously.

The dragoon's allowance of equipment for the march was greatly reduced, as in fact all other baggage; and even two ambulances, brought for the sick, were loaded with corn until they might be needed.

The corn wagons finally arrived, and were instantly taken and packed by great exertions, for the march.

Due to the Indians in front and all around them, Cooke read to the officers assembled in front of the mounted regiment, adding a few words expressing his confidence in their every exertion to meet the expectations of the commander of the army.

Not only did the cold blasts and heavy snows swoop in as a surprise, for the impression of a sunny temperate season had been expected, it fell upon the troopers not prepared for an ordinary winter's cold.

The horses were all blanketed from that time, and on the march led and mounted alternate hours, besides dismounting on difficult ground, same as the hostile Indians. But Ian and Shenga's band had a herd of spare horses for alternate riding, and as one mount tired, another was always there for a fresh mount. And they scouted tirelessly for good grass and let their horses graze the bunch grass to the roots.

At night Ian's warriors would raid Cooke's camp and steal away several horses each time. Cooke had to start guarding the horses and mules all night.

When finding on the river very good grass, the dragoons, after marching eight miles, made camp and herded the horses and mules, no corn was issued in the camp, save a half-feed to the horses the next morning. The Indian's main body rode twenty miles ahead of the troopers but snipers continually harassed the dragoon stragglers.

The Indian riders kept the dragoons and train under constant observation, harassed their outposts, drove off several herds of cattle, and burned three wagon trains. Ian and Shenga's band continuously withdrew towards the mountains to the west.

An express-man, a mounted messenger, was hired to carry a letter to communicate with Fort Leavenworth, but the man was shot through the head by the hostiles and his horse dragged him across the rough prairie ground for two miles, dead.

Next morning was very cold, the few tents were with difficulty folded and packed, having remained frozen from the sleet two nights before.

Five wagons and teams of the worst mules were that morning left in camp, to return to the Platte after resting two days.

Twenty miles were accomplished, against an excessively cold headwind. The horses were mostly led. The fatigue of walking up and over the high hills, in the face of the wind, was very great. A bad camp with poor hill-grass and a cold rain was made on a creek.

One of the hunters brought in at night four hundred pounds of good buffalo-meat, and also a canteen of petroleum from a spring at the base of one of the small black mountains near the trail. Five empty wagons and teams were ordered back to the other wagons left several days before.

The next day, the Dragoons found the ground once more white and the snow falling, but then very moderately.

Cooke marched as usual. But the north wind and drifting snow became severe. The air seemed turned to frozen fog, nothing could be seen. The troopers were struggling in a freezing cloud. Every so often a powerful war arrow would shoot out of the mist, disabling over seven troopers. The hostiles were relentless in avenging their dead comrades.

Now the streams became choked with snow and ice. Finally, the guide led them to a great granite rock, but all too small for the promised shelter. Only a part of the regiment could huddle there in the deep snow, while the long night through the storm continued, and in fearful eddies from above, before, behind, drove the falling and drifting snow. Thus exposed, in the hope of grass, the poor animals were driven with great devotion by the men once more across the stream and three-quarters of a mile beyond to the base of a granite ridge, but which almost faced the storm. There the famished mules, crying piteously, did not seek to eat, but desperately gathered in a mass; and some horses, escaping the guard, went back to the ford where the lofty precipice first gave them so pleasant relief and shelter.

The morning light had nothing cheerful to reveal, and the air was still filled with driven snow. The animals soon came, driven in, and mingled in confusion with men, crunching the snow in the confined and wretched camp, trampling all things in their way. It was not a time to dwell on the fact that from that mountain desert there was neither retreat nor any shelter near, but a time for action. No murmurs, not a complaint was heard, and certainly none in their commander's face a doubt or cloud; but with stern manner, he gave the orders for the march.

And then the sun showed its place in the sky, and their hearts beat lighter.

But for six hours the frozen fog fell thickly, like snow, and again they marched as in a cloud.

The deep snowdrifts impeded them much and in crossing a river the ice broke in the middle. On the trail they found the bodies of three frozen outriders.

The mercury that morning marked forty-four degrees below freezing-point, but the march was started before eight o'clock, and soon a high northwest wind arose, which with the drift, gave great suffering. Few could ride long. The snow was blown deep in the creek valley, to which the hills gave little shelter. On them the guide said, there was some grass; but few animals went, and none stayed there, so bitter was the wind.

Twenty-three mules had given out, and five wagons and the harness were abandoned at the camp.

The next day the snow was deep and drifted; the officers and men leading had to break through the drifts on the trail, where the wagons had to follow. The cloud was still on them and freezing in their faces. Seven hours thus the valley was regained, and the wagons arrived at night. The animals were driven over the ice to herd on the high hills bounding the very narrow valley; but in the night a very great wind arose and drove them back from the scant bunch-grass there, freezing to death fifteen. They had there for fuel, besides the sage, the little bush-willow sticks.

Shenga Wassa and Ian's chief men who had long experience of the great plain's winter's advised him that the cold and snow would do their killing for them, so the little band decided to call off the fight and hole up in some camps where the summer-killed buffalo jerky was cached for such emergency on the winter trail. As they kept in their warm teepees while the snow and sleet storms raged outside, they sat out the remainder of the winter planning their spring war expeditions against any remaining troopers.

Back at the dragoon column, the northeast wind continued fiercely, enveloping them in a cloud, which froze and fell all day. Few could face that wind. The herders were to bring up the rear, with extra but nearly all broken-down mules, but could not force them from the dead bushes of the little valley, and they remained there all day and night, bringing on the next day the remainder of the mules, that had not frozen. Thirteen miles were marched, and the camp was made four miles from the top of the pass. A wagon that day cut partly through the ice of a creek, and there it froze so fast that eight mules could not move it empty. Nearly all the tent-pins were broken in the last camp; a few of iron were substituted. Nine trooper-horses were left freezing and dying on the road, and a number of soldiers and teamsters had been frostbitten. It was a desperately cold night; the thermometers were broken, but, by comparison, must have marked twenty-five degrees below zero. A bottle of sherry wine froze in a trunk. Having lost about fifty mules in thirty-six hours, Cooke left a wagon in the bushes, filled with seventy-four extra saddles and bridles and some sabers. Two other wagons, at the last moment, he was obliged to leave, but empty. The carbines were then issued to the mounted as well as the dismounted men.

The next day it was pleasant in the forenoon to men well wrapped and walking in the sun. The guide's search resulted in his reporting "no grass." There remained but one day's corn after that night. It proved intensely cold, and the mules for once were ordered tied to the wagons. They gnawed, and destroyed four wagon-tongues, a number of wagon covers, ate their ropes, and getting loose ate the sage fuel collected at the tents. Some of the tents they also attacked. Nine died.

The fast growing company of dismounted men marched together as a separate command by day. In the morning a number of them were frostbitten from not being in motion, although standing by fires.

That day eighteen miles were marched to Big Sandy, where the guide found grass, and fuel with it, so good that the next day was made a day of rest; the animals were all herded at the grass. Fifty horses had been lost.

November 14 was cold with a dense fog, which caused much delay and difficulty in collecting the animals. Later in the day the weather had much moderated.

On the 15th they reached a government mail station. Nine wagons were left at the house, and forty-two mules, with teamsters to herd them.

The sick report had rapidly run up from four or five to forty-two; thirty-six soldiers and teamsters having been frosted. A man named Migette was authorized to collect and winter such animals as he might find surviving on the trail.

The next day they had to face a very severe wind. Twenty horses were abandoned in that twenty-four hours.

The guide was sent to look for grass the next morning and found some, so the regiment marched, leading the horses six miles and encamped there.

On November 19, they marched, leading through the mud and snow. Cooke's command was in desperate straits, so he decided to spend the winter there in a temporary establishment, which he named Camp Gordon. He had 144 horses left, having lost 134. Most of the loss had occurred in comparatively moderate weather. It had been of starvation. The land was a lifeless, treeless, grassless desert; it contained scarcely a wolf to glut itself on the hundreds of dead and frozen animals which for thirty miles nearly abandoned and shattered property; they marked, perhaps beyond example in history, the steps of an advancing army with the horrors of a disastrous retreat.

It had been a terrible experience. Constant snowstorms had been encountered; the temperature dropped to minus sixteen degrees; the draft animals and beef cattle weakened pitifully because of lack of forage. As a result they dropped alongside the road and in camp by the dozens and quickly froze. Progress was so slow that the last fifteen days they were only able to negotiate thirty-five miles!

All of this suffering was directly attributable to the Secret Committee of the West's desperate attempt to stop a major war on the plains. General Wilkinson disregarded all prudent reasoning about wintering on the plains and had ordered the expedition to start entirely too late in the season. It had been launched against competent military advice. Final blame must be squarely placed upon the Grand Conspiracy in utter disregard for the dragoons and the stupidity of the politicians' ignorance in Washington of such a conspiracy.

So ended this most remarkable march in Cooke's wide experience. His solicitude for his men and animals, his courage under highly adverse conditions, his efficiency in handling his command won the praise of all his superior officers, including those involved in the treasonable conspiracy. In early spring his command returned by way of Bent's Fort, Colorado, and the Santa Fe Trail.

The Massacre

*T*he United States government had finally devised a plan to take care of the Indian problem . . . that is, exterminate all wild, uncivilized Indians.

The warriors of the Seminole in Florida and the Apache of Arizona/New Mexico Territory had proven fierce adversaries so they were the people to be exterminated by the War Department.

General Jesup wrote to his superiors, "In regard to the Seminole, their country is an unexplored wilderness, the interior of which we are as ignorant as of the interior of China. We exhibit in our present contest a nation employing an army to attempt to remove a band of Indians from one wilderness in Florida to another in Arizona/New Mexico."

"My decided opinion is, that unless immediate emigration be abandoned, the war will continue for years."

To this the Secretary of War replied that the government desired the removal of the Seminole to the West as early as practicable, no matter the cost in lives or expense.

The United States Army, the Grand Conspiracy, the Spaniards, Texians, frontiersmen, Mexicans, ranging companies—all were involved in the exterminating war. The number of soldiers would be increased, until they would cover the country as the grasshoppers cover the fields.

"Bury the hatchet," said the envoys extraordinary of the government, "and the soldiers will return whence they came."

All that was . . . was only another lie in the long list of lies.

Shenga Wassa and her little band of followers, approximately three hundred souls, had made camp near a little stream at the edge of the foothills of the Rocky Mountains. They decided on a performance of the Ghost Dance—their religious dancing ceremony with their Messiah in attendance.

A hole was dug in the ground and into it was fitted snugly a large tin bucket, bottom upwards. Each musician took a stick, about eighteen inches long, notched from one end to the other. One extremity of this stick was held in the left hand, and placed in contact with the edge of the tin bucket. In the right hand, the performer held a small piece of wood, square or rectangular in shape, and from three to four inches in thickness, and scraping this upwards and downwards on the notched stick, he produced the ravishing music which so delighted the dancers. The men and squaws arranged themselves into two lines so that the sexes stood opposite and faced each other. When the music commenced two squaws clasped hands, advanced to the male line, and choose their partners; two more in the same manner made their selection and so on until all were supplied. Then the males and the females from their respective lines advanced towards each other with a trot and a swaying motion of their bodies, until the couples were almost face to face, and then with similar backward movements returned to the places from which they started. This alternate advance and retreat was all there was to the particular dance, but the participants apparently enjoyed the exercise immensely, and continued the dance until they were completely exhausted.

After a rest another ceremony started. The dance was a slow, grave and solemn gesturing, accompanied with singing and the sound of the timbre1, led by Shenga Wassa, the rest imitating her movements and repeating the words of the song as they uttered from her lips.

Their timbrels, or tabret, was a musical instrument in the form of a hoop, edged round with rings or pieces of brass to make a jingling noise, and covered over with tightened skin like a drum. It was beat with the fingers, and corresponded to the normal tambourine. All the women followed after her with timbrels.

Shenga Wassa's idea of the gift of prophecy, understanding mysteries, and faith to accomplish results, by will, singularly coincided with the Jewish ideas as expressed in I Corinthians 8:2, wherein these subjects are thus recited:

"And though I have the gift of prophecy, and understand all mysteries, and all knowledge; and though I have all faith, so that I could remove mountains, etc."

The singing were more like chants, like the echoes of whispering or moaning forests, set to human words; of the dusky throats that, without training, yet sang together with never a discord; of the love-songs that had in them the minor cadences of sadness.

In the low, glowing light of the fire, when the group around it faded in the darkness, she seemed to forget her many listeners, and talked on as if to only Ian. To the rest it was as if they had met a stranger there that evening for the first time, and found her interesting. Even Three Bears dropped his slightly contemptuous manner toward her, a change to which he was as indifferent as to her coolness. It may have been Shenga's songs in the evening that unlocked his heart. It may have been a dash of restlessness that urged him to enjoy it for a little time only—this association that suggested so much he had long been a stranger. Whatever the impulse was, it showed a side of his nature that only Shenga saw.

At Ian's request she would repeat some remembered Indian song. Ian would hum the plaintive airs with her and dance before the campfire in Indian fashion. Even after the rest had quietly withdrawn and rolled themselves in blankets for the night's rest, Saba, Three

Bears, and several other chief men still sat around the fire with old legends for company and with strange songs in which the music would yet sound familiar to any ears used to the shrilling of the winds through the timber or the muffled moans of the wood dove.

And in the sweet dusk of the dark, Shenga, the first to leave the fire, lay among the odorous, spicy branches of the cedar and watched the picture of the group about the fire. All was in darkness, save when a bit of reflected red would outline a feature.

But the voices of the final three, dropped low though they were for the sake of the sleepers.

*   *   *

Ian and his friends decided to journey down to a small settlement so they could learn from the trappers, mountain men and emigrants news on the whereabouts of the army and rangers. No one knew them there so they wouldn't be recognized.

Saying goodbye, Shenga Wassa seemed somewhat melancholy and Ian mentioned he might not go as this sadness was not like Shenga, but she insisted that he should go with his friends.

A puff of wind sent Shenga's hair blowing across her face and Ian brushed it back carefully that he might see her eyes; but the caress in the movement was as if given to a child. There was unspoken warmth in her eyes and speech. She looked at him as she did love.

Goodbye—goodbye," she murmured as her hand touched his chest at the shoulder and gently swept diagonally across his chest to his waistline—the sign language of goodbye. She was so gentle—the touch of her hand on his breast was tremulous.

Ian's companions for the short sixty mile journey were Baredran, Jamie Bill, Sergeant Beidler and four other troopers Ira Hammond, Luke Griffin, Oddie Blackburn and Snowd Bell who had deserted from Fort Leavenworth to join Ian.

It took two easy days of riding to get to Willow Bar run by a mountain man by the name of Else Campbell. (Willow Bar was in the northeastern part of the present Cimarron County, Oklahoma).

That evening Ian, the sergeant and several others accompanied him to the tavern. It was a large barn-like room, the scene of eating, drinking, smoking, lounging, sleeping, . . . and gambling. After two drinks of Missouri rye, he found himself one of seven around a table in a corner, and the "papers" in motion; every man "bragging" according to his pile. He was emphatically on his "own hook," not knowing where his friends had disappeared to—a stranger in a strange place. Soon he counted eight or ten different tables, each surrounded by players, maybe fifty men, all cursing or talking loudly; most intoxicated, disputing, and quarreling.

Being careless, fortune favored him, and as his "pile" grew, so the circumstances caused him to several times adjust his Colt to increase the visible protrusion of the handle of his trusty revolver to those around the table. Perhaps it was an instinctive action upon the maxim, "do at Rome as the Romans do." As one of the gamblers across the table from Ian ran out of money and left swearing about his bad luck, a wealthy civilized Mohave Indian by the name John Oatman, took his chair. After his "pile" disappeared, he seemed to have a good hand but no money, so he calmly said that he would give his right eye, if he could stay in the game. Of course, this interested the rest of the gamblers at the table at the unusual offer, so he was dealt two more cards. When he lost the pot, the winner demanded payment. He hesitated for a moment while the demand was repeated by the surrounding crowd of drunken onlookers. As the tension built up, he plucked his eye right out of its socket, and rolled the glass eye across the table to the winner. There was unbelief for a moment, then the unruly drunks, burst out laughing and hee-hawing.

Soon Ian's fortunes turned and he found himself losing all he had gained and a small amount more. He left the game as his money ran out and went seeking his friends.

Oatman, his money and eye gone, left the table and joined Ian at the bar with his companions. The more intoxicated he became, the more he talked. It seemed that his wife was suing him for some of his money. Both lived near his gold camp, in which the Mohave chief was interested. In the division of communal property, Oatman, getting his half of the household furniture, sawed one table and a chest of drawers in two and had then removed his half of the furniture from the Oatman house.

While using dynamite in working the mine, Oatman lost part of his scalp and an eye. Since then, he had taken delight "scalping himself" by removing his wig to frighten his own children and the other boys and girls of the tribe. Moreover, Mrs. Oatman complained her husband spent most of his money buying glass eyes, which he lost many of them at poker.

When bedtime came, Ian was spreading his blankets outside on the ground when the owner offered shelter so they could sleep better. Ian, still under the influence of the rye, came inside, spread his blankets, laid down, and soon fell asleep.

It was not long before other visitors commenced coming in, and several times on partially awakening he found himself so crowded that he could not move without disturbing a neighbor; on further awaking to the situation, he found that he could not get out without walking over several sleepers, and that his blankets were not only furnishing bedding for himself but for numerous others. So there was no way but to lie still and rest as well as he could.

At daylight he awoke and took a look at the sleepers. The room was fully-packed so thick it was impossible to count them or distinguish who was who. His bedfellows were men, women, and children piled in promiscuously, regardless of sex, age, or nationality. As soon as he could pick his way out, he seated himself on a stone and ate an early breakfast with several of his friends.

The man who had won a lot of money at the gambling table last evening was found dead with his throat slashed. Ian thought that maybe it was good that he lost.

Gathered at the ranch or passing through were professional leeches, backwoodsmen, arrogant swash-bucklers from the eastern states, Yankees, Iowans, Irishmen, professional gamblers, whiskey-dealers, general swindlers, disappointed lovers and black sheep. Kit Carson and Jedediah Smith who Ian had become acquainted with were passing through the country to the mountains.

There was gold-fever, bad liquor, faro, monte, rouge-et-noir, quarrels, oaths, pistols, knives and dancing. In the melange was one conspicuous gap. There were at the ranch, appallingly few women of the homemaking, respectable sort, and not many women at all, and most of those ladies were recent and dubious accessions of St. Louis.

A few frame shanties were pitched together as if by accident. There were tents of canvas, of blankets, of brush, of potato sacks and of old shirts, with empty whisky barrels for chimneys and smoking hovels of mud and stone. Coyote holes in the hillsides were forcible seized by men, and pits and shanties with smoke issued from every crevice; piles of goods and rubbish scattered broadcast in pell-mell confusion.

As Ian and Jamie were preparing to leave, they encountered a group of ten men coming in off the trail, leading four unmounted horses among them. They were a villainous crew to look upon, a rough, sneering, swaggering bunch of daredevils. Most of them were young men, large of frame, dressed in coarse clothes, and all armed with rifles, pistols, and knives.

As they dismounted, the bottles passed from one coarse, tobacco-stained mouth to another, with boasting and swearing between drinks. The leader of the band rode alongside Ian for a word, "We come onto two new settlers, young men, and their families, down the trail five miles back," he said.

"The men said they was on their way to their claims west a little distance."

"Two of the boys burnt their wagons, goods, and all. We took their horses and told the women to walk back to Massachusetts quick. There was two babies in the crowd, and one of the boys suggested they could drop 'em into the Arkansas River if they were heavy."

A roar of laughter followed this brutal recital. Then with oaths, and foul and cruel jests, the rabble continued its way to other deeds of like fiendishness. Major Buford, a renegade ranger title rather than military rank, had come with his brutal gang to assassinate anyone they felt like. They branded women, stripped starving children naked, robbed of husbands and fathers, and plundered all their possessions. Should they be left beside the smoking embers of their wagons, it mattered nothing to him.

"What's the next number on the program, Major?" one of the band asked.

The Major looked at Jamie and Ian and said matter-of-factly, "Well, I think we'll take these fine horses."

Jamie Bill

Courtesy of Rox's Images

Jamie and Ian had suspected such a maneuver and had their Colts ready for action. In a split second both drew their revolvers and fired a deadly volley; every bullet plowing through the chests of the men. The murderous gang had never encountered the deadly repeating Colt revolvers and professional gun fighters such as Ian and Jamie. In a few seconds it was all over, with the ten prairie pirates dead from hot iron in their hearts. Jamie and Ian had just rid the country of ten wild beasts. No judges, no lawyers, no expenses of a trial—just quick justice. They were the forerunners of a new bred—the frontier law-and-order marshals.

Ian and Jamie gathered the horses and the provisions the gang had robbed from the settler families and turned back on the trail to help the two women to a caravan coming along the trail.

Against the lawless piracy the traders and immigrants were at a great disadvantage. There were tricky politicians and adventurers, outlaws, who in the name of Indian warfare brought dishonor and murder to a cause they claimed to defend. But they formed only a tiny percent of the growing population. Men were chopped in the face with hatchets and left to perish in the freezing cold. Mutilated men were flung into their houses, whose wives became maniacs from the sight of them. Wagons burned, with all clothing and bedding, leaving helpless women and naked children alone on the cold, forsaken prairie in the desolate midnight hour; men forced to flee for their lives, and, under promise of protection, cut down as they fled. These deeds and others too vile to set on record, unbelievable now for their demoniac fiendishness, were a part of the history-making of those days in Kansas Territory of peril and power. For power went with those criminal hordes of prairie pirates.

*   *   *

The small band had rode hard all day as Ian wanted to get back to Shenga Wassa. He missed her smile more and more as time passed and soon she would have their baby, which Ian was looking forward to, with happy thoughts of family life with his beloved.

At midday there was a hasty lunch of jerky while in the saddle, but in the evening all were prepared for rest and enjoyment of buffalo steaks and talk—or, as some expressed it, "swappin' lies"—around the fire.

*   *   *

The band of hired rancheros—organized robbers and murderers—from Aaron Burr's settlement, had found the Dreamers. These rancheros hovered on the flanks of the frontier army and succeeded at different times in surrounding small detachments of soldiers. Just two days previous, they had killed a Lieutenant Potter, of the dragoons. Potter had gone out with three men in search of the colonel. Their bodies were mutilated, scalped and horses stolen, so the whole scene was blamed on murdering Indians by the relief soldiers who found their remains.

As the rancheros charged the camp, Shenga Wassa sat cross-legged on the ground, on this solemn occasion, and sang a death song, which every Indian sung, whenever they anticipated approaching death, or suspected death was about to overtake them.

Her wailing song was interrupted by a deep, hard cut of a soldier's saber down across her chest and abdomen, killing her and her unborn child. As the blood gushed from her body a deadly lance was thrust into her, a faint cry of a dying child issued from her womb. Mortally wounded, she struggled to stand up to meet her God, but was trampled down by another charging ranger's horse. Unable to rise, the life blood of her and her unborn baby drained from her in a trickle into the stream already red with others blood and then came death . . . to Shenga Wassa! The Grand Conspiracy of the West had done its work well.

The warriors put the squaws and children together and surrounded them to protect them. When the troops came up to them, they ran out and showed their persons to let the soldiers know they were squaws begging for mercy, but the soldiers shot them all. A soldier came up to a squaw whose leg had been broken, with drawn saber; she raised her arm to protect herself, when he struck, breaking her arm; she rolled over and raised her other arm, when he struck again, breaking it, and then left her without killing her. There was indiscriminate slaughtering of men, women and children. A little girl about six years old wandered away from the group; she proceeded but a few steps when she was shot dead.

The women and children were huddled together and most of the shots were concentrated on them. A ranger who rebelled at the massacre of the women and children was told by one of the officers, "Damn any man who sympathizes with the Indians." The trooper told him, "But pledges were given the Indians!"

The officer's reply was, bringing his gun close to the troopers face, "We have come to kill Indians, and I want no prisoners," as he shot the last woman.

*   *   *

Ian woke with a start in the first light of day! Still asleep, his body jerked upright and a mournful scream wailed from his soul that told him something dreadfully wrong was happening.

As Saba, Three Bears, and Sergeant Beidler rushed to him, he stood up and uttered, "Shenga is dying!"

"I know," Saba answered him sorrowfully. He then turned to Three Bears and curtly ordered, "Get three of our fastest horses, so he may go to Shenga!"

Ian's mind was in a blind haze as he thought of the pain and suffering his soul told him was happening to Shenga Wassa. Saba grabbed his shoulders firmly and spoke concisely and abruptly, "Go! We will follow as soon as we can break camp!" As Three Bears brought up the horses, Ian jumped onto one of them as Three Bears thrust the other two bridle reins into his other hand.

Ian, without further word, kicked his boot heels hard into his black, spirited charger. Off they flew with Ian holding tightly to his extra mounts. It was thirty miles and one horse could not run at full speed with a man load on his back for that distance.

Soon the perspiration of his mount was fretted into a white lather. At seven miles his steed was visibly winded with foam rolling from his mouth from exhaustion. Ian sprang nimbly from his worn-out horse onto one of the fleet Indian ponies he was leading. Thoroughly used up, his former mount slowed to a stop, breathing heavy and terribly hard, trying to get enough air to stand up.

In eight miles his second pony was expended and he jumped onto the last mount. As they sped across the prairie, Ian, not aware of it with his only thoughts with Shenga's welfare, whipped the pony mercilessly to reach her as soon as he possibly could.

Suddenly the little pony ran its heart out and stumbled and fell as its heart burst from extreme over-exertion. Ian, now plainly alarmed, hesitated not a moment, and picked himself up and ran as fast as his legs would carry him. In a few minutes, he realized that he had to pace himself slower like the Indians do, so he could traverse the remaining miles. He slowed to a steady jog as the rain started. The rain against his face revived him somewhat from his ordeal. Over rocks he ran, through the small streams without slowing. Finally he came into sight of smoke from the teepees and wagons burning fiercely in the light rain.

Finally he reached the encampment, waded across the wide shallow stream and discovered his beloved Shenga.

Ian knelt down and lifted her body into his arms watching for some show of life in her closed eyelids and parted lips. And then with a great shivering breath, he drew the still face to his own, and in a half-motherly way smoothed back her hair as if she had been a child, whispering over and over: "Not dead, my Shenga! Not you, my love! Don't leave me!"

When the remainder of his friends arrived at the massacre site, he was still holding her. The fury of the storm had increased. Out in the open country it hammered mercilessly on the flat, resistless, grassy plains. It wrenched in wrath at every tree and shrub and the fleeing rangers and rancheros. It screamed in anger down every open draw and shaded ravine. It hurled its violent rage upon every human and dumb animal.

The sweep of the winds was unchecked on the flat plains.

Ian looked into Saba's sad face and ordered, "Kill them! Kill them all for what they have done! The first man who brings me a prisoner will be shot."

By this time the native telegraph had informed neighboring camps and a number of warriors had gathered for revenge. With a roaring wail they charged after the fleeing murderers, knowing well of the terrible vow of revenge of the dog soldiers, Ian had proclaimed martial law and the war chiefs assumed sole command of the reprisal expedition.

Whatever chance the butchers had of escaping Ian's warriors was washed away by the cloudburst that turned the ground into a quagmire.

Ride! On through the rush of the rain, on over the dreary desolation of water, now floundering ankle-deep through the tenacious mud—down the slippery sides of the "coulees," through the foaming waters of the streams, swirling and rushing along in muddy torrents.

Up, Indian ponies, up the steep banks, slipping and stumbling over rain-loosened stones, on over the prairie again.

Ride! On toward the solitary station of soldiers the rancheros and rangers rode, the water streaming from their oil-skins, dripping from their wide-brimmed hats, and running down the flanks of their tired horses. Three unlucky drowned in crossing a river. The Indians had now caught up to the fleeing murderers, and arrow after arrow found their mark. One rider was shot through the leg by an arrow that pierced his horse's belly eight inches. Another and another hit his chest and side as the mount slowed because of the wound. His mount in pell-mell flight gave out and fell and rolled over several times, crushing his rider.

Push on! The panting horses, upward and still onward, now rounding some queer tower-shaped mass of sandstone, now sliding down some steep little descent, horses with all four feet together, haunches almost touching the ground, into a sea of mud at the bottom, floundering through and climbing upward again.

The trail grew rougher; the red sticky mud adhering to the hoofs, the men covered with it from head to foot, save where the rain washed it off their slickers.

The fury of the storm let up and the gray of the sky started clearing. All along the chase trail was ghastly evidence of savage fury. In a gulch, lay a ranchero's body with six arrows in it. His horse had made a vigorous spring up the opposite bank but lost its footing on the slippery verge, and after a desperate scrambling, rolled with his rider floundering in the mud at the bottom. A hundred yards away three rancheros lay with bullet-holes in their breasts and their bodies hacked and mutilated. A little further another body lay on its back, with the head pillowed on his dead horse—by his side was a rifle.

Two miles from him a man lay with a lance thrust through his chest. For twenty miles lying here and there were bodies of Shenga's murderers. It was a scene of overwhelming vengeance.

Hour after hour the rangers and rancheros rode, until with a final spurt they crossed the butte in front of them, and there, broad, curving gracefully through the wide valley, shining like silver in a sudden burst of light that broke through the cloud masses above, there flowed the Arkansas.

Hurrah! Down the hill side and out over the short stretch of green plain to the brink of the stream, and wet, dead tired, hungry, and thirsty, the rangers pulled up their smoking, panting horses at the log-fort of the soldier's station, beyond which, nestling in the shelter of cotton-wood and willow trees, gleamed the white walls of several dozen tents, marking the camp of the little detachment of troopers, a solitary outpost of the regular United States Dragoons.

There also were flannel-shirted, heavily booted government teamsters who had been sent out with their supply train. They had drawn the wagons up in a square to resist the attack made by the little band of about eighty Indians. The soldiers joined forces with the teamsters and the rangers and rancheros, and by firing from behind the protection of the wagons succeeded in driving off the Indians and killed a number of their horses. The hostiles were reinforced by fifteen other braves who had been straggling along the trail mutilating and scalping the bodies. A hard fight was kept up for an hour until more troops arrived from a nearby caravan about dark, having been sent in answer to a courier who managed to elude the attacking party. The troops charged on a gallop and the Indians retreated, having lost several, killed and wounded, besides a number of their horses.

*   *   *

A number of women had arrived and took Shenga's body from Ian's arms for burial. He continued sitting cross-legged in the mud as he mourned his loss. Shenga Wassa was the dearest creature he had ever met or ever expected to meet this side of heaven. She loved with all her heart, laughed like a gentle spring wind; her voice like soft church bells tinkling in the breeze.

He remembered her singing voice, saying she would never leave him. Now she was dead: he would never hear her whispers; feel her warm gentle touch. He loved her so—but she loved everything: God, the wild creatures, life. . . .

After night lunch, she would sit by him, singing softly and as hauntingly as an angel sent to earth to shine in his life as the one good and holy thing.

"I should have never let her out of sight," he lamented. "What I would give to hold her tight again, to kiss her goodnight."

"I shall never love anyone else to the day I die," he swore to himself.

As he saw Saba nearby, he vaguely remembered what he had said when Ian told him Shenga was dying. He slowly got up and walked over to the bereaved Saba; he stood in front of him, and questioned, "How did you know Shenga was dying?"

Saba thought for a moment as if uncertain he should tell him—as a warrior he would not, but as a friend he did.

"You killed her because you did not believe—truly believe."

Ian reacted spontaneously by hitting Saba in the face with a smashing blow, which staggered him backward but managed to keep on his feet. Ian lunged at him with the whole fury of his body, at the revolting thought of Saba's words. He would do anything to keep Shenga alive and safe and yet Saba was accusing him of her death! With animal ferocity he vowed to kill him!

But he was no match for Saba, who deflected Ian's lunging and grabbing his shirt slammed him into a tree trunk hard, with all his strength, which was considerable.

The blow to his head and back against the tree stunned Ian momentarily as Saba pushed his drawn knife into Ian's throat a fraction of an inch, then in earnest promise to him, "Friend or no friend, never do that again, or I will kill you! Never . . . or you will die!"

As he sheathed his knife, he let go of Ian who sank to the ground from lack of breath. As he got his breath back, he now realized what he had done. Ian could never hurt Saba, his and Shenga's dearest friend and protector. He thought about what Saba had said and he was right. Ian claimed he believed but somehow for some reason he could not find it truly in his heart to believe with all his heart and soul. There was something that kept him from putting his total belief in Shenga. Maybe it was his society training and experience. A white man, supposedly educated and intelligent, just could not completely believe in a Messiah, in a personal Messiah. No! No! This was not possible. Maybe almost 2,000 years ago, but not in this time and on these plains of Kansas. No!

Saba knelt and explained to Ian, "She told me it was time that we depart—I to die, you to live. I leave you in the storm! The spirit voices spoke to her with articulate words in the ripple of the river, in the vesper bells, in the rustling of the leaves, and in the sighing of the wind."

"Her voices had told her she would be taken before midsummer. I must leave you," Saba said she had told him.

*   *   *

When Shenga's body was brought back to the nearest camp, the mourners put on coarse and tattered garments, blackened their faces, and, sitting upon the ground near her body, bewailed her death in tones of the deepest grief and despair.

The women kept up a constant wail until exhausted, when another set took their place and thus the mourning and the great lamentation kept up until after her burial service.

All the tribe wore leather strings tied around their wrists and ankles for the purpose of reminding them of her death.

Shenga's body was dressed in her best garments and laid in the center of the village with her baby in her arms. Fires were kindled and continued all night, the object being to light her spirit on its journey to the spirit land. Ian, with his face blackened and hair cropped in the universal sign of mourning, sat motionless at Shenga's side all night long in sorrow and grief with the wailing of the women filling the night. Nearby, Saba mourned in silence and alone.

After sunrise Shenga's body was tied up in a blanket, which she possessed when alive, and borne to a spot some hundred yards distant, where her funeral pyre was being raised on the highest point of ground. The entire camp and visiting mourners followed: the women crying and wailing greatly. The body was laid on the ground while the pyre was being built. This occupied considerable time, during which the mourning was kept up in loud and wild wailings. The females were blackened around their chins, temples, ears, and foreheads, and cried. They often prostrated themselves upon the ground. The pyre was finished and Shenga's and the baby's remains were placed upon it in a reclining position with all her beads, baskets and earthly effects. This done, the pyre was fired all around and as the blaze enveloped the bodies, the mourners gave way to unbounded grief.

Their Messiah was dead and was returning to the spirit world whence she came, and Ian's "Beautiful Flower," whom he loved dearly, was being consumed by the fire.

Saba, standing at the foot of the pyre gave utterance to his sorrow in loud and broken strains. He was naked, except a small girdle round his middle. As he half-cried, half-sung his sorrow, he would occasionally speak something distinctly but without appearing to address himself to the people or any portion of them.

In the course of the ceremony, groups of Indians would occasionally gather around him. On one occasion he drew marks in the sand as he spoke. He said, "We are like these lines. Today we are here and can be seen; but death takes one away, and then another, as the winds wipe out these lines in the sand, until all are gone!"

Drawing his hand over the marks, he continued, "They are all gone even now; like them, we will all be wiped out, and will be seen no more!"

Ian standing quietly near the pyre, suddenly and slowly walked closer to the blaze, stopped, then walked straight into the fire crying out, "Shenga! Shenga!" as if to join her.

He was stopped just inside the blaze by an apparition of a raging white buffalo bull that would not let him join Shenga Wassa in her spirit journey. The apparition held his head low and with menacing horns kept Ian at a distance as he pawed the earth with his hoofs and bellowed terrible threatening roars. As quickly as it appeared the white buffalo disappeared.

The circle of gathered chiefs sadly leaning with bowed heads, upon sticks, were slow to react, then two of them leaped forward and grabbed Ian's arms and pulled him from the flames. He struggled ferociously to free himself from their grasp, but the two chiefs held him firmly as he continued to call out her name.

After a few moments of struggle, he fell to the ground on his knees as Shenga's body was consumed by the flames. During the whole time the mourners kept up intense feelings of grief and anguish.

As the scaffolding of the funeral pyre collapsed and the fire ebbed down, the chiefs loosened their grip on Ian's arms and left him alone in his sorrow. All the mourners ceased their wailing and all that could be heard was the quiet sobbing of several women and the crackling fire. One of the chiefs thrust his walking stick into Ian's hand.

Ian grasped it momentarily, then raised to his feet without a word, turned and went into the desert to be alone in his grief. Jamie Bill, Ian's woman-man friend, strapped her revolver on her hips, slipped a bullet bandolier across her shoulder, packed her knapsack with beef-jerky, and slung six water canteens over her other shoulder. Pulling her sloppy felt hat down over her forehead, and grasping her rifle, she followed Ian into the Llano Estacado—the great desert.

*   *   *

One late afternoon he stopped on a high point that overlooked the plains. This country was the bottom of a sea, warped and twisted and heaved up by a gigantic upheaval in eons past. The hills and buttes had disintegrated and fell down with their bases covered with deep reddish earth. Wind and water had eroded the faces of cliffs with thousands of odd and grotesque cuts.

Rugged lava crests were seamed and hacked with ravines and gashes of all shapes. The desert was unsurpassed for dryness by any area in the whole world. The steep sand hills, bluffs of sandstone and shale, its 120 degree sun, the killing dryness of the wind, whirlwinds twisting across the plains, its rattlesnakes and gila monsters, were all strange and weird. The desert for miles was furnace dry, barren, with little vegetable life but for the cactuses, and they were tough skinned from the terrible heat and they appeared dead rather than alive. A few shriveled sprigs of grease-wood, a speck or so of sagebrush grew at great intervals, and in shady crevices a lonely spot of green grass, or something else, grew in the burnt, baked clay and sand. Here and there was a mesquite, a patch of crown and sagebrush struggling for survival. The Prickly pear spread its flat, jointed limbs into the heat of the day. There were signs of springs, which form pools ordinarily, but in this dry season they had disappeared.

The rays of the sun, reflected back from the surface of the plains, dazzling and paining Ian's inflamed eyes. His weariness was aggravated by mirages reflecting with tantalizing distinctness the limbs and branches of the young cottonwood along the banks of non-existent distant rivers.

As Ian watched the whirlwinds pirouetting gracefully along the ground, the murmur of the gentle wind rose into a gale, then gave way to a harsh scream of the meanest of all storms—the sand-storm.

The sky became overcast, assuming a dull-gray color, which soon changed to a yellowish-brown, from the mass of sand and dust held in suspension in the air. The higher hills turned purplish-black, as the tornadic winds wreaked destruction upon the land and blew a smothering mantle of dust upon the landscape.

The dust entered Ian's eyes and hung upon his lids, lashes, and mustache and upon his lips. It was a struggle just to get enough air to breathe as nature, unrestricted in this desolate land, tried to kill all plant, animal and human.

On the fourth afternoon, Ian sat motionless on a rocky prominence for a long while thinking about life . . . and death. Jamie Bill, two hundred yards behind Ian, sitting astride her horse whose head nearly touched the ground, to escape the blinding sand, tried to peer through the storm from under her slouched hat. She gripped the saddle tightly to keep from being blown off her mount by the gusts of sand. Finally the winds died down to a gale.

Covered with dust and completely worn out from battling the storm, Ian, a proud man, could not fall onto his knees; to no one; not even God. He felt he had to stand up to adversity, to evil, to the world and be counted. Here was a man, a true man which God respected, his indomitable spirit, his incessant trying to correct wrongs, to help his fellow man and woman during their short journey through his life—a helpmate to those who had lost their dignity of life.

Ian's mind told him if one is to be saved, we have to save one's self in this corrupt world. Many find no help in the church. Only a fraction have emerged from the dark ages. People under great stress naturally gravitate to the occult . . . to supernatural influences and phenomena . . . and in this searching the initiate finds such supernatural secrets. Only to these seekers, is the knowledge tendered, in the here and now, overlooked by the common man and woman. As fish are taken out of the water, God cast a hook into Ian's nose and drew him nearer. Ian struggled as the ancient captives who were led by their conquerors by hooks made to pass through their noses. As a fish in the sea, Ian could not conceive of any other existence apart from his anguish and resisted all attempts to get outside of it for even a moment. But through all of Ian's agonizing physical pain and mental distress with blood from the unseen hook flowing profusely down his face, the Lord did not relent. God thought Ian was worth saving.

Ian's body though of the earth and animated as a physical organism was also spirit and stood to his Creator as a son to his father.

It came to pass after several days of intense mental suffering on the sun-parched desert a revelation came to Ian and he fell to his knees, fighting the kneeling inch by inch, but it finally happened. After witnessing all of this, his man-woman friend came to his side and stood beside him.

And a voice said to Ian, "Stand upon your feet and I will speak with you."

The Spirit entered into Ian and set him on his feet. And out of the whirlwind, He said to Ian, "Son of man, I will grant you a gift I seldom grant any mortal."

After a time, Jamie Bill quietly said, "Let us leave this place, Ian."

"To friends, to life, to carry on Shenga's work."

*   *   *

The journey back did not take as long as the first, as Ian rode behind Jamie on her horse. Jamie shot a rabbit and roasted it over a cactus fire. After a good night's sleep, they bathed in a warm mineral spring found among the rocks. Like Adam and Eve before the eating of the fruit, they found no lust for the other's body. The mineral waters cleansed the old lives from their bodies and the world took on an altogether different look.

Terrible War on the Plains

*I*n the war, the Cheyenne, in their wild and savage way, fought well for their country and in their history, during the past few years, had been written in blood. Innocent settlers suffered cruel outrages at their hands; women and children went down to horrible deaths through their revengeful rage, and burning houses had lit their pathways of devastation. They in turn were hunted like wolves and shot down like mad dogs, until they were becoming a wreck of their former greatness.

Perhaps their savage and cruel war, with its attending horrors, were but the legitimate fruit of bad policy and mismanagement of Indian Affairs. Willful indifference to or misunderstandings of the condition and circumstances of the Indians and their relations to the government, which in times past had too often permitted dishonest agents to be the intermediaries between the government and them, and through weakness or cowardice had at times paid more heed to the clamors of rapacious miners and settlers of the white race than to treaty obligations.

The Cheyennes were at first friendly to the whites but they subsequently became one of the greatest terrors of the frontier. The men of the Cheyenne rank as high in the scale of bravery, energy, and tenacity of purpose as those of any tribe, and in physique and intellect they were superior of those of most tribes and the equal of any tribe. Under the most demoralizing and trying circumstances preserved in a remarkable degree, that part of their moral code which relates to chastity (pure respect to unlawful sexual intercourse). Public sentiment was so strong with them in regard to this matter that they had been, and still were noted among all the tribes which surrounded them for the virtue of their women.

In dress and general appearance they differed little from the Arapaho and Sioux. Their vocal language was difficult to acquire, Ian found, and was noticeable for the rapidity with which they could articulate in making their speeches and harangues. It literally flowed forth in a constant and swift stream.

In the degradation of their barbarism, in many of their customs, and in their faith, there was much to condemn, but a close study of their character, at peace and at war, reveal much to admire. It has often been asserted that the cruelties and tortures which at times had been inflicted by Indians upon their unfortunate and helpless captives had been, and is, the practice of all Indians. The Cheyenne make war as terrible as possible to their enemies, and when influenced with the passion of revenge, tender infants and pleading women go down before the same war-club that crushed the skulls of dead fathers and husbands, but they did not burn their captives at the stake, flayed alive, or any other torture inflicted on prisoners captured by these fierce, and enterprising Indians. Sickening mutilations of the dead characterized the Indian wars by the Indian and the whites.

There was no more serious phase of the Indian problem presented to the American frontier than that offered by the Apache tribes. Aided by the desert nature of their country, they resisted the advance of the whites longer than any other Indian nation. They fought with bravery and inconceivable cunning. They made their name a terror to a section of country five times larger than all New England. They kept miners for years from treasure deposits that were regarded as of fabulous richness. They gained the reputation of being the most cruel Indians that were known in the United States. People, willing to extend sympathy and assistance to other Indians, stood aghast at the work of the Apaches. Given their opinions that nothing but the extermination of the tribe could ever rid New Mexico, and what would become the state of Arizona, of a constant liability to outrage and devastation. In connection with this reputation was the fact that the Apaches were among the least known of the Indian tribes. Not only had their hostile attitude prevented white men from associating with them, but even when brought in contact with the whites, they maintained a jealous reserve as to their habits, particularly those of a religious character. By way of example, it was commonly believed they did not bury their dead, and never touched a dead body except in cases of necessity.

Colonel Cremony, who had excellent opportunity for knowing, insisted they bury their more prominent men, at least, with great ceremony.

The Apaches spoke the same language as the Navahos and Lipans. They were in nine tolerable distinct tribes in earlier times, but through confederations and factional separations in the course of their long warfare, some of this identity was lost. There were the Chiricahuas, Gilenos, Mimbrenos, Mescaleros, Jicarilles, Pinalenos, Mogollons, Coyoteros, and Tontos.

The Apache were always known as wild Indians. The Spaniards never obtained any control over them, and the Mexicans never retained any control. Between these two peoples there was almost continuous war. The condition of the people of the Northern Mexican settlements was such that there was little chance of successful opposition to the Apache. They were poor and hardly more advanced in knowledge than their Indian enemies.

As a general rule it was found cheaper and more agreeable with the warlike spirit of the Mexicans to buy peace from the Apache than to fight them.

It was not strange that the Mexicans appeared cowardly. The great mass of the people was in a state of peonage in bondage for debt. They were without organization and had nothing in life to stimulate them to bravery.

The Americans, who went into the Apache country prior to the frontier army, were on a different footing from the Mexicans. They were chiefly trappers and traders, and though many of them had Mexican wives or mistresses, quite as many had their marital companions from among the Indians. They were so seldom attacked that the Mexicans accused them of having secretly traded with the Apaches. Their immunity was really due to constant preparation for attack as the Apache never attacked except by surprise. In 1837 the Mexicans offered one hundred dollars for the scalp of an Apache warrior, fifty for the scalp of a squaw, and twenty-five for that of a child. They also gave to the scalper any booty that he might take from the Indians. In addition to the scalp bounty, the trappers were induced to this by pay from the owners of the Santa Rita copper mines. At any rate the trappers made a feast and invited to it a number of Mimbreno warriors, who accepted this hospitable bidding. To one side of the area where his feast was spread he placed a howitzer, loaded the muzzle with slugs, nails and bullets, and concealed under sacks of flour and other goods. In good range he placed a sack of flour, which he told the Apaches to divide among themselves. Unsuspicious of wrong, they gathered about it. Johnson, of the trappers, touched his lighted cigarrillo to the vent of the howitzer and the charge poured into the crowd, killing and wounding many people. The party of trappers at once followed up the attack with their rifles and knives. A goodly number of scalps were taken, but the treachery was terribly repaid.

Another party of fifteen trappers was camped on a stream a few miles distant. The surviving Mimbrenos went to these unsuspecting men and murdered every one of them. Their vengeance did not stop at this. The copper mines of Santa Rita were furnished with supplies from the city of Chihuahua by guarded wagon trains that brought in provisions. The time for the arrival of the train came and passed, but no train appeared. Days slipped away; provisions were almost exhausted; the supply of ammunition was nearly gone. Starvation was imminent.

The only hope of escape for the miners and their families was in making their way across the desert expanse that lay between the mines and the settlements. They started, but the Apaches, who had destroyed the train, hung about them and attacked them so persistently that only four or five succeeded in reaching their destination.

A few years after American troops occupied this country, vigilance committees of California filled Arizona with the most villainous collection of white men that ever breathed. There was a tragedy in which the principle performer was John Gallatin. He was a desperate scoundrel and had gathered about him a band of cut-throats whose infamous characters were excelled only by his own. The governor of Chihuahua undertook the task of making these men useful to the state by paying them thirty dollars for each Apache scalp they secured. They brought scalps in profusion, but the Apache raids were not diminished. On the contrary, large numbers of Mexicans and friendly Indians were assassinated and scalped in the midst of the settlements.

The suspicions of the Chihuahuans were excited, and Gallatin was at length discovered taking the scalps of some Mexicans who his people murdered. This accounted for the extraordinary activity of the Apaches, and Gallatin and his band left the country. They gathered up some twenty-five hundred sheep as they went along, and with these made their way to Aaron Burr's territory that he had purchased and became part of the "Grand Conspiracy."

The scalp-bounty system was not given up by the Mexicans, and what is more remarkable, man-hunters were allowed to pursue their occupation on the American side of the line for the scalp markets of Chihuahua and Sonora.

Lieutenant Drew was visited by such a party, who coolly proposed to massacre the Indians who were under his protection, while they were preparing to go onto a reservation. These people did not care a straw for the depredations committed in this or any other country; they worked for the money a scalp brought, and one from a friendly Indian was worth as much as one of any other.

After the massacre of the miners, the Mimbrenos held possession of the Santa Rita mines for a dozen years undisturbed. The place became known as their great stronghold, and no white men were able to break through its surrounding wilds.

In what is now Western Arizona, there lived the less nomadic bands of the Apache. These Indians were more closely surrounded by white neighbors and nearer to the locations of American troops; besides, they were of a more peaceful character than the other tribes. There were several bands that were quite agricultural in their pursuits, notably that of Miguel, who kept back in the mountain valleys and took little or no part in any of the wars.

Miguel's village, with a white flag flying over each lodge, was found in the heart of the White Mountains by Captain Perry. His forces were on an exterminating expedition, but these Apaches showed so much sincerity in their professions of peace that even the Mexican scouts said they could not fire on them. For these Apaches the White Mountain reservation was established, and to it others gathered as they learned they could surrender and remain at peace in their own country.

Their numbers gradually increased until it reached five hundred ten. They were very destitute and almost naked, but they were willing to work to obtain clothing, so they were set to gathering hay. They cut it with their knives and brought it in on their backs, but by this slow method they furnished the post with one hundred fifty tons in less than two months, besides gathering large quantities of mescal for their own use. As the weather grew warmer they were allowed to move four or five miles farther up the Arivapa, to some land that they wished to cultivate, and here they were counted and rationed every third day.

Lieutenant Whitman was in charge of the small outpost with fifty infantry. The Indians were well-behaved, and the system of counting made it impossible for them to go any great distance from their camp. The ranchmen in the neighborhood were on friendly terms with them and had made some contracts for their services in the coming harvest.

On April 28th a large party of Americans, Mexicans and tough Papago Indians left Tucson, with the avowed determination of killing these Arivapas. Lieutenant Whitman, having received word of this movement by a messenger, at once sent two men to the Indians to tell them to come in, but in an hour the messenger returned and informed him that it was too late.

The camp was strewn with the mutilated bodies of women and children, and their lodges were burning. The post-surgeon, Doctor Briesly, with twelve men, was at once dispatched to the slaughter with a wagon, to bring in any wounded that might be found. Doctor Briesly said, "on my arrival I found that I should have but little use for wagon or medicine; the work had been too thoroughly done."

The camp had been fired and the dead bodies of some twenty-one women and children were lying scattered over the ground; those who had been wounded in the first instance had their brains beaten out with stones. Two of the best-looking squaws were lying in such a position, and from the appearance of the genital organs and of their wounds, there was no doubt they were first ravished and then shot dead. Nearly all of the dead were mutilated. One infant of some ten months was shot twice and one leg hacked nearly off. While going over the ground, the doctor came upon a squaw scared of the Americans but was unhurt. He was unable to get her to come in and talk, she not feeling very sure of his good intentions.

The next morning, Lieutenant Whitman went out with a party to bury the dead. He thought the act of caring for their dead would be an evidence to them of his sympathy at least, and the thought proved correct, for while at the work many of them came to the spot and indulged in expression of grief, too wild and terrible to be described.

Their camp had been surrounded and attacked at daybreak. So sudden and unexpected was it, that no one was awake to give the alarm, and the lieutenant found quite a number of women shot while asleep beside their bundles of hay which they had collected for the army to bring on in that morning. The wounded who were unable to get away had their brains beaten out with clubs and stones, while some were shot full of arrows after having been mortally wounded by gunshot. The bodies were all stripped naked. Of the whole number killed and missing, about one hundred twenty-five, only eight were men, all the rest were women and children.

It was said later that the men were not there; they were all there. On the 28th the soldiers counted one hundred twenty-eight men, a small number being absent for mescal. About their families taken captive, they pleaded with Whitman to "get them back for us; our little boys will grow up slaves, and our girls, as soon as they are large enough, will be diseased prostitutes, to get money for whoever owns them. Our women work hard and are good women, and they and our children have no diseases. Our dead you cannot bring to life, but those that are living we gave to you, and we look to you, who can write and talk and have soldiers, to get them back."

Lieutenant Whitman told them, "I pledge my word I will never rest easily, day or night, until they would have justice."

Whitman told his superior officer, "I would as soon leave the army as to be ordered away from them, or to be obliged to order them away from here. You know that parties who would engage in murder like this, could and would (and have already) make statements and multiply affidavits without end in their justification. This situation may be made either a means of making good citizens of them and their children, or drive them out to a hopeless war of extermination. They ask to be allowed to live here in their old houses, where nature supplies nearly all their wants; they ask for a fair and impartial trial of their faith, and they ask that all their captive children living may be returned to them. Is their request unreasonable?"

The frontier press does not always represent the feeling of the majority of a community in these matters. It is sensational on all subjects, and it was down on Indians on all occasions, on the supposition that this course was popular. It is popular in time of war. After all, the Americans were only stealing the lands, killing their people, that is all. Misrepresentation may then be carried as far as in politics, or farther, for them there was but one side to be heard. But there is no community so depraved as to favor assassination in time of peace, and this was downright assassination. Whatever provocation there existed was in the offense of other Indians. The massacre could not even be justified on the theory that it was an application of lynch law, for lynching is resorted to for the purpose of just punishment, irregularly of course, but still for the exclusive purpose of punishment. The camp was plundered, women were ravished, and the children carried away were sold for the profit of their captors. It ranked as a crime committed by criminals.

The massacre naturally raised a whirlwind of indignation in the East among those who advocated peace, and even conservative people who had not been inclined to Indian-worship recoiled at this atrocity.

*   *   *

There were a large number of Indians who were sufficiently humbled by war to be ready for reservation life, under control of the Indian Department. There were also many who had

not been humbled, who had never been conquered, and who considered themselves the superiors of white men in all respects except number and equipment. It was erroneous to suppose
that this latter class would live peacefully on reservations. No warlike Indian ever submitted to
reservation restrictions until he had been beaten. He cannot be a savage ruler and a humble
pupil at the same time. He cannot feel that fighting is the only work a man ought to do, and
yet take kindly to ploughing. His spirit must be broken in some way, or his nature changed,
before he will submit to it. The right or wrong of breaking his spirit is another question; the fact
remains that he must be born again into civilization, if he ever attains civilization.

Both Sam Houston of Texas and President Andrew Jackson knew they could not stop
the emigration of the white settlers onto Indian lands and the broad panorama of history
was to be played out on these plains in blood and cruelty with all the sorrowful attendant
consequences.

Among many tribes there are brothers by adoption, and the tie is held as sacredly as
though created by nature. One cold, wintry morning in the late fall, while yet the gray shadows of darkness hovered mistily over crag and gorge, some of Ian's band of Indians charged
down upon a renegade ranger's camp sleeping in fancied security of canyon. One of Ian's
party, Two Bears by name, rode a horse, which became crazed by excitement and unmanageable, and being wonderfully fleet, dashed with him ahead of all others into the very center of the ranger's camp, where men were running in wild confusion, where bullets were flying thick and fast, and the ranger's were making a sharp resistance to protect themselves.

Ian, seeing the trouble Two Bears was in, dashed after him, urging his own fast pony
forward with vigorous strokes of the whip, at the same time throwing himself from side to
side of his pony to avoid the shots of the rangers.

Thus he followed Two Bears through the bushes and across the stream, down among
the camp, and into the very center of the rangers, where Two Bears' horse had fallen dead,
shot through the neck. Two Bears had scarcely touched the ground when Ian, sweeping
past, took him behind himself and bore him away from death. Ian had saved Two Bears'
life at the risk of his own, and thence forward the two were much together, and became
brothers by adoption. Ian never thought he had done anything very noble, but keen-eyed,
brave, loyal, wiry little Two Bears deeply appreciated the service Ian had rendered him, and
there would have been glad sunshine in his heart if an opportunity presented itself for him
to reciprocate the gallant action.

Afterwards, when the two were on war parties, and they met other parties and questioned why Ian, a white man, rode with Two Bears. Two Bears would answer in sign language; bringing the tips of the extended, and touching, first and second fingers of the right
hand against lips, back of fingers up and horizontal, other fingers and thumb closed, carry
the hand some inches straight out from the mouth—this meaning, brother.

Bear hunting to Two Bears was a most exciting sport. His weapon consisted of a long pole, to one end of which was attached, by means of small strips of rawhide a steel spear, four inches long and two inches wide. He had another weapon which he used, but not so commonly as the spear, which was made by wrapping several sharp-pointed spikes together so their points extended outward something like the bristles of a hedge-hog when rolled up. This *chevaux-de-frize* was fastened to a long pole, then was used like a spear. This weapon was used to worry the bear by first irritating the animal until, enraged, it rushed upon its assailant. Two Bears then defended himself by presenting his spike weapon, which the bear would seize only to wound itself. More violently enraged with these self-inflicted injuries, the bear endeavored to destroy the spikes by biting and squeezing them, until it actually killed itself.

In using the spear there was more danger incurred than from the spiked weapon, for when a bear was wounded with a spear it attacks the hunter, who sometimes becomes the victim. Nothing can equal, for ferocity and vitality than the grizzly bear of North America. Yet terrible as it is when fully aroused, Two Bears not only attacked, but slew it with no other weapon than a long spear.

Should Two Bears be wounded in these dangerous attempts, which he frequently was, he thought himself lucky, as such wounds were considered evidence of prowess, and to be killed by a bear was esteemed a happy death.

After its death the bear's head and paws were cut off and the head impaled on a spiked pole in front of his teepee to show off his prowess. The claws were kept for good luck, which sometimes were worn for years tied to a string about the neck.

It was very common to find the ears, jawbones, skull, and paws of bears killed, hung up in trees where they are supposed to exercise a most serviceable influence in keeping off evil spirits and bringing good luck to the village.

*   *   *

The United States had hardly a handful of cavalry hence the long campaign of minor affairs that had to follow. To force used against him, the Indian would yield nothing. In battle he never surrenders and he never accepts capitulation at the hand of others. In war he does not ask or accept mercy and does not grant mercy.

As most of the men who had murdered Shenga Wassa and her village wore army clothing and the army troopers helped them after the massacre, Ian naturally assumed that the United States Army had committed the barbarous deed. He had lived and fought with the Indians to accept their thinking that revenge must be satisfied.

Ian and his warrior army kept up a running hit and run warfare. Fleet small forces would strike and run, these attacks many times covered hundreds of miles distant, back and forth, up and down the frontier. At the apex of one of these campaigns, being two hundred miles from Fort Leavenworth before turning and doubling back south from the fort, Ian conceived in his mind to satisfy the revenge of Shenga Wassa's death. The Post Commander seemed to have the most prominent role in the murder; didn't he send Ian to find her?

In the attire of a civilized Indian he easily slipped onto the military reservation. He was dressed in slouchy army blue coat and trousers, which were a little too short, a pair of old fashioned iron spectacles without glass lenses rested uneasily on his nose. A calico shirt, a paper collar, and black "fly" cravat (necktie), which was of course askew, completed his attire.

The officers of Fort Leavenworth were assembled in the presence of the colonel commanding, as was the daily morning custom. It had long been the practice of that veteran soldier to require all his commissioned subordinates to put in an appearance at his office immediately after the ceremony of guardmounting. He might have nothing to say to them, or he might have a good deal, and he was a man capable of saying a good deal in very few words, and meaning exactly what he said. The meetings were by no means unpopular features of the daily routine. The officers were permitted to bring their pipes or cigars and take their after-breakfast smoke in the big, roomy conference room just outside his office. Any matters affecting the discipline or instruction or general interests of the command were brought up; both sides of the question were presented, if a question arose, the decision was rendered then and there, and the officers were dismissed for the day with the customary, "That's all, gentlemen." They left the office well knowing that only in the event of some sudden emergency would they be called again or disturbed in their daily vocations until the same hour on the following morning. Meantime, they must be about their work—drills, if weather permitted, stable-duty, no matter the weather, garrison courts, boards of survey, the big general court that was perennially dispensing justice at the post, and the long list of minor but none the less exacting demands on the time and attention of the subalterns and company commanders.

To his lieutenants, the commander seemed at times greatly preoccupied. Courteous, grave far beyond his years, silent and thoughtful, he impressed them all as a man who had suffered too much ever again to be light-hearted.

As Colonel Williams walked to his immense desk to take care of some correspondence, the door slowly closed and clicked shut. He sensed this was unusual and, as he turned to ascertain if the door had closed, he found a heavy .44 caliber revolver in his face. As Ian cocked the pistol, Colonel Williams wondered what was the reason of such irrational behavior.

He said nothing, letting Ian talk.

"Why did you murder my Shenga Wassa?" he asked the Colonel.

"I didn't kill her, Ian," Colonel Williams replied. "I was only directed to find her, that is all."

"But why did you want to locate her?"

"I do not know. The orders came from General Wilkinson, Commander of the Army of the West."

Ian considered this for a long moment; maybe the colonel did not have her killed.

"Tell me colonel that you did not kill her!" Ian begged for the truth. "Tell me that it is not true. I shall believe you. I cannot believe myself, when I say it."

"It is not true," answered the colonel earnestly. "I pledge my word of honor—it is not true," he repeated the words slowly and emphatically.

Ian knew Colonel Williams was an honorable officer, perfectly honest; as brave a man could be, conscientious and laborious. He was a man for whom Ian had a very high regard, and for his truthfulness Ian had the greatest respect. He was a very valuable man, and his soldierly example was of the highest value in the new army. A nation is fortunate that possesses such soldiers as Colonel Williams.

"I know it is not, when you say it," Ian said as he uncocked his revolver and slowly put it in his belt. "But it is all so terrible, so horrible!"

The colonel turned away from Ian, his eyes moist from the realization that his dreams had escaped him.

Colonel Williams continued, "I say—and I say it after years of reflection—that the more a man of honor and reputation of his cloth, the less can he afford to take a position in the Army of the United States. Why? Why, because the great mass of the people have no conception whatever of the duties that devolve upon the military, of the life they lead, of the trials they encounter. In time of peace they think they have no use whatever for an army, and declare that they do nothing but loaf and drink and gamble. The public is taught to think so by the newspapers of great cities, and, never having a chance to see the truth for themselves, they accept the views of the journalists, who really know no more about it than they do, but do not hesitate to announce as fact what exists only in their imagination."

"I was five years tramping, scouting, skirmishing all through the Indian Territory without ever seeing the inside of a city. We lived on hard tack and bacon and what we could pick up when we couldn't get them. We lost many a good soldier in Indian battle during that time, and at last I got a wound that laid me and sent me back home. I had not seen the place in seven years. Dozens of my relatives and old schoolmates lived there, and I looked forward with pleasure to the rest and joy I should have at the old firesides. I didn't suppose that people really believed all the outrageous flings the newspapers had indulged in at the expense of the army. Do you ever see anything good of an army officer in any paper until he's dead?"

Without answering his question, Ian quietly left the Colonel to his private thoughts.

The next day while sitting in his office with a friend, chatting cheerfully, the colonel complained of the close atmosphere of the room. His friend stepped out for a moment, leaving Colonel Williams handling his saber. Immediately after, hearing a groan, he hurried in to find that the colonel's head had fallen forward on the point of sword, which entered his brain through the right eye, causing death instantly.

Captain Boone's letter reported the death of the commandant of the post: Colonel Williams, "who departed this place at 2 o'clock yesterday afternoon."

Mindful of the virtuous reputation of the army, the new commandant caused a severe reprimand to be issued to Captain Eustace Tremor of the First Dragoons. He had asserted that it was a suicide. Later upon "due consideration of the case," his death was certified accidental. The "most reliable authority" stated that, "due to having only partially recovered from an attack of brain-fever."

His military career had been unusually brilliant, promotions rapid, prospects bright, and possessing the regard and confidence of a large circle of friends.

God's action within men is sometimes manifested in positive achievement and sometimes in the endurance of pain and frustration.

*   *   *

The Indian firestorm of war continued relentless. On his way back to Indian Territory just south of the Arkansas, Ian met up with a small band led by Three Bears, previously known as Two Bears, but he had killed another bear on a marauding expedition.

The outriders of the band intercepted a messenger for the Grand Conspiracy. They attacked and lanced the trooper. As Ian arrived at the scene, the ranger shed tears and tried to make a noise but was unable to because of his wounds. He died minutes later. In his saddlebags, Ian discovered a communication from the Grand Conspiracy along with $16,000.00.

*   *   *

A small troop of cavalry encamped on the Flint Hills high prairie to rest their horses, which were in poor condition. It had been hot and the grass was very dry. Indians had been seen hanging about all day, but the soldiers did not expect an attack this close to Fort Leavenworth.

Two hours before sundown the troopers had just finished eating supper when all at once fire broke out in a circle around their camp just out of rifle range. There was a strong south wind, and before they knew it, the tall grass was blazing furiously—the flames leaping twenty feet high, coming on the run!

In desperate haste, the troopers set a counter-fire all around their camp, beating out the flames nearest them with grain sacks and saddle blankets. The men knew that their lives were at stake. For fifteen minutes they fought like demons, blinded by smoke and ashes, their hands and faces blistered by the flames. The men were utterly exhausted; hardly no one had breath to speak. The lieutenant who led the fire-fighting, with hands and face blistered in several places and his mustache and whiskers, the first he had ever grew, were utterly ruined. He could not wash on account of the burns, and dipped his face and head deep down in the precious spring of water and held his hands under to relieve the pain. His experience was that of most of the troop. Fortunately, they had quite a quantity of antelope tallow, which was warmed and applied to their burns. Undoubtedly the Indians had set fire to burn them out. The troops were notified at retreat roll call that they would move out at daylight. The guards were doubled and they rested as best they could. They were eager to avenge their ruined whiskers but the Kaws were gone.

*   *   *

Column of route! Winding over the trackless prairie through the gray sagebrush, a thin blue thread in the immense space about it, the command moved out. Prairie, more prairie, still more prairie on every side, until lost and melting into the horizon. No sign of life relieved the monotony of the scene, except, perhaps, an occasional coyote away in the distance sneaking off to shelter, or the prairie-dogs popping into their little burrows with shrill barks of alarm and defiance. Now and again the bleached skull and black horns of some defunct buffalo gave silent token of the countless herds that roamed unrestrained across the boundless plains. The sun rose higher and higher in the sky, beating down with pitiless rays and dazzling eyes with its brilliant light. The alkali dust stirred up by the beat of the horses' hooves hung over the column in thick, stifling clouds, making eyes and nostrils tingle.

If there were only a breath of air, ever so gentle, to carry the dust-cloud a little to one side, and to relieve them from the parching heat. Most of the men had laid off their coats and were riding in their shirt-sleeves; some of the men had stripped to their undershirts. Little was said. The choking dust smothered all desire for conversation, until they began to feel a softer pressure under the horses' feet, and gradually the cloud subsided as they rode over and around some rolling, grassy mounds. They saw before them a green line of willow-brush, indicating the proximity of water. The column did not halt, but pushed on over the little yard-wide stream, as they found its waters so full of alkali as to be unfit for use.

Prairie again all around them, but more rolling, and covered with long, waving grass; in the distance clumps of bright green cottonwoods. They halted for a moment on the brow of a high butte to rest their heated horses and throw themselves down in the soft grass. Someone had saved a canteen full of coffee, and from this they had a refreshing drink, and with cigarettes lighted, enjoyed their short rest. Ahead of them, on the top of the next butte, they could see the staff reclining on the grass. The captain had evidently been at it again, for they could hear the hearty laugh of the adjutant as he rose. The staff trumpeter sounded the order to mount again and away they went brushing through the high grass. They were comparatively free from dust now, and although the sun shoots down its fiercest heat as the hour of noon passed, they could bear it more easily. The scene, too, was refreshed by the wonderful color of the rolling hills far in the their front, where the millions of wild flowers covering their smoothly rounded sides blending their bright hues harmoniously in strong contrast with the deep-blue shadows of the mountains. As they neared the cottonwoods the rushing of a stream was heard, and they were soon standing on its high banks, looking down upon the swift-flowing torrent. The signal to let their horses drink was given, and they scrambled down the steep sides and forded the rapid current, rising almost up to their knees as they sat in their saddles; the thirsty animals sucked in the sweet water, cooled by the melting snows of the distant mountains.

The days wore on in this manner. Now they traversed tracts of cactus desert, now dipped down through some sudden break in the plains, and forded streams more or less deep and rapid. Now they climbed over mound-shaped buttes until they entered a little grassy valley, and halted there to await the arrival of the wagon train and to make their camp for the night. The horses were immediately unsaddled, hobbled, and driven off by squadrons to water and to pasture. The men, tired by the long ride, lay about in groups, some dozing, saddles for pillows, under the shelter of leafy little huts, constructed with astonishing rapidity from the pliant branches of the dwarf willows, cut with their sheath-knives from the river brink close by.

The cook had already prepared a little "snack" for them to stay their appetites until dinner and although it consisted chiefly of the remnants of the biscuits baked for breakfast; the contents of some round, gaudily labeled tins of beef or tongue, with a taste of jam or a pickle for a relish, and something from a field flask to wash it all down with. The most elaborate picnic spread in the world could not have been better. The quartermaster rode in just as they were lighting up their pipes to report that the wagons were near at hand. He was hot and thirsty, like a man who has seen nothing to eat or drink for a week. Soon they heard the cracking of the whips, the braying of the mules, and the creaking and groaning of the wheels as the long line of canvas-covered, heavily laden wagons came lumbering up to the camp ground. Speedily the tents rose in well-ordered lines, fires were lighted, and every preparation made for dinner and a comfortable night's rest. Some of the troopers took their towels and strolled down to the river for a bath, or to wash some article of clothing with a piece of toilet soap—laundries being one of the luxuries of civilization which they had parted with some time ago. The mosquitoes were not so bad here this evening as they were a few days ago in one camp they occupied. One could bathe with more or less comfort. Besides, they were hardened to them by this time, if one can ever become hardened to the sting of a Kansas plains mosquito.

Few of the men were about. Those not on duty of some sort were mostly in their tents; a few were fishing for carp, and the horses and mules were grazing quietly on the hillsides on whose tops the troopers could see the mounted figures of the guards outlined against the sky. The little valley, only an hour or two ago a solitary oasis in the wilderness, already took on the appearance of having been inhabited for weeks.

The column of soldiers was accompanying several emigrant wagons and a stagecoach, which carried several important travelers. The presence of the pretty emigrant girls caused some of the younger dragoon to strut like peacocks. When something unusual in petticoats was sighted, the word spread down the column with lightning swiftness. The girls considered the soldiers a lively feature of the dull region. For the troopers part, it was reported that one of the girls had actually been seen—that is, evidently, wearing a "tournure" (bustle), the latest in graceful fashion. Upon seeing the modish bustle, many a "Bold Tim" among the dragoons probably wished for war with England and a long sojourn in St. Louis to view many such ladies.

For their own part, the emigrants were "much gratified" with seeing the company marching gaily past their wagons.

But the excitement of the day was when his lordship and the grand dame of the stagecoach would walk beside their carriage to get daily exercise. Despite the simplicity of her dress, which though of rich material was severely plain, she was one of those women who seem formed by nature to excite men. She wore no jewelry except a silver medallion that Ian Douglass had given her—for she was Louisa, his first love. Clara, the black negress, and Louisa took turns caring for a little two year old boy. The elderly Sir Charles was escorting her through Indian Territory as he had journeyed with the caravan that Ian's dragoons had escorted to Santa Fe previously.

Sir Charles, both during the war and since, had seen staff duty that had brought him into social and political circles in Washington. He had learned there the lesson that an ounce of influence was worth a pound of pure record; that in most matters affecting army legislation, it was the men who were the farthest away from the army whose opinions Congress sought. In all appointments to the staff departments, personal and professional excellence might plead in vain unless backed by senators by the score. That while judicious use of the gifts that God had put in his way in the shape of the public press might result in the gradual rearing of a monument of popular esteem, a single unguarded word or petulant expression, would tumble the whole fabric about his ears.

Sir Charles and Louisa had convinced the president to give Ian full amnesty, an official forgetting or overlooking of offenses, in other words, a general pardon of offenses against the government. The other traveler was a young chief by the name of Lone Elk. He had gone east to Washington, D.C. on business affecting his tribe to work out details for future protection of their hunting grounds from the white settlers. He had been attacked with vomiting of blood during his stay in the capital, which soon brought him to great weakness, so that the delegation lost all hope of his recovery. In that extreme and afflicting situation, Lone Elk had recourse to prayers and implored the aid of Jesus Christ. Then a fellow chief, being filled with faith, drew near to the bed of the dying Lone Elk and exhorted him to put all his confidence in the Great Spirit. Showing him the cross of the Savior, which he had about him, he offered it to the sick man's lips, and saying, "Dear nephew, embrace the crucifix with confidence. Jesus Christ can do everything. He will give you health and bring you back safe and sound to the bosom of your family."

He embraced the cross with a pious ardor and full of faith. The spitting of blood ceased, and from that day his strength gradually returned to him.

"I hope," said the good chief, "that my healing will help to bring all my people to the knowledge, service, and love of the Great Spirit."

Lone Elk spoke little and when he spoke at all, his words were brief. His eyes were like black steel, and his figure grew slighter, and seemed to grow taller as he spoke. He had handsome high features and his face was without a sign of emotion like a red marble mask. After they reached Indian Territory he donned a ghost shirt, a sign of priesthood in the Indian Dreamer religion. Around his neck hung a medallion draped over the shirt, which hung to the middle of his chest. The president had presented each of the chiefs with such a large miraculous medal, which they received with the liveliest gratitude, promising to wear them as souvenirs of fidelity to their promises.

The Ghost Dance religion bothered the government greatly, for religious zealots who were fanatically committed to their cause always concerned established governments. But this did not disturb the small detachment of troops as a good share of the soldiers were catholics as were most military posts. The catholics had their own zealots, the Jesuits, who they tolerated, even admired for their activity to make changes in the established order of things and explicit faith free from the clearly developed church thinking. This unreserved "Society of Jesus" founded by Ignatius Loyala in 1534, were considered by church hierarchy as crafty, intriguing, and equivocating men of God. They were necessary in the order of things.

On their solitary mules they traversed the unknown west two hundred years before other white men, converted pagans to Christianity. They built missions, established a form of government and compassion for the poor Indians. Many times they were tortured and killed for their efforts, but these adversities and hardships failed to lessen their faith. Their motto, "Trust Jesus," carried them through many dangerous and painful endeavors, while their fellow priests were more timid and cautious.

Now, in the 1800s, the precursors of the new religion, the Dreamers, were predestined to bear torment, suffer infliction of severe pain, coercion, and anguish identical to Jesus' followers. Many a so-called "Christian" were hesitant to unduly condemn them as they risked a place in purgatory for an eternity to expiate their sins against their fellow men and women. Others thought, to hell with purgatory, to hell with God, kill these damn Indians! Their lives are nothing, didn't the price of their scalps go down from one hundred dollars to now the bloody deed was only worth twenty-dollars, which the Mexicans paid and the United States government condoned by looking the other way. An Indian's grave in a small corner of 640 acres of good land worth a hundred times more did not bother them.

But this thinking caused countless innocent's deaths through the Indians' passions for revenge and bloodshed for bloodshed. Many a new mound under the snow that winter was marked by a rude slab bearing the inscription: "Beloved wife and infant child."

"Fours left, 'aarch! Halt, right dress, hrrunt!" The little detachment stood in line while the senior sergeant, saluting, turned it over to the command of the officer. Sturdy, hardy fellows, this little company of American cavalrymen. From that veteran weather-beaten soldier on the right there to the blond-haired, red-cheeked lad who had but recently joined with the last batch of recruits from the east, they, in their easy-fitting, serviceable blue uniforms, looked ready for anything that may turn up from a game of baseball to a fight with the Indians.

The ringing voice of the soldierly young adjutant swung the column around and started its day's march. Days passed in this way. They crossed the great plains almost imperceptibly reaching a higher altitude day by day.

A train on the march under these circumstances made a picture not soon to be forgotten. Over the level prairie the wagons rumbled along quietly and smoothly enough. At the occasional coulees there had been some hard pulling, but the patient, strong, willing army mules—most unjustly derided of four-footed beasts—dragged the heavy supply wagons through one after another, and the line stretched its slowly moving length out over the prairie again, at the head the quartermaster, sometimes some crony, the doctor perhaps, riding with Sir Charles to keep him company.

Priding himself in the efficiency and appearance of the dragoons, the lieutenant felt in a patronizing mood toward the officers' laundresses who had a bad time during the crossing of the prairies. He believed that women had no place with a company on active service.

*   *   *

White Eagle (Ian) was reconnoitering the small village of Tousac. This preliminary inspection was made alone so as not to arouse any suspicions. Attired as a half-civilized Indian, he did not attract any of the rancheros, in fact he had selected a day when they were absent from their garrison.

A band of rancheros—organized robbers and murderers—hovered on the flanks of the supply trains. Half-Indian and half-Spanish in their extraction, shriveled though muscular in their frames, dark and swarthy as they were, these men were the Arabs of the American continent. Living half of the time in the saddle—for they were unrivaled horsemen—with lasso in hand, they traversed the vast plains. Their costume generally consisted of a pair of tough hide leggings, over which is a blanket with a hole in the center large enough to allow the head to be thrust out, and which fell not ungracefully over their shoulders, leaving ample room for the play of their arms. Add to this a broad straw sombrero and the lasso hanging ready for use at his girdle, and you have the ranchero as he appears in time of peace or in pursuit of his occupation. Join to this a long lance with a sharp spear-head, ornamented with a strip of red bunting, on a horse as wild and unmanageable as himself, and his belt plentifully supplied with pistols and knives, and you have a ranchero as a member of the troop of banditti, or as a soldier in a body of cavalry. Cowardly as they generally were in the open field, yet in conflict among the chaparrals of Mexico and Indian Territory or in an ambuscade, they were indeed a formidable enemy. Their power of enduring fatigue was almost inexhaustible, and a scanty meal *per diem* of jerked beef and plantain (a tropical nutritious fruit similar to a banana) sufficed them for months.

Such are the rancheros, and under disciplined control they could be rendered the best light troops in the world. These were the men who comprised the great body of the Mexican cavalry, and they were to the armies of that nation what the Cossacks are to the Russians—ever on the alert, never to be surprised, and untiring in the killing of the foe when plunder, no matter how trifling, was to be obtained.

The village was situated on a small stream. Tousac was enclosed with a mud wall with a handsome mission in the center square, indeed most all villages of North Mexico were the same. The mission was surrounded by a powder magazine, quarters for the Rancheros, and few iron field pieces on miserable truck carriages. The village population was fifteen hundred souls, which consisted of civilized Indians, but much mixed blood. The square enclosure of mud walls had houses forming the inside of the walls. The walls of several feet thickness were made of unhewn stone and lime.

The little village was reached over a comparatively level rude wagon-road, the creek admitting of being forded at this season. There was a stone bridge that was used to gain access to the main gate. The road to Tousac passed over a broad plain, generally uncultivated, comparatively uninhabited, without a stick of timber and rarely a drop of running water. The soil was very arid, and the vegetation scanty. A canal brought the water of a river, which was about eight miles distant, to the town. The market place, now deserted in the middle of the afternoon, was protected from the sultry heat of the sun by a rough framework with plantain leaves.

White Eagle strolled unchallenged, in fact all the rancheros were in a plundering raid elsewhere and the inhabitants were enjoying their daily siesta nap after the noonday meal.

Ian was astonished to find, enclosed in the mud walls of the cathedral, rich paintings and the patron saint as large as life, ornamented with gold and silver. The mission cathedral was a very decent Gothic building. Erected in 1807 with one priest, four monks, and three nuns constituting the church with the same profusion of paintings and statuary which is to be found in all Mexican churches. There was a wax figure of the Saviour laid in the tomb, of life size, and unusually beautiful. There were three representations of the crucifixion, as large as life, and of different shades of color, each retaining all the features to which are accustomed in the portraits of Christ, somewhat strangely, combined with the peculiarities of the physiognomy of two of the three races which comprised the population.

White Eagle stood alone in the church before the altar. He thought many thoughts—Shenga Wassa, his life, the killings, the innocent deaths and the futility of it all. He was angry with himself; he had thought revenge and killings would help erase the loss of his dear Shenga Wassa, but he was wrong—it would not bring her back. She was gone . . . gone forever!

He drew his saber and hacked relentlessly at the altar and anything else within his reach with both hands with all his strength. As he tired, he was even more dejected, his spirits totally depressed, and he cast his saber away and prostrated himself on the stone floor and suffered his frustrations alone.

After a long while he rose to his feet and left the church with renewed spirit after pouring out his lamentations of grief and sorrow. He was now truly embarrassed . . . a man was not supposed to lament one's grief but to deal with it head on. Sinful or not, he prayed to end it all . . . to take him as He had Shenga Wassa. The task given him was too much, too difficult for a mortal, but he would carry on as best he could and have faith along the way. Ian was a sorrow laden man. The best of causes have had to fight their way to triumph through a long succession of failures and disappointments, and many of the assailants have died in the breach before the fort has been won. The heroism they have displayed is to be measured not so much by their immediate success, as by the opposition they have encountered, and the courage with which they maintained the struggle.

Most men are the moral slaves of the class or caste to which they belong. There is a sort of unconscious conspiracy against each other's individuality. Each circle and section, each rank and class restrains him. It requires strength and courage to swim against the stream, while any fish can float with it.

The Indian race was dying, being exterminated, and Ian in a righteous cause was a determined man who would stand upon his courage, as upon a granite block and, like David, go forth to meet Goliath, strong in heart, though a host was encamped against him. He would not die on his knees but stand upright and fight to the end.

As Ian left the church, there was a slight movement in the dark recesses in the shadow of a pilaster projecting from the adobe walls of the cathedral. A young woman in the dress of a Carmelite nun witnessed the grief of Ian Douglass. She looked remarkably like Shenga Wassa as she touched her forehead in the sign of the Cross!

*   *   *

Back at the caravan that Louisa was journeying with, passed close by a blackened smoking heap of ashes—all that was left of a ranch that stood there—and a short distance farther on they slowed up a little at the still burning ruins of another house.

"It's the Jones' boy's ranch," said a veteran trooper.

"By Jiminy, the Injuns is makin' a terrible clean sweep of the kentry!"

That they had not been long gone was evident. Two half-charred wagons stood in the "corral," the wooden fence of which was brightly burning, the flames licking the edge of a great wood-pile that even as they passed burst into flames. In a small field of waving corn joining a potato-patch the carcass of a mule was lying right on the bank, the red blood still flowing from a hole in its head, a large dog, a hound, was stretched lifeless. Near a pile of debris, which may have been a kitchen or other out-house of some kind, for a pot or two and tin camp-kettle were hanging from the low fire-seared branches of a tree nearby; a few chickens shrilly cackling were huddled together.

The next morning the quartermaster, before turning his stock from the corral, got upon a wagon wheel and looked over the prairie of a long distance, as far as he could see up and down the river, and saw no signs of horses or people, except several of the picket guards on the hills overlooking the valley. He gave the order to let the cattle out, and they passed out slowly and in a string, marching a long distance towards the hills, when all at once large numbers of Indians sprang up as if from out of the ground, mounted, yelling, and with rattles of some kind in their hands and tied to the tails of their horses. They charged among the cattle, lancing a few. The immense racket and smell of blood so frightened them that none were saved.

The lieutenant thought it imprudent to leave the camp without defense, and sent only about twenty of the dragoons to recover the cattle, if possible. They followed about a mile, when a regular engagement took place. The Indians appeared to be on the retreat; this was only done to get the men as far as possible on the prairie. About one hundred Indians had been stationed on the opposite bank of the river, and they now charged across, came up in the rear of the dragoons, and completely surrounded them. They now had it hand to hand—four to six Indians upon one trooper at a time. The engagement lasted twenty minutes, and five of the soldiers were killed and six wounded. The Indians scalped three of the troopers. Some of them had as many as twelve to fifteen wounds from arrows, and were horribly mutilated; the throat of one was cut from ear to ear—the ears of another were cut off.

Saba, the head chief of the war-party was attracted to the stage coach of which he had not seen before on the frontier. As he approached, Lone Elk stepped out of the coach and rising to full height gave the sign that he was a Crow chief.

Saba signaled to the dog soldiers to do no more harm to the occupants in the stagecoach as Lone Elk signed that they were friends. But that did not include the soldiers and emigrants which continued fighting for their lives.

As Louisa and Sir Charles stepped from the coach Louisa screamed as she saw a warrior pick up Clara who had been walking and holding Michael, and laid her across his horse and sped away while another grabbed the crying toddler and also galloped away in a cloud of dust.

Both would be dead soon. Covering her ears with her slender hands to keep out the screams of the dying and the cries of Clara and her son, she burst into a passion of tears and fainted. As Louisa fell to the ground, several buttons on her blouse ripped off, partially revealing her breasts, between which lay a gold medallion. Saba recognized the unique medal that Shenga had given to Ian to ensure his safety on the plains and Ian had in turn given it to Louisa for her safety amongst the Indians. Immediately Saba shouted out the command to withdraw and the fighting stopped as the Indian band rode away from the carnage of the battle.

After burying the dead and placing the wounded in wagons the little caravan continued on to a small military post. The officers there had brought their families to visit them, and it was a novel sight to see delicate and refined ladies and pretty little children seated around the camp-fire and listening to the lively music of a really excellent string-band, made up from among the enlisted men.

The women tried to comfort Louisa in her grief, but to little avail. The strain of those long sleepless days of watching, waiting, hoping, praying in helplessness and despair, losing Clara and little Michael was too much to bear. She just stood at the edge of the camp staring out into the prairie most of the time, imagining the sufferings of her beloved child.

Two days of grieving had past when two lone Indians showed up on the prairie carrying a white flag of truce which indicated they wanted to parley. As the oft-repeated tap-tap-r-r-ratatattat of the drum over by the commandant's office, and the excited voices of some of the troopers armed themselves to receive the visitors, the captain rose up from his half-reclining attitude, and stepped to the window to see what reason there was for the unusual stir.

As Ian and Three Bears dismounted, their sweat-covered horses stood with heaving flanks, heads bowed down, necks out-stretched, before the door of the office, and an Indian scout squatting on the ground, rose and held the bridles loosely in his hand with an air of stolid indifference. Ian, still wearing his disordered dress he had worn in Tousac—loose gray shirt, mud-splashed blue regulation trousers, bead-embroidered, yellow-fringed, and betasselled buckskin leggings—showed he had ridden hard and fast.

The commandant, standing in front of the open door, looked up into Ian's face and discovered he was a white man. Ian asked to see the white woman on the stagecoach. The young soldiers gathered around Ian and Three Bears clearly nervous as the two were armed for warfare. But the commandant, an old and tried veteran knew never ask an Indian for his weapons while under a flag of truce, ushered Ian into his office for privacy as he sent a corporal to fetch Louisa. Three Bears preferred to remain with the horses.

As Louisa entered the room her head was drooping low, her hands clasped together, her bosom heaving from running to Ian, and her breath fluttering away. She had grown years older in two days.

As Ian approached to embrace her, still frantic from the loss of the baby and Clara, she stepped closer and beat upon his chest with all her strength, taking out all her sorrow and distress in her pounding fists.

Ian understood her immense grief and let her pound him relentlessly to vent her anger, not raising a hand to defend himself from the woman he loved.

She screamed repeatedly over and over, "You killed our son! You killed our son!"

After a time her strength left her and her arms fell to her waist in total despair.

Ian felt terribly sorry for her and he reasoned that only one thing could ease the intense ache in her heart and soul in the death of their son whom she had carried in her womb for nine months and for over two years now was her greatest joy and love. And now he was gone! Dead at the hands of some Indian!

He drew his revolver and pushed the heavy pistol into her shaking hands, and said, "Kill me, stop the killing of innocent children, even my own son!"

He spoke, his deep voice firm, as he saw a way out of his misery and suffering, "Take my life for his life! Please!"

Louisa in her state of utter despair and helplessness, grasped the only solution, she reasoned, was to end the life of the one who had caused all her grief.

She raised the heavy revolver to Ian's face and with trembling fingers slowly cocked the trigger. For a long while she tried to pull the trigger, but her heart would not let her do it. Quivering involuntarily, she came to her senses and laid the gun on the nearby table.

"I cannot," she pitifully pleaded, "I cannot kill my God!"

And before she could retreat, his strong, trembling hands seized her drooping head, and between them held her face with its dark, lustrous, swimming eyes, with checks still tear-wet, yet burning with blushes chasing each other to her very brows, her soft red lips trembling at the corners.

Her eyes lifted to his worshipping gaze, and she could not repel any longer. One swift glance, and if any vestige of doubt remained, it vanished then and there. No woman on earth could have looked into his eyes and denied the love that burned within them—all her own, all her own!

Impulsively she raised her soft lips to his face and kissed him enthusiastically. After the long embrace, she drew a little ways from him and said, "It is all too terrible!" She shook her head against his shirt, hiding her face.

"Nothing but death, death, everywhere—our dear son, the soldiers, and their brothers, Clara, the innocent emigrants—one after the other." Her gentle face was undeniable sad and Ian remembered Saba had uttered these same thoughts at Shenga Wassa's death.

Unknowingly to both of them, two more Indians were coming in, having been assured safe passage by the white flag. Through the open door walked Clara carrying little Michael!

Louisa and Ian were both stunned, unbelieving the glorious sight. Louisa grabbed both and gave them a long, firm embrace. Then she gently took baby Michael in her loving arms. Drawing her son to her breast, clasping him in her sheltering arms, her motherly heart gave way, and rocking to and fro in wordless joy, mingled her tears with those of her beloved child—the sobbing, clinging little one, crying "because momma cries."

She shivered violently as she thought of a few minutes ago when she had almost destroyed everything in their life and had momentarily lost her faith. She thanked Almighty God over and over that she never took that drastic action against her only true love.

*   *   *

The experience of the past few days taught Louisa much. She felt her heart stronger and richer for its lessons, and she looked back on that memorable time as something she would not willingly had missed in her life. She learned that one may be reduced to great straits, may have few or no external comforts, and yet be very happy with that satisfying, independent happiness which outward circumstances cannot affect.

Michael was a loving, affectionate boy—a good child.

Louisa never realized, but did now, the full force and beauty of the Indian custom, living in the midst of dangers seen and unseen, these people every morning looking reverently up to the Great Spirit, and thank Him that they were still alive. So when with each returning day they saw their children safe and well, their first feeling was, gratitude to the Master of Life, who was their only refuge, had not removed them from His everlasting blessings.

Around the campfire that evening, Clara related the story of the return of herself and Michael. They had both been taken to an encampment about four hours' journey. She had been given a horse to ride and as the baby was scared and cried all the time, they let Clara hold him. At the camp some of the women and young warriors had never seen a black person and it seemed to puzzle the superstitious Indians as perhaps a sign of bad luck.

Then Saba returned to the village and told them that the baby's mother wore the medallion the Messiah had given White Eagle (Ian). A young woman by the name of Mo'ki who seemed a very important person (Ian remembered she was the First Disciple of Shenga Wassa) insisted the baby and Clara be returned. The warrior who had seized Clara consented, but the one who had kidnapped Michael refused the order from Saba. He had backed up against a large tree as the village chiefs became angry at his refusal. As she watched the fearful situation of the Indian holding the child tightly to his chest, Saba had suddenly loosed an arrow from his powerful war bow. The arrow pierced the warrior's forehead, went through his brain killing him instantly and out the back of his skull. It embedded in the tree six or eight inches. The baby was taken by Mo'ki, and Saba accompanied them back hence they were taken. At last look, Clara noticed the dead warrior was still hanging to the tree by the arrow.

The next several days were unbelievable joyful, as Ian and Louisa renewed their friendship and both enjoying little Michael.

Louisa was one of those women who seem formed by nature for the sole purpose of being sacrificed to the welfare and happiness of others, and who, in that sacrifice, found her own happiness. She had bound her life to her son.

Sir Charles discussed the amnesty that President Jackson was thinking about granting Ian. He was willing to forget offenses against the government and a general pardon if he would stop his depredations upon the whites. Ian discussed with Sir Charles the possibility of setting aside lands for the Indians and giving them state or national status with their own self rule. Oklahoma Territory would be a suitable area for the Indian Nations.

The white men treated those who contested possession of the Plains against them as barbarians. The Plains Indians reversed this designation. They considered the white man the actual barbarian.

Indian fury, fired to unprecedented savagery by Shenga Wassa's brutal massacre had spent its force. The red man's raids of retaliation had ravished the frontier from one end to the other. Transcontinental travel had been almost paralyzed. Stock had been driven from isolated emigrant trains. Lives of hundreds of soldiers, teamsters and emigrants had atoned for Shenga Wassa's killing. Their thirst for revenge having been satisfied, avenging warriors had quit the warpath to retire peacefully to the hunting grounds between the Washita and the Arkansas Rivers. The road to Santa Fe was once more open. Peaceful trading had been re-established in exchange for pledges from the Great White Father that the red man would not be molested in those areas set aside for his exclusive use.

The Cherokee, Osage, Pawnee, Creek, Cheyenne, Arapaho, Iowa, Kickapoo, Pottawatomie, Choctaw, Chickasaw, Kiowa, Comanche, Apache, Seminole, Wichita, Missourian, and other Indian tribes were to be involved in the relocation.

Only the Dog Soldiers were disgruntled. They refused to sign the treaties because it required them to give up their favorite hunting grounds. But they were merely sullen, rather than actively hostile. Comparatively few inconsequential raids into Texas because of the "ranging companies" hostile actions against them had marred tranquillity of the region.

While the Indians thus were attempting to adjust themselves to the new order of things, willing to go to any reasonable limit that they might hunt and dwell in harmony with their unwelcome neighbors, new strife was being fomented by the invaders. The red man was the hapless victim of an old feud between the contentious factions of the Whites; the War Department and the Interior Department.

Indian agents insisted their charges craved permanent peace, pointing to their repeated surrender of lands and further retirement from the lands of Plains commerce as proof of this desire. Militarists warned that the Indian agents were being duped. They magnified every overt act on the part of the Indian. Minor raids by small, unattached bands frequently were heralded as forerunners of a general uprising again. They argued the only way to settle the Indian question was by armed subjugation by forcing at point of the bayonet every Plains Indian to give up his nomadic life and to settle down to the white man's mode of living within the confines of restrictive reservations.

Sir Charles said he would convey this thought to the President and was hopeful that it was probably the best solution that could be obtained, imperfect as it was.

Before dawn a courier galloped into camp, the horseman enveloped in fur and frost and steam from his panting steed. He handed a note to Ian.

The note was short and to the point. The Rancheros of Tousac had raided an Indian camp and killed a number of them and taken twenty-six scalps. This must be stopped, so Ian prepared to leave. Sir Charles and Louisa's little party were leaving also for Saint Louis. He told Louisa in parting, "I long to see your face, to hear your voice, to look into your glorious eyes, they have overmastered me time and again. God knows my love and honor has been yours a long, long time."

He hugged Michael, his son, and gently handed him to Clara; he kissed Clara on the cheek and thanking her for all the courtesies and help she tendered to Louisa.

In leaving, he turned and bent and kissed Louisa on her wet cheeks. She threw her trembling arms around his neck and clung to him in the agony of departing.

*   *   *

Ian and his band of a hundred warriors, young and old, lay in ambuscade of Tousac. They waited for the sun to rise hoping to catch the rancheros asleep. His force was strung out for over six hundred feet, and as soon as the heavy wooden gates opened for the peon women to fetch water from the canal for preparation of the morning breakfast they would attack.

Saba was squatted on his haunches on one side of Ian and Jamie Bill on the other, setting on the canal bank out of sight of the rancheros, silently loading her carbine; her repeating revolvers already loaded.

As the band spread out in a line of skirmishers for the fight, they then sat quietly until the sun rose and the gates opened. From the direction of the village cathedral, a sweet singing voice wafted gently through the morning air and over the stream to Ian's ears. As he leaned forward and cocked his head to the side to hear the sound clearer, there was no mistake about it. It was his beloved Shenga Wassa's voice he had listened to for many nights before the campfire on the plains and in the recesses of the cave on Holy Mountain!

He whispered, "Shenga, Shenga Wassa!" As he repeated the dead Messiah's name, his voice increased to a loud calling, "Shenga, Shen. . . . ga!" as the song continued issuing from behind the walls.

Saba, grabbed him by the nape of the neck, and thrust his head into the water to muffle the voice of Ian. Even under the water, Ian continued to call out her name, but only a mummer rose out of the water in violent bubbles. Saba raised Ian's face out of the canal then ducked his head again to stop him.

The heavy gates swung open and the Mexican rancheros raced across the stone bridge over the moat in full force to attack the warriors. The ground thundered beneath the hooves of their charging horses. Today they would take more scalps!

Saba, seeing the element of surprise was no longer with them, climbed the steep bank of the canal, and yelled in a loud shout, "Retreat! Retreat!"

As the warriors scampered in a hasty run to their horses, the trio climbed out of the canal, and prepared to do battle with the murderers. Saba, as chief, had been taught all his life, when the odds are too great, retreat to fight again. As Jamie Bill and Ian stood alone to face the horde sweeping toward them, several dog soldiers decided to die with Ian, an honorable death about which would be sung around their campfires for many moons.

The cavalry charged and, in a giant wheeling maneuver, spaced its musketry the length of the Indian line. Even the most valiant warriors could not stand up under such odds and fell back or died.

Ian was almost instantly disabled in both his arms, losing first his sword and then his reins and followed by a few of his men, who were presently cut down, no quarter being asked nor given. Ian was carried along by his horse, until receiving a blow to his head by a saber. He fell on his face to the ground.

Recovering, he raised himself a little to look around, being at that time in no condition to get up and fight, when a lancer, passing by, struck his lance through his back, as he cried out, "You are a dead man, Yankee."

His head dropped, blood gushed into his mouth, a difficulty of breathing came on. Ian thought all was over.

The rancheros charge carried them through Ian's little band of warriors. Jamie dismounted in front of Ian and faced the charging horsemen alone taking down a half-dozen with her accurate and deadly carbine. When she ran out of ammunition, she drew her Colt repeater and picking up Ian's from his side, stood up on both feet firmly planted and with cool head, free from excitement, passion, and fear, killed and wounded many a horseman before they could reach Ian. Then a lance thrown hard, hit her chest and she staggered back and fell dead next to Ian—never to see her seven brothers and her beloved Texas. She loved him well enough to die for him.

The ranchero artillery fired salvos of grapeshot into the thinning Indian ranks but the banditti came on anyway. Ian regained consciousness, weary and worn out, less from fatigue than anxiety. Ian's horse had received a shot through the leg and one through the flap of the saddle, which lodged in his body, sending him a step beyond the pension list.

Gradually, the Indians dwindled into a solitary ragged line of skirmishers. Most of his warriors were lying literally dead. The smoke still hung so thick about that he could hardly see anything. Ian walked a little way to each flank to get a glimpse of what was going on but nothing met his eye, except the mangled remains of men and horses. It was at the center of the line where the killing ground piled highest with dead.

The clouds broke at noon; the sun shone out a little just as the battle finished. The sunlight mingled with cannon smoke as the battle raged and it seemed the Indian forces was vanquished on the bloody field.

Not long afterward, an infantryman stopped to plunder him, threatening his life. Ian directed him to a small side pocket in which he found three dollars, all he had, but he continued to threaten Ian, and Ian said he could search him. This he did immediately, unloosing his shirt and tearing open his coat and leaving him in a very uneasy posture. But he was no sooner gone than an officer, bringing up some troopers, happened to halt where Ian lay, stooped down and addressed him, saying he feared he was badly wounded. Ian answered that he was. Ian complained of thirst, and the officer held his brandy bottle to his lips, directing one of the soldiers to lay Ian straight on his side and place a knapsack under his head. He then passed into the action.

By and by, another infantryman came up, a fine young Mexican man full of ardor. He knelt down and fired over Ian as the Indians counter-attacked, loading and firing many times and conversing with Ian gaily all the time. At last he ran off saying, "You will be glad to learn that we are going to retreat. Goodbye, my friend."

A little later two squadrons of cavalry passed over Ian in full trot, the horses' hooves lifting him from the ground and tumbling him about cruelly.

The battle was now at an end. The shouts, the imprecations, the outcries, the discharge of the musketry and cannon were over and the groans of the wounded all around him became every moment more and more audible. He thought the night would never end.

About this time Ian found a soldier of the infantry lying across his legs. He had crawled there in his agony, and his weight, his convulsive motions, his groans and the air hissing through a wound in his side distressed Ian greatly. The last circumstance most of all, as Ian had a wound of the same nature himself.

Ian turned to get more comfortable and looked into Jamie Bill's lifeless face and wept, "I'm sorry, Jamie . . . I'm sorry," as he removed the Colt revolver from her hand and the holster from her delicate waist.

Say what you will, there is something more truly Christian in the man and woman who gives their time, their strength, their life, if need be, for something not themselves. Whether they call it their friends, their country, or their family—and this spirit of giving one's life, without calling it a sacrifice, is found nowhere so truly as on the frontier

The Indians believed and so did Ian that there is a time to live and a time to die. A good death is far better than a wasted life. A person lives but so long as their life is worth more than their death. The longer life is not always the better.

When day broke, a cart came for Ian on the fields of death and he was placed in it and carried to the village of Santa Maria, five and a half miles off. Ian had received seven wounds. He was saved by the excessive bleeding, but in a very hopeless state. He had been hit by a musket ball which pierced the leather part of his old conquistador helmet he sometimes wore into battle and received a saber slash which could have sliced deeply into his lungs if had it not struck the leather bandolier across his chest.

He fell into deep unconsciousness for two days. As he slowly came back to life, he looked up into the beautiful face of Shenga Wassa! He went unconscious again due to his lost strength. The nun had some knowledge of surgery, and repaired the open cuts by using the needle and sinew thread. During the closing of the wounds, Ian was awakened by the pain, but said nothing, only looked at the nun through hazy eyes at the miracle of Shenga Wassa's return.

Afterwards she dressed the wounds. Although the operation of probing and cleansing them was perfect torture, he submitted to it patiently and without a sound of complaint, although he did wince from the pain several times.

As she finished, Ian tenderly and weakly grasped her hand and whispered "Shenga . . . Shenga, my love!"

The nun leaned close to Ian so he could hear her say. "I am not Shenga . . . I am Sister Nicaela of the order of Carmelite Nuns!"

Ian had heard of the Daughters of the Blessed Virgin Mary. This ancient order originated on Mount Carmel in 1562 in Avila, Spain by St. Teresa of Jesus. The sisters nurse the sick and serve the interests of God's glory, her own perfection, and the good of souls.

Ian argued, "You are Shenga Wassa—my wife!"

She replied, "I am Sister Nicaela," and showing him the silver ring she wore on her finger, "I am married to Jesus."

That ended the conversation as he had little strength as she attempted to make him eat. Maybe she was not Shenga Wassa but her kind, loving consideration deeply impressed him.

Saba and several other warriors who had returned to be again with him, carried the severely wounded Ian on a travois to a nearby hot springs that issued from the metamorphic rocks. The water was strongly alkaline with temperatures of 98 degrees to 107 degrees which had been visited by the Indians for years on account of the curative properties of the waters. As she immersed him in the warm waters and bathed his wounds, he felt his strength returning and the wound healed remarkably fast. The government had sent a geographical survey west of the 100th meridian and had analyzed the chemical properties of the spring. The curative chemicals consisted of

Carbonate of soda	30.80
Carbonate of lime	9.52
Carbonate of magnesia	2.88
Carbonate of iron	4.12
Sulphate of sodium	29.36
Sulphate of magnesia	18.72
Sulphate of lime	3.44
Chloride of sodium	4.16
Siticale of soda	4.08
Chloride of calcium	trace
Chloride of magnesium	trace

Total grams solid residue per gallon   107

The main spring flowed 8,000 gallons per minute. These springs had long been used for rheumatic afflictions.

As she bathed Ian's naked body, her habit hung tightly to her body as she sat close to Ian in the warm springs, revealing a full feminine figure with mature protruding breasts. Sister Nicaela ignored his inspection of her body. The Carmelite nuns are called to a life of love demanding total dedication to God. Retaining the spirit of her desert heritage, the Carmelite pursues the contemplative ideal, divine intimacy, while embracing the world with her apostolic prayers and effectiveness of their sacrifices, making her a collaborator in the redeeming work of Christ.

While tending his wounds in the spring, she removed her bandeau (the white linen cloth worn around the forehead to which the veil is attached) and the wimple, a linen starched covering, which fitted the sister closely about the neck, throat, face, and head. It was once common attire for women. It is also known as a barbette. With her head uncovered, she was Shenga Wassa's perfect image, except for her close cropped hair cut in traditional nun fashion.

And as she chanted Indian prayers over Ian, he was certain she was Shenga Wassa.

Three Bears had killed a coyote and it was cooked over a slow fire in boiling water all day long to get rid of the wild taste, then Ian ate several pieces for quick strength. Saba brought in a fresh killed buck deer and the antlers were cut into small pieces and boiled for three days. Sister Nicaela dropped some secret red berries into the brew and Ian sipped a drink of the concoction as Nicaela insisted. He could feel life and strength flowing back into his body.

Nicaela had been an extern sister at the convent, a member of the cloistered order of nuns who lived within the convent, served as portress and done shopping. She accomplished a variety of manual work, and vowed a strict fast and perpetual abstinence. If she was not Shenga Wassa, she had an uncommon knowledge of Indian habits, nature and womanly duties. She prepared a sweat lodge with a small hole, a foot deep, dug out in the center of the floor space, to serve as a receptacle for the heated stones over which water was poured to produce steam. She piled the dug earth in a small hillock a few feet in front of the entrance to the sweat lodge, which always faces the east. This small mound was called the thi'aya in the Arapaho language, the same name also applied to a memorial stone heap or to a stone monument. It was surmounted by a buffalo skull, as it always is, and placed so as to face the doorway of the lodge.

Although Nicaela had constructed the sweat lodge the same as Shenga Wassa, and spent several nights in the lodge with Ian, she kept her distance from Ian, even though he held her tenderly several times and kissed her full on her lips. She seemed to suffer his attentions so Ian, even though he had passion for her as he had for Shenga Wassa on their wedding night, which was spent in such a sweat-lodge, he respected her perpetual abstinence and never violated her body. Nicaela slept next to him that night and in the morning she still retained her innocence.

Saba and the other Indians had no problem with reincarnation. The notion that the "life" may be transferred from one body to another was wide-spread among the American aborigines. Shenga Wassa, the Messiah of the "Ghost-Dance Religion," or Dreamers as some called them, taught that the Indian dead were to be resurrected, the old life restored, and even the game of former days to be brought back. Christian influences were at work here, but they fell on well-prepared aboriginal ground.

Although the Indians were being converted to Christianity, many still retained some of their ancient superstitious feasts and ceremonies, one of which is so remarkable that it must not be passed unnoticed. In the village that Ian's small band was visiting on their journey north, once a year there was a great festival, prepared for three successive days, which they spent in eating, drinking, and dancing. Near this scene of amusement was a dark cave, into which not a glimpse of light could penetrate, and in which were prepared places to repose on. To this place persons of both sexes and of all ages (after they had physical development to beget children) and of all descriptions, went to the cave, where there was an indiscriminate orgy of rape and intercourse, as chance, fortune, and events allowed. These orgies had great similarity to the ancient mystic rites of Greece and Rome.

The practice of periodic relaxation of social restraints has been followed by the majority of people, and is the unconscious response to a real social need.

The study of the orgy as a normal phenomenon throws light on the whole mechanism of society. Primitive "bursts" and modern "Bank Holiday" mafficking fulfill an identical purpose, and their conditions are identical, though more stringent in the case of early society.

The life of a native is hedged in with arbitrary rules that must be obeyed, often at the peril of their life. To the casual onlooker the native may appear to live a perfectly free life; in reality he does nothing of the kind; indeed, very much the reverse.

The orgy is to the routine of ordinary life what the religious feast is to the fast. It supplies a rest and a change, but particularly an emotional and physical expansion and discharge of energy. Excess and dissipation are almost inevitably involved, but they are not in principle essential conditions. Nor again, is the criminality, which often appears. The functions in which this neuromuscular discharge takes place are those belonging to the general muscular system—eating, drinking, and sex. The main psychological element, relief from restraint, is connected with others—the play-instinct, the pleasure of exhilaration and neuromuscular excitement, and religious enthusiasm in many cases. The economic conditions of Indian life, themselves suggest periodic excess. The Indian hunter often practically fasts for days together. He is disciplined to this, and especially capable of gorging himself when he has killed his game. This capacity indeed is part of his survival value. In origin an unconscious social reaction, their orgy has clearly been thus understood in later ages and accepted. Having a function to fulfill in every orderly and laborious civilization built upon natural energies that are bound by more or less inevitable restraints, it has been deliberately employed in great religious ages, the rule of abstinence being tempered by permission of occasional outbursts. Possible such regulation of excess and dissipation has assisted the general development of self-control.

In the case of feasts of first fruits, the sudden access of a supply of food and liquor inevitable encourage an outburst. The young people engage in games and dances, feats of strength and running. After these are over the whole camp give themselves over to disorder, debauchery, and riot. In their games they did honor to the powers of nature, and now, as they eat and drink, the same powers are honored in another form and by other rites. There is no one in authority to keep order, and every man does what seems good in his own eyes. People are even permitted to abuse the chief to his face, an offense which at any other time would meet with prompt vengeance and an unceremonious dispatch to join the ancestors. At times during the festival the grossest liberty prevails; neither theft, intrigue nor assault is punishable, and each sex abandons itself to its passion. It was a time of general license and the people were supposed to be out of their senses, and therefore not to be responsible for what they did. Some Hos of North India have a strange notion that at this period (harvest festival) men and women are so overcharged with vicious propensities that it is absolutely necessary for the safety of the person to let off steam by allowing for a time full vent to the passions. After eating and liquor-drinking people expand in other ways. The feast is unrestrained revelry during which servants forget their duty to their masters, children their reverence for parents, men their respect for women and women all notions of modesty, delicacy, and gentleness; they become raging bacchantes, men and women become almost animals in the indulgence of their amorous propensities.

Man is credited with an evil imagination, though this imagination or disposition was not the result of the fall of Adam and Eve. Sin is regarded as a state, as well as isolated act. The universality of sinfulness is sometimes emphasized. Sin is occasionally spoken of as inherent in man from his birth.

While Ian and Three Bears were hunting, this riotness reached its apex and Sister Nicaela, screaming and praying, was dragged into the dark cave and raped by a dog soldier caught up in the "harvest festival" of the moment.

Having satisfied his physical-neuro excitement and pagan religious enthusiasm he exited the cave and continued his debauchery of drunkenness and excess eating. When Ian and Three Bears returned with an elk, Ian could not locate Sister Nicaela and upon inquiry was informed that she was in the cave. Worried about the festival that had occurred during his absence, he must find her to protect her from the rites of the village.

He quickly picked up a faggot from the large campfire where various wild game was being cooked, and entered the dark cave.

Several couples were still engaged in the sexual passions, undisturbed by his presence. He finally located Sister Nicaela, her gown still up at her thighs, her guimpe which normally covers the chest was ripped open revealing her bosoms. Her chest was heaving in a spasm of frightened crying and knowing her body had been violated and her marriage to Jesus and total abstinence vows broken. All she could do was to lay there and hold her string of beads crying the rosary of devotion.

Ian passed the firebrand to Three Bears and carried her tenderly from the cave. He laid her on a buffalo robe a little ways from the carnival of riot and debauchery and sat with her to ward off any more harm to her.

Three Bears knew he should honor the religious festival of the local camp but his Messiah had been violated, and to him that was an unforgivable sin of the first order.

The warrior who had perpetrated the act was soon identified and tied to a cross in the center of the camp. Three Bears, a highly respected chief known throughout the Indian

Territory explained to the onlookers that their Messiah had been outraged and death of the warrior was the only satisfaction, notwithstanding the festival proceedings.

He took off his bear robe and held it over the flames until it blazed fiercely as the robe caught fire. He calmly walked over to the cross and threw the blazing robe over the hapless warrior.

Nicaela screamed and turned her head from the horrible scene as the sweet, sickening stench of burnt human flesh wafted over the camp.

The warrior let out no scream and bravely died for his misdeed. His crime was not of evil intent. He did not realize she was considered a Messiah. He had done wrong and thereby invoked the law of retaliation, or quick justice. The honor of his tribe was the first and most predominant emotion of his heart.

The Indian custom of burning at the stake was one which has been the subject of severe criticism and condemnation among the white race. It was, however, their established mode of putting an offender to death.

According to their law the fate of transgressor was death; so under our law, the fate of one who commits treason against our government, who is regarded as our enemy, is death. As between the Indian and ourselves, it is merely a question as to the mode of executing the law.

He met death in a heroic manner. He held his honor and respect of his tribe in so high esteem that he preferred it to life, and suffered the most exquisite torture rather than dishonor it. Such was the peculiarity of native Indian character.

The next day all was back to normal as Ian, Nicaela and Three Bears continued their journey. Every day Ian saw more and more of Shenga Wassa in Nicaela. Nicaela in great distress had discarded her brown habit and scapular of Our Lady of Mount Carmel, her black veil, white guimpe (a white linen starched rounded cloth which covered the chest), and her white choir mantle, for the typical Indian attire and let her close-cropped hair grow in the style of Shenga Wassa. The only articles of former dress she retained was a leather belt with a rosary and crucifix attached. Ian noticed her silver ring had been removed.

Jackson Grove Incident
Walnut Creek, Arkansas River,
Indian Territory

*T*he spring thaw had set in at Fort Leavenworth. The winter winds had ceased to sweep down from the barren grasslands of the Missouri breaks, a time when men and their horses began to move restlessly about within the confines of barracks and stables.

Colonel Kearny, back from a court-martial at St. Louis wrote the War Department, "I have 350 efficient and well-mounted men ready for service. If there is anything to be done, we are all desirous of entering upon it."

In May orders came down, positive as well as permissive to send the Dragoons where needed to afford protection of the Santa Fe traders. A government caravan, loaded with military stores had left Fort Leavenworth for the long and dangerous journey of more than seven hundred miles over the great plains, which that season were infested by Indians to a degree almost without precedent in the annals of freight traffic.

The train was owned by a Mr. H.C. Barret, a contractor with the quartermaster's department, but he declined to take the chances of the trip unless the government would lease the outfit in its entirety, or give him an indemnifying bond as assurance against any loss. The chief quartermaster executed the bond as demanded, and Barret hired his teamsters for the hazardous journey; but he found it a difficult matter to induce men to go out that season.

Among those whom he persuaded to enter his employ was a mere boy, named McGee, who came wandering into Leavenworth a few weeks before the train was ready to leave, seeking work of any description. His parents had died on their way to Kansas, and on his arrival at Westport Landing, the emigrant outfit that had extended him shelter and protection in his utter loneliness was disbanded, so the youthful orphan was thrown on his own resources. At that time the Indians of the great plains, especially along the line of the Santa Fe Trail, were very hostile, and continually harassing the freight caravans. Companies of men were enlisting and being mustered into the United States service to go out after the Indians, and young Robert McGee volunteered with hundreds of others for the dangerous duty. The government needed men badly, but McGee's youth militated against him, and he was below the required stature; the mustering officer rejected him.

Mr. Barret, in hunting for teamsters to drive his caravan, came across McGee, who, supposing that he was hiring as a government employee, accepted Mr. Barret's offer.

By the last day of June the caravan was all ready, and on the morning of the next day, July 1, the wagons rolled out of the fort, escorted by the company of volunteer United States troops.

The caravan wound its weary way over the lonesome trail with nothing to relieve the monotony save a few skirmishes with the Indians; but no casualties occurred in these insignificant battles, the Indians being afraid to venture too near on account of the presence of the military escort.

On the 18th of July, the caravan arrived in the vicinity of Fort Larned. There it was supposed that the proximity of that military post would be a sufficient guarantee from any attack of the Indians; so the men of the train became careless. As the day was excessively hot, they went into camp early in the afternoon, the escort remaining in bivouac about a mile in the rear of the train.

About five o'clock, a hundred and fifty painted Indians, under the command of Little Turtle of the Brule Sioux, swooped down on the unsuspecting caravan while the men were enjoying their evening meal. Not a moment was given them to rally to the defense of their lives, and of all belonging to the outfit, with the exception of one boy, not a soul came out alive.

The teamsters, every one, were shot dead and their bodies mutilated. After their successful raid the Indians destroyed everything they found in the wagons, tearing the covers into shreds, throwing the flour on the trail, and winding up by burning everything that was combustible.

On the same day the commanding officer of Fort Larned had learned from some of his scouts that the Brule Sioux were on the warpath, and the chief of the scouts with a handful of soldiers was sent out to reconnoiter. They soon struck the trail of Little Turtle and followed it to the scene of the massacre on Cow Creek, arriving there only two hours after the Indians had finished their work. Dead men were lying about in the short buffalo grass, which had been stained and matted by their flowing blood and the agonized posture of their bodies.

Moving slowly from one to the other, the lifeless forms still showed the agony of their death-throes. The chiefs of the scouts came across the bodies of two boys, both of whom had been scalped and shockingly wounded, yet, strange to say, both of them were alive. As tenderly as the men could lift them, they were conveyed at once back to Fort Larned and given in charge of the post surgeon. One of the boys died in a few hours after his arrival in the hospital, but the other, Robert McGee, slowly regained his strength, and came out of the ordeal in fairly good health.

The story of the massacre was related by young McGee after he was able to talk, while in the hospital at the fort; for he had not lost consciousness during the suffering to which he was subjected by the Indians.

He was compelled to witness the tortures inflicted on his wounded and captive companions, after which he was dragged into the presence of the chief Little Turtle, who determined that he would kill the boy with his own hands. He shot him in the back with his own revolver, having first knocked him down with a lance handle. He then drove two arrows through the unfortunate boy's body fastening him to the ground, and stooping over his prostrate form ran his knife around his head, lifting sixty-five square inches of his scalp, trimming it off just behind his ears.

Believing him dead by that time, Little Turtle abandoned him, but the other Indians, as they went by his supposed corpse, thrust their knives into him, and bored great holes in his body with their lances. After the Indians had done all that their ingenuity could contrive, they exultingly rode away, yelling as they bore off the scalps of their victims, and drove away the hundreds of mules they had captured.

When the tragedy was ended, the soldiers, who had from their vantage-ground witnessed the whole diabolical transaction, came up to the bloody camp by order of their commander, to learn whether the teamsters had driven away their assailants, and was too late what their cowardice had allowed to take place. The officer in command of the escort was dismissed from the service, as he could not give any satisfactory reason for not going to the rescue of the caravan he had been ordered to guard.

When news of this outrage reached Fort Leavenworth Headquarters, Kearny heeded the warning of the foray. As soon as the weather permitted patrolling, he sent out Captain Nathan Boone (son of old Daniel Boone) with three Fort Gibson companies to reconnoiter the prairies as far as the alkaline flats of the Canadian River, and to afford protection to the Santa Fe traders. Kearny gave the four companies in the Fort Leavenworth area to Captain Philip St. George Cooke with definite instructions to protect the caravans from *any* attack.

The dragoons were well equipped, each trooper with a Prussian-model saber, breech-loading Hall's carbine and one Harper's Ferry percussion pistol. Fifteen supply wagons with six-mule teams and two howitzers made up the train. The companies paraded in the barracks square of Fort Leavenworth in the morning. At the end of the inspection, the dragoons were called to attention; the bandmaster raised his staff and, as the fifes began to squeak "The Girl I Left Behind Me," the regiment marched out the gates of the Fort.

The omens for success were favorable. Not only were the horses and men in fine condition, the supply train ample, and the officers experienced, but the state of training and discipline was excellent. At the first night's encampment, tents and even cooking fires were automatically "dressed right"—a far cry from the days when an ignorant regiment had lain shivering in shingle huts around Fort Gibson.

Some traces of the spring mud still lingered in shady places, cutting the day's march down to ten miles, but the command was in good spirits.

The marches quickly fell into a routine. Reveille was at dawn, with no dawdling permitted, the better to accustom the dragoons to quick response, for this was the favorite hour of Indian attackers. Morning stable call was blown; the horses were taken out from the picket lines to be groomed, grazed, and inspected by careful sergeants and company officers. Breakfast for the men followed with the officers eating well secluded in their mess tent, served by their slaves, to whom the rank and file referred to as "black Hussars." The slaves were usually merry, but quickly became doleful in any sort of rain. With mess over, the wagons were loaded with camp equipage and their "forward" was blown. Broken only by a long noon halt, the march continued until late afternoon or such time as wood, water, and grass were found close together. Then the processes of morning were reversed.

The horses were inspected for saddle sores or other marks of ill usage. Quite soon, the tents were up, but already the mess fires afforded the brightest illumination in the camp. The guard was told off, paraded, and sent either to rest or posts of duty. The noise of cooking died away; for a time there was yarning or card-playing before the fires, then the last formation was held-tattoo, to make sure that every man was armed. The bugler blew "Lights Out" (taps had not yet been composed), and silence fell over the camp, broken only by snores, the pawing of a picketed horse, and the reassuring voices of the sentries.

It was hard for Captain Cooke to leave his wife and their new daughter so few weeks after her birth but Kearny had received permission to go; Julia Turner Cooke was born at Fort Leavenworth just three months earlier.

Worse still, Rachel Cooke had become the victim of a grievous accident at her husband's hands. He was unfortunate as to wound his wife very severely by the accidental discharge of a pistol in his hands. The ball entered her jaw about an inch and a half and passed out through the under-lip, carrying away one half of her teeth.

Cooke was much attracted to his wife, and was very unhappy at having been the instrument of inflicting on her such suffering. He was extremely desirous to obtain for her as speedily as possible the professional aid of a surgeon dentist in order to mitigate as far as he could this serious misfortune.

*   *   *

Treachery on the Santa Fe Trail was not confined to the streams and mud-holes. It is true that, at least within the territories of the United States, bandits seldom annoyed the caravans of the traders.

American citizens traveling with westbound caravans could take pride in the prompt justice of their government.

Cooke's caravan, marching with considerable difficulty, for as the result of a late spring and wet weather, the grazing was poor and the prairie soft. The supply wagons and their howitzers bogged down with aggravating frequently, but in the weeks to the rendezvous at Council Grove, those annoyances were reduced. After waiting two days at the grove, Terrett joined with A Company from Fort Scott, and the traders announced themselves ready to depart. Cooke began to watch for a likely spot in which to winter his men, for Kearny had warned him that he might be sent on to Bent's Fort and so unable to return to Fort Leavenworth before the coming of cold weather.

Dropping Captain SW. Moore and C Company to ride with the mired and overloaded caravan, Cooke and the remaining three companies rode to Walnut Creek. On June 14, they met Boone's detachment from Fort Gibson, together with the wagon train of Charles Bent and Ceran St. Vrain, en route from Bent's Fort to the settlements. Here, all halted because of the flooded streams. Cooke dined with Bent and Manual Alvarez, the former American consul at Santa Fe. Cooke also botanized and noted in his diary the military features, or lack of them, of the country. He then meditated the frontier of the United States, "It is not extraordinary that . . . desperate, heedless, small parties should meet their fate in this lawless wilderness; the wonder is, that so many escape. If the power and almost certain punishments, of our best internal government, do not prevent daily murders and robberies . . . can they fail to occur here, where struggling parties of Indians are tempted by their poverty, and the almost certainty of escape from detection and punishment? Our government is scarcely bound in duty to protect such rash and vagabond men . . . as three buffalo-calf hunters from Missouri who were ambushed on the Pawnee Fork, practically within easy ride of six companies of United States Dragoons."

Charles Bent, also, marked time while St. Vrain went back with wagons to collect five boatloads of furs marooned somewhere on the stretches of the Arkansas River; an experiment in bringing the pelts to St. Louis by water had quite obviously failed. On the other hand, there was too much water on the prairies, for the lagging wagon train was impeded by bog on ground that usually was firm. Cooke rode out to hunt buffalo, and looked forward to the promise of a "general assemblage" at Walnut Creek.

To most military leaders operating on the Plains, Indians were Indians, regardless of who the offenders were, it was common practice to take the nearest red man to task for any offense committed anywhere by any Indian. It was typical of frontier injustice in those days that though the Cheyenne, Arapaho, Kiowa, and Comanche were the ones against whose treaty rights these offenders operated, yet it was these same tribes who were punished by the government.

Map–Western United States

Topping the plains of Texas only a few miles south of the main Canadian River rises what once was a beautiful, clear water stream. Paralleling its broad-channeled neighbor almost to the ninety-seventh meridian, it suddenly swings south past the Arbuckle Mountains, then east and south again, forming the borderline between the now Marshall and Bryan counties, before emptying in Red River.

Unlike most of the Plains rivers, its narrow channel runs deep, confined between rather precipitous banks. It drained one of the most fertile valleys in all of Oklahoma Territory. From its source to its mouth is fringed with heavy growths of a variety of trees, preponderantly cottonwoods, elms and hackberries. All of its main tributaries also were wooded. Along its banks grew an equally large variety of bushes, tall grasses, luxuriant short grasses, and wild flowers. As far back as tradition runs and history records, it was a wildlife paradise. In this region vast herds of buffalo were accustomed to winter. There was forage, not only along the main stream, but also along its numerous tributaries, that was protection from sweeping winds. Deer, antelope, wild turkey, pinnated grouse and quail abounded. Game animals and game birds in countless thousands never left its environs.

Because of this remarkable abundance of game, the stream derived its name from Choctaw words meaning "Big Hunt." Choctaw and Chickasaw and others of the Five Civilized Tribes had hunted its southern and eastern extremities more than a century ago. Small parties sometimes risked conflicts with the plains tribes by venturing far up its course. From the easternmost slope of the Wichita to the plains of Texas, it was the favorite hunting ground of the Kiowa, Comanche and Lipan, or Plains Apache. These tribesmen ranged south, west and north. It furnished part of the fare for remnants of the Caddo and Wichita tribes. From the North came bands of Cheyenne and Arapaho in ever-increasing numbers to lay in a winter's supply of meat, especially after overland trail of commerce had begun to drive buffalo from the region of the Missouri, Platte, and Arkansas Rivers. Years of harassment by the soldiers had worried their leaders into seeking an amicable agreement over lands so that the Indians might hunt without molestation. Some were so eager for a cessation of hostilities, always incited by troops, that they were even willing to try their hands at agriculture. The great majority, however, preferred to continue their lives as roving huntsmen yet within such reasonable restrictions as would prevent collision with settlers and soldiers.

Here was what the Indians wanted more than anything else—assurance of peace and freedom from aggression by the bad white men who heretofore had caused so much resentment among the red men.

Thus assured, the Indians were willing to make the same kind of promises to the whites. They agreed to deliver up any of their own people who should stray from the straight and narrow and to permit the government to withhold any of their monies to pay for any legitimate claims of damage done by their people.

They obtained for their reservations and hunting grounds most of the territory from the southern line of the proposed State of Kansas to Red River not reserved for the other tribes. In the words of the treaty, this territory was "hereby set apart for the absolute and undisturbed use and occupation of the Indians herein named, and for such other friendly tribes of individual Indians as from time to time they may be willing, with the consent of the United States, to admit among them; and the United States now solemnly agrees that no person except such officers and agents, and employees of the government as may be authorized to enter upon Indian reservations in discharge of their duties enjoined by law, shall ever be permitted to pass over, settle upon, or reside in the territory described in this article, or in such territory as may be added to this reservation for use of said Indians."

General W.S. Harney, who headed the military group when the famous Medicine Lodge Peace Treaty was negotiated, once said: "I never knew an Indian chief to break his word. I have lived on this frontier fifty years, and I have never yet known an instance in which war broke out with these tribes that the tribes were not in the right."

They appealed to Charles Bent to try to arrange such a treaty council for them. He did so. Cheyenne and Arapaho persuaded the Comanche to join. An effort was made to bring in the Kiowa, too, but the Kiowa, at that time were enjoying one of their sporadic wars against the Ute, so they refused. The other tribes, however, met a commission at Bent's Fort, south and east of Denver. There they entered into extended negotiations. No definite agreement could be reached at that time. The commissioners wanted to exclude the Indians from the Republican and Smoky Hill regions. These were favorite hunting grounds of the Cheyenne and Arapaho. The region the commissioners wanted the Indians to accept as their reservation had been virtually cleared of buffalo. Agriculture could be successfully accomplished only through irrigation. The council finally broke up without signatures of the Indians to these terms.

Particularly adamant in their refusals to cede the Republican and Smoky Hill hunting grounds were the entire Dog Soldier chiefs. Not one of them would put his mark to the treaty offered them.

They obtained promise of the Government to construct at some place near the center of these reservations, permanent agency buildings. These buildings were to include a warehouse for the use of the agents in storing goods belonging to the Indians, an agency building for the use of the agent, residences of the carpenter, farmer, blacksmith, miller and engineer and school buildings as well as a sawmill, grist mill and shingle mill.

There were to be separate reservations for the Cheyenne and Arapaho and for the Kiowa, Comanche, and Apache. Cheyenne and Arapaho lands were established in the northern portion of this area—Kiowa, Comanche and Apache lands in the south. Each of these groups was to have its own central agency and agency buildings.

They obtained promise of individual allotments for any that desired to try their hands at agriculture and services of competent instructors and necessary implements. They obtained promise of annual issuance of clothing and subsistence.

They also obtained the right to hunt unmolested on any of the land south of the Arkansas so long as the buffalo should range thereon in such numbers as to justify the chase.

Government machinery always did move slowly, most exasperatingly so, for the treaty to be amended by Congress ratified and promulgated. Meantime, the military forces were not content to let well enough alone. Many of the Army's acts aggravated the Indians. The red man could not understand why the Great White Father was so slow about providing for them, as he had promised to do. He seemed to expect them to move on to their reservations immediately, although no steps had been taken to care for them there, in accordance with terms of their agreement. He apparently was making no appreciable effort to provide them with the things he had promised them, so that they could begin to "travel the white man's road."

While pacific agencies in the east were striving to aid Indian agents of the west in getting the government to ratify the treaties and carry out its part of the contract expeditiously and faithfully, military leaders still on the Plains were invoking every pretext to move against the Indians throughout the summer. They were even planning a tremendous winter campaign in direct conflict with the letter as well as the spirit of the treaties.

Not only did the Indians have to contend with the army, but also a growing horde of lawless white men. Along the Santa Fe Trail a noisy tide came scurrying in disorder; drunken men, boasters, and bullies gathered from the mud-banks of the Missouri. They were all heavily armed. They rode horses of a nondescript variety. Their words were mingled with oaths and coarse jests and the rallying cry of this outlaw pack was "a good Injun is a dead Injun." Many craved action. Where? Activities against the Plains Indians offered the only prospect for killing and fun. This in the hay-day of licensed lawlessness.

W1th any sort of man who would carry arms, on any sort of horse that could carry a man, and with a wagon bearing ammunition, provisions, and the inevitable jug of Tennessee rye, they came forth by bands, for one purpose, to wipe from the land every Indian.

Fifteen hundred strong, they swept all over the frontier. Some gathered on the banks of the Arkansas, and their campfires signaled hatred, destruction, loot, and murder to the defenseless land through which the Arkansas wanders on its way to meet the Missouri. They wanted to fight, these valiant rangers, else they would not have volunteered; they wanted to kill, else they would not fight; they wanted to plunder and destroy, else fighting and killing were a waste of energy.

These invading bands were all ready to exterminate the Indian camps. The Indians numbered perhaps five hundred warriors.

A few gentlemen led the rabble. And they were dangerous, for they were the brains of the crowd. But they all had something in common, they all wanted to fight, and they all wanted to kill some Indians badly, and they all wanted whiskey and they all wanted to get the job done.

Their camp was no cavalry quarters like Fort Leavenworth. They couldn't be held back much longer if something didn't happen soon. They figured they could swoop down on the Indian camp and beat them into the bushes in one setting. They were the most lawless gang of robbers and cutthroats. Some of them, a precious few, but some, ought to have known better than to be caught in among them.

But the Indians were not scared.

It was the darkest hour the territory had yet known. The Indians would not give up their right to live here.

Ian thought, "This war was so contemptible, so unjust, so uncertain." He reasoned his soul would rise to meet the duty of the hour. But here were all the cheap things of strife, the petty subterfuge, the swinish appetites, the brutish cruelty, the things that in his Christian home had been taught all his life to despise. He did not know then that these things belong to war, even to just war, and without them wars could not be.

It is not the province of history to frivolously object to the decrees of fate. We may recognize inexorable necessity when we meet it. We may know how certain eventualities stand, how they have been and are likely to be, though we are unable to weigh or measure them, or tell why they are so. What seems to us wrong in the abstract may when interwoven in the scheme of the universe be right; we do not know.

We see the titles to all civilized lands running back to their acquisition by bloodshed and fraud; ownership changing on the approach of superior strength. Various names being given to various sorts of robbery, as right of conquest, right of discovery, the word *right* not signifying so much that which is just and proper as that which is strong. What is right? The dictionary makes sad work of it trying to tell.

To whom does this land belong, to the king of Spain or England or the aboriginal occupants? The reply of history is "To whomever possesses the power to hold it." Possession was the point, and the power to hold possession.

After all has been said, it is plain that the acquisition of title, the claims to ownership of lands aboriginal or ancient must not be tested too closely by any code of ethics, other than the ethics of superior strength, if we would not have brought home to us the fact that every foot of this earth has been many times stolen from its possessors.

In the eyes of civilization Indians had no rights. Wild lands when wanted by civilization had only to be taken and wild men like wild beasts must give way before the stronger arm.

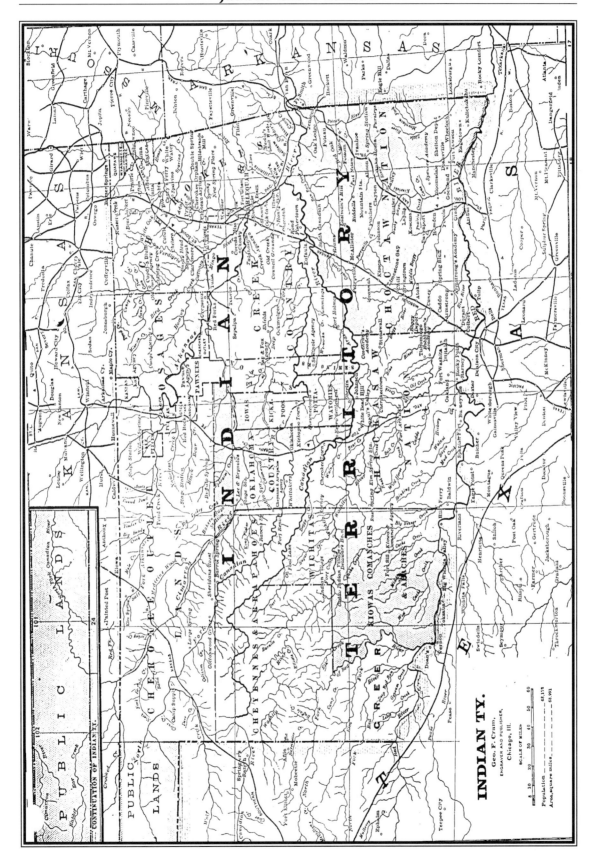

They had souls, yes, convoked wisdom had so decided, but the swarthy natives of America were not human, as the white Europeans were human.

And these same Puritan white Europeans found a new happiness, the happy pursuit of holding black Africans in slavery.

The people of the states, south and north, were rapidly as possible clearing the country of its aboriginal population as they cleared it of its wild beasts, by killing them, burning their towns, and driving them farther back into the wilderness. The government, that abstract irresponsible thing at Washington where its thieving agents are concerned, was fathering and flattering these children of nature, herding them in reservations and giving them for their comfort trinkets, blankets, missionaries, surreptitious whiskey, and the white man's diseases.

If we're to carry upon our shoulders this sin of our fathers to the third or fourth generation, and for many more, we may take this for our consolation, that it is fate under whose inexorable decree we suffer. That the mere contact with civilization is too often fatal to the Indian, that along the lower levels of savagism kindness kills as surely if not as quickly as cruelty. If indeed the rifle is not more merciful than measles, smallpox, syphilis, tuberculosis, and the rest.

The world was made for man, that is to say for civilized man. Naked wild men and wild beasts must not occupy land wanted by mounted men in clothes that is if the latter are strong enough to take it. True, all were once savage, inhabiting the woods, but then the fittest survived, you know. Well might the Indian say to the white man, "Take our land if you must, kill us if you enjoy slaughter, but spare us your sham goodness, hypocrisy, and lies."

It is idle to talk of the rights of civilization. Civilization has no rights not held in common with savagism. Let us rather be honest with ourselves and others, and say openly to the native, "You have that which we want and are going to take; be quiet and submissive and we will give you something; make us trouble and we will kill you." For this civilization has itself proclaimed, if not in words at least in deeds.

*   *   *

Black Coyote had selected a site farther west than any of the others. His was an ideal location. A high ridge rose to the south, a higher one to the north, their summits being scarcely two miles apart. His chosen campsite was flanked on the west by a tree-fringed branch of the Washita. Below him another tributary flowed through a break in the southern hills. At the western edge of the flat bottoms, the Washita made a small sweep to the north, came back south and then formed a larger horseshoe bend to the north. South of these two comparatively small bends an elevation rose rather precipitously. The westernmost protected pocket was ideal for Black Coyote's camping purposes. It was just large enough to accommodate the three-score lodges of his immediate following. Ample forage for the herds of the village was to be found in the ravines to the west.

Black Coyote had chosen for his lodge site a spot under a cottonwood tree on the river-bank at the western extremity of the smaller of the two bends. Only one was farther west than his was. It was that of Big Thunder, a blood relative of Black Coyote and father of the budding warrior, Little Raven. A few others had pitched their teepees in that vicinity, but the greater part of the village was located in the larger bend, a snug, cozy camp.

The pony herds were collected from their wider range on every side to browse and graze in the ravines, sandhills and groves up-stream. Their trail from the main village crossed the Washita near Black Coyote's lodge, where an easy fording of the stream was possible. From there it ran west through the immediate sandhills to the main foraging area.

Conformation of the river and crowding hills prevented other villages being established in the immediate vicinity; but two miles farther down stream the Washita swept to the north and east in a tremendous oxbow more than a mile deep. Inside this loop the land was almost as level as a floor. Along the western side, that nearest Black Coyote's band, Little Raven's Arapaho installed themselves. Earlier in the summer, Kiowa also had been camped there, but recently had moved, leaving behind some thirty lodges of Kicking Bird's band, the only Kiowa on the upper reaches of the Washita. These occupied part of the huge bend with the Arapaho. In a succession of smaller bends just below, Medicine Arrow's Cheyenne, Little Robe's Cheyenne, more Arapaho, a few Apache and Comanche populated the valley a distance of several miles. In all, more than five hundred tribesmen were encamped there at the beginning of the summer. Along the Washita, were nearly all the other non-reservation Indians of the Southern Plains. Their hunt had been eminently successful. Curing strips of buffalo meat hung from every lodge-pole. Piles of cured buffalo hides waited final dressing and crude manufacture into garments, robes or lodge coverings. Huntsmen and warriors whiled away the time shaping new bows, shafting arrows, running bullets and puffing on their long-stemmed pipes.

The Indians liked their agent. His friendly attitude, his sympathetic understanding of their problems drew them to him. Already some of the older chiefs were beginning to be interested in the plans he told them the Great White Father in Washington was making for their future security.

Periodical trips to visit the new agency, obtain supplies and confer with the representative of the Great White Father broke the monotony of camp life.

On the north side of the Arkansas, a dozen Cheyenne were the first to sight the raiding free-booters and irregular soldiers. The lawless white men were moving along at a leisurely trot. Discovering they were being followed, they increased their pace to a gallop, but they could not distance the fleet ponies of their pursuers. Cutter, in charge of the ruffians, halted his men in a ravine, dismounted them, and forming them in a circle, prepared to fight it out in white man fashion.

Normally the Indians would have fought cautiously, once they had their foes at their mercy. They seldom took unnecessary risks and they might have wiped out this group without loss to themselves, but it so happened that Saba was one of the Cheyenne and Saba was supposed to bear a charmed life. His protective medicine was an oddly shaped war-club, which, according to the tradition that came to him with it, rendered its possessor invulnerable. This same tradition demanded that its possessor perform deeds of valor in keeping with the knowledge that he could not be harmed.

So Saba rode bravely in, discharging his rifle in the very faces of the little circle. Around and around the huddled dozen he rode, firing and reloading and firing again. Within a few minutes the little band of rangers was the center of a moving ring of death. Sioux joined the Cheyenne to pour bullets and arrows into its ranks. Eventually the last man was killed.

Then the Indians dashed in. It was the first time the braves had obtained a good chance to register vengeance on the rangers for burning their villages. Two of their number had just fallen. This called for further revenge. They stripped every body, mutilated the corpses and before departing, rode by, shooting arrows into them. When another irregulars force eventually found the missing detachment, the bodies were fairly bristling with shafts.

Had soldiers scored a similar victory, the official government narrative would have set it down as a "glorious victory in fair fight." Being an Indian triumph, it was termed a "massacre," and this massacre immediately became one of the incidents by which the ranging companies justified their merciless persecutions of a later day.

*   *   *

Ordinarily, Plains Indians were in no hurry to crawl from their buffalo robes on early autumn mornings. They had few early chores demanding such inconvenience, but Black Coyote was one of the early risers, despite the lateness of his retirement the previous night. He was filled with foreboding.

Emerging from the low entrance to his lodge and straightening to his full height of slightly less than six feet, his eyes rove about the village. Beyond the top of the teepees in the bend east of him the sky was brightening, heralding the rising of the sun. Wisps of smoke curled from the apertures at the apex of more than one lodge. To the north the rugged knolls of the flanking ridge loomed dimly through the branches of the trees and a heavy blanket of fog. To the south it was one solid landscape, rising less sharply than that on the other side of the Arkansas. The scene was peaceful enough.

Suddenly an Indian woman burst into view, running down the pony trail as fast as frightened moccasin feet could carry her.

"Soldiers! Soldiers!" she cried as she saw the figure of Black Coyote outside his lodge.

Back into his lodge plunged the chief. Immediately he reappeared, rifle in hand. By that time the breathless messenger had splashed through the creek and was standing in front of him gasping her story.

The master of the her lodge having decided the night before to move down to one of the other villages as soon as possible; she had gone to fetch the family horses. While moving up the trail through the timber, she had heard horses approaching. At first she caught a glimpse of the outlaw pack moving rapidly toward her. Without stopping long enough to estimate the size of the party or to attempt to identify it, beyond her was a body of mounted soldiers, she had ran back to camp to give the alarm.

This unheralded visit in the early morning, its surreptitious approach, recalled vividly to Black Coyote's mind another morning several years previously when, also at the earliest break of day, an avenging major had led a murdering horde into another camp under very similar circumstances.

Painful memories of his own narrow escape, the death and mutilation of so many of his tribesmen on that occasion, caused the head chief to resolve that his village this time would not wait to be fired upon before taking flight. He would arouse the camp. Ordering the woman to go through the village and cry the alarm, Black Coyote pointed his rifle in the air and pulled the trigger to awaken those who might still be asleep.

Meanwhile, hearing the excited voices of the woman and Black Coyote's sharp commands, those in nearby lodges had scrambled from their teepees, sensing something was wrong. Told of approaching rangers, they too sped away to aid in arousing the village.

It was customary for important men of the tribe to keep a pony or two tethered near their lodge for emergency use of convenience so that it would not be necessary to go to the main herd every time a mount was desired. One was staked near Black Coyote's teepee. His wife untied this pony and led it up to her husband. At that instant came a trumpet's blast from the timber in the direction of the advancing rangers. Shouted commands, an ear-splitting cheer, a thunder of hooves, and a crashing of under-brush left no doubt of the hostile nature of this visit. Answering shouts from all sides of the village also told the chief that his camp was being charged from every side except the riverside. His rifle was empty. He had not reloaded after firing his warning shot. He could not offer armed resistance. Leaping to the back of his pony and pulling his faithful squaw up behind him, Black Coyote made a dash for the river, hoping to beat the rangers to it and make his escape down the north side of the channel.

Even as he dug heels into his pony's sides and gave it the word, the head of the charging column, led by Cutter himself, burst into view a few yards away. A volley came from pistols and carbines, and Black Coyote felt the burning sting in the pit of his stomach. One bullet had found its mark. He swerved to the right, still riding for the stream. Another slug struck him in the back between his shoulder blades just as his pony splashed into the channel; he collapsed, sliding into the water, dead. On dashed his thoroughly frightened horse. By the time it reached the top of the opposite bank, it was riderless. Black Coyote's wife had entered the happy hunting grounds on the heels of her illustrious mate. Thus, the greatest of all Cheyenne chieftains, first in war in the days when he thought the Indians might successfully resist seizure of their lands, and first in peace when he became convinced in the futility of the unequal struggle, became the first to fall.

On into the startled village raced the rabble, shouting, shooting, and slashing. Pistols were discharged in the very faces of Indians as they thrust heads from their lodges to see what the cause of all the commotion. Sabers struck down others. Any head which appeared was an immediate target, whether that of warrior, woman or child. A warrior leveled his pistol at Cutter. Cutter beat him to the shot. The Indian fell pierced through the head. Those on the side of the village nearest the river, attempting to escape in that direction, ran into the charging rangers of Meyer, Thomas, or Alders, which had completed their encircling movement. No quarter was shown in that first wild dash by the converging lines of horsemen. There was no semblance of military formation. Breasts of the women were slashed by sabers. Arms and legs were hacked nearly off and bodies otherwise mutilated.

Some of the rangers could not resist the temptation to belt their first Indian scalps.

Soon the outlaw pack began to group in pursuit of fleeing Indians. From every side came the loud shots of carbines. Occasionally an Indian rifle answered, but these were notable for their infrequency. So sudden had been the attack, only a few of the Indians had opportunity to arm themselves. Most of these who did had only a bow and arrows. They were powerless to offer serious resistance. Flight was their only hope.

Those villagers whose teepees stood nearest the river fared better than their friends in the center and on the south side of the camp did. The first to dash through the water and scramble up the opposite bank found themselves running away from scouts and sharpshooters. They also encountered irregular soldiers, mounted and dismounted on the route to the river, but the fugitives took the only avenue left open to them, the channel itself. It was misery to wade its waters, but it was either that or bullets. Women and children, as well as braves, plunged into the stream. Most of them were scantily clad. Many were without moccasins on their feet. Frequently the water reached to the armpits of adults who had to carry the children through these deep pools to prevent their drowning. Desperately they splashed their way beyond the lines of their enemies. Eventually some made their way, half dead from exhaustion and fright, to the Arapaho village of Shenga Wassa and Ian. Here they found refuge. Here they were given dry clothing and food and found relief before the campfires of friendly neighbors.

Shenga had foretold the massacre.

As the outlaw band reached the south bank of the Arkansas, they came under intense and accurate gunfire and arrows, so severely that they had to withdraw after over a dozen or so ruffians lay dead at the water's edge.

Two headmen, Sitting Antelope and Big Crow, noting that all rangers had centered their attention on the camp, made a break for a low ridge farther south. If they could gain this objective, they could continue unobserved. They were nearing the protection of two pointed knolls when a single horseman spied them and gave chase. Limping from his wound, Big Crow was being quickly overtaken. His companion refused to leave him. Sitting Antelope was unarmed. Big Crow had only his cap-and-ball pistol and a knife. Yet they decided they would put up a fight when over-taken. Slipping his knife to Sitting Antelope, Big Crow pulled his ancient firearm from his belt as the ranger rode up. Dodging a sweeping saber, Big Crow suddenly thrust the muzzle of his pistol almost against the stomach of the braggart and pulled the trigger. The outlaw soldier slumped in his saddle. Big Crow yanked him from the saddle.

Meantime, Sitting Antelope had seized the horse's bridle. As the rider crashed to the ground, Sitting Antelope assisted Big Crow to mount. Then he swung to the horse's back behind Big Crow. The horse was put to a run. Before the fugitive could gain the top of the ridge, however, a squad of ruffians, which came riding from the east gave chase.

Seeing that the fleeing pair would gain the crest ahead of them and likely would out-run them, the rangers turned their attention to a group of Indians escaping on foot between them and the river. Toward this group the irregular soldiers rode. Halfway to the group they encountered a boy, named "Crazy," because of a mental affliction, and an old man. The murderers killed both of them.

Little Beaver, twelve years old at the time, came near forfeiting his life for the sake of a pistol his father, Wolf Looking Back, had given him. The lodge of Wolf Looking Back stood almost in the center of the village. It was so far removed from the point of the first attack that all of his family could have made their escape had they so desired. Only Little Beaver and his father took flight. His mother, Red Deer, remained in the lodge. When almost to the timber, Little Beaver thought of his forgotten gun. He decided to return for it. Scarcely had he secured this treasure and regained cover of the river's bank when plunderers raced by.

By this time, his father had disappeared in the timber. Thus separated from him, Little Beaver joined a group consisting of three women, three children, and two young braves making their way toward the lower camps under protection of the high riverbank. At one place they found the water to be too deep to be waded in safety. They decided to take a shortcut, even though by doing so they were compelled to cross an open space. They now were nearly a mile below the village and they thought they might escape detection, but they were soon discovered. This was the group toward which the buccaneers rode when they gave up the chase of Sitting Antelope and Big Crow.

The two young braves with the group were named Blind Hawk and Bear. Seeing the rangers coming, Bear said to Blind Hawk, "Here come the soldiers. They will catch up. Maybe so, they will kill all. Let us run. The soldiers will see that we are braves and that the others are women and children. Maybe so, they will pay no attention to the women and children but will ride after us. While they are chasing us, our friends can escape."

By this time the group had waded across the river to the north side. Hawk accepted the challenge of their plan. Immediately they dashed away, running as fast as they could. They ran directly west, toward some high hills beyond which they knew were the camp of other Indians.

The lawless white men splashed through the waters of the river at full speed but the out-law soldiers did not give chase immediately after the fleeing braves. They first rode up the bank of the river to the women and children. Instead of killing them, the sergeant-major was detailed to escort them back to the village, there to be turned over to Cutter. Then the pursuit of Blind Hawk and Bear was continued.

By this time the fleeing youths had put several hundred yards between them and their pursuers. Hope now began to grow in the breasts of these youthful Indian heroes that they might escape the death they had considered certain when they commenced their sacrificial dash. Beyond the next rise, only half a mile distance lay the camp of the Arapaho. Should they be able to top this rise before being overtaken, they might escape. Once their pursuers sighted the immense Arapaho village and that of the Kiowa, the pursuers certainly would turn back; so the youths reasoned.

On they pushed. Then hope began to wane as their strength failed. On solid ground they might have won. The horsemen bore down on them. With safety for the staggering youths almost in sight, the troopers drew within range and opened fire. Down went Blind Hawk and Bear.

No sooner had the detachment rode after Blind Hawk and Bear than Little Beaver grasped his pistol. It was in a holster secreted under his arm. There it had been unobserved by the rangers. Little Beaver urged the squaws to detract attention of their single guard so that he might get out his gun and shoot the sergeant. They then would be free.

The squaws demurred.

"Maybe the gun is not loaded," objected one.

"That would be bad."

Little Beaver was forced to admit he was not certain, but he thought it was loaded. He tried to keep it loaded at all times.

"What if you do not kill the soldier?" wailed the other. "Then the soldier will kill us all."

Cautiously, Little Beaver sought to examine the gun. The guard noticed his move. The sergeant commanded the boy to surrender his pistol.

Little Beaver complied. Then the return to camp was resumed. Herding his charges in front of him, the sergeant whose name was Kennedy, continued to ride his horse.

The start west had been made from the north side of the river. Prisoners and guard had crossed a little branch running into the Arkansas and were moving up the slope when one of the squaws chanced to glance toward the river only a short distance away. She saw the figure of a mounted Indian flash past a break in the timberline. Another and still another followed. She knew word of the battle had reached the other villages and that in a few minutes the valley and hills would be literally alive with warriors rushing to the scene of action.

Oh, for an opportunity to delay her own party! Chance of rescue would be much better if they could be discovered by their friends before reaching the top of the hill, for beyond might be a large number of pursuers.

Suddenly she had an inspiration! The two smallest children were without moccasins. Their feet were bleeding from contact with the rocks and the brush of the riverbank they recently had left.

Halting, she directed the attention of Kennedy to those bleeding feet, making signs that she wanted to bind them up. The squaw tore the sleeves from her dress and began to wrap them around the lacerated and swollen extremities of the children. She was as deliberate as she dared to be; yet avoided creating suspicion of the alert sergeant who had them in his charge. Occasionally, she would look up at the make-believe soldier, crooning sympathetically to the children. Not only did she look at Kennedy; she looked past him and what she saw sent a thrill through her crouched frame. A horseman had dashed out of the timber and was riding hard for the little group. Back of him came three others.

Excitement she could not conceal must have shown in the squaw's eyes. That or something else caused the sergeant to turn his head toward the river at that instant.

Throwing his carbine to his shoulder, the free-booter fired in the general direction of the on-rushing Arapaho.

One of the Indians' rifles blazed a reply. Both shots went wild.

Digging his heels into his horse's sides, Kennedy headed for the main body of pursuers, attempting to throw a new shell into his carbine.

Freed from their guard, the Indian women and children broke for the river, most of them to be picked up behind warriors who now began to swarm to the river.

They were carried to the Arapaho village of Shenga Wassa.

So intent on his chase had been ranger Langes, his men had failed to notice what was happening behind them or observed activities in the valley at their left. By the time Langes had overtaken and slain the two young braves he and his detachment had been pursuing, he heard shots and shouts to his rear. He turned in time to see Kennedy dragged from his horse and killed. He also observed other warriors riding up the valley on the north side of the Arkansas.

Putting spurs to their tired horses, the murderers set out to retrace their steps.

From the first, it was apparent they would have to fight their way back to the main body of soldiers in the sacked and burning village. The four Arapaho who had accounted for Kennedy now had been joined by five others and were riding to meet the soldiers head on.

Their horses too nearly spent to make a run for it, Langes decided to dismount his men that their aim would be better. Employing such tactics of the cavalry of that day, every fourth man leading horses of three other comrades.

Orders were given to dismount, kneel and prepare to fire. Their fire was withheld until the nine Indians riding down on them divided suddenly. Not a bullet found its mark. Circling, the Indians emptied their rifles at the soldiers, also ineffectively. Then they charged the led horses, hoping to stampede them. A few did break loose.

Loading as they advanced, the plunderers moved forward a few rods and as the Indians swooped down upon them again, they discharged another volley. Timing the blast accurately, the Indians threw themselves to the opposite side of their racing ponies. Not one of them was struck.

Alternately halting to deliver a volley at their circling foes and then, advancing a short distance while reloading, the beleaguered men slowly moved toward safety.

Before Langes had covered more than a fraction of the distance to camp at this slow rate of retreat, the numbers of the Indians had multiplied many times. Soon the Kiowa and Cheyenne, as well as the Arapaho were all around them. This circling Indians formed a whirling ring of death, which drifted slowly westward. Through it, Langes could not break. Indian reinforcements now were pouring in with increasing rapidity as warriors rode up from the more distant villages.

Langes and his men's progress grew slower and slower. Enveloping ranks of Indians became more and more daring as braves vied with each other in riding close to the outlaw pack. They reached the ravine in which Kennedy had been killed. Further advance seemed impossible. So far their ranks still were intact, but the last of their horses had been stampeded or slain. Immediately in front of them, the branch creek formed a bend to the west. Its banks were steep, preventing the Indians charging close from that direction. Tall grasses and weeds made it possible to drop from sight by lying prone on the ground. Here Langes decided to make a stand.

Cutter's command was little more than a mile away. Even if Cutter did not yet know the plight of Langes' rangers, certainly the sound of firing soon would be heard and relief would be sent.

Ordering his men to form themselves in a circle, feet to the center, faces to the foe, Langes prepared for a courageous defense of that position until rescued.

Soon he was to discover that the very conformation of the stream, which had caused him to select the spot for his last stand, was proving more of a hazard than a protection. While the banks prevented horsemen charging his position from that direction, the Indians soon began to dismount and to use these same barriers to shield themselves from sight of the enemy and their bullets as they maneuvered to within a few feet of the prostrate men. From there they could shower the area with arrows, or direct effective rifle fire every time a man would raise his head above cover to reconnoiter the situation or take better aim. Wild grasses and wild sage, which screened the soldiers from sight of their foes, also prevented them seeing their opponents. It was either take chances of hitting their mark by firing in the general direction of the Indians, or risk inviting a burst of bullets and a shower of arrows by rising to their knees.

Minutes passed. Carbines in arm, lifted above cover, popped an ineffective slug aimlessly beyond. Ears were strained to catch the sound of charging cavalry hooves, but the only hoof-beats audible were those of the swift ponies bringing new reinforcements of the already overwhelming force of Indians circling and shouting and shooting.

Carbines barked with less frequency. Rifles rattled faster. Popping of pistols came only from the outer circle, none any longer from the center. The painted, whooping Indians swirled nearer. They sensed the beginning of the end of the fight.

From the east came a new war whoop. Bursting from a single throat, it came nearer and nearer. Down the hillside rode a solitary warrior brandishing above his head an oddly shaped war club. His pony was lathering from a hard ride, still being urged forward at breakneck speed.

The warrior was Saba, who had headed the avenging circle of Cheyenne and Sioux at the beginning of the battle.

How long Langes might have held out but for the arrival of Saba is problematical. His enemies had not dared to charge his position up to that time, but Saba never hesitated. He had sized up the situation the instant he topped the hill. Immediately he had concluded that his belated arrival called for a rash display of valor. He determined to deliver. Straight toward the bandit soldiers ring he headed. Into it he dashed. Over the prostrate invaders he rode. As he was about to emerge from the opposite side of the circle of doomed men, a bullet struck him in the stomach. His horse cleared the fatal spot with its rider, mortally wounded, slumped onto its neck. Saba's medicine had failed him at last, but his example demanded the Indians to strive to equal or excel his bravery. There was a concerted rush to follow the trail he had blazed.

Even if the ranger's main body had come to Langes' rescue then, they would have been too late. The fact that none of those who followed Saba was killed or wounded indicates that only a few of Langes' men were still alive at that time, or their ammunition had run out.

Ian and his gathered headmen on an overlooking knoll, gazed down on the bodies of Langes and his twenty-eight men lying in a circle of death. Those who had shot down the surprised warriors and women and little children were all dead with the exception of one trooper. The only Indian wounded here was Saba.

The renegade sergeant major stood alone, wounded in several places, his ammunition expended, saber in hand, surrounded by a crowd of triumphant warriors. Not a shot was fired at him. No effort was made to kill him.

An old Indian fighter, he knew the meaning of this kindly demonstration. Merciful death had overtaken all his comrades. He was to be reserved for torture. In his prolonged agonies, his enemies would find consolation for the injuries the troops had inflicted upon them.

Realizing all this, he saw his only hope of escaping torture was in so exasperating the Indians that they would kill him at once. Seeming to surrender, he walked toward the chief, with outstretched hands. With a quick thrust, the sergeant major's sword passed through the chief's body.

One instant of terrified surprise on the part of the Indians, the next, twenty bullets of hot lead in the sergeant major's body.

The troopers went into battle that morning with at least one hundred rounds of ammunition each and, since they appreciated the necessity of conserving these precious supplies as much as possible, the exchange of shots lasted a long time. There was a pile of empty cartridges near each dead plunderer.

But Cutter was too interested in events transpiring within the village itself to be concerned with disaster of any of the men. Each lodge was being searched for hiding squaws and papooses, for arms, ammunition, provisions and robes. Deeply engrossed in the work of plunder and destruction, Cutter did not notice the increasing number of warriors making their appearance on the ridges north of the river. All were hideously painted, decked out in full war regalia. At the time they made their spectacular dash into Black Coyote's camp, they believed the hundred slumbering inmates of those lodges were the only Indians in the vicinity. By mid-morning, however, so many braves had appeared on the surrounding hills he wondered if it had been possible for that many to escape the net they had set so carefully. When their numbers continued to increase and they began harassing them on all sides, his early surprise turned to concern.

From a sister of Black Coyote, who he had captured, he learned that they had stumbled into the greatest concentration of Indians on the Southern Plains of the Western Territory.

Destruction of the village and the captured pony herd was yet to be accomplished. While lodges blazed, the huddled terror-stricken groups of ponies withered before carbines of those men assigned to their slaughter.

Not daring to rush the village for fear of bringing death to their women and children held captive, they contented themselves with repeated attempts to draw the free-booters out of their protected position for a test of fighting ability, but they would not accept the challenges. Only when pressure became unbearable did they strike back. Even then they limited their counter-attacks to the shortest of sorties. Never did they trust themselves far enough from the main body of the invading pack to enable their alert, hard-riding foemen to cut them off and force a decisive battle.

Huge piles of teepees, buffalo robes, buffalo meat, saddles, bows, arrows, and other plunder had been reduced to smoldering embers. The last of four hundred captured ponies had been shot, that is, all except those appropriated to their own use by the rangers and those reserved to transport prisoners and such of the booty as was to be taken.

Encouraged by the ease with which they had captured Black Coyote's camp, Cutter believed he would have no serious difficulty completing subjugation of the others.

They shot the Indians from their ponies and treated the wounded with savage cruelty, scalping and flaying them alive, so that even a number of scoundrels not drunk—who were hard-boiled enough—were shocked.

The leading tracker and guide protested vigorously that Black Coyote's camp had been only a small outpost, isolated from the Dreamer's larger villages, that surprise had much to do with their quick triumph there. He warned that Cutter's men had outnumbered Black Coyote's warriors, but the odds were with the braves now. They were thoroughly aroused, thirsting for vengeance, and eager to draw the soldiers into the open where they could be attacked.

*   *   *

All this occurred at Walnut Creek about three miles east of the present town of Great Bend, Barton County, Kansas.

In the evening Cooke received the surprising news that a Mexican escort was just across the Arkansas River from the Caches, having come up by forced marches from Santa Fe after insistent order from Santa Anna to Armijo.

In the morning, Cooke rode out to see for himself; it was true but the Mexican commander politely refused Cooke's invitation to cross the river for an exchange of courtesies on the grounds that he had positive orders forbidding it. Cooke became thoughtful at the implications of the message, but contented himself by forming his dragoons on the river bank and saluting the Mexican lancers with the howitzers.

*   *   *

It was an uneasy village that waited, wondered and watched while they were being surrounded by the irregular soldiers of the Plains, Boone and his troopers from Arkansas,

Cooke's dragoons from Fort Leavenworth and the rancheros from Mexico and Burr's banditti. The Indian exterminating expeditions were fresh in their memories. They still could see children ruthlessly shot down, women vulgarly mutilated, ghastly corpses of warriors who had died in defense of the helpless, scalped, mangled, strewn over the ground or heaped in gruesome piles. Ashes where lodges had stood floated in memory before them. That tragedy had struck their people from skies as peaceful as those of the present. Did these approaching soldiers plan a similar fate for this village? The warriors were determined not to be caught off guard.

Ian had much trouble of keeping the headmen in line with his plans. Many thought now was the time to show the Great White Father in Washington that he could not continue to mistreat the Indians who always had yielded to demands for more and more of their lands. If they did not strike now, they might never again have such an opportunity to assert their strength.

Young braves were not alone in suggesting these actions. Rebellion which had been smoldering in the breasts of their elders threatened to burst forth, to be transformed from thought to demands for action. They could see that if the United States government continued to encroach upon their hunting grounds, if soldiers were to be permitted to search out their villages for slaughter, pillage and destruction, there never could be any peace or any security for their families. Why not fight it out to the finish now, rather than be constantly harassed?

However, the leading chiefs of the Kiowas, reversed their first clamor for reprisals. So too, did the war chiefs of the Arapaho and Cheyennes. To punish the innocent soldiers for the guilty was the white man's custom, not that of the Indians now. Yes, few years before, they still retained their old ways, but whether they knew it or not, they were becoming more civilized.

The chiefs however were not willing to place their people in further jeopardy by remaining in the path mostly likely to be taken by Cooke's invading troops, if; as expected, they would treat all Indians the same as the ranging soldiers had dealt with Black Coyote's band. Here in the western extremities of Western Territory, they could seek safety in flight to the desert wastes of the Staked Plains. Across the Great American Desert, they could fare better in the mountains. There some protection could be obtained from the wintry winds. There game was more plentiful. There was an abundance of good water, however the region to the west was not so good. Streams in that gypsum country made Indians sick.

Ian and Shenga took no chances. They directed the women and children out onto the plains west to the El Llano Estanado. If Cooke insisted upon war, Dog Soldier warriors would cover the retreat, and fight to the death if necessary. Ian could take no chances of being destroyed by Cooke, Burr's banditti, rancheros from Mexico and rangers from Texas.

At first light of the following third day, the trumpets sounded reveille in a lively manner. Those leather-lunged trumpeters raised a tremendous racket. All was life and bustle among the men as they went trooping off; some, tin cup and platter in hand, for breakfast and the steaming hot coffee that the cooks were already preparing, some to look after the horses or to make a hasty toilet by the stream; the dogs, of which there were several in the command, barking and jumping up to their masters with morning greetings, or foraging around the mess tents in search of a stray bone or other such luxury. The horses and mules, refreshed by the night's rest, were neighing and stamping, awaiting the coming meal, "stable call" having been sounded immediately after reveille, and the men attended to the wants of their trusty four-footed friends. It did not take long to make toilet and pack the equipage, ready for the "strikers" to take away to the baggage wagons.

The second bugle call in Cooke's camp sounded boots and saddles. As if an electric shock had traversed the assemblage, the scattered groups formed in ranks. Another trumpet blast. Like one man they rose into their saddles and sat motionless. Still another signal and like a machine started by some invisible power the column moved. The columns formed with the band at its head. The band struck up a stirring march. The column headed toward the Indian camps. Immediately, alert Indian scouts dashed to Ian's camp to give the alarm.

At this alert, Ian ordered the warriors surrounding the village to assemble and prepare to meet Cooke's dragoons.

Cooke, riding ahead of the main body of troops with a sizable bodyguard, neared the waiting Indian army. There was a smart, tidy look about the men.

Ian watched the dragoon commander from a position of a few paces before his chiefs. Long legs, neatly encased in semi-tight fitting buckskin leggins, draped moccasin feet well below the body of the spotted pony upon which he sat. A loose-fitting jacket of skins was caught about a slender waist by a heavy-buckled belt. From this belt hung two holsters, one on each hip, holding his Colt revolvers. Alongside was a keen, long-bladed hunting knife. Across his shoulders, broad with vigorous manhood, was slung an unstrung bow, made from bois d'arc wood and an unadorned quiver of steel-tipped arrows. His hair which he had let grow was caught in twin braids. Entwined with flannel ribbons of brilliant crimson and green, they reached well down below his shoulders and his arrow-straight back. No saddle or blanket cushioned his seat on the back of his spirited mount. The sole item of riding equipment was a short lariat tied loosely to the under jaw of the pony after the fashion typical of Plains Indians.

His mount was decorated with bright long zigzag lines down each leg, across his rump and neck. These lightning marks intent was to speed the warrior and his horse on their way into battle and to terrify a man's foes, since they would also recognize that his vision had given him lightning power. The enemy's problem of the moment would be how to cope with lightning power.

Golden eagle tail feathers were tied to the mane and tail of his war horse. Its tail was tied up in a common Plains custom when preparing for battle. The tail was folded and bound together with buckskin strips. The feathers added to a spectacular effect. White coup lines were painted on his steed's nose, and red circles around the horses eyes "to improve the animal's vision in warfare."

He was a man ready for battle to the death. In fact, every warrior had put his war clothing on so as to prepare him properly for death. The imposing figure of Medicine Arrow was decked in full ceremonial regalia.

Poor Elk rode a fine and spirited wild horse, which was as white as the drifted snow, with an exuberant mane, and its long bushy tail sweeping the ground. In his hand he tightly drew the reins upon a heavy Spanish bit. The eyes of this noble steed seemed to be squeezed out of its head; its fright, and its agitation had brought out upon its skin a perspiration that was fretted into a white foam and lather. The warrior's quiver was slung on his back, and his bow grasped in his left hand, ready for instant use, if called for. His shield was on his arm, and across his thigh, with a beautiful cover of buckskin. Thus armed and equipped was this dashing cavalier; nearly in the same manner, all the rest of the party; and many of them leading an extra horse, which was their favorite war horse. He was gallant and had a wonderful appearance of a warrior. Others carried lances fourteen feet in length.

Another chief; White Wolf; faced the direction of the dragoons and with impassive countenance said slowly, "While winds blow and the Arkansas runs down to the Missouri, we are ready to fight here and now." Every man with that spirit brings the strength of ten the men in his fighting arm.

The chief wore a robe of white wolf-skin, upon which was painted a hieroglyphics account of his warlike achievements.

The band was highly ornamented; paint of every hue was upon their bodies. Their heads were decorated with feathers. Long strings of wampum hung from their necks. Some wore glittering armlets and collars of tin. Their heads were shaven, and covered with vermillion, and from the top of each hung a scalp lock, generally adorned with an eagle's plume. As much care had been bestowed upon the horses as upon the riders. They moved forward with proud step, conscious of the haughty character of White Eagle who led them, but this feeling was as much owing to the horsemanship of the riders as to the spirit of the animals themselves, for there was no class of people better able to show off the points of a horse than the Indians who live on the horseback from childhood.

Saba was astride his war horse on a little knoll some distance from the converging armies. He was visibly badly wounded from the attack with Langes, but he insisted to view the anticipated battle. Father Gregg had offered his staff topped with the Christian emblem of the cross for Saba to lean on. Father Gregg had covered the cross with a purple cloth signifying the expression of sorrow. Father Gregg sat on his mule at Saba's side administering

Christian Last Rites and the medicine man prayed to the Indian Great Spirit for compassion and mercy. Both of their faces indicated a deep feeling of sharing the suffering of Saba.

Saba sat erect, back straight and firm countenance on his face that gave encouragement and support to his people.

The Indian's cavalcade moved to meet that of the white man. Gloom was not caused by doubt of their own ability to cope with the soldiers in actual battle. It was concern for their families. It was disappointment, that certainly such a large force of troops, whose leaders seemed determined to goad Indians to desperation, but they would face the issue bravely and without any display of weakness. They would put on a bold front when they met their unwelcome guests. All were decked out in their finest.

Every Indian in camp on this morning walked with firm step, and gloom had fled away with the shadows of the night. The impending danger was not lessened, but the spirit of the braves made a much stronger force than the enemy had counted on.

Ian shouted stern orders to his warrior chiefs on either side:

"I'yu ha' thiba' nawa

A' nani'sa'na---E'e'ye'!

Bi' toa'wu--E'e'ye'!"

Then turning to Three Bears on his other flank, commanded in hissing, choking Cheyenne syllables, his arm and hand swung vigorously:

"Nanisa' Taqu' thi - Chinachi' chiba'iha

Ni' nch-a- wa na

Nibal' naku' nithi."

Ian's friends, Sergeant Tom Beidler, Pierre Baudron, Charlie Pickett, and Big Jim Kendall at his side with ready rifles, looked at each other, not understanding the command.

Beidler looked at Ian bewildered and puzzled. Ian was speaking in tongues; tongues he did not know! Beidler frowned somewhat at the miracle, but the urgency of the moment dismissed any further thought on the matter as Ian continued shouting his courses of action, not realizing he was talking several Indian dialects.

"Ha'nae' he Ya' ga' ahi' na

Sa' niya' gu' nawa - abe' e' ye'"

As the two columns came within sight of each other, the chiefs and headmen spread out in front of the other warriors. It was a colorful and brave display. Back of them came their followers, and still farther in the rear rode a scattered few, ready to bear quick news to the other villages should hostilities be started.

To those eager messengers who rode far in the rear of the Indian lines, it looked like battle. Without waiting to see the outcome, they dashed away to give the alarm in the villages. Flight of non-combatants commenced immediately; fugitives taking with them only such articles as they could carry easily and which would not hamper them in making a quick get-a-way. Lodges were left standing.

While still quite a distance apart, the rival lines halted. From one side rode forward a group of officers, from the other Ian, Three Bears and chiefs. Once more Poor Elk declared his intentions of shooting Captain Cooke as soon as they met. Again he was restrained.

Apparently those with Cooke and Boone who knew Poor Elk had pointed him out to the captain, for, as the emissaries came face to face, Cooke addressed himself to this warrior instead of to any of the other chiefs. Poor Elk glared steadfastly into the captain's face for some little time.

There was a decidedly business-like look about both men and horses.

"Do the Indians want war, Ian?" Cooke finally addressed him, recognizing his friend of years past.

Ian took the challenge and looked him straight in the eyes with ill-concealed hostility, not far removed from contempt.

"If Indians wanted war, would he bring few warriors so close to so many soldiers; so close to big guns?"

Then the talk shifted to the others, Three Bears, head of the Dog Soldiers doing most of the speaking for the Indians. He urged Cooke not to come any nearer the camps for fear of alarming the villages.

"Indians remember when soldiers came up like this and killed everybody. Our women and children are afraid of soldiers," he said.

But Cooke was not acquiescent. He reiterated his intention of moving up close before pitching camp. He actually was waiting for Nathan Boone's arrival with his company of dragoons. He had learned that West Point tacticians knew nothing of the Plains method of fighting, that there was a great deal of difference between leading a saber charge against a massed body of troops and attempting to get within striking distance of the phantom warriors of the prairies.

But, by sheer determination, rigorous discipline and tireless energy he had the 1st Dragoons (later changed to the First Cavalry) whipped into shape to give a better account of itself than any other outfit to rid the Western Kansas and Oklahoma Territory of a fancied Indian menace. Cooke was ready for battle and there would be no backing away from a fight, no matter what the outcome.

He remembered that Lieutenant Douglass, one of the most brilliant tacticians ever to ride the plains was their Great Chief, and he remembered his last encounter with his friend wherein he lost his entire command to his cunning and determination and the winter weather. But Cooke would not back down from his duty to his country, even if it meant death to himself and his command.

1ST CAVALRY

2D ARMORED CAVALRY

3D ARMORED CAVALRY

4TH CAVALRY

5TH CAVALRY

6TH ARMORED CAVALRY

7TH CAVALRY

8TH CAVALRY

9TH CAVALRY

10TH CAVALRY

ARMY DIGEST, United States Army
December 1967

But then, he said with finality, there would be no further discussion of the subject. He had letters of specific instruction from President Jackson, which were to be opened upon contact with any hostiles and he had not read those yet.

At that moment an Indian rode up out of a ravine common on the southern plains and rode slowly out in front of the line of dragoons.

Several Arapaho gaahi' na (coyote men), with outstretched arms in the direction of the slowly approaching rider shouted, "Da' chi' nathi', na" (The Messiah). Coyote men, an order of warrior of middle age acted as pickets or lookouts for the war party. When the band was threatened, it was the duty of these men, usually seven or six, to take stations to keep watch and give timely warning in case of the approach of anyone. It was an office of danger and responsibility and was held in corresponding respect.

As the rider approached the party of chiefs, Ian and Cooke at the other end of the column of dragoons, Ian recognized her as Shenga Wassa (Beautiful Bird), atop a beautiful decorated war pony. Her steed was a gorgeous spotted horse, a very rare breed. Ian had only seen a handful of them in the whole Western Plains. The Indian hieroglyphics were outstanding in their red, black, white, and deep blue colors. A large white feather plume in her hair, Shenga Wassa sat upright in the saddle with great dignity and grandeur, head upright with majesty.

The farthest gaahi'na galloped along side his Messiah. He wore a white buffalo robe as a symbol of his duty, and had his face painted with white clay and carried in his hand the ya' haga' ahi' na or "coyote gun," a club decorated with feathers and other ornaments and covered with a sheath of bear gut. This society must be unmarried and remain so while in office. They were never all off duty at the same time, at least half were always on guard, one or more coming down at a time to the village to eat or sleep. They built no shelter on the hills, but slept there in their buffalo robes, or sometimes came down in turn and slept in their own teepees. They usually, however, preferred to sleep alone upon the hills in order to receive inspiration in dreams. If attacked or surprised by the enemy, they were sworn to fight to the death. The corresponding warrior of the same society among the Cheyenne carried a bow and arrow instead of a club.

In spite of the guerrilla-like and careless look of the troopers, Ian could not help but admire the soldierly ease and grace with which they sat in their saddles, ranks well aligned, shoulders squared, heads erect, eyes to the front, their harness and equipments shining in the sunlight, not a buckle or strap out of place, carbines clean, and resting at their sides ready for immediate use, brass-shelled cartridges peeping from the well-filled prairie belts. And their horses! Ian had never seen better mounts. They had been in the field for weeks, and had passed through stream and canon, over plain and desert, through thick alkali dust and sticky mud, yet how their coats glistened, and how proudly they arched their necks and chomped their bits. Though the uniforms were dim and weather--beaten, though the harness and saddles were of the simplest description, with little or no attempt at ornamentation, the troopers and horses looked ready for instant work, and work too, of the most serious kind. And well had they proved by many a hard ride, by many a wakeful night, with hunger and thirst, and the exposure by the pitiless sun, harder to contend against than their Indian adversaries of the wilderness, their readiness at all times; for this was a famous regiment, and their motto. "Toujours pret" (always ready) which they proudly bore was no idle boast.

Ian thought for a moment, as he viewed the fine troopers the country had and the finest of the plains Indians caught up in the book of history, wherein so many would be martyred for each of their causes.

But he quickly came back to the reality of the moment. Here and now, all were witnessing a miraculous moment in time. The Almighty God of both civilizations had sent a living angel; sometimes that happens once in a thousand years, a sight few men ever witness.

The troopers had all heard about the girl Hasanun. Had not the horrible ballad of vulgar, lewd humor of the Ghost Dance Dreamers become a favorite song among the troops?

Ian thought "it took our own Aryan ancestors untold centuries to develop from savagery into civilization." Was it reasonable to expect the Indian could do the same in 200 years? There was something terribly unfair about all this.

Four or five of the Eastern-Episcopalian and Southern Baptist boys, and Kentucks and Tennessee backwoods men realized what was happening and in deep humility slipped their old regulation slouched hats off as she passed by. One straight, fine looking young trooper wearing a great, broad-brimmed "cowboy" hat pulled down over his eyes, gently removed his hat and made the sign of the cross. He had been with the troopers who had murdered this prophet and her unborn child. He knew he was witnessing a very rare occasion—resurrection (bringing back to life) on these Southern Plains of Indian Territory. It was the favor a voice promised Ian in the desert. Ian knew this was no supernatural happening, not to a supernatural being, only a natural thing for one with divine power.

Shenga Wassa halted between Captain Cooke and Ian who were about twenty paces apart. Saying nothing, she looked intently at the captain for a long moment as if reading his mind. Ian slowly guided his mount close to Shenga's and spoke to Cooke.

"This is Shenga Wassa, the Hasanun!"

Ian could see Cooke could not, or would not believe the statement; he knew she was gone, the Grand Conspiracy of the West had saw to that, but . . . he knew his friend Ian believed it, so he must respect that.

Cooke nodded and tipped his hat slightly in courteous acknowledgment. As he looked at Shenga Wassa he fondly remembered his own wife and knew what this Indian woman meant to Ian.

Cooke, still looking at Shenga Wassa said forcibly and positive, "It cannot be. The Hasanun is dead!"

"Look at me!" Shenga replied. "Here I am!"

Shenga Wassa had thrown a challenge directly at Captain Cooke; this did not necessarily bother a West Point officer, but it entered his mind as to how he would write up the report of battling a spirit? . . . a dead girl?

The army would not take such explanation lightly, and he would probably be ridiculed out of the service. This possible event bothered him greatly at this time in his career.

Continuing these thoughts he replied, "I war not with the dead!"

Shenga, in great compassion said, "Listen to me! I would not have you be so grieved for your wife." Meaning that his wife would fully recover from the wounds he had inflicted on her.

She then continued, "Do not render the land barren of fruit, nor spill the dripping rain of death in fierce war," knowing that this confrontation could turn into a prairie fire that would consume all Indians and whites in the region.

Looking straight into the captain's soul she pleaded, "Let my people be!" She hesitated a moment then continued, "Not many years from now you will be asked the same favor by another young religion by the name of Mormons!"

Cooke had never heard of the name Mormon, but he had made up his mind that the Indian Messiah spoke the truth and knew things beyond his comprehension.

"Where will you go?," Cooke inquired.

Shenga spoke in slow broken English and coupled it with sign language so all the chiefs knew what she was saying.

Pointing her arm to the west she replied, "Across the Jornada de Muerte . . . Journey of Death."

This was a large desert called various names, sometimes El Llano Estanado, Staked Plains, and the great American Desert. The Comanche and Kiowa lived on the edge of this forlorn desert.

After pondering the request for quite a while, he replied, "I shall give you an answer tomorrow."

Shenga, satisfied with his response, turned her horse back toward the village. The meeting was over. Tomorrow answers would be forthcoming, but Ian was already putting a plan into action; he waited on no man to decide his courses of action. Ian decided to let the enemy react to him, not vice versa.

Back toward their villages turned the Indians and the soldier column returned to their camp.

Ian went to tell Chief Saba of the news that the battle would wait for another day. As he approached Saba, he never acknowledged Ian's arrival. Ian was now visually worried.

As he neared Saba, he noticed blood dripping down his leg, off his moccasin into a large puddle on the dry ground. The closeness of Ian's horse startled Saba's mount and jerked to one side. Saba slowly pitched forward and then fell to the ground, breaking the staff with the cross falling into his life-blood with Saba on both. Saba, a great chief and disciple of the Messiah, was dead. The brave true heart was stilled forever.

*   *   *

The meeting the next day was short and more military-like. Both White Eagle and Captain Cooke were accompanied by a dozen or so men of each force. Cooke informed Ian that President Jackson's private orders instructed him to protect the caravans.

In the other message, President Andrew Jackson had tendered Ian Douglass a general pardon of offenses against the government. The full amnesty included an honorarium of Brevet Major in recognition of professional services. Not a word in its curt formality disclosed the reasons of policy for the secret instruction from the War Department that concisely pardoned Ian, but reading between the lines the honor was for thwarting the traitorous designs of the Grand Conspiracy and Her Catholic Majesty of Spain to establish a new Spain.

The note also indicated that the government had already taken action to make Oklahoma Country, Indian Territory to the Red River. The Indians were becoming convinced, although against their will.

Captain Cooke smartly saluted the superior ranked Brevet Major Ian Douglass in leaving. Ian gave the Indian sign "Goodbye, friend," and turned to start the trek across the Jornada de Muerte.

The chain was at last broken for a time, the chain of evil inflicted and evil repaid, only to lead to further infliction and further repayment, had been brought to a temporary close.

*   *   *

The order was given to return to the dragoons encampment. The troopers wheeled in a quarter turn at slow march.

Two Scottish Highlander pipers in their colorful tartans led the columns of troops while two others mounted on their chargers beat out the slow cadence on their drums attached to their saddles.

As they marched past Ian the flag bearers lowered their staffs to salute position to honor Ian, now Major Douglass.

In return, Ian smartly saluted English style. His ancestors came from the Highlands of the Scottish Isles.It was common politeness for the clans to courteously respect their fellow celtic ancestors on ceremonial occasions, even though they were rival antagonists at this time, serving in different armies.

The Governor of Georgia, in desperate straits with the Cherokee and Creek mutiny, recruited a detachment of Highlanders to help restore the peace of the infant colony.

The clans of the Highlands were characterized by persons of almost gigantic build, corresponding strength of arm, and valour indomitable, always requesting duty in the front line of battle.

In England, their name became the dread of the border tribes, in times when Scotland sorely needed such a shield.

Highland Clans and Tartans

R.W. Munro, Published by Octopus Books, Limited, London 1977

The Morton family of the Douglass Clan were said to have aided the escape of Mary Queen of Scots from Lochleven Castle.

The arrival of the ship Hector at Pictou, Nova Scotia, in September 1773, with about 200 emigrants who had sailed from Lochbroom Wester Ross, is looked back to as the first wave of a mighty tide which swept westwards across the Atlantic from the Scottish Highlands.

These men carried the fame of bonnet, plaid and bagpipes throughout the world.

It was estimated that up to 12,000 Highlanders were enlisted in the Seven Years War,—although the figure has been put much higher.

Cattle raising was the main occupation of Highland farmers, but in the 1760s sheep farming was introduced from the Lowlands and it spread rapidly as the century advanced. A cash economy gradually replaced the old pastoral way of life; and a wish for paid employment spread.

Social readjustment, poverty, overpopulation, rising rents, bad seasons, and more shipping all contributed to emigration to America.

Ian's mother's side of the family was the Conner's of Ireland who left their homes after suffering many hardships.

During the Ireland potato famine over 1,000,000 Irish farmers perished so their great emigration to America started.

After overcoming the initial difficulties, they encouraged others at home to follow.

The "great dispersal" had been substantially begun, and as the years passed, the flow increased in volume.

The fame of the Highlanders and the glamour of the tartan were again being carried to the outside world.

After the Cherokees signed a peace treaty, many of the Scots elected to stay on as citizens of Georgia and Carolina colonies.

The dispersal of the Irish and Highland clans were somewhat similar to the American Indian displacement, except the Indians decided to resist the massive eviction from their lands.

Jornada de Muerte

*B*ack at the camp, Shenga instructed the tribes, "Gather the people, assemble the elders, gather the children and those that suck the breast, and leave this place." All were far away when the troopers rose in the morning.

Cooke's Indian scouts reported that the village, alarmed by approach of such a large body of troops and fearing an attack was imminent, had fled.

Here, indeed, was disappointing news to the captain. The teepees were empty; only Ian and his small band of rear vanguard were left. The Indians were not to be deceived by promises of security. Those in other villages had been assured of their safety, only to be attacked and massacred. The chiefs and their headmen had profited by this previous display of bad faith on the part of soldiers and escaped from harm's way to take their chances of survival on the dreaded desert of Death.

Soon after nine o'clock in the morning, Ian and his men were on the trail. It was not hard to find or difficult to follow, at first, at a rapid pace. It headed west. Across innumerable streams it led and still westward, then north, easily discernible for awhile, then it grew dimmer and smaller. Soon it faded entirely. More than one thousand Ghost Dance Dreamers were gone.

Behind Shenga Wassa the villagers strung out for well over a mile, dust from the scraping travois, from the horse herd which the boys were driving, from the interweaving horses of the women. Old men and women rode the travois atop piled teepees and parfleches, so did young children. Stolid babies swathed to the chin in cradles stared out from their mother backs. The women who managed all this were shrill and profane. There was an incessant brawling of excited dogs.

Shenga Wassa was a comforter and helper to other women less brave and capable than she was. The animals were rested and prepared for the fearful jornada, just ahead.

Beyond the sandhills was an immense barren plain without wood or water, stretching for fifty miles by the most direct route to the Cimarron River. For four-fifths of the distance, there was not a single landmark, and no trail to follow.

Wagon masters laid their course by compass on that prairie ocean, level as the calmest sea.

The day before, the women had been busy cooking meat, filling the skin pouches with water, and preparing supplies for the long trip through the desert. They knew it would be at least four or five days before they found water or fuel for cooking.

As to the horses, they had to do without a drink. Their masters therefore took care to see that they had a good rest, ample time to graze, and a bellyful of water before they started.

Unfortunately, the first five miles through the sandhills, was sand that was soft and deep like an ocean beach, and by the time the animals had reached the level plain beyond, many of them were already tired, hot and thirsty. The passage of the sandhills caused the caravan to move at a snail's pace.

On they plodded, and the sun and wind, to say nothing of dread of the desert, made every man, woman, and child thirsty beyond their wont.

The jornada was no mere trap for greenhorns. Veteran mountain men died there. Of these, no better man ever stood in moccasins than Jedediah Smith, one of the finest fellows and most competent explorers of the West, a gentlemen in buckskins, with a courageous heart of a bear. When only thirty-three years old, he started for Santa Fe with his own wagons. There was no trail to follow and Smith had no guide. For three blistering days the party was lost on the desert.

The only trails to be seen there were those of buffalo—broad beaten highways, leading—at certain seasons, to water. Knowing the habits of that animal, Smith believed the trails would lead to water, though they ran off every which way. But, he was mistaken. There was then no water at the ends of those trails. He rode alone, leaving the wagons to find help for his comrades. That was Jedediah Smith all over. He was a genuine Christian—probably the only one among the Santa Fe traders. With parching lips and tongue, he kept going, and at last he found a stream, or rather, the dry sandy bed of a stream. The Cimarron!

Smith spurred forward looking up and down the river for a pool. There was none. He dismounted eager to slake his thirst, so that he would have strength to carry the word to his comrades, back there in the burning heat. Anxiously, he dug barehanded in the sand, scooping out a basin two feet deep. The water began to seep in. Smith watched it, smiling with cracked lips. His comrades were saved, now! He sat and watched the basin fill up, then stooped to drink. When he raised his head, he found himself surrounded by Comanche.

They were on horseback. When he tried to mount, they frightened his horse, shot and lanced him. Smith jerked out his holster pistols; tried to defend himself. He dropped two of them, but he had no chance. They killed him. All that was known of his death was what they told some Mexican traders, to whom they sold his weapons.

Smith was a good friend of the Indians, and did not approve the cruelty with which some of his companions treated them. He was also a scholar, in his way, loved literature, and had prepared a geography of the Rocky Mountain region. But to the Comanches, he was just a scalp.

*   *   *

On the second day into the desert, Shenga Wassa started having labor pains. Her baby was to be born here on the desert, so with several women they left the column for the occasion. The women were old and experienced squaws. The sitting position of child birthing was the most common, but sometimes the lying down and other positions were assumed. In the sitting position, it was customary for the assistants, as soon as the pains set in, to frequently lift the patient up by the arms.

Ian and a medicine man stood close by until the childbirth was over. After giving birth, Shenga rested only minutes, then rejoined the caravan. The girl child was more beautiful than any mortal.

Ian, concerned that the walking and the heat would weaken her still more, built a travois to carry her this day. In the building of the travois, the teepee poles were fastened at their smaller ends by hide thongs, which passed over the pony's withers, and the larger ends of the poles drag on the ground. The poles become shafts behind the animal where the load was fastened. Small children were frequently placed in a wicker-work basket fastened to these poles, and for supporting the sick and wounded, the skin of a freshly-killed animal robe or blanket was fastened to the pole, forming a bed upon which the sick or wounded persons recline. Two poles only, as a rule, were used for this purpose.

By this time the thousand warriors, women and children who had started the trek had separated into four smaller parties for the journey across the desert; some turned to the north, others west and Ian's band took the southwest route, to be reunited either in part or in full at a prearranged point. Their goal was the wild hunting grounds along the still distant rivers.

The little band came upon a prairie-dog town of considerable size. The "wish-ton-wish," as the Indians called them, resided in towns or villages, having an evident police established in their communities.

The sites of their towns were generally on the brow of a hill, near some small creek or pond, in order to be convenient for water, and that the high ground, which they inhabit, may not be subject to flooding. Their residence, being underground, is burrowed, and the earth brought out is made to answer double purpose of keeping out the water and affording an elevated place in wet seasons to repose on, and to give them a further and more distinct view of the country. Their holes descent in a spiral form.

The prairie dogs, or wish-ton-wish, were of a dark brown color, except their bellies, which were white; their tails were not so long as those of gray squirrels, but were shaped precisely the same. Their teeth, head, nails, and body were those of the perfect squirrel, except that they were generally fatter than that animal.

The Indians killed great numbers of these animals with their rifles and arrows and found them excellent meat after they were exposed a night or two to the frost, by which means the rankness acquired by their subterranean dwelling was corrected. As they approached their towns they were saluted on all sides by the cry of wish-ton-wish, from which they derive their name with the Indians, uttered in a shrill and piercing manner. Then they retreated to the entrance of their burrows, where they posted themselves and watched even the slightest movement of the people. It required a very nice shot with a rifle or arrow to kill them, as they must be shot dead, for as long as life exists they continue to work into their cells. It was extremely dangerous to pass through their towns, as they abounded with rattlesnakes, both of the yellow and black species. Strange as it may appear, the wish-ton-wish, the rattle-snake, the horn-frog with which the prairie abounds (termed by the Spaniards the chameleon from their taking no visible sustenance), and a land tortoise, all take refuge in the same hole.

Outriders rode in to relate that banditti were following and closing rapidly on the little band. Ian had only a hundred dog soldiers and two hundred women, children and old people.

He reasoned that they were from Aaron Burr's settlement and out for scalps. He had reasoned right. The Grand Conspiracy had doubled the price of the Indians' scalps, women, children, old men, any Indian, to fifty dollars. So they left the women and children guarded by two dozen warriors and the rest rode out to receive the charge of the Mexican banditti lancers.

As they rode, Ira Hammond, the young man who had been with him since early Fort Leavenworth days said he had no fear of being shot; the only fear he had was the Mexican lasso or lariat.

Ian had decided to use different tactics from those customarily used by the Indian. They had captured several artillery pieces with sufficient shells and powder to practice their aiming and accuracy. As the riders, rode in, keeping Ian informed of the enemy's advance, they took positions upon the top of a small knoll directly in the line of the march and waited for the lancers to arrive. Two cannon were set up and ready to fire, with bowmen on both sides. Normally Indians did not stand and fight, but the little detachment knew they must do so to save their fleeing women and children.

Sergeant Beidler dismounted to tighten up the "cinch" of his weather-beaten saddle. Finishing, he swung into the saddle again, and went cantering down the slope, his charger snorting with exhilaration of the anticipated battle in the keen morning air.

Ian reasoned the slope up the knoll would slow their charge and give his bowmen a chance to thin the charger's ranks. The Indians formed a line to receive the lancers. Soon they appeared in about equal number as the Indians. Before they were in rifle and bow range, Sergeant Beidler and the Indians he had trained were ready to receive the charge of cavalry. When the advancing column was within close range a deadly fire of canister from the eighteen-pounders thinned their ranks. On they came, and as they reached the foot of the slope, the bowmen loosed their deadly arrows into the onrushing banditti. As they reached the summit the battle became hand to hand. The Indians fought with ferocious tenacity, with persistent and relentless attack, to protect their families.

One ranchero got to within lance range and thrust it at Ian in a quick stabbing movement. Ian whirled out of the way and the lancer fell from his horse with a 40-caliber bullet right over his heart.

The rancheros, like the Indians, never fought a one-on-one basis, and as their numbers were getting less and less, turned and retreated down the hill, Beidler's artillery doing great execution to their rear.

Their leader Perkins who had escorted Ian to the prairie prison several months before, had his head carried off by an eighteen pound ball; he had no chance for last dying words.

They reined up a half a mile from the Indian position behind a rock ledge and waited for reinforcements from Burr's settlement. The reinforcements never arrived.

*   *   *

The fierce Apaches still remembering the massacre of their women and children previously now saw their opportunity for blood revenge on Burr's settlement. The Apache, well armed and mounted, began the attack by stampeding the cattle. About twenty rancheros started to recover them if possible. They followed about a mile, when the attack on the settlement commenced. The Indians driving the cattle appeared to be on the retreat; but it was only done to get the rancheros as far as possible on the prairie. About a hundred Indians had been stationed nearby, and they now charged, came up in the rear of the rancheros, and completely surrounded them. They now had it hand to hand—four to six Indians upon one ranchero at a time. All rancheros were killed. The Apache scalped six of the men.

As the warriors poured into the garrison office the four rancheros officers begged them not to kill them. The braves told them they were going to kill every ranchero in Indian Territory. Long deadly arrows flashed though the air—then another and another, but the major did not die easily. Dying, but still standing, one impatient Indian sent a bullet through his chest. As he fell, a chief leaped forward, grabbed one of his pistols, and shot him in the face.

The attacking Indians found several rangers in a house. They knocked them down nearly unconscious, then stripped them of their uniforms, and threw them naked out onto the dusty street. They marched them about the streets, prodding them with their lances, and pushing arrow tips into their flesh, inch by inch. Those that couldn't walk were dragged along.

If the rancheros were looking for equally ferocious adversaries as their own atrocities, they had found them. Massacres for massacre, the Indians were equal to the rancheros.

All along the road was ghastly evidence of Indian fury. In a gulch, lay a body. A hundred yards away was a teamster with two bullet holes in his breast. A little further down the canyon a body lay on its back, with the head pillowed on large rock. By his side was a rifle.

Half a mile from him a man lay naked, with a bullet hole through his head. It was a scene of overwhelming desolation. All the buildings but one were burned down. No sign of life was near, and the absence of life was emphasized by the haphazard scattering of articles of all kinds over the ground, indicated pillaging before the burning. Lying here and there were bodies of victims. A priest lay naked, on his back, one hundred yards from the ashes of his house. A bullet had pierced his brain. Around his neck was a chain, by which he had been dragged from the storehouse.

Another man's corpse lay over in the field, with a bullet through the heart. Another laborer, lay naked, shot through the left breast.

*   *   *

Back at the scene of the encounter of the Rancheros and the Indians, Mexican lance thrusts ended the lives of seven warriors. Others received from two to eight lance wounds, mostly when unhorsed and incapable of resistance.

Ira was killed and was found with a new lariat wound two or three times around his body.

The rancheros waited for replacements to arrive, and when they did not appear, they retreated back to the settlement, now burned to the ground. Aaron Burr's cherished design of forcing secession of the country west of the Mississippi and an invasion and conquest of the West was dead.

Shenga Wassa's and Ian's band continued their way across the desert with women, children, teepees, dogs, "travois," and the large pony herd, to the fastness of the mountains.

Ahead were the much-dreaded sand hills, an immense field of steep sand ridges, without shrub or vegetation of any kind, looking like a piece of Arabian desert transplanted into this plain; like the bottom of the sea uplifted from the deep. Soon they arrived at the foot of the sand hills, and they commenced traveling very slow. There was nothing around them but the deepest and purest sand, and the animals and walking people, especially children could only get along in the slowest walk, and by resting at short intervals. At last the horses were exhausted; they would move no more and they had not yet reached half their way.

In this dilemma, Ian put his own riding horse to the travois, and they moved forward again. In the meantime dark night had come on, illuminated only by lightning that showed them for awhile the most appalling night-scene, as the column moved along as slow and solemn as a funeral procession; ghostly riders on horseback, wrapped in blankets or cloaks. About midnight, at last they reached the end of the sand hills, and encamped without water.

They had now traveled four days in the desert, the last two without water. The greatest conceivable torment is that where no water is found. Want of food is no comparison. After the third day there is no suffering from hunger, but day and night, asleep and awake, the only thought or dream is for water, water, and water!

Along the route lay the bones of ten teamsters who had perished in the desert from want of water.

During the day they came in sight of a range of hills, and from the appearance of the country and the many birds flying around a particular location, Ian thought they should find water. He left his horse at the foot of the hills and by great effort arrived at the point. Looking down into a deep crevice in the rocks, he discovered a pool of water that had flown into the crevice from the surrounding surface during the rainy season, and enough remained to relieve all immediate wants. He was so weak that it was only by great effort and risk of life that enabled him to get to the water. He dipped the water into his boot and drank from it by a single swallow, resting between for some time, and then went to the relief of his horse, carrying both boots full and allowing him to drink from the top of the leg. Setting them down on the ground, he would press down until all was gone. Thus the process continued until the wants of the others and horses were satisfied.

In consideration of the tired, hungry children, they came to halt several times, and rested.

After an hour's rest they resumed their journey and although their only conveyance was several travois, so crowded as to be very uncomfortable, the little travelers bore the journey bravely. But when they reached the foothills, just beside a deserted Indian camp, their horses fairly gave out again and a large campfire was made; buffalo robes were laid on the ground, and the weary travelers found a temporary resting place.

Shenga passed the hours of waiting, holding her newborn baby to her breast. When all the tired ones were still, the silence was only broken by the crackling of burning embers, the occasional falling of rock from above, the hooting of an owl, the dismal howling of the wolves in the forest. Ian sat there looking at the weary forms so ill protected from the chilly night. The thought of the children being safe kept his heart warmed and comforted.

Shenga shivered with the external chill, but hugging her baby close, and committing all to the care of Him who never slumbers nor sleeps, sank into an unconscious sleep.

A little after noon the caravan came to a warm spring. It was clear, pure water in a large basin of rock, with sandy bottom, out of which several warm springs gushed out of the surface. All took a bath and had a good time. It was a very bold spring at the foot of a small mound apparently of volcanic origin. The water boiling up through the sand over a large space some two or three rods across and apparently walled up, raising the water to some four feet in depth. The temperature was just right for a comfortable warm bath and drink, and a stream of water flowing from it sufficient to run a mill.

They had crossed the Jornada de Muerte losing only three children and two old people. A little further into the hills the three hundred souls collected in the mountains. Their position there was almost impregnable with breastworks thrown across the trails where they practically hung in mid-air, with a solid rock wall on one side and a precipice on the other. There was no other entrance to the mountain retreat except for several trails through narrow openings in the rocks. With rifle fire, lance, and arrows dispatched from both sides of the canyon—a direct assault was suicidal.

Around the campfire while Shenga breast-fed her little infant girl, Ian would reminisce and review the past experiences and events, for the lessons he had learned from them. Why did the Almighty send Shenga Wassa back to him and her people?

A logical explanation was that God creates man and woman, such as Shenga Wassa and Ian, each to do their proper work, each to fill their proper sphere. Neither could occupy the position, nor perform the functions of the other. Shenga Wassa existed on her own account, as Ian did on his, at the same time that each had intimate relations with the other. Humanity needed both for the purposes of the race, and both must necessarily be included. Everything created has a specific purpose; Shenga's purpose was not completed, perhaps that is why her soul returned. Shenga Wassa kindly explained to him, "As for reincarnation, it is simply the passage of the soul from one body to another. In the vast ocean of renewed births there are innumerable streams of existence."

The notion of transmigration, the passage after death of the human soul from the mortal body to a new incarnation in another body, necessarily rests upon a belief that the soul itself is immortal or at any rate more lasting than the body. The migration of souls is made to serve another and still higher and more direct purpose, the justice of God. By means of migration the soul has fulfilled the object of its creation—to pass through man and woman and to lift them higher and bring them nearer the divine; its ultimate result is to be the rule of heaven upon earth.

The word which he commanded to a thousand generations (Ps 105:8) is interpreted to mean that it refers to the same soul passing through innumerable generations, for God's command has been given once to all the souls, and these souls are reincarnated over and over again.

This doctrine of metempsychosis (the passage of the soul from one body to another) was borrowed from ancient religious systems. The Palestinian Targumim show traces of it, inasmuch as in some places they speak of a second death, which can only mean at least a life twice repeated upon earth; this is possible only if the soul migrates from one body to another. With the appearance of the Zohar, the older kabalistic literature was pushed into the background, and many an ancient mystical treatise was forgotten.

Reincarnation has been widely accepted by the religions and philosophies of the Orient.

The Zohar, a Jewish cabalistic (or kabbalistic) book attributed to a second-century teacher, contains a complete cabalistic theosophy, treating of God, the cosmogony (the genesis or origination of the universe), and cosmology (the general science or theory of the material universe, its parts, laments and laws), of the universe, the soul, etc. Its contents indicate it is the work of many authors, periods, and civilizations.

Cabala was a kind of system of occult theosophy (religious thought in which claim is made to a special insight into the divine powers latent in man) or mystical interpretation of the Scriptures among Jewish rabbis and certain medieval Christians, at first handed down orally through chosen individuals, but later committed to writing.

The cabalists assume that every letter, word, number, and accent of Scripture contains a hidden sense; claim to know the methods of interpretation for ascertaining these occult meanings; and vie with each other in giving them, even pretending to foretell events by these methods.

Reincarnation was a reality to Shenga, not a mystical theory. It was simply a manifestation of divine favor. The natural and supernatural could very well be connected and the unending series may form a whole, and there may be new terms not yet discovered beyond the whole of it.

This spirit world, strictly speaking, belongs to a realm above ordinary categorical logical thinking and as such is beyond the province of logic proper.

The soul does not depend on the body for its ultimate being, or dies in the physical dissolution of death, but simply that the connection of soul and body is not artificial, temporary, or alien.

Shenga Wassa's spirit assumed some material body, in order that it could be seen through the medium of natural sight. The natural eye ordinarily cannot see the soul because of some veil that hides the supernatural.

Shenga, though female, was not born of a female; she sprang, the myth tells us, mature and fully armed from the Master of Life. Yet she was a woman—a female divinity sprung solely from divinity. She divinely foreknows.

Souls of the dead may be reincarnated in human bodies. Ghosts, as distinguished from souls or spirits, are of a more substantial character. They are a ghostly appearance of the dead, but they assume material forms, and at times enter into human relations with living people, even marriage and parentage.

*   *   *

Her sobs were for those who strove and failed, acting bravely a silent and desperate part in the tragedy of human existence. Her pitying gaze was ever bent on those whose youth bore no flower in its branches.

Her heart was filled with grief at the woe of those who stood at the dying of the day; at the end of the long and lonely trail with the work of their life all around them unheeded.

*   *   *

One morning, months later, a young woman, Mo'ki, the Messiah's disciple, rode into camp. Everyone had thought she had perished in the attack upon the village by the Rangers but her body was never found. She related what had happened on the fateful day.

That morning while it was still dark, she was lying in her teepee and suddenly awakened and felt the beat of galloping horses against the ground, which she lay.

The dogs began to bark loudly. She sat up, then scrambled to her feet just as a war-whoop shrilled at the far end of the camp. She ran out of the tent and looked around her. Enemies were charging the camp, which was suddenly alive.

All around her was confusion. The old men were yelling advice. Young men dashed by to catch their horses or galloped past to meet their enemies. She could see the flash of guns and hear them crashing as the charge swept home.

Women and children sped by her away from the battle, running in all directions to find a place of safety. Mothers were lugging their babies or dragging older children by the hand; frightened girls were clutching their blankets under their chins, and matrons puffing for breath. Hobbling old women made off as best they could with their sticks. Children cried, dogs yelped, horses reared and plunged, but above all she was conscious of the sound of the shooting.

Already the rangers were among the tents, firing at everybody who came out of them. Some of the Cheyenne were killed before her eyes.

All this she saw in a moment. Then she was running as hard as she could go towards the bluffs, stumbling through the morning light. She could never remember how, but at last she arrived, panting and trembling, among the rocks. As it grew lighter she cowered back among them and found a shallow cave where she could hide.

By that time her enemies had driven her people out of the camp and set the tents on fire. The Cheyenne had been surprised and overwhelmed by numbers. Shortly after sunup, her enemies took the captured ponies and rode away.

In the afternoon when the Cheyenne were sure that their enemies had gone for good, several old men came out of hiding into the valley where the camp had been, and began to call the people together. Over and over again for a long time they kept calling until most of the people had assembled. Fall was coming on. They had no horses with which to hunt, and all their food, bedding, and tents had been destroyed. Some of the people were almost naked, just as they had jumped from their beds when the camp was attacked. A council was held and they voted to strike out afoot, looking for another camp of their tribe. So the people straggled away to the north and west.

Courtesy of Veawpa (Leky) Ondej

Mo'ki

Before they left, the old men walked around and called again like camp criers, throwing their voices as far as possible. The old men feared that some of their people might still be hidden, and they did not wish to leave anyone behind.

In the cave with the woman was another person, a young boy. They were both frightened almost to death and dared not look out of the cave all day. Even when they heard the old men calling the people, the woman and the boy were afraid to budge out of hiding. They stayed in the cave, and the Cheyenne, who supposed they were dead or captured, finally went away and left them.

All night long the two of them remained in the cave without food, fire, or water. It was cold that night, and they had no buffalo robes to keep them warm. In the morning they were starving and shaking with chill. Everything was quiet. The woman looked out of the cave. She could see no danger. Still they waited there, for they were badly frightened. But at last they became so hungry that they sneaked out, went down into the valley, and prowled around where the camp had stood. Everything had been burned. The whole place was covered with heaps of ashes where the teepees had been. They poked around in the ashes and found a small piece of dried beef charred by the fire. The woman divided it with the boy and they ate it between them.

They were very thirsty then, and went to the spring for a drink. The woman drank only a little water, but the boy lay down on the ground, stuck his lips in the cold water, and filled himself with it. Immediately he took a chill, and in a little while was dead. She tried to help him, but he was puny and almost naked, and the woman had nothing with which to cover him. She was left alone. . . .

Mo'ki had not even a knife. She took thongs from the fringes of her dress and made snares of them. Next morning she found a rabbit in one of the snares, and ate it raw. The meal gave her fresh courage, and she went to work and made more snares, which she set all up and down the valley. In this way, she captured other rabbits. From time to time she moved her camp a mile or two so that she was always able to catch more. She skinned the rabbits and tanned the skins, using their sinews for thread and a sharp thorn for an awl. In this way she sewed the rabbit skins together and made herself a fur robe. This kept her warm for the time being. But winter was ahead and she knew that without a buffalo robe, she would freeze when the cold weather came.

Buffalo were to be seen all around her, but she could not kill them, because she could not make a bow and arrows without a knife. In her despair, she stood up and raised her open hands to Man Above, praying: "Take pity on me. Help me get to my people, and I will make the Sun Dance."

The very night after she made her vow, Mo'ki had a dream. In her dream she was walking across the prairie, looking for edible roots and small animals which she could eat. As she passed over a hilltop, she saw the whole country with all its streams and hills spread out before her like a great map all dotted with buffalo. She stood on the hilltop and looked at the beautiful country. In her dream, as she passed on over the country before her, she came to a level place between two buffalo wallows. There she saw a knife lying on the ground and her heart was glad. She bent down and picked up the knife. That was the end of her dream.

When Mo'ki woke up, she took her robe of rabbit fur, her snares, and her root-digging stick and started off over the prairie on the trail of her people, looking for small animals which she might catch and eat. Suddenly, that afternoon, as she passed over a hilltop, she saw the whole country with all its streams and hills spread out before her like a great map all dotted with buffalo.

She was astonished, for it was the same country she had seen in her dream. Mo'ki was encouraged. She went straight to the level place between two buffalo wallows where she found the knife in her dreams. When she came to the place, there was the knife on the ground. Mo'ki picked up the knife and was happy. She held up her hands to Man Above, gave thanks, and renewed her vow.

"Ah-ho, Ah-ho," she said.

A bunch of buffalo was grazing not far from where she stood. The woman sharpened her knife against a stone and sneaked up towards the buffalo. Her mouth watered as she looked at them. She was sick of rabbit meat, and longed for a warm robe instead of the tattered patchwork of rabbit-skins she was wearing. She went very slowly and carefully, creeping up-wind through the tall grass. Buffalo do not see well, and these could not smell her because of the wind.

There was a cow lying asleep on the edge of the herd. Mo'ki crept up on the cow from behind, slipped along to its head, and cut its throat with a swift slash. Then she jumped away.

The cow scrambled up and staggered about, coughing out its life, soaking the grass with blood. After a while it fell down, struggled a little, and lay still.

Mo'ki butchered the cow and ate some of the warm liver seasoned with gall. Then she skinned the cow, cut two dozen sharp stakes, and pegged the skin flat on the prairie. While it was drying, she jerked the beef, so that she had plenty of meat to eat. She knew it would be very difficult to kill another buffalo as she had killed that one. When the hide was dried, she scraped it clean with her knife and tanned it with the brains and liver of the buffalo. Then she had a warm robe and plenty of meat.

She made a bow and four arrows and found flint arrowheads for them as she wandered over the prairie. At first she could not hit anything, but in time she learned to use the bow and killed other buffalo and made herself a small tent of the hides. She jerked all the beef and had enough to keep her all winter. When spring came, she had seen no human being since the fight in the valley. She made a pack to carry her belongings in and plodded on to the north.

It had been so long since she had seen a person that she did not expect to see anyone.

One day as she was walking over the open prairie, she saw Indians on horseback coming. She was frightened. "They will kill me," she thought.

She tried to run, but they were on horseback and galloped straight at her. She was surrounded. They were Arapaho, allies of her people. She threw down her pack and held up her hands in the sign for peace. They saw that she was a Cheyenne and did not harm her.

She could not speak their language, but told them who she was and all her story in the sign language—all but her dream about the knife. She thought it would not be wise to talk to strangers about the favors of Man Above.

The Arapaho were friendly and said they would take her with them. They were going on the summer buffalo hunt, but they were not going towards the camps of her people. They could not give up their hunt to take her home at the time. When they did return, Mo'ki left to join Shenga Wassa and her people. They welcomed her as one returned from the dead.

*　　　*　　　*

A little six-year-old Sioux boy sat with the others around the campfire and listened with great interest of the Ghost Dance Dreamers and remembered them throughout his life. In later years he would be known as Sitting Bull.

*　　　*　　　*

And thus it ended . . . this story of Shenga Wassa. Myth or Messiah . . . we will never know, we can only imagine, for her work and name expired with the generation that heard her speak. She had no disciples like the Christus to spread her gospel, only Ian Douglass and Reverend Father Gregg who disappeared into the vast wilderness of the western United States after the obscure incident on the Arkansas River in Kansas Territory that changed the course of history.

She had the gift of prophecy and clairvoyance and of healing by a mere touch and the gift of tongues and believed in the reality of constant communication with the spirit world.

But this we do know, she lived and loved and bore the burden of the knowledge that her people would suffer greatly. From the tears of this Indian girl, amid the death-throes of an ancient race's encounter with civilization, there emerged a new race . . . the Western man and woman of the United States of America.

Her prophecies were fulfilled and remnants of the Great Indian Nations still survive. The Dreamer Religion did not die, but that is another story . . .

Kansas
Ghost Woman

Epilogue:
Later Chapters in the Book of Destiny

*D*espite efforts of the military to keep the nation incited by misleading stories of Indian depredations, the populace was beginning to sympathize largely with the Indians. Washington became convinced the situation could be adjusted more quickly and more economically, as well as more honorably by diplomacy than by force of arms.

But at the same time, the government found the Indians less willing to risk their newly regained freedom on documents which became "mere scraps of paper" whenever designing white men believed themselves able to tear up those treaties with impunity. They had been double-crossed too often to be rushed into new pacts. Constant excuse for military operations against the Plains Indians was to "make the Indians live up to their treaty obligations."

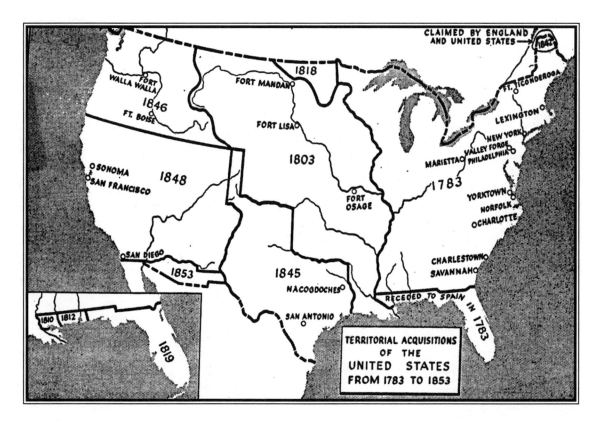

TERRITORIAL ACQUISITIONS OF THE UNITED STATES FROM 1783 TO 1853

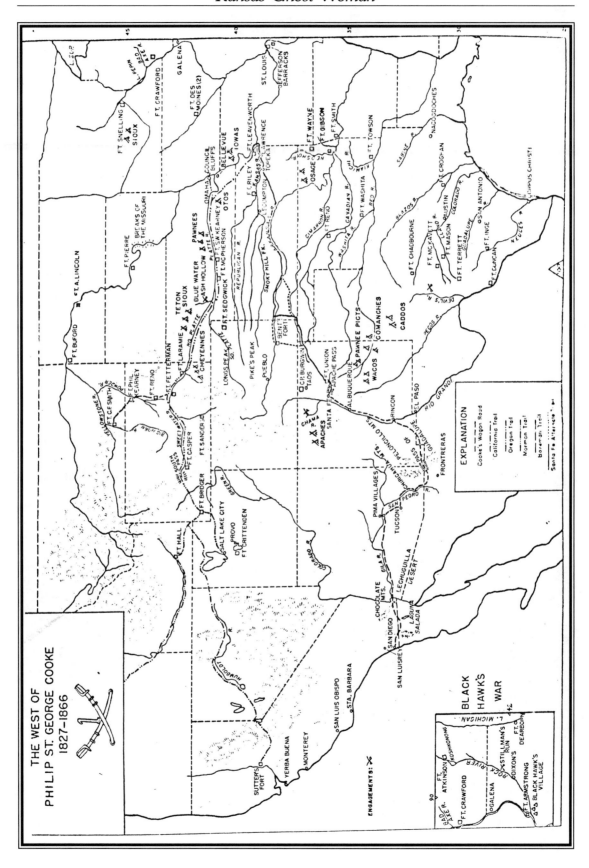

THE WEST OF
PHILIP ST. GEORGE COOKE
1827-1866

EXPLANATION

Cooke's Wagon Road
California Trail
Oregon Trail
Mormon Trail
Bozeman Trail
Santa Fe Alternate

ENGAGEMENTS:

BLACK HAWK'S WAR

*   *   *

Philip St. George Cooke was to serve his nation for forty-six years, a span of unbroken military duty which even today remains something of a record, and which was to affect the destinies of entire nations.

Years later other men signed the protocols, but the Gadsden Purchase was directly inspired by Cooke's wagon road to the Pacific. It was a barren, bitter land, but Major General Philip St. George Cooke, the man who always accepted the challenge of the harder course, would probably have been content with having his name forever linked with the last territorial acquisition to round out the boundaries of the nation which he served so well.

*   *   *

And of Ian Douglass? . . . his life? It had been given at last to the wild places he loved. He left his mark on humanity.

*   *   *

The house in which Sarah Knox died still stood in 1955, though in moldering condition with part of the roof caved in—the cattle's winter hay stored in one end of the drawing room. Some two hundred yards away, beyond a high wall of aged japonicas, lies the cemetery. A chaste marble tomb surmounts Knox's brick-covered grave with four rounded columns supporting the top slab, which bears the simple inscription:

> Sarah Knox Davis
> Wife of Jefferson Davis
> Died September 15, 1835
> Age 21

During the Great War of the Rebellion, Federal troops burned Hurricane. They also burned all but a few of Jefferson Davis' books.

*   *   *

Knox's father, Zachary Taylor, so adamantly opposed to the marriage, was appointed to command the American forces in Louisiana and Texas at the outbreak of the Mexican War and was directed to make the advance into the disputed territory which brought on the war. Winning two battles against the Mexicans, he followed them into Mexico, and there defeated Santa Anna in the crowning battle of the Buena Vista campaign. He was elected President of the United States of America in 1848. The struggle over the question of the admission of slavery to the territory taken from Mexico occupied his term in office. He died in Washington, July 9, 1850.

*　　*　　*

Jefferson Davis resigned his seat in the United States Congress to enter the Mexican War and with his regiment, the 1st Mississippi Volunteers, he joined General Zachary Taylor on the Rio Grande and fought at Monterey and Buena Vista, where Colonel Davis was wounded. He declined a brigadier-generalship offered by President Polk. He was elected United States Senator and held the office of chairman of military affairs and in debate was known as the champion of slavery and states' rights. He assisted in the election of Franklin Pierce and when Pierce became president, Mr. Davis was made Secretary of War. In 1857, he re-entered the senate. In 1860 he received votes for presidential nomination at the Democratic National Convention, but declined the honor. When Mississippi seceded from the Union, Mr. Davis resigned his senate seat and the following month was appointed commander-in-chief of the southern army. On February 18, 1861, he was elected President of the Confederate States of America. He was indicted for treason in 1866, but was never brought to trial. He was included in the general amnesty declared in December 1868. Mr. Davis died December 6, 1889, still a champion of states' rights.

*　　*　　*

Aaron Burr was reduced gradually to obscurity and poverty, and died, on Staten Island with scarcely a friend at his side. This terminated the career of one who played a prominent part of the great stage of public life in the days of Washington, Jefferson, Hamilton, and Jackson.

*　　*　　*

The American government had a problem killing the new religion of the Indian Dreamers. Other religious extravagances such as the Flagellants, Dance of Saint John; an epidemic of maniacal religious dancing in 1374; of Ranters, Quakers, and Fifth-Monarchy Men, the Shakers, Kentucky Revivalists, Beekmanites and other messianic excitement usually crested and quiet would be restored after the excitement had waned. But the Dreamers religion paralleled the Christian doctrine somewhat and prevailed, although greatly diminished through extermination of the race, intimidation, through fear of reprisal and threats. Did not the white man's Bible teach that "I will pour out my spirit upon all flesh, and your sons and your daughters shall prophesy, your old men shall dream dreams, your young men shall see visions?" (Joel 2:28)

*　　*　　*

The remote in time or distance is always strange. The familiar is always natural and a matter of course. Beyond the narrow range of our horizon, imagination creates a New

World, but as we advance in any direction, or as we go back over forgotten paths, we find ever a continuity of a succession. The human race is one in thought and action.

The systems of our present civilization have their origin and interpretation in the customs and rites of our own barbarian ancestors, and of our still existing aboriginal tribes. The Indian messiah religion is the inspiration of a dream. Its ritual is a dance, the ecstasy, and the trance. Its priests are hypnotic and cataleptics. All these formed a part of every great religious development of which we have knowledge from the beginning of history.

In the ancestors of the Hebrew, as described in the Old Testament, we have a pastoral people, living in tents, acquainted with metal working, but without letters, agriculture, or permanent habitations. They had reached about the plane of our Navaho, but were below that of the Pueblo. Their mythological and religious system were closely parallel. Their chiefs were priests who assumed to govern by inspiration from God, communicated through frequent dreams and waking visions. Each of the patriarchs was the familiar confidant of God and his angels, going up to heaven in dreams and receiving direct instructions in waking visits, regulating his family and his tribe, and ordering their religious ritual, in accord with these instructions.

The whole of the prophecies is given as direct communications from the other world with the greatest particularity of detail.

In the New Testament, representing the results of six centuries of development beyond the time of the prophets and in intimate contact with more advanced civilizations, we still have the dream as the controlling influence in religion. In the very beginning of the New Testament, we are told that, while Joseph slept, the angel of the Lord appeared to him in a dream, and as a result "Joseph raised from sleep did as the angel of the Lord had bidden him." The most important events in the history of the Messiah are regulated, not in accordance with the ordinary manner of probabilities, but by dreams. So Wovoka, asleep on the mountain, goes up to the Indian heaven and is told by the Indian God of the coming restoration of his race.

As Be ank'i of the Kiowa claimed to bring rain and snow at will, the Jewish Messiah's disciples said that even the winds and sea obeyed Jesus.

Fasting and solitary contemplation in lonely places were as powerful auxiliaries to the trance condition in Bible days as among the tribes of the plains.

We see the same phenomena that appear in the lives of religious enthusiasts from Mohammed and Joan of Arc down to the prophets of the Ghost Dance.

Dancing, which forms so important a part of primitive rituals had a place among the ancient Hebrew and of their neighbors, although there are but few direct references to it in the Bible. The best example occurs in the account of the transfer of the ark to Zion, where there were processions and sacrifices, and King David himself "danced before the Lord with all his might."

How easily the memory of even Jesus might have been obliterated from the minds of his followers almost before it was born. Many today think that all else granted that if Paul had not immediately followed him, his work and name would have expired almost with the generation that had heard him speak.

Like Jesus, Shenga Wassa did not write.

*   *   *

As the white man had his Indian problem, so the Indian had his problem, which was the white man problem, whose civilization first cast its shadow upon him in North America, when De Soto marched through his country, murdering his people and destroying his property, the beneficent influence of which he could not just then well understand. It afterwards appeared upon him at Plymouth Rock, when the Puritans pilfered his property, and made war on his people. He was told that the white man had a religion, which instructed mankind to live peacefully, quietly and charitably, and to love his neighbor as himself. When the same people drove him from his country, murdered his people, robbed him of his lands, and cast among them destruction by his firewater, they lost faith in white man's profession of friendship and became reluctant to accept his religion and his civilization. The Indian wonders how it is, if the white man's civilization tends so much to better the conditions of mankind, that the white man had, in his society, so many crimes and offenses, and that he has been compelled to put forth so much exertion to resist those evils. He wonders how it is that the white man's society, according to his own account, is so thoroughly permeated with crime and sin, and how it is, if his civilization is so good and beneficial to mankind, and effective in its good purposes, that all these evils are not held in check by its beneficent influences.

To the Indian, the white man's civilization is a series of inconsistencies, with its artificial burdens abhorrent to the Indians' primitive nature and instincts.

General Wilkinson's resolve to be the "Washington of the West" made him a traitor to Burr. On a trip to Washington, D.C., the president asked Wilkinson if he knew or had heard of any enterprise being on foot in the western States. Wilkinson replied that he had heard nothing on the subject, and asked him what the enterprise was to which he alluded.

The president then said, "Yes, my friend, a great number of individuals possessing wealth, popularity, and talents, are, at this moment, associated for purposes unfriendly to the government of the United States. Colonel Burr is at their head."

At the last moment, then, Wilkinson shrank from the work expected of him. The probability is strong that he always meant to do so. That he was a weak, vain, false, greedy man is likely enough. That carried away by the magic of Burr's resistless presence, and hoping the scheme would never involve him in its fold, he suggested, encouraged, and aided it, is very probable. That he had given Burr to understand in some vague way, that he would strike a blow, which would begin a war, whenever it should be needed, is also probable. That he chose the part he did choose from a calculation of advantages to himself, from motives mean and mercenary rests upon evidence that convinces.

Nevertheless, the fact remains that he did not "strike the blow"; he did not involve two nations in war; he did not shape his course according to the wishes of Aaron Burr, but instead to the orders of Andrew Jackson.

If he was a traitor, he was a traitor to his confederates, not to his country, his commission, and his flag. True, the country, particularly the western states, desired war, and would have applauded him for beginning it. But to a soldier, his country speaks only through the commands of its chief.

There were several millions of dollars in the bank to carry out the scheme. President Jackson issued a proclamation, and sent it flying through the States, paralyzing the enterprise as it flew. The president's proclamation did not mention Burr's name. It merely announced that unlawful enterprises were on foot in the western states, warned all persons "to withdraw from the same without delay," as they will answer the contrary at their peril, and incur prosecution with all the rigors of the law," and commanded all officers, civil and military, to use their immediate and utmost exertions to bring the offending persons to deserving punishment.

While Wilkinson was still in some doubt what course to pursue, he received a letter from an acquaintance in Natchez that stated a well-authenticated rumor was afloat. "A plan to revolutionize the western country had been formed, matured, and is ready to explode, and that Kentucky, Ohio, Tennessee, Orleans, and Indiana were combined to declare themselves independent." Proposals had been made to some of the most influential characters of St. Louis, by an accredited agent of the conspiracy, to join the plan. Then it was that the general, perceiving the golden opportunity, fully resolved to set up in the character of Deliverer of his Country.

There was a charge that Wilkinson sent a confidential agent, Walter Burling, to Mexico, to demand of the Viceroy a compensation of two hundred thousand dollars for his services in suppressing Burr's expedition. The Vice-Queen of Mexico, after her husband's death, asserted it repeatedly to Colonel Richard Raynal Keene, an Irish gentleman in the Mexican service.

*   *   *

In . . .

1836—Arkansas was admitted into the Union

1836—Battle of the Alamo

1845—Texas admitted into the Union as a slave state with the Red River to be its northern boundary

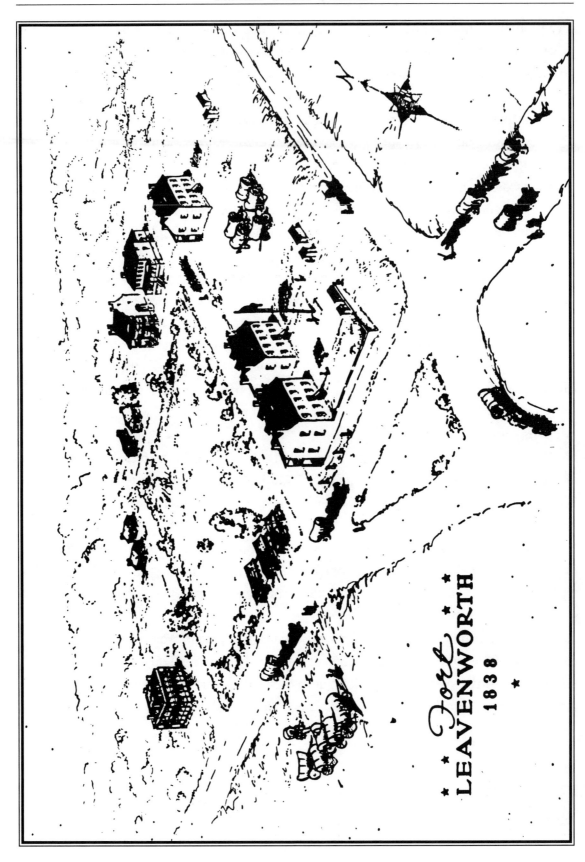

Fort
LEAVENWORTH
1838

1846—War with Mexico

1846—Iowa admitted into the Union

1848—Peace with Mexico brings a vast increase of territory

1856—Kansas was refused admission into the Union because Kansas desired freedom of slaves with statehood

1859—Oregon admitted into the Union

1861—Kansas admitted into the Union as a free state

1864—Nevada admitted into the Union

1867—Nebraska admitted into the Union

1870—Texas re-admitted into the Union after the War of Rebellion

1876—Colorado admitted into the Union

1889—The president signs the bill making North Dakota, South Dakota, Montana, and Washington states of the U.S. on February 22

1889—The Oklahoma Indian Country was opened up to white settlement on April 22

Remnants of the small and great Nations of the Plains Indians exist today in Kansas and Oklahoma; five tribes are situated in northeast Kansas and thirty-seven tribes throughout Oklahoma.

Tribes in Kansas

Tribe	Council House located in:
Kickapoo Nation	Horton
Iowa Nation (area Sioux Tribe)	White Cloud
Prairie Band Pottawatomi Nation	Mayetta
Sac Nation	Reserve
Fox Nation	Reserve

Tribes in Oklahoma

Tribe	Council House located in:
Absentee Shawnee Tribe	Shawnee
Apache Tribe	Anadarko
Caddo Tribe	Binger
Cherokee Nation	Tahlequah
Cheyenne-Arapaho Tribe	Concho
Chickasaw Nation	Ada
Choctaw Nation	Durant
Citizen Band of Pottawatomi	Shawnee
Comanche Tribe	Lawton

Delaware Tribe of East Oklahoma	Bartlesville
Delaware Tribe of West Oklahoma	Anadarko
Eastern Shawnee Tribe	Seneca, Missouri
Ft. Sill Apache Tribe	Perkins
Kaw Tribe of Oklahoma	Kaw City
Kickapoo Tribe of Oklahoma	McCloud
Kiowa Tribe	Carnegie
Loyal Shawnee Tribe	Jay
Miami Tribe	Miami
Modoc Tribe	Miami
Muscogee (Creek) Nation	Okmulgee
Osage Nation	Pawhuska
Ottawa Tribe	Miami
Otoe-Missouri Tribe	Red Rock
Peoria Tribe	Miami
Ponca Tribe	Ponca City
Quapaw Tribe	Quapaw
Sac and Fox Nation of Oklahoma	Stroud
Seminole Nation	Wewoka
Seneco-Coyuga Tribes	Miami
Tonkawa Tribe	Tonkawa
United Keetoowah Band of Cherokee	Tahlequah
Wichita Tribe	Anadarko
Wyandotte Tribe	Wyandotte
Yuchi Tribe	Sopulpa

Indian Nations University is located in Lawrence, Kansas.

These Native Americans share their heritage through dance and music in powwows throughout the year. Powwows (social dances and get-togethers) have been an integral part of the Native American culture for centuries. Their songs represent 500 years of tradition. The songs are haunting and powerful, and the shaking of the gourds in time with the drum beat seems to hypnotize. Drums are set up on the periphery of the dance areas and each drum group sings from their own repertoire of songs. As many as fifteen northern drum groups perform at a large powwow.

Images of exquisitely beaded and feathered dancers whirling to the cadence of the loud and rhythmic drumbeat harkens you back to the mists of time.

When you witness the young warriors carrying their babe's close to their hearts in the ceremonial dances and their womenfolk in traditional dress and shawls holding feathered fans and their little toddlers hands both dancing in the sacred circle, and the professional drummer groups pounding out the beat, you are transported back into ancient times. These dances are a demonstration of traditions with all age groups joining in the spiritual celebration, including children, adolescents and teenagers growing to manhood and womanhood, young adults and their old people. With faces painted, swirling in elaborate dips and swirls that make the brightly-colored yarn, beads and feathers of their costumes ripple and churn, and the tinkling of their metal decorations give the spiritual and joyous celebration a spectacular quality.

Powwows have become major events in Kansas and Oklahoma cities, which have large Indian populations

Indian culture is alive in Kansas. The ancient prairie of the largest grazing area in the world are in their original state except for the immense buffalo herds being replaced by a million cattle grazing on three million acres of the Flint Hills.

*   *   *

History makes records of heroes who fell fighting bravely—of those who survived and of great deeds of daring done and suffering endured. But, there were other heroes who won no stars, who received no ovation, and whose histories were never written, but who none the less were martyrs to their country.

They were the frontier mothers and children weeping and praying and working to keep the home bright and comfortable for the soldier when he should come back. And many fair, smooth faces, grew pale and seamed with care and anxiety, many brown heads of the brave women turned to gray, and their erect forms became bent with the laboring and the years.

And during the waiting, many small children in voices broken with sobs would ask, "Mother, did you pray for father tonight?"

She would reply: "Yes, my son, mother never forgets that."

"But, mother are you sure?"

"Yes, dear one."

"Mother, won't you kneel down here by me, and pray for him again?" And side by side the two or three or four knelt humbly, the mother with her arms about the youngest sobbing child, while she prayed most earnestly for the precious one far away. Then, the dear children would cease their weeping, and kissing mother for herself and "father," would lay down to sleep saying: "Mother, I don't think God will let father be killed."

But, alas! Many hearts were broken when the list of the "dead and wounded" reached the home.

*   *   *

There was another kind of dreaming that was done in the American wilderness, and you must know about this too, for otherwise you cannot know the hill yonder or the ground upon which your house stands or where you saw the red hawk yesterday. Unless you know about these other dreams you can never understand either the land itself or the Native Americans who inhabited it.

In every part of America, Indians once lived, and wherever they lived, they made their myths and legends, creating another world behind the visible world around them. They peopled it with gods and half-gods, and around these mythical beings stories grew . . . stories which often came to be attached to specific places - some mountain or stream or valley where once upon a time a strange thing happened.

To most of us this "other America" is an undiscovered country. We think of America as too new to have a mythology of its own and the word carries us back to ancient Greece and other Old World regions whence came the only myths that we know. The fact is that America, too, is a land of fascinating legend; it is no raw new upstart with anything to offer except its physical attractions. It was eons before we came to it and its hills and valleys have as long memories as those of the Hellenic imaginings which are surely more interesting to us because they are native to our soil.

Army Men Who Shaped
The Nation's History Westward
The Army Pioneers

They stride forever through the pages of American history—these men of the U.S. Army who made their mark not only as warriors but also as nation builders—Army men who pioneered the expansion of the Republic in its growth to greatness.

Today active and former Army installations mark the progress of the Army westward from Governors Island in New York harbor to Fort Niagara to Fort Leavenworth to Fort Vancouver on the Pacific coast. The Nation has erected monuments commemorating the battles fought, the victories won, and explorations made. They pay tribute to the role played by the Army in building the Nation.

Some of these memorials tell the story of struggle and discovery, of expansion and progress, of victories and defeats. Some tell of bloody struggles between red man and white, of Northerner and Southerner, brother against brother, with the end result, a nation united. Others are memorials to hardy pioneers who braved the windswept prairies and snow-blocked mountain passes to claim and develop the land.

The Army's role as a nation builder began early with the Lewis and Clark expedition in 1804. Although the objectives of the expedition were cultivation of friendly relations with the Indians and extending the external commerce of the United States, the explorers' observations about hitherto unknown animal and plant life, of mineral and other natural riches, of massive rivers and endless miles of prairie awaiting the farmer's plow struck a spark that was to ignite the western movement that ended only upon the shores of the Pacific Ocean. While Lewis and Clark were exploring beyond the Missouri, Lieutenant Zebulon Pike was sent on a similar expedition to the headwaters of the Mississippi. In 1807 Captain Pike accompanied by a small band of soldiers explored what is now Colorado—a feat that led to the naming of the famous peak that bears his name.

After the War of 1812 John C. Calhoun as Secretary of War established a line of military posts and trading houses that extended into the Indian territories west of the Mississippi. Army surgeons on these posts kept detailed day-to-day weather records. When these records were compiled years later, they constituted the basic data for the first scientific study of weather in the U.S. and the most complete data of its sort then in existence.

Captain Benjamin L.E. Bonneville's explorations from 1832 to 1835 produced the first authentic reports and maps of the entire Northwest. In 1832 also, Lieutenant James Allen and his little detachment accompanying the Schoolcraft expedition explored the sources of the Mississippi and revealed valuable data on Minnesota's mineral deposits.

The work of Lieutenant John C. Fremont in opening the West earned him the nickname, "The Pathfinder." A skilled topographical engineer, he traced and mapped the routes later used by emigrants across the Southwest to California. His enthusiastic reports about the area sparked a flood of emigration.

It was under the sponsorship of Jefferson Davis as Secretary of War that five routes for the transcontinental railroad were surveyed, four of which were eventually used. It was also Davis who influenced Congress to complete the Gadsden Purchase, adding a 29,670 square mile area to the United States.

ARMY DIGEST
December 1967

Postscript to this History

In November 1993, President Clinton signed the Religious Freedom Restoration Act.

News Release, Washington, D. C., *Associated Press,* Saturday, April 30, 1994:

President Clinton and Vice-president Gore and their wives attended a 2½-hour meeting with Indian leaders from around the country, including those in Kansas. It was the first such meeting since 1822, and probably the first ever to which all 547 federally recognized tribes were invited. The event was complete with prayers in Indian languages to the beat of drums.

President Clinton said the government would work to allow Indians to practice their own religions as they wish, including the use of eagle feathers in ceremonies.

News Release, *Associated Press,* May, 1994, reported an order was issued this week by United States Magistrate William A. Knox that the act *clearly makes accommodations for Indians, even in prisons, to practice their religion and will no longer be required to cut their hair, and will be allowed to build a sweat lodge to perform religious rites.*

Thus, over 150 years of intolerance and banishment of Native Indian religions, including the GHOST DANCE, sometimes known as the DREAMER RELIGION has ended.

Indian Agency Apologizes for Legacy

By Matt Kelley
Associated Press

WASHINGTON—The head of the federal Bureau of Indian Affairs apologized Friday for the agency's "legacy of racism and inhumanity" that included massacres, forced relocations of tribes and attempts to wipe out Indian languages and cultures.

"By accepting this legacy, we accept also the moral responsibility of putting things right," Kevin Gover, a Pawnee Indian, said in an emotional speech marking the agency's 175th anniversary.

Gover said he was apologizing on behalf of the BIA, not the federal government as a whole. Still, he is the highest-ranking U.S. official ever to make such a statement regarding the treatment of American Indians.

The audience of about 300 tribal leaders, BIA employees and federal officials stood and cheered as Gover finished the speech.

"I thought it was a very heroic and historic moment," said Susan Masten, chairwoman of California's Yurok tribe and president of the National Congress of American Indians. "For us, there was a lot of emotion in that apology. It's important for us to begin to heal from what has been done since non-Indian contact."

Although Gover's statement did not come from the White House, President Clinton's chief adviser on Indian issues, Lynn Cutler, said the White House did not object to it.

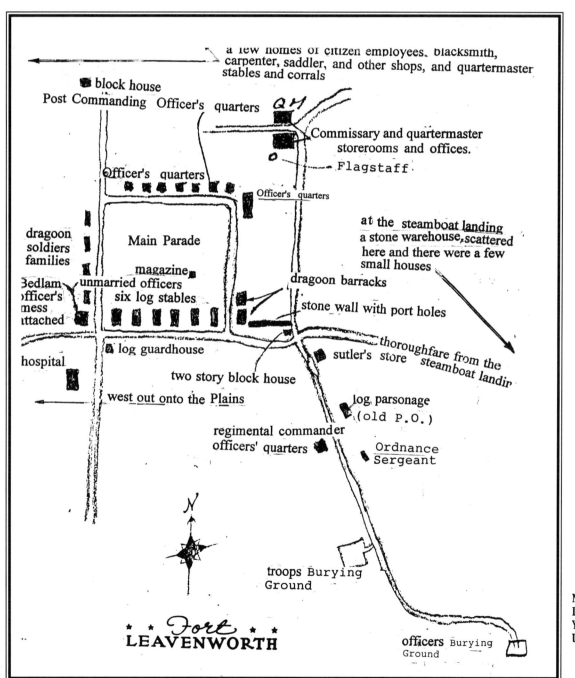

a few homes of citizen employees, blacksmith, carpenter, saddler, and other shops, and quartermaster stables and corrals

block house
Post Commanding Officer's quarters QM

Commissary and quartermaster storerooms and offices.

Flagstaff

Officer's quarters

Officer's quarters

dragoon soldiers families

Main Parade

magazine

Bedlam officer's mess attached

unmarried officers
six log stables

at the steamboat landing a stone warehouse, scattered here and there were a few small houses

dragoon barracks

stone wall with port holes

log guardhouse

hospital

two story block house

west out onto the Plains

thoroughfare from the steamboat landing

sutler's store

log parsonage (old P.O.)

regimental commander officers' quarters

Ordnance Sergeant

N

troops Burying Ground

★ ★ *Fort* ★ ★
LEAVENWORTH

officers Burying Ground

Mr. Percival Lowe's "Five Years a Dragoon"

Gover recited a litany of wrongs the BIA inflicted on Indians since its creation as the Indian Office of the War Department. Estimates vary widely, but the agency is believed responsible for the deaths of hundreds of thousands of Indians.

"This agency participated in the ethnic cleansing that befell the Western tribes," Gover said. "It must be acknowledged that the deliberate spread of disease, the decimation of the mighty bison herds, the use of the poison alcohol to destroy mind and body, and the cowardly killing of women and children made for tragedy on a scale so ghastly that it cannot be dismissed as merely the inevitable consequence of the clash of competing ways of life."

Saturday, September 9, 2000
A2 St. Joseph (Mo.) *News-Press*

"KANSAS became not only a Free Territory (anti slavery), but the stronghold of Union and Liberty in the West, a mighty fort garrisoned upon the borders of hostile countries."

The Gateway of History
The Worlds' Famous Events
By Edward S. Ellis and Charles F. Horne, Ph.D.
1913

References

Important sources of Kansas history are found in the following books, periodical literature, newspapers, Annual Reports of the United States Government Bureau of Ethnology, all of which I have drawn on heavily.

I have overwhelmingly restricted my research to works originally printed over one hundred years ago.

In the writing of this book, I have made extensive use of the writings of men and women living in those years. They are listed in the Bibliography which is appended. Much of this narrative was drawn from the original diaries, notes and official government documents.

Bibliography & Suggestions for Further Reading

United States Bureau of Ethnology Fourteenth Annual Report to the
Secretary of the Smithsonian Institution
1892-93, Washington Printing Office 1896
Subject: The Ghost Dance Religion

Life, Letters and Travels of Father Pierre-Jean DeSmet, S.J. 1801-1873
Printed 1905

Periodical Rosicrucian Digests

The Journals of Francis Parkman—The Oregon Trail Journal—1840

Indian Sign Language—W.P. Clark, U.S. Army
L.R. Hamersly and Co. 1885

Massacres of the Mountains
By J.P. Dunn, Jr., M.S., LLB
Harper and Brothers, Franklin Square
New York 1886

Journal of a Santa Fe Trader 1844-1847
By James Josiah Webb, 1818-1889
The Arthur H. Clark Company
Glendale, California 1931

The Deserter
By Charles King
J.B. Lippincott Company 1901

Jefferson Davis—American Patriot 1808-1861
By Hudson Strode 1955
Harcourt, Brace and Company, New York

General Court Martial Orders
Headquarters Department of the Missouri, Fort Leavenworth, Kansas

Army Research and Development News Magazine
June-July 1969
Article—Ancient Greek Tragedy, Present-Day Ethics

Early American Dress
Edward Warwick, Henry C. Pitz, and Alexander Wyckoff
Publisher Benjamin Bloom, New York 1965

The Complete Story of the Galveston Horror, fully Illustrated
Written by the Survivors

Sins of New Orleans

Mexico, Its Geography—Its People—Its Institutions
By Thomas J. Farnham
H. Long and Brothers, 32 Ann Street, New York 1846

Unknown Mexico
By Carl Lumholtz, M.A.
New York, Charles Scribner's Sons 1902

History of America Before Columbus
By P. De Roo, Member of the Archaeological Club of the Land Van Waes and
of the United States Catholic Historical Society;
Honorary Member of the American Catholic Historical Society of Philadelphia
Volume 1 American Aborigines
J.B. Lippincott Company
Philadelphia and London 1900

The Old Santa Fe Trail
The Story of a Great Highway
By Colonel Henry Inman, Late Assistant Quartermaster, U.S. Army
The Macmillan Company
New York and London; Macmillan and Co., Ltd. 1897

Beacon Lights of History
By John Lord, LL.D.
Vol. VII American Statesmen
Publisher Fords, Howard and Hulbert, New York 1886

Aaron Burr
Historical Brief Biographies
James M. Murphy, S.J., Ph.D.
Fairfield University, Fairfield, CT 1997

The French Quarter
By Herbert Asbury
Garden City Publishing Co., Inc.
Garden City, New York 1938

Annals of the West
Principal Events
Western States and Territories
Compiled from the most authentic sources
Published by James R. Albach
St. Louis 1852

History of the State of Kansas, Illustrated
Chicago: A.F. Andreas 1883
Reproduced by Saint Benedict College, Atchison, Kansas in cooperation
with the Kansas State Historical Society, Topeka, Kansas 1976

Horse, Foot and Dragoons
By Rufus F. Zogbaum
Harper and Brothers, New York and London 1888

The Mythology of all Races in Thirteen Volumes
Volume X, North American
By Hartley Burr Alexander, Ph.D.
Marshall Jones Company, Boston
Printed April 1916

The Bible as Literature
Old Testament History and Biography
Buckner B. Trawick, Professor of English, University of Alabama
Barnes & Noble, College Outline Series No. 56

A History of Kansas
By Nobel L. Prentis
Published by Caroline Prentis
Topeka, Kansas 1909

Damaged Souls, IV, Aaron Burr
By Gamaliel Bradford
Printed 1922
Atlantic Monthly Company
Cambridge, Massachusetts

Acknowledgments

Reverend Father Clarence F. Stolz, contemporary Episcopal priest, former rector of Trinity Episcopal Church, Atchison, Kansas, former chaplain University of Kansas, and University of Texas, Austin, now retired.

Reverend Father Angelus Lingenfelser, monk, teacher, rector, former business administrator of Benedictine College, Atchison, Kansas, publisher of *History Of Kansas.*

National Archives—Washington, D.C.

Historical Archives—Fort Leavenworth, Kansas, without whose reference materials this book could not have been written.

The ruts of the wagon road climbing up the steep slopes from the Missouri River still remain to this day. The Main Parade still dominates the Post and Corral Creek seems haunted by Waddell and Majors huge wagon trains gathering for the trek westward.